C000175112

ANIMAL
FREE
SHOPPER

First published June 1991
Second edition published June 1993
Third edition published April 1995
Fourth edition published November 1997
Fifth edition published June 2000
Sixth edition published October 2002
Seventh edition published July 2005
Eighth edition published November 2008
Ninth edition published November 2010
© The Vegan Society

ISBN: 978-0-907337-33-1

Design by doughnutdesign.co.uk

Printed on recycled paper

Published by
The Vegan Society
Donald Watson House, 21 Hylton Street
Birmingham, B18 6HJ, United Kingdom

Tel: 0121 523 1730
Local call rate: 0845 45 88244
www.vegansociety.com
Registered Charity No. 279228
Company Registration No. 1468880
VAT Registration No. 448 5973 95

CONTENTS

- Although, as far as is practical, the publisher has taken care to ensure the accuracy and reliability of information supplied to it, the reader should bear in mind that manufacturers may make alterations to the constituents, derivation and testing of their products *at any time*. The diligent animal free shopper always checks a product's ingredients listing (where one is provided!) before making a purchase.

- The absence of an (apparently) animal free product does not necessarily mean it does not meet the Society's **ANIMAL FREE CRITERIA** (page 8). Product categories that are obviously or typically animal-free (tinned fruit, tea, coffee, nuts, dried pulses, beans, peanut butter etc) have been excluded. Additionally, despite repeated approaches, some manufacturers/distributors (including a number whose products have appeared in previous editions) failed, or simply refused to supply the information requested.

- In order to make effective use of this guide, it is suggested that the new reader familiarises him/herself with the location of the **KEY** (page iii) and **CONTENTS** (page i) — and, at least initially, regularly consults the **PRODUCT INDEX** (page 392).

- The inclusion of a product should not be construed as constituting Vegan Society approval for the product, its intended use, or its manufacturer/distributor (see **OTHER ETHICAL CONSIDERATIONS**, page 43).

- The listing of products under 'Healthcare' is not intended to take the place of advice provided by health care professionals.

- The guide is also online at *www.animalfreeshopper.com* and is updated frequently.

KEY

The entire range of the company's products is animal-free
(see **ANIMAL FREE CRITERIA**, page 8)   ☺

The company is an authorised user of the Vegan Society Trade Mark   TM
(but not all its animal-free products may be registered)
(see **VEGAN SOCIETY TRADE MARK**, page 6)

The company has at least one vegan proprietor   ❶

The company's entire product range is organic   ✿

The company has a policy of ensuring that (as far as is possible and   🚫
practical) the production of its products has not involved the use of
genetically modified material
(see **GENETICALLY-MODIFIED ORGANISMS**, page 8)

The company has a policy of not   🐇
conducting nor commissioning animal testing

The company has signed up to the Humane Cosmetics Standard   👁
(see **ANIMAL TESTING CRITERIA**, page 8)

The company has a policy of using only ingredients which have not   ✂
been tested on animals by, or at the initiative of, the company or its
suppliers since a specified date (Note: In the product listings, the year
follows this symbol — eg a1976 cut-off date appears as ✂1976)
(see **ANIMAL TESTING CRITERIA**, page 8)

Food and Drink products in **bold** are registered to use
The Vegan Society Trade Mark

w = with (product listings only)

Some of the companies without symbols may meet some of the
above criteria but this has not been confirmed.

WWW.VEGANSOCIETY.COM

Log on to the website of the world's premiere vegan organisation

- Shop securely online for Vegan Society goods
- View listings of all Vegan registered products
- Become a member
- View Factsheets
- Information
- News and developments
- 'Why Go Vegan' section
- Links to other great vegan/veggie web pages
- Link to Animal Free Shopper website which is regularly updated

Return for updates and latest information

THE NO. 1 SITE FOR VEGAN SURFING

INTRODUCTION

Welcome to the ninth edition of the *Animal Free Shopper*, The Vegan Society's indispensable guide to each and every vegan product we are aware of on sale in the UK. The Vegan Society has now been established for more than 65 years and animal-free products have never been easier to get hold of.

Veganism is increasingly mainstream and no longer viewed as a bizarre 'fad' diet. Veganism is regularly featured in newspapers and magazines. The number of vegan guides, cookbooks and publications continues to grow. An increased awareness of the realities of animal exploitation has meant that many people are cutting down on their consumption of animal products and searching for cruelty-free alternatives.

In relation to global climate change, the United Nations (UN) report *Livestock's Long Shadow* states: "The livestock sector is a major player, responsible for 18% of greenhouse gas emissions measured in CO_2 equivalent. This is a higher share than transport." (Transport causes 13.5% worldwide.) The same report found that "The livestock sector emerges as one of the top two or three most significant contributors to the most serious environmental problems, at every scale from local to global."

The UK's obesity crisis is of concern to many people, and studies have found vegans on average to have lower Body Mass Indexes (BMIs) compared with non-vegetarians. The 2009 review *Health Effects of Vegans Diets* noted that compared with vegetarians, "vegans are thinner, have lower total and LDL cholesterol, and modestly lower blood pressure".

The consumption of greater quantities of fresh fruit and vegetables is now widely encouraged by the UK government's 'five a day' programme, and lentils, beans, wholegrains and pulses are accepted in the mainstream as nutritious foods. 'Meat Free' and 'Dairy Free' markets are growing considerably.

While the labelling of products is improving all of the time, there are few things worse than scrutinising an ingredients list only to be confronted with obscure names, arrays of E numbers, or the dreaded unspecified 'flavourings'. By carrying this pocket-sized guide with you, it's easy and hassle-free to choose from thousands of animal-free products.

With the *Animal Free Shopper*, the hard work is already done for you. We've contacted hundreds of manufacturers – not just of food and drink, but also of toiletries, cosmetics, clothing and other products – to find out which of their products are vegan, and we have used that information to compile this easy-to-use guide.

The *Animal Free Shopper* includes products from supermarkets and independent retailers as well as guidance on additives and E numbers. In terms of background information on veganism, the *Animal Free Shopper* also includes a section on nutrition and some facts and figures about animal exploitation. There are so many reasons to go vegan, for the benefit of people, animals and the environment, that the question is no longer 'why go vegan?' but rather 'why not?'

MISSING, PRESUMED VEGAN

Although we've tried to make the *Animal Free Shopper* as comprehensive as possible, you may still come across products that are vegan but are not listed. There are a number of reasons for this, the main ones being:

- companies failing to respond to our requests for information;
- lack of confidence on the part of the compilers that the manufacturers/ suppliers really understand the ANIMAL-FREE CRITERIA (see page 8);
- companies supplying incomplete or inadequate product information.

PLAYING DETECTIVE

Though experienced in investigating the animal-free credentials of a product, there are limits to The Vegan Society's capabilities. Food processing technology is a vast, complex and rapidly changing subject. Unless we obtain evidence to the contrary – or the details provided are clearly suspect – The Vegan Society has to accept the information provided (normally in the form of a written declaration) in good faith.

However, playing detective isn't the sole province of The Vegan Society. Enquiries from members of the public are often more effective than those from an organisation, so please do contact companies for vegan lists and if you would like to see changes in their formulations or labelling. Use the ANIMAL-FREE CRITERIA (see page 8) as the basis for your approach, and check ADDITIVES (see page 12) to identify E numbers that could be animal derived. You will quickly be able to determine whether the person responding to your enquiry is sufficiently knowledgeable to provide you with plausible product information.

Many larger companies have technical departments where staff have more information than staff in customer services.

Confirming the animal-free status of a product can be thrilling, but be prepared for frustration and disappointment on occasion. That said, discovering that an apparently animal-free product is not suitable certainly isn't wasted effort. Manufacturers take note of consumer interest and will, sooner or later, act. Be encouraging and explain that vegan products appeal to almost any customer. Plant-based food attracts healthy eaters, vegetarians and people on many religious diets, as well as vegans themselves, while many consumers are seeking cruelty-free goods and products with environmentally friendly credentials.

In addition to drawing the attention of manufacturers to the unmet needs of animal-free shoppers, it is equally important to tell them that you buy their products precisely because they are animal-free.

It is all too easy to complain and accuse companies of 'discriminating against vegans' or 'condoning animal suffering', but letters and phone calls of an encouraging nature are likely to elicit a receptive response and, ultimately, produce the desired outcome.

LOOKING AHEAD . . .

Research for the *Animal Free Shopper* never ceases, and The Vegan Society needs you to be part of this process. If you obtain a vegan list from a manufacturer please forward the information to our office. If you discover that a manufacturer has introduced an animal ingredient into a product that was previously animal-free, please share your findings by contacting us at:

The Vegan Society
Donald Watson House
21 Hylton Street
Hockley
Birmingham
West Midlands
B18 6HJ

t 0121 523 1730
f 0121 523 1749
e info@vegansociety.com.

thePhoneCo·op
it's your call

Get home phone and broadband from The Phone Co-op and support The Vegan Society

The Phone Co-op is focussed on giving you what you want: good value, excellent service and a socially responsible, environmentally sustainable approach to business. When you sign up to our services we will give 6% of your ongoing spend back to the Vegan Society.

SUPPORTER OFFER

£10 OFF your first bill when you sign up to one of our packages

Vegan

Quote AF0020 when calling

Call: 0845 458 9040
Visit: www.thephone.coop/vegan

A LITTLE BIT ABOUT THE VEGAN SOCIETY

The Vegan Society promotes ways of living free from animal products, for the benefit of people, animals and the environment.

Established in November 1944, the Society was founded by a group of vegetarians who had recognised the ethical compromises implicit in lacto-vegetarianism. Among the founding members was Donald Watson, who coined the word 'vegan' by taking the first three and last two letters of 'vegetarian'.

Today, The Vegan Society continues to highlight the problems caused by an unhealthy dependence on animal products. We are a registered educational charity, focused on the provision of information on all aspects of veganism. We publish a quarterly magazine, *The Vegan*, which is free to members and available to buy in some health food shops or directly from the Society. We also publish several books, including *Plant Based Nutrition and Health*, and a variety of leaflets, booklets and information sheets. The Society's website *www.vegansociety.com* contains lots of information

www.vegansociety.com

on veganism and has a news headlines section. Additionally, we offer advice on vegan pregnancy and parenting, have an interactive CD-ROM for young people and run a speakers programme which includes a network of school speakers. The message of The Vegan Society is simple: **go vegan – for people, animals and the environment.**

The Vegan Society needs funds to continue its work. If you would like to support this work please consider becoming a member so that you can help us continue to promote compassionate vegan living. You can join the Society using the membership form at the back of this book, through our online shop at *http://shop.vegansociety.com*, or by calling 0121 523 1731.
Thank you very much for your vital support.

OUR TRADEMARK

Some of the products listed in the *Animal Free Shopper* are in bold. These are all of the products that, at the time of going to press, were registered to use The Vegan Society's trademark sunflower logo.

The trademark was conceived as a way of helping people to shop for animal-free products in 1991. Only Vegan Society registered products carry the trademark.

The trademark allows consumers to make easy, informed choices about the suitability of purchases and enables us to work with companies who are willing to recognise their vegan customers. With thousands of items now bearing our familiar logo, and through international recognition of the trademark, our influence has never been greater. We have registered vegan alternatives to just about everything: vegan ice cream, margarine, cheese, seafood, wines, chocolate and jewellery! The trademark covers household items such as cosmetics and bath products, cleaners and soaps, and has attracted a lot of interest from producers of remedies and supplements.

Have a flick through the guidebook to see the huge number and variety of animal-free products that are registered with us, and remember to ask the manufacturer of your favourite products whether they have registered with The Vegan Society yet – the symbol you can trust.

VEGAN SOCIETY TRADEMARK STANDARD

NO ANIMAL INGREDIENTS
The manufacture and/or development of the product, and where applicable its ingredients, must not involve, or have involved, the use of any animal product, by-product or derivative.

NO ANIMAL TESTING
The development and/or manufacture of the product, and its ingredients, must not involve, or have ever involved, testing of any sort on animals conducted at the initiative of the manufacturer or on its behalf, or by parties over whom the manufacturer has effective control.

The Vegan Society understands the word "animal" to refer to the entire Animal Kingdom, that is all vertebrates and all multicellular invertebrates. The word may be used either as a noun or an adjective and to refer to either a species or an individual animal, depending on context. Unless otherwise stated, it usually means non-human animals.

  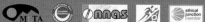

GENETICALLY MODIFIED ORGANISMS

The development and/or production of genetically modified organisms (GMOs) must not have involved animal genes or animal-derived substances nor be tested on animals. Products put forward for registration which contain or may contain GMOs must be labelled as such.

ANIMAL TESTING CRITERIA

It remains the case that different animal protection groups and manufacturers promote a number of variations on the complex 'not tested on animals' theme. Depending on one's perspective or strategy, all have their strengths and weaknesses.

The criteria used to complete the Animal Free Shopper recognise that most substances have been, and some may continue to be, animal tested and so requires that a product's manufacturer has not initiated testing on either the finished product or, where applicable, the ingredients. In other words, a company has not contributed to animal testing with the products listed in this guide.

NO ANIMAL INGREDIENTS

As with the trademark criteria, the manufacture and/or development of the product, and where applicable its ingredients, must not involve, or have involved, the use of any animal product, by-product or derivative.

NO ANIMAL TESTING

The development and/or manufacture of the product, and where applicable its ingredients, must not involve, or have involved, testing of any sort on animals conducted at the initiative of the manufacturer or on its behalf, or by parties over whom the manufacturer has effective control.

FIXED CUT-OFF DATE

A company that has adopted a fixed cut-off date (FCOD) has a policy of not using ingredients that have been tested on animals after a specified date. In addition, the company will not initiate animal tests on its finished products. The Cosmetics Industry Coalition for Animal Welfare (CICAW) encourages cosmetic companies to adopt an animal testing fixed cut-off date — preferably 1976 (the year the EU required all new ingredients to be safety (animal) -tested).

See 'Vivisection' (page 28) for more details on animal testing.

GLOSSARY OF ANIMAL SUBSTANCES

* indicates that non-animal (synthetic, vegetable or plant/mineral-derived) versions/sources by the same name are known to exist.

• **albumen/albumin** egg white *Use/s: food binder* • **alpha hydroxy acids (AHAs)*** naturally occurring chemicals derived from fruit or milk *Use/s: cosmetics* • **ambergris** morbid concretion obtained from the intestine of the sperm whale used in perfumes and cigarettes • **amino acids*** 'building blocks' of proteins • **amniotic fluid** fluid surrounding the foetus within the placenta *Use/s: cosmetics* • **amylase*** enzyme in saliva and pancreatic juice • **anchovy** small fish of the herring family, often an ingredient of Worcester sauce and pizza toppings *Use/s: flavour enhancer* • **angora** fibre obtained from rabbits or goats *Use/s: clothing* • **aspic** savoury jelly derived from meat and fish *Use/s: glazing agent* • **astrakhan** skin of stillborn or very young lambs from a breed originating in Astrakhan, Russia *Use/s: clothing* • **beeswax* (E901)** secreted by bees to produce combs *Use/s: furniture- and floor-polishes, candles, cosmetics* • **bone/bonemeal** animal bone *Use/s: horticultural fertiliser, bone-china ornaments, crockery, supplements* • **brawn** boiled meat, ears and tongue of pig *Use/s: foodstuff* • **bristle*** stiff animal hair, usually from pigs *Use/s: brushes* • **calcium mesoinositol hexaphosphate** *Use/s: baked goods, soft drinks, processed vegetables* • **capiz** shell *Use/s: lampshades* • **carmine/carminic acid (E120)** red pigment obtained from cochineal *Use/s: food and drink dyes* • **casein** milk protein *Use/s: cheese* • **cashmere** fine wool from the cashmere goat and wild goat of Tibet *Use/s: clothing* • **castoreum** obtained from the anal sex gland of the beaver *Use/s: fixative in perfumes* • **catgut** dried and twisted intestines of the sheep or horse *Use/s: stringed musical instruments, surgical stitching* • **caviar(e)** roe of the sturgeon and other fish *Use/s: a relish* • **charcoal*** charred bone or wood *Uses: clarifying agent* • **chitin** organic base of the hard parts of insects and crustaceans e.g. shrimps, crabs *Use/s: conditioners and skin-care products, thickener and moisturiser in shampoos* • **chamois** soft leather from the skin of the chamois antelope, sheep, goats, deer etc. *Use/s: cleaning cloth* • **cholecalciferol** see vitamin **D3** • **cholic acid (E1000)** extracted from the bile of cows *Use/s: emulsifier* • **civet** substance scraped from glands in the anal pouch of the civet cat *Use/s: fixative in perfumes* • **cochineal (E120)** dye-stuff consisting of the dried bodies of scale insects, used for making carmine *Use/s: red food and drink colouring* • **cod-liver oil** oil extracted from the liver of cod and related fish *Use/s: food supplement* • **collagen** constituent of connective tissue which yields gelatin(e) on boiling *Use/s: cosmetics, sausage skins, supplements* • **coral** hard calcareous substance consisting of the continuous skeleton secreted by coelenterate polyps for their support and habitation *Use/s:*

jewellery, ornaments • **deoxyribonucleic acid (DNA)*** controls protein synthesis/stores genetic information. Found in all animal and plant cells *Use/s: cosmetics, genetically modified organisms, shampoos* • **down** underplumage of fowls (especially duck and goose) *Use/s: filling quilts, pillows, sleeping bags, padded clothing* • **dripping** melted animal fat *Use/s: frying* • **eider down** small, soft feathers from the breast of the eider duck *Use/s: filling quilts* • **elastin** protein uniting muscle fibres in meat *Use/s: moisturiser in cosmetics* • **fatty acids*** organic compounds: saturated, polyunsaturated and unsaturated • **feather** epidermal appendage of a bird *Uses: fashion accessory, feather dusters* • **felt*** cloth made of wool, or of wool and fur or hair *Use/s: clothing* • **gelatin(e)** jelly obtained by boiling animal tissues (skin, tendons, ligaments etc.) or bones *Use/s: confectionery, biscuits, capsules, jellies, photographic film, match heads* • **glycerin(e)/glycerol (E422)*** clear, colourless liquid which may be derived from animal fats, synthesised from propylene or from fermentation of sugars *Use/s: solvent for flavours, texture improver, humectant* • **hide** animal skin (raw or tanned) *Use/s: clothing and footwear, clothing accessories, upholstery* • **insulin*** pancreas of cattle, sheep or pigs *Uses: managing diabetes* • **isinglass** very pure form of gelatin(e) obtained from the air bladders of some freshwater fish, especially the sturgeon *Use/s: clarifying alcoholic drinks, jellies* • **keratin** protein found in hair, horns, hooves and feathers *Use/s: shampoos and conditioners, fertiliser* • **L'cysteine hydrochloride (E920)*** manufactured from animal hair and poultry feathers or synthetically from coal tar *Use/s: shampoo, improving agent for white flour* • **lactitol (E966)** produced from milk sugar *Use/s: sweetener* • **lactose** milk sugar *Use/s: tablet filler, sweetener, carrier for flavouring agents, especially in crisps* • **lanolin(e)*** fat extracted from sheep's wool and hide *Use/s: cleaning products, an emollient and emulsifier used in cosmetics, especially lipsticks* • **lard** fat surrounding the stomach and kidneys of pigs, sheep and cattle *Use/s: culinary* • **leather** tanned hide (mostly from cattle but also sheep, pigs, goats etc.) *Use/s: clothing and footwear, clothing accessories, upholstery* • **lecithin (E322)*** fatty substance found in nerve tissues, egg yolk, blood and other tissues, mainly obtained commercially from soya bean, peanut and corn *Use/s: emulsifier in baked goods and confectionery* • **lutein (E161(b))*** deep-yellow substance found in egg yolk, obtained commercially from marigold *Use/s: food colouring* • **lysozyme (E1105)*** enzyme which may be derived from eggs *Use/s: preservative* • **mohair** cloth or yarn made from the hair of the angora goat *Use/s: clothing* • **musk*** substance secreted by glands of the male musk deer *Use/s: perfume* • **oleic acid*** fatty acid occurring in animal and vegetable fats *Use/s: soaps, cosmetics, ointments* • **oleoic oil** liquid obtained from pressed tallow *Use/s: margarines* • **oleostearin** solid obtained from pressed tallow *Use/s: soap and candles* • **oestrogen*** female sex hormone from cow ovaries or pregnant mares' urine *Use/s: cosmetics, body-building supplements, hormone creams* • **parchment*** skin of the calf, sheep or goat, dressed and prepared for writing etc. • **pearl** ('Mother of', or 'cultured') concretion of layers of pain-dulling nacre formed around a foreign particle within the shell of various bivalve molluscs, principally the oyster *Use/s: jewellery and decorative* • **pepsin** enzyme found in gastric juices *Use/s: cheese making* • **placenta** organ by which the foetus is attached to the umbilical cord *Use/s: cosmetics* • **progesterone*** sex hormone *Use/s: hormone creams* • **propolis** bee glue, used by bees to stop up crevices and fix combs to the hive *Use/s: toiletries and cosmetics* • **rennet*** extract of calf stomach containing the enzyme rennin which clots milk *Use/s: cheese, junkets* • **reticulin** one of the structural elements (together with elastin and collagen) of skeletal muscle • **ribonucleic acid (RNA) *** see **deoxyribonucleic acid (DNA)** • **roe** eggs obtained from the abdomen of female fish *Use/s: a relish* • **royal jelly** food on which bee larvae are fed and which causes them to develop into queen bees *Use/s: food supplement* • **sable** fur from the sable marten, a small carnivorous mammal *Use/s: clothing, artists' brushes* • **shellac (E904)** insect secretion *Use/s: hair spray, lip sealer, polishes, glazing agent* • **silk** cloth made from the fibre produced by the larvae (silk worm) of certain bombycine moths, the harvesting of which entails killing the insect *Use/s: clothing, cosmetics* • **sodium 5'-inosinate** occurs naturally in muscle, prepared from fish waste *Use/s: flavour enhancer* • **sperm oil** oil found in the head of various species of whale *Use/s: candles* • **spermaceti wax** fatty substance found mainly in the head of whales and dolphins *Use/s: medicines, candles, cosmetics* • **sponge*** aquatic animal or colony of animals, characterised by a tough elastic skeleton of interlaced fibres *Use/s: bathing aid* • **squalene/squalane*** found in the liver of the shark (and rats) *Use/s: toiletries and cosmetics* • **stearate*** salt of stearic acid *Use/s: body-building supplements* • **stearic acid (E570)*** organic acid prepared from stearin • **stearin(e)*** general name for the three glycerides (monostearin, distearin, tristearin), formed by the combination of stearic acid and glycerin; chiefly applied to tristearin, which is the main constituent of tallow and suet *Use/s: medicines, skin softener in toiletries and cosmetics* • **suede*** kid-, pig- or calf-skin, tanned *Use/s: clothing and footwear* • **suet*** solid fat prepared from the kidneys of cattle and sheep *Use/s: cooking* • **tallow** hard animal fat, especially that obtained from the parts around the kidneys of ruminants *Use/s: soap, candles* • **taurine*** amino acid • **testosterone*** male hormone *Use/s: body-building supplements* • **urea*** nitrogenous waste formed in the liver and excreted by the kidneys *Use/s: toiletries and cosmetics* • **vellum*** fine parchment prepared from the skins of calves, lambs or kids *Use/s: writing material* • **vitamin A*** (retinol) derived from fish-liver oil or egg yolk *Use/s: cosmetics, food supplement* • **vitamin D3 (cholecalciferol)** vitamin derived from lanolin or fish oil *Use/s: vitamin and food supplements* • **velvet*** fabric made of silk, cotton, rayon or nylon *Use/s: clothing* • **volaise** ostrich meat • **whey** residue from milk after the removal of the casein and most of the fat, by-product of cheese making *Use/s: margarines, biscuits, crisps, cleaning products* • **wool** hair forming the fleecy coat of the domesticated sheep and similar animals *Use/s: clothing including felt, mattresses.*

More e-numbers are listed in the following **ANIMAL-DERIVED ADDITIVES section.**

ADDITIVES

A food additive alters the properties of a basic foodstuff or mixture of foodstuffs for the purpose of achieving one, or a combination, of the following: aiding the production process, preserving, or modifying consumer perception. The majority of additives possess no nutritional value.

All the countries of the European Union share a common list of additives. They are preceded with an 'E' to show they have been approved for use within the Union and must be displayed on the labels of all foods containing them. Some additives have no E-numbers and therefore do not have to be declared. These include solvents like ethanol used to dilute other additives such as colourings and to extract flavours. Flavourings constitute the largest group of non-E number additives.

Colourings and dyes that are approved for use in the cosmetics industry within the EU are allocated a Colour Index ('CI') number.

The addition of substances to modify food is by no means a new phenomenon. Salt, for example, has been used as a preservative since about 3000 BCE. However, the sheer number of additives available for use today, the routine and insidious use of animal-derived substances, and the totally unnecessary, morally objectionable requirement to test many new additives on animals all provide the animal free shopper with an incentive to avoid additive-containing products where alternatives are available.

ANIMAL-DERIVED ADDITIVES

• **E120 (CI75470)** carmine/cochineal • **E542** edible bone phosphate • **E901** beeswax • **E904** shellac • **E913** Lanolin • **E966** Lactitol • **E1000** Cholic Acid • **E1105** Lysozyme • **calcium mesoinositol hexaphosphate** • **lactose** • **sperm oil** • **spermaceti**

POSSIBLY ANIMAL-DERIVED

• **E101** riboflavin, lactoflavin, vitamin B_2 • **E101a** riboflavin 5'-phosphate • **E153** (believed animal-free version only may be used in food) carbon black, vegetable carbon • **E161(b)** lutein • **E161(g)** canthaxanthin • **E236** formic acid • **E237** sodium formate • **E238** calcium formate • **E304** Fatty acid esters of ascorbic acid, ascorbyl palmitate and ascorbyl stearate • **E322** lecithin • **E325** sodium lactate

• **E326** potassium lactate • **E327** calcium lactate • **E304** fatty acid esters of ascorbic acid, ascorbyl palmitate and ascorbyl stearate • **E422** glycerol (glycerine) • **E430** polyoxyethylene (8) stearate, polyoxyl (8) stearate • **E431** polyoxyethylene (40) stearate, polyoxyl (40) stearate • **E432** polyoxyethylene sorbitan monolaurate, polysorbate 20, tween 20 • **E433** polyoxyethylene sorbitan mono-oleate, polysorbate 80, tween 80 • **E434** polyoxyethylene sorbitan monopalmitate, polysorbate 40, tween 40 • **E435** polyoxyethylene sorbitan monostearate, polysorbate 60, tween 60 • **E436** polyoxyethylene sorbitan tristearate, polysorbate 65, tween 65 • **E442** glycerol • **E470(a)** sodium, potassium and calcium salts of fatty acids • **E470(b)** magnesium salts of fatty acids • **E471** glycerides of fatty acids, glyceryl monostearate, glyceryl distearate • **E472(a)** acetic acid esters of glycerides of fatty acids, acetoglycerides, glycerol esters • **E472(b)** lactic acid esters of glycerides of fatty acids, lactylated glycerides, lactoglycerides • **E472(c)** citric acid esters of glycerides of fatty acids • **E472(d)** tartaric acid esters of glycerides of fatty acids • **E472(e)** mono and diacetyltartaric acid esters of glycerides of fatty acids • **E472(f)** mixed acetic and tartaric acid esters of mono- and di-glycerides of fatty acids • **E473** sucrose esters of fatty acids • **E474** sucroglycerides • **E475** polyglycerol esters of fatty acids • **E476** polyglycerol esters of polycondensed fatty acids of castor oil, polyglycerol polyricinoleate; polyglycerol esters of dimerised fatty acids of soya bean oil • **E477** propylene glycol esters of fatty acids; propane-1,2-diol esters of fatty acids • **E478** lactylated fatty acid esters of glycerol and propane-1,2-diol • **E479(b)** thermally oxidised soya bean oil interacted with mono- and di-glycerides of fatty acids • **E481** sodium stearoyl-2-lactylate • **E482** calcium stearoyl-2-lactylate • **E483** stearyl tartrate • **E491** sorbitan monostearate • **E492** sorbitan tristearate, span 65 • **E493** sorbitan monolaurate, span 20 • **E494** sorbitan mono-oleate, span 80 • **E495** sorbitan monopalmitate, span 40 • **E570** fatty acids (including myristic, stearic, palmitic and oleic), butyl stearate • **E572** magnesium salts of fatty acids (including magnesium stearate); calcium stearate • **E585** ferrous lactate • **E626** guanylic acid • **E627** guanosine 5′-disodium phosphate, sodium guanylate, disodium guanylate • **E628** dipotassium guanylate • **E628** calcium guanylate • **E631** inosine 5′-disodium phosphate, sodium 5′-inosinate • **E632** dipotassium inosinate • **E633** calcium inosinate • **E634** calcium 5′-ribonucleotides • **E635** disodium 5′-ribonucleotides • **E635** sodium 5′-ribonucleotide • **E640** glycine and its sodium salt • **E631** disodium 5′-inosinate (IMP) • **E920** L-cysteine hydrochloride • **E921** L-cystine • **E1518** glyceryl mono-, di- and tri-acetate (triacetin) • **calcium heptonate** • **calcium phytate** • **diacetin** • **glyceryl** • **leucine** • **monoacetin** • **oxystearin** • and **any unspecified flavourings.**

Lactic acid as an additive is highly unlikely to be derived from dairy (in general commercial terms, 100% of the commercial market is from vegan sources) but if you want to be positive, you should contact the manufacturer.

ANIMAL-DERIVED CARRIERS

Some additives that are not animal derived may involve the use of gelatine as a carrier. These include E104 quinoline yellow, E160a(i) mixed carotenes and E160a(ii) -carotene.

WHY ANIMAL-FREE?

Well, why not? By adopting a vegan diet you can:

● help stop animal exploitation and slaughter
● considerably reduce your environmental impact
● avoid contributing to the hunger of the world's poorest people
● start to feel good about the choices you make every day.

Let's start with the most common reason for going vegan, to save the animals...

CATTLE

Beef Cattle
2.6 million cattle were killed for meat in the UK in 2008. Cattle raised for meat come from two sources, either from animals bred specifically to produce calves for meat production, or the surplus calves created by the dairy industry. It is estimated that around 50% of UK beef is produced from surplus dairy calves.

Some pure bred beef cattle are being bred to be so muscular (and therefore 'produce' more meat) that the breeding cows are unable to give birth and their calves must be delivered by Caesarean section. In effect, cattle are being bred who are unable to reproduce naturally, for the sake of profit.

Meat cattle may live outdoors, be kept indoors on slatted floors with no bedding, or be kept inside during winter. American style feedlots (which are basically battery farming for dairy cows) are gradually being brought in to the UK's system. Indoor cattle may be tethered to prevent them from moving. The calves may be subjected to castration and dehorning, and calves with too many teats may have the extra ones chopped off with scissors.

They will usually be allowed to live for 1-2 years, of a natural lifespan of 25. Cattle are usually slaughtered by first being stunned with a captive bolt, then being hung up by a back leg and bled to death (sometimes cattle are both stunned and killed electrically). Stunning is not always adequate. The animals may face distress and injury from the inadequate or inappropriate restraints and pens. There is potentially very significant pain and distress from the slaughter methods.

Dairy Cows
In order to produce milk the dairy cow must give birth to a calf. As soon as the calf is born s/he forms a strong bond with her/his mother. Yet within two days the calf and mother are usually separated, causing them extreme distress. It is well documented that the cow continuously calls after her calf. This aspect of the dairy industry is inescapable: to leave the calf with her/his mother would cause a loss of revenue because the calf would drink milk that the farmer wants to sell. Therefore it is not a viable option.

The Mother
Three months after the loss of her calf, and while she is still producing milk, the cow is usually made pregnant again. She is put through this exhausting procedure not once but three or four times, until she is deemed to be of no further use to the farmer, whereupon she is killed. More than 20% of dairy cows sent for slaughter have been found to be pregnant and more than a quarter of these pregnancies were in the third trimester.

The Calf
Female calves are often kept to replace old cows and endure the same conditions as their mothers did before them. Male calves of pure dairy breeds are considered too scrawny to rear for beef so are usually sent abroad for veal or killed as useless by-products of the dairy industry.

Organic Milk Production
It is important to differentiate between organic and cruelty-free. Organic does not mean cruelty-free. On organic farms the dairy cow still has to deal with continual pregnancies, forced separation from her calf and slaughter. Castration and disbudding (dehorning) of calves may still be carried out and both can be acutely painful. Under the organic system calves cannot be exported for veal. A small number are raised in the UK to produce rose veal, which involves less confinement and a better diet for the calf, but the calves are still killed at a fraction of their normal life span so that humans can eat their flesh.

BROILER CHICKENS

Almost 800 million chickens were killed for meat in the UK in 2009.

Approximately 98% of all broiler chickens are kept in large, closed sheds with no daylight, often in cramped conditions. Industry guidelines currently allow chickens to be kept at 18-19 birds per square metre, which leaves a space smaller than an A4 piece of paper per chicken and is less than the legal minimum living space required for a battery hen. An official figure allowing a maximum of around 19 birds per m^2 is expected to be made law in England (the EU-wide figure will permit 21 birds per m^2). Even chickens sold as 'free range' are usually kept in large sheds and may be kept at a density of 13 chickens per square metre.

Chickens are often unable to carry out their natural behaviour such as pecking and dust bathing and often cannot even stretch their wings. Lighting is kept deliberately low to discourage activity, leading to eyesight problems. The lighting period is kept long to encourage the birds to eat more, denying them adequate time to rest.

Broiler chickens are bred to put on weight extremely quickly: most conventionally reared chickens go from hatching to reaching their slaughter weight in just six weeks. This abnormally fast growth rate puts massive strain on their body, leading to lameness and heart failure. Some die from starvation or thirst because they can no longer walk to their feeding areas, or from heat stress owing to the high temperature inside their shed. The sheds are not cleaned out during the chickens' lifetime and as a result they suffer breast blisters and burns to their feet and legs from the ammonia produced by their own waste.

At the age of six weeks the chickens are caught and transported to the slaughterhouse. They are usually killed by being shackled upside down by their legs, which itself causes them pain and distress, stunned by immersing their heads in electrically charged water tanks and then killed by bleeding. Smaller birds or those who struggle in their shackles may miss the water bath and bleed to death while still conscious. A significant proportion are killed by gassing. More than 10,000 birds per hour can be killed in some slaughter units, raising concerns about the handling of the animals.

EGGS

The laying hen

Today's egg laying hens are descended from the Red Jungle Fowl (*Gallus gallus*) of Asia which lays around 60 eggs a year. Modern breeds of domestic hen have been selectively bred to lay over 300 eggs a year.

Selective breeding for high egg production has resulted in distinct strains of birds for egg laying and for meat production. Birds of the laying strain do not make good meat birds and as a result male birds of the laying strain, who neither lay eggs nor produce meat efficiently, are killed when a day old.

Female hens in egg farms suffer from a range of welfare problems and restrictions during their lifetime. When the productivity of the flock falls the hens are sent for slaughter and are quickly replaced with more profitable animals. Laying hens are normally only kept for about one year before they are slaughtered - their natural lifespan is around seven years. This slaughter of 'spent' hens takes place even in free-range systems.

FARMING SYSTEMS FOR EGG-LAYING HENS

Battery Cages

In the UK, nearly 17 million laying hens are kept in battery cages which are so small that they cannot stretch their wings, peck, scratch the ground, or perform other natural behaviours such as dust bathing, perching and laying their eggs in a nest.

Battery cages provide a floor space of 550cm² per hen of cage area, equivalent to a piece of A4 paper. A battery cage typically contains four or five hens. The cage floors are sloped up to 21.3% (or 12 degrees) depending on the floor type which may consist of wire mesh. The slope is so that the eggs roll forward for collection by the farmer and puts painful pressure on the hen's toes, causing damage to the bird's feet.

Hens housed in battery cages are susceptible to feather pecking (whereby the hens will attack and peck each other) which occurs in situations of social and physical stress. Feather pecking has also been described as redirected ground pecking because caged hens are unable to ground peck. Feather pecking leads to feather loss and hens may cannibalise birds with exposed flesh. In an effort to prevent feather pecking, farmers debeak the birds (see *debeaking*).

The lack of exercise and high egg production can lead to brittle bones that are easily broken. The Institute of Food Research in Bristol found nearly 30% of caged birds had broken bones by the time they reached the water bath stunner in the slaughterhouse.

Battery systems are to be outlawed in Europe from 2012, but the so-called 'enriched cages' that will replace them are little better.

'Enriched' Cages

Enriched cages must provide at least 750 cm^2 per hen, of which 600 cm^2 should be 'useable area', the remaining area being shared space for items such as a nest box. Enriched cages should have litter, a claw-shortening device and a perch. The extra space in enriched cages is equivalent to roughly a postcard-sized piece of paper when compared to a battery cage and the facilities provided still deprive the birds of the ability to fulfil their natural behaviours.

Birds in enriched cages have slightly better bone health compared to those kept in battery cages, but their bones are still classed as osteoporotic. Birds in enriched cages still exhibit feather-pecking behaviour and are therefore debeaked (see *debeaking*).

Barn Systems

"Barn" eggs are produced from hens kept in flocks confined to a shed with no access to the outdoors. Hens may be stocked at a density of 12 hens per square metre. Litter should be provided for scratching and dust bathing but only needs to cover one third of the ground surface. Nest boxes should be provided at 1 nest box for every 7 hens or a communal nest for every 120 hens. Perches should also be provided allowing 15cm of perch per hen. Hens in barn systems are debeaked in an attempt to control feather-pecking behaviour.

"Free" Range

Birds in free-range systems are stocked in sheds at a density of up to 9 hens per square metre. In addition the hens must have continuous daytime access to open runs that should mainly be covered with vegetation and at a maximum stocking density of 2,500 birds per hectare which equates to 4 square metres per hen. Birds in free range systems may be debeaked to combat feather pecking.

Debeaking

Hens' beaks have an extensive nerve supply, but to combat feather pecking famers debeak them. During debeaking or 'beak trimming' a red-hot blade sears off the end of the bird's beak. Debeaking occurs in caged, barn and free-range systems.

Debeaking is a serious mutilation which results in a significant reduction in preening and pecking afterwards. This reluctance to use the area after amputation is thought to be guarding behaviour in response to pain and discomfort. As feather pecking occurs among stressed birds unable to fulfil their natural behaviours debeaking adds insult to injury by punishing the birds for the systems they are kept in.

Malignant Tumours

Another welfare problem associated with selectively breeding hens to lay more eggs is the development of malignant tumours of the oviduct. In one investigation, a significant proportion of malignant tumours of the oviduct were identified in 20,000 'spent' layers selected from ten different farms. The researchers concluded, "... the increase in the prevalence of the (magnum) tumour coincides with continued selection of fowl for high egg production".

Slaughter of Spent Hens

Most egg-laying hens in the UK are sent for slaughter after a year of egg production. The hens are caught and bundled into crates before being transported by lorry to the slaughterhouse. One study found that at the time of catching and crating, levels of the stress hormone corticosterone in battery hens were 10 times higher than normal. Around 30% of battery hens arriving at the slaughterhouse are reported to have at least one freshly broken bone. The number of freshly broken bones in live birds prior to slaughter and the number of old healed breaks has been described as 'unacceptably high'. 'Spent' hens are considered to be of low value and after slaughter their flesh will be used in chicken soups, pastes, pies, pet food, etc.

Slaughter of Cock Chicks

For every hen hatched for egg laying there is a cock chick that is killed because he is the wrong strain to be raised for meat. Common slaughter methods include gassing, neck dislocation and the 'macerator', a device that shreds chicks alive. Over 40 million day-old chicks are killed in hatcheries in Britain every year.

FISHING AND FISH FARMING

Today it is rarely disputed that fish feel pain; in fact, evidence suggests that fish feel pain, fear and psychological stress and have the capacity to suffer. Not only is fishing cruel but our demand for fish is unsustainable, with many fish populations on the verge of collapse. Omega 3 fatty acids found in fish can easily be gained from plant based sources. By switching to a plant based diet, you're saying "no" to cruelty and giving the world's oceans and waterways a chance to recover.

State of the Oceans

Approximately 80% of the world's fish populations are either fully or over-exploited. In 2006, around 82 million tonnes of fish were caught from the oceans, with a further 10 million tonnes caught from inland waters. The Food and Agriculture Organization of the United Nations (FAO) projects an increase in fish consumption of 40 million tonnes by 2030. If current trends continue it is projected that species that are currently fished will collapse by the middle of this century. In addition to dwindling fish populations, the biodiversity of the oceans is being lost too. Coral reefs are dying at an unprecedented rate, averaging a loss of 600 square miles per year, (or 1% of the total), since the late 1960s. Tropical and subtropical coastal mangrove systems, vital for healthy coral reefs, are being felled and converted to ponds for prawns and shrimps destined for the Western market. Around 20% of the world's mangrove systems have been lost since 1980.

Factory Fish Farms

Some argue that the only way to meet the future demand for fish is to farm them. Fish farming (aquaculture) is now the world's fastest growing food production industry, growing at nearly 9% a year since 1970. Both marine and freshwater fish are farmed. In 2006, 47% of the world's food supply of fish came from farmed fish. In salmon farms, 50,000–75,000 fish can be crowded together in a single underwater cage, resulting in each 75cm long salmon having the equivalent of a bathtub of water to swim in. Trout are usually confined at even higher densities (equivalent to as many as 27 trout to one bathtub). The stress caused by these unnatural conditions (a wild salmon will swim thousands of miles to return to its spawning ground) leads to physical injuries and increased susceptibility to disease. Official figures show that mortality rates among farmed fish are high, 20% of fish may die before they are "harvested".

Disease

Parasites and diseases are common problems for intensively farmed fish. The large concentrations of fish in fish farms attract sea lice, often causing such severe damage to the fish that the skull becomes visible, a condition known as 'death crown'. Other diseases that affect farmed fish include bacterial kidney disease, furunculosis, infectious haematopoietic necrosis and kudoa (soft-flesh syndrome). Antibiotics are administered in an attempt to keep disease at bay. The widespread use of antibiotics in aquaculture has led to several strains of antibiotic-resistant bacteria. Diseases from farmed fish spread to nearby fish populations resulting in increased mortality in wild fish.

Slaughter

In fish farms fish may be starved for up to two weeks before slaughter to empty the gut and reduce the risk of their flesh becoming contaminated during the gutting process. Slaughter methods include clubbing, suffocation in air or on ice, percussion stunning or carbon dioxide stunning. Whichever method is used their gills are then cut to enable the fish to bleed out. The European Food Safety Authority stated in their 2004 report that "many existing commercial killing methods expose fish to substantial suffering over a long period of time". It is not only the fish themselves that suffer. Every year thousands of fish-eating species, including birds and seals, are shot by fishermen and fish farmers. Between 3000-5000 seals are legally shot in Scotland by fishermen and licences are issued for the shooting of cormorants. Around 100,000 albatrosses are killed on longline fishing hooks every year.

INSECTS

Shellac

Lac are insects (*Laccifer lacca*) that live on lac trees, where the female secretes a protective resin over herself. It is this resin, along with encrusted live insects, that is scraped from the trees and used to manufacture shellac. About 200,000 insects are killed for 1kg of shellac. India, Thailand and China are the main exporters. Global production is estimated to be 20,000 tonnes a year. Shellac is used as a glaze for fruit (such as those surprisingly shiny supermarket apples) and sometimes in paint, varnish, tablets, cosmetics, confectionery, floor polish, wood finish and even as a stiffener in hats. It is also occasionally used in the production of dental impression trays and (partial) denture production, and as a fuel in fireworks because of its colour. In foods it is sometimes labelled as E904. Whilst synthetic resin could easily replace shellac entirely, public demand for 'natural' products may actually be encouraging greater production.

Cochineal

Cochineal, also known as carmine, is a red dye used in clothing, cosmetics and foodstuffs. It consists of the dried bodies of *Dactylopius coccus,* an insect indigenous to Central and South America. The insects are killed by immersion in hot water or dried in sunlight or an oven. The method depends on the end colour required. It takes about 150,000 insects to make 1kg of cochineal dye. Cochineal often commands five times the market price of synthetic raw food dyes. Peru produces most of the world's cochineal, with the Canary Islands, Bolivia, Chile and Mexico also exporting. It is found in marinades, alcoholic drinks, bakery products and toppings, cookies, desserts, icings, pie fillings, jams, preserves, juice beverages, sauces and sweets. It can be labelled as "carmine", "natural red 4", "C.I. 75470" and "E120". The pharmaceutical industry uses cochineal to colour pills and ointments. It is also used in cosmetics.

Silk

Silkworm is the common name for the silk-producing larva of several species of moth. The larva is not a worm at all but a caterpillar. The adult moths are extinct in the wild but are reared in large numbers by the silk industry. Silkworms feed mainly on the leaves of the mulberry tree. Silkworm farming is called sericulture.

Typical Commercial Silkworm Production

The first stage of silk production is the hatching of the silkworm eggs, which takes place in a controlled environment. The female lays 300 to 400 eggs at a time, each about the size of a pinhead. The female dies almost immediately after depositing the eggs. The larvae hatch in about approximately 10 days and are about 0.6cm long. Once hatched they are placed under a layer of gauze and fed large quantities of chopped mulberry leaves. Each larva will eat 50,000 times its initial weight in plant material. After four to six weeks, when the larva has achieved its maximum growth, it stops eating, changes colour and attaches itself to a compartmented frame, twig, tree or shrub in the rearing house ready to become a chrysalis.

A Hard Day's Night

Over the next four days the silkworm spins a fibrous cocoon around itself. The cocoon is secreted as a continuous silk fibre up to a mile long from special glands in the silkworm's head. If the adult moth were allowed to emerge from the cocoon naturally, it would secrete an alkali, which would eat through the cocoon. To prevent this the silkworms are killed by heat to preserve the silk cocoon, by immersion in boiling water, steaming or drying in an oven. Only enough adult moths are allowed to emerge to ensure the continuation of the species.

Hundreds Die

The amount of useable silk from each cocoon is small, so it takes hundreds of tiny lives to produce just one silk scarf or tie.

Stud Bank and Breeding Research

A limited number of pupae are allowed to complete their chrysalis stage, the resulting silk moths being the stud bank that produces eggs to breed future generations of silkworm. Researchers are keen to establish silkworm varieties for low-cost cocoons, disease resistance and polyphagy (ability to utilise more than one type of food). As with other types of animal farming, research and technology are used to increase production.

Say No *to* Silk

Silk may be used for suits, coats, trousers, jackets, shirts, ties, lingerie, hosiery, gloves, lace, curtains, linings and handbags. Synthetic fibres such as nylon and polyester are stronger and cheaper than silk. Rayon, composed of cellulose, is another alternative to silk. Fibres from bamboo can be made into fabrics that look and drape like silk. Bamboo fabric is growing in popularity as a more environmentally friendly fabric since bamboo grows easily without any chemical input and helps to stabilise soils.

Honey

Honey, and other bee products such as beeswax, propolis and royal jelly, are animal products and therefore vegans do not consume or use them. In common with other animals kept to produce food products bees are farmed and manipulated, and the honey they produce for themselves is taken from them. Vegans do not eat products taken from any animal, including bees, because it is neither desirable nor necessary to exploit animals in order to obtain food for humans.

To produce honey, worker bees drink nectar from flowers and store it in their honey stomach, where the nectar is mixed with secretions from two glands (including the salivary gland) which will transform the nectar into honey. On returning to the hive the worker bee transfers the nectar to a 'house' bee who drinks the nectar, and may regurgitate and re-drink it several times to mix more secretions with the nectar and may pass it on to another bee to do the same, and then places it in the honeycomb. Each worker bee will produce 1/12th of a teaspoon of honey in her lifetime.

The queen bee is usually killed every year and a new queen introduced to the colony. The queen may have her wings clipped to preventing her from flying; this is to stop the bees carrying out their natural instinct to swarm (the old queen and a large proportion of the bees leaving the nest once the colony has provided a new queen to replace her).

Far from being 'just' simple insects, bees have a complex communication system, display co-operative behaviour and take part in activities such as collective decision-making, organisation and conflict resolution.

Farmed bees are vulnerable to insect attacks and diseases such as American Foulbrood and European Foulbrood, Varroa mites and associated viruses, which have increased significantly in the UK over the last 5-10 years, along with a decline in bee numbers.

One method of dealing with American Foulbrood is to burn the hives while all the bees are inside. Other bee products include beeswax (E904), royal jelly, propolis, venom and bee pollen. Bee products are used as ingredients in cosmetics, candles and toothpaste and as a glaze on sweets.

With so many delicious plant-based alternatives to honey available, there is no need to take honey from bees.

WOOL

Wool production is unavoidably linked to the meat industry. Sheep are farmed for both their wool and their meat: the sheep whose wool is taken will inevitably end up on someone's plate. Many of the lambs produced yearly by ewes kept for wool will be sold straight for meat. Some wool is taken from slaughtered sheep, known as "skin wool".

In the UK, several million lambs are subjected to painful tail docking and castration without anaesthetic every year. Lambs will show signs of pain for several days after being castrated. Lameness due to foot rot is a major welfare problem in UK sheep flocks and is considered an unavoidable part of sheep farming. Many of the lambs born into the industry do not survive their first few days of life - lamb mortality is around 15% in the UK. The process of being sheared is stressful for the sheep.

Australian sheep are commonly subjected to mulesing, a painful procedure where flesh is cut out from their tail area without anaesthetic, to discourage flystrike (maggots attacking the sheep's flesh). Despite the existence of less painful methods of prevention mulesing is still inflicted on many merino sheep, which has led to some major British manufacturers boycotting the use of Australian wool in their products. Some sheep from Australian flocks may be killed during droughts if there is not enough water and food to go around.

Lanolin is a grease which is secreted from sheep's skin and extracted from wool. It is mainly used in cosmetics and to produce vitamin D3, which can be used as a food additive or in supplements, sometimes only labelled as 'vitamin D'. ('Vitamin D' may refer to either to D2 or D3. D2 is the form of vitamin D that is suitable for vegans.)

With so many plant-based and synthetic fibres to choose from, there really is no need to take wool from sheep.

24

PIGS

More than nine million pigs were killed for meat in the UK in 2009.

Most pigs in the EU are raised in intensive farming systems. The majority are kept in appalling conditions: overcrowded, filthy sheds with bare concrete or slatted floors, and barren environments in which they are unable to carry out basic natural behaviours. Although pig welfare in the UK is reported to be not quite as bad as in many other countries, it is estimated that around 40-50% of British pigs are kept in barren environments with no enrichment.

More than 60% of UK sows give birth in farrowing crates. The sow is put in the crate a week before she is due to give birth and kept inside it until her piglets are weaned. The crate prevents her from moving other than to stand up and lie down. She is unable to carry out nest-building or fulfil her instinctive maternal behaviour towards her piglets.

Of the remainder who farrow outdoors, most of their piglets will be transferred indoors by four weeks of age. Only 5% of pigs are reared outdoors and just 1% spend their entire lives outdoors.

In many countries, sows are kept in sow stalls for the entire duration of their 16.5-week pregnancies – metal cages so narrow that the sow cannot even turn round. Sow stalls have already been banned in the UK and Sweden and an EU ban is due to come into force in 2013. However, even after the ban farmers will be permitted to keep sows in sow stalls for the first four weeks of their pregnancies.

The sow will be inseminated again within five to ten days of her piglets being weaned, to repeat the cycle approximately every 140 days. This continues until her 'productivity' declines, when she will be killed. For most sows this will be some time between their second and eighth litters.

Piglets are usually weaned at four weeks of age, much earlier than their natural weaning age of 16 weeks. They commonly suffer from digestive disorders resulting from the sudden removal of their mothers' milk, since they are too young to digest other foods properly. This is 'managed' by routine use of antibiotics. Early weaning is not carried out for the benefit of the sow or piglets, but to allow the sow to be made pregnant again as soon as possible.

Piglets are subjected to various painful procedures including tail docking, teeth clipping and castration, usually without anaesthetic.

Tail docking, where a portion of the piglet's tail is cut off, is carried out to reduce injuries from pigs biting each other's tails. This behaviour is often caused by frustration and boredom at their poor living conditions, particularly lack of straw. 80% of UK pigs and 90-95% of pigs in the EU as a whole are tail docked even though routine tail docking is illegal in the EU. Routine teeth clipping is also banned in the EU, yet around 57% of pigs in the UK have their teeth clipped. It is deemed 'necessary' by some because sows have been bred to produce much larger litters than they naturally would, resulting in the piglets having to fight one another to reach their mother's teats, which risks injury to the sow.

Although castration is uncommon in the UK, overall in the EU 77% of male piglets are castrated without anaesthetic.

Leg disorders are a major problem in farmed pigs, caused by genetic selection and being fed high energy and high protein diets.

Pigs bred for meat are normally killed at 4-6 months of age. Most pigs are stunned with electrical tongs, usually in a group pen where still-conscious pigs can see the others being stunned, then hoisted up by one leg and bled to death. Stunning is not always effective due the tongs not being positioned accurately. Approximately one third of pigs are killed by gassing, which has been shown to cause significant distress to the pigs in the moments before death.

FUR

Global sales figures for fur totalled over £8 billion in the year 2007/08. Fur may come from fur farms or from wild animals. The United States is the world's largest supplier of skin from wild animals. Other countries include Canada and Russia. Trappers use a variety of traps including steel leg-hold traps (now banned in Europe), which do not kill the animal outright and cause immeasurable suffering. Wild animals trapped for their skins by today's fur industry include raccoons, opossums, red foxes, coyotes, bobcats and beavers.

80-85% of fur sold comes from animals farmed in fur farms. Animals such as mink, foxes and rabbits are imprisoned in row upon row of wire cages until they reach the age at which they will be killed for their fur. Europe alone produces over 25 million mink pelts a year. In the UK, long-term campaigning has led to the farming of animals exclusively for their fur being outlawed. Rabbits killed for fur are not a "by-product" of the meat industry. Rabbits bred for the fur trade are a different strain from those bred for the meat trade.

Confined animals can show signs of stereotypical behaviour such as rocking, self-mutilation and cannibalism. Cage sizes in fur farms vary from country to country. Mink cage sizes in Scandinavian fur farms are typically 45cm high, 30cm wide and 90cm deep. In other countries cage sizes may be even smaller. The animals are killed by gassing, neck-breaking, lethal injection, or anal electrocution.

Real fur trim can be found on inexpensive garments such as coats and jackets. Many consumers are unaware that they may be purchasing real fur, since there is no legal obligation to label real fur or label a garment as containing real fur.

LEATHER

The sale of leather makes a sizeable contribution to the viability of the meat industry, contributing up to 10% of the market value of the animal. Leather is not a by-product of animal suffering - it is a contributing factor.

Leather products are not environmentally friendly either. In its natural state as hide or skin, leather would be totally unsuitable for commercial use and would rapidly rot. To make it pliable and longer lasting, the removed animal skin is treated with a wide range of environmentally damaging chemicals such as lime, alkalis, sulphides, ammonium salts, biocides, sodium hypochlorite, fungicides, tanning chemicals, dyes, ammonia and lacquers. In the UK the off-cuts are stained and incinerated or are sent to a rendering plant.

In addition to chemical pollutants, tannery effluent contains large amounts of solid pollutants such as proteins and hair and can be toxic to aquatic life. Many tanneries have relocated their operations from developed to developing countries, which now produce over 60% of the world's leather. Labour is cheaper and human safety laws and environmental regulations are less stringent in most developing countries, meaning that today's cheap leather goods may come at a high cost to humans in the developing world. Hides may be exported from the UK to tanneries abroad for treatment, only to be re-imported as leather goods, increasing the product's environmental impact.

Purchasing leather goods helps to make the rearing and killing of millions of animals a profitable concern. Alternatives to leather include Lorica and hemp, from

27

which vegan shoes and clothing are made. See the clothing section of the *Animal Free Shopper* for a range of vegan footwear suppliers.

VIVISECTION

Every year millions of animals are subjected to painful experiments. According to UK Home Office figures, three and a half million animals were experimented on in the UK in 2008. Sadly this figure represented an increase on the previous year. More than half (65%) of the experiments were conducted without the use of an anaesthetic. In addition millions of purpose-bred animals which are disposed of 'unused' by the vivisection industry are not included in the figures. Nor are those animals killed for blood and tissue products.

Animal experiments are an unreliable way of developing successful medical treatments for humans. The relevance of animal models to human health is questioned because of differences between the species. Animal models are poor models for human disease and cures that would be effective in humans are missed because of the differences. Also debilitating side effects such as depression, fatigue, nausea, headaches, dizziness, hallucinations and blurred or double vision cannot be predicted as they cannot be observed or measured in animals. A review has pointed out the discordance between animal and human studies which may be due to bias or *the failure of animal models to mimic clinical disease adequately.* A British Medical Journal editorial concluded that positive results in animal studies rarely translate to the clinical domain. Previous analysis suggested that only about a third of highly cited animal research translated at the level of human randomized trials. Prior to this publication there was concern that much animal research into potential treatments for humans is wasted because it is poorly conducted and not evaluated through systematic reviews.

An increasing number of scientists and medical professionals are publicly voicing their concerns about the continued use of animals in medical research. A survey of General Practitioners conducted by TNS Healthcare on behalf of the Safer Medicines Campaign found that 82% were concerned that animal data can be misleading when applied to humans and that 83% would support an independent scientific evaluation of the clinical relevance of animal experimentation. Though the UK government has yet to commission such an evaluation, a number of studies question the use of animal models in human medical research. An article in *New Scientist* magazine raised concerns that systematic evaluations reviewing the validity of animal testing are lacking and that those studies that had evaluated the relevance of animal data to humans have found it to have little credibility. For example a 2006 study found that more than two thirds of cited animal research studies did not translate into any meaningful research for people.

SPIRITUAL

Central to the beliefs of many people following an animal-free lifestyle is the desire to strive to reduce harm and show reverence for life, embodied in the spirit of *ahimsa*, the Sanskrit word for non-killing and non-injury championed by Mahatma Gandhi.

Some animal-free shoppers regard the principle of compassion as a major part of their spiritual practice and consider that their animal-free lifestyle is a practical application of their faith, giving them a sense of inner peace.

For a list of organisations that hold vegan and kindred spiritual views, visit www.vegansociety.com/lifestyle/faith or contact the Vegan Society office for a paper copy of our *Spiritual Faith* fact sheet.

ENVIRONMENT

World meat production has quadrupled in the past 50 years and farmed animals now outnumber people by more than three to one. The livestock population is expanding faster than the human population and is projected to continue to expand as the Chinese middle classes increasingly adopt meat-centred diets and as the Western taste for meat, eggs and dairy products continues to grow (along with our waistlines).

This trend will contribute to continuing malnourishment in the developing world, global warming, widespread pollution, deforestation, land degradation, water scarcity and species extinction because more animals mean more crops are needed to feed them: the planet cannot feed both increasing human and farmed animal populations.

So if we are trying to reduce our car use, limit the amount of water we waste, become more 'energy-efficient' and generally lessen our environmental impact, we must also examine one of the most important factors of our personal ecological footprint: what we eat.

CLIMATE CHANGE

When carbon dioxide, methane and nitrous oxide are released into the air they blanket the Earth, trapping heat inside the atmosphere. This is known as the greenhouse effect, and it keeps our planet at a temperature at which life can thrive. The problem is that the massive increase in the output of these and other greenhouse gases since industrialisation has caused the effect to intensify.

Meat eating is responsible for nearly 40 percent of all biological methane emissions. Methane is produced by bacteria in the stomachs of sheep, cattle and goats and is released through the animals' bodily functions. Molecule for molecule, methane is 23 times more potent than carbon dioxide as a greenhouse gas.

Factory farming uses massive inputs of fossil fuels. The vast majority of this energy is used in producing, transporting and processing feed.

A vegan diet uses substantially less energy than a diet based on animal products and therefore contributes much less to air pollution, acidification, oil spills, habitat destruction and global warming.

The felling of forests to grow food for the exploding population of cattle, pigs and chickens results in fewer trees to absorb carbon dioxide and is a major contributor to global warming.

DEFORESTATION

We need forests. They store large amounts of carbon dioxide, release oxygen, regulate climate, prevent floods, protect soils and harbour millions of varieties of plant and animal species. They are also home to tens of thousands of indigenous people whose livelihoods and ways of life are rapidly being destroyed.

Forests are being destroyed not only to provide wood, paper and fuel but also to provide land for grazing cattle and for growing crops to feed farmed animals. The World Resources Institute (WRI) assessments suggest that 20-30 per cent of the world's forest areas have already been converted to agriculture.

As agricultural lands become more and more degraded, most of the land for replacement and expansion comes from the world's forests. The expansion of agricultural land accounts for more than 60 per cent of deforestation worldwide. Most of this land is used to graze beef cattle. The United Nations Food and Agriculture Organisation (UN FAO) report: *Livestock's Long Shadow* states that "by the year 2010 cattle are projected to be grazing on some 24 million hectares of neotropical land that was forest in 2000." This process has become known as the 'hamburgerisation' of the forests.

OVERGRAZING

The WRI states that nearly 40 per cent of the world's agricultural land is seriously degraded. The International Food Policy Research Institute (IFPRI) predicts that if land loss continues at current rates an additional 150-360 million hectares could go out of production by 2020.

Increasing population is therefore not the only factor that we have to consider when looking at future food production. Viable agricultural lands are diminishing, so there is less and less productive soil per person. Continuing to intensify production on already degraded lands is not a sustainable solution.

Overgrazing is responsible for 35 per cent of soil degradation, deforestation for 30 per cent and agriculture for 27 per cent. The main causes are directly or indirectly related to the consumption of animal products.

It is a vicious cycle in which declining soil fertility pushes people to find new land to expand the agricultural base. This often leads to deforestation, which in turn causes soil degradation. This process is the epitome of unsustainable agricultural practice.

WATER SHORTAGES

The United Nations Water Assessment Programme states that "at the beginning of the twenty-first century, the Earth, with its diverse and abundant life forms, including over six billion humans, is facing a serious water crisis." This situation is predicted to worsen as our population expands and consumption per capita increases with more and more people adopting resource-intensive Western meat eating habits.

It takes at least three times the amount of water to feed a meat eater compared with that used to feed a vegan. This is largely because arable land has to be irrigated to make it agriculturally viable and to increase and improve crop yields. As has been shown, much of this land is entirely wasted by growing feed crops for livestock rather than food for direct consumption by people. The water used on this land – as well as that consumed direct by livestock – represents yet another wasted resource. Since a large percentage of the crops fed to European farmed animals are 'grown' in developing countries, this wasted water comes not only from European reserves but also from the very countries where drinking water is most scarce.

WATER POLLUTION

Agriculture is the number one water polluter. Slurry from cattle and other livestock pollutes groundwater, streams and rivers. The livestock sector is probably the largest sectoral source of water pollution. Manure and slurry contain high levels of nitrogen and phosphorous. These elements can leach into groundwater and run off to pollute lakes, killing the fish and endangering the health of humans and other animals. Ammonia is also given off and can cause acid rain. Additionally, demand for animal feed is one of the major reasons behind the intensification of crop production. It is estimated that more than 4.5 billion litres of pesticide are now used annually in the UK. The harmful environmental effect of pesticides is well documented. They can affect wildlife populations – from beetles to songbirds – and many are also deemed detrimental to human health.

TANNERIES

In its natural state as hide or skin, leather would be totally unsuitable for its current uses and would rot rapidly. To make it pliable and longer lasting, the removed animal skin is treated with a wide range of environmentally-damaging chemicals such as lime, sodium sulphate, sodium sulfhydrate, emulsifiers, degreasing agents, salt, aluminium, sulphuric acid, chromium sulphate, caustic soda, formic acid, aniline dyes, and various other chemicals.

Tannery effluent contains large amounts of solid pollutants such as proteins and hair, and can be toxic to aquatic life. Many tanneries have relocated their operations from developed to developing countries, where labour is cheaper and human safety laws and environmental regulations are less stringent. Hides may be exported from the UK to tanneries abroad for treatment only to be re-imported as leather goods, increasing the product's environmental impact.

Far from being a by-product of the meat industry, leather is a significantly profitable part of the slaughtered animal.

GLOBAL FOOD SECURITY AND
THE BENEFITS OF VEGAN, STOCK- FREE FARMING

Growing plant crops to eat 'first hand' makes much better use of resources than animal farming does. One billion people around the Earth are under-nourished, mostly in the developing world. Meanwhile, the United Nations says that over three billion people could live on the grain fed to farmed animals. This is why more and more people are realising the threat that animal farming poses to global food supplies in a world where the human population is projected to grow to 9 billion by 2050.

The farming of animals reduces the food supply for humans because farmed animals use at least half of their food energy for their own life processes (such as movement and metabolism). Instead of farming animals, we can grow plant crops for humans to eat direct, and this will help to ease the global food crisis.

STOCK-FREE FARMING – BENEFITS FOR FARMERS

- Stock-free farmers (arable farmers who don't use manures or other products from farmed animals) avoid the reliance on the livestock industry to produce manure. They are unaffected by fluctuating costs of animal feed and can function well without subsidies.

- Stock-free farms avoid the worry of animal diseases such as Bird Flu, BSE, bluetongue, Newcastle Disease and foot-and-mouth.

- In the UK stock-free farming offers an alternative to the tight margins and low farmer confidence that are currently placing many dairy farmers in a precarious situation.

- Green manures, crop rotation and composting are low cost techniques that can be used in the UK and in developing countries, and training to grow nutritionally balanced plant diets could be made available.

- In the developing world, vegan farming reduces the risk of conflict over scarce water and grazing land and does not require reliance on domestic animals for food when the survival of the animals can be uncertain, for example in times of drought.

HOW MUCH PLANT-BASED FOOD CAN WE PRODUCE?

DEFRA estimates that in terms of calorific requirements UK agricultural land could produce more than enough food from arable production for the entire population.

The area currently being used for crops in the UK is 4.7 million hectares. It is estimated that only 3 million hectares would be required to feed the UK population on a vegan diet, so it is likely that sufficient quantities of suitable land would be available for arable use without having to plough pasture.

A STOCK-FREE LANDSCAPE

Many people may find it difficult to envisage a countryside other than the existing familiar landscape shaped by current farming practices. However, it can be shaped in other ways. For example, land which is currently used for grazing could be used for leisure purposes, fruit and nut trees, biomass and providing woodland habitat for wildlife. Woodland is also a carbon sink, which will help to reduce net carbon emissions.

HEALTHY EATING FOR VEGANS

Sandra Hood BSc (Hons) SRD

One of the most important ways to influence our health is through our diet and as vegans, we often feel that we have to prove that we can be healthy and that we are getting enough of this or that particular nutrient. However, it is all too easy to become obsessed with meeting the nutritional requirements of the general population and forget to look at the other side of the coin and how protective a vegan diet can be.

The mainstay of a healthy diet is plenty of unrefined carbohydrates, such as cereals, pulses and whole grains, plus the important vitamins, minerals and phytochemicals found in fruits and vegetables, and the essential fatty acids found in nuts, seeds and oils. This healthy eating diet has been shown not only to prevent illness but also to treat it. Compared with omnivores, vegetarians have been shown to be at lower risk for conditions such as constipation, diverticular disease, gallstones and appendicitis. Vegan diets have also been used to treat diseases such as angina, diabetes, high blood pressure, rheumatoid arthritis and kidney disease.

In recent years there has been a lot of emphasis on vegans adopting a more raw food oriented or fruitarian diet, and no doubt we should all be including more raw foods in our diet. However, it can also be very bulky and unsuitable for infants and children. Cooking may damage some plant nutrients, but in many cases it alters the structure of nutrients in a way that may actually increase the availability of phytochemicals, resulting in significant health effects. For instance, lycopene (a carotenoid and precursor of vitamin A) is far better absorbed from cooked tomatoes than from raw ones. To maximise benefit from the plant nutrients in the diet, therefore, it is best to include a variety of both raw and cooked foods.

The following paragraphs give a brief outline of nutrients that may be of particular interest to vegans. There are very few rules about what you should or should not eat, but it is important to ensure a reliable source of vitamin B12, and if sun exposure is limited vitamin D supplements or fortified foods should be used.

Aim to eat a variety of whole foods, including the following food groups on a daily basis:

- Fruits
- Vegetables
- Nuts and seeds
- Cereals
- Pulses

ENERGY

Carbohydrates

These are the main energy foods, and half your energy should come from carbohydrates. There are two types of carbohydrates: starchy foods and sugary foods. Try to choose mainly starchy foods such as whole grain bread, pasta, rice, potatoes and cereals. Vegans generally have a high fibre diet with less reliance on refined carbohydrates; in the refining process, essential nutrients are lost.

Fibre

This is the part of a plant that cannot be digested. All plant foods contain fibre. There are two categories of fibre, soluble and insoluble, and most plants contain a mixture of the two. Insoluble fibre adds bulk to stools and ensures that food passes quickly and easily through the intestinal tract. Soluble fibre, found in peas, beans, oats and lentils, has been shown to reduce blood cholesterol levels. Vegans have been shown to consume 40 to 50g of fibre per day compared with 30 to 40g per day for vegetarians and 10 to 20g per day for omnivores. Recommended minimum intakes are 18g per day and the World Health Organisation (WHO) recommends an upper limit of 54g per day. It has been suggested that intakes comparable with those of vegans would be beneficial for health.

It has been reported that excess fibre may reduce the absorption of certain minerals, but high fibre whole foods provide enough extra minerals to more than compensate for any losses incurred. When fibre does bind with minerals, they can be partly released during the fermentation of fibre by bacteria in the large bowel.

Fats

Fats provide vitamins and energy, are essential for the manufacture of hormones and are important for insulation and protection. Fat should provide approximately 30% of adult energy requirements while infants need a higher intake. Most people are confused about the type and quantity of fats. Whether a fat is solid or liquid at room temperature, it will contain the same amount of calories. The main constituents of all fats are fatty acids, which may be saturated, monounsaturated or polyunsaturated, depending on the number of double bonds between the carbon atoms in the molecule. As the number of double bonds increases, the fats become more unsaturated or oily. There are more than 40 fatty acids found in nature.

There is no physiological requirement for dietary fat, only for essential fatty acids.

These are the polyunsaturated fats:

- Linoleic – sunflower, corn, safflower and soya oils
- Alpha-linolenic – linseed, walnut and rapeseed oils

Humans and other mammals lack the enzyme to synthesise them, so they are essential in the diet.

Saturated fats

Saturated fat has been linked with heart disease; it raises cholesterol levels in the blood, and the higher your cholesterol level the greater the risk of suffering a stroke or heart attack. Meat and saturated fat go hand in hand, and animal products are the greatest sources of saturated fat in the Western diet. Milk fat is more than 60% saturated fat, compared with 6 to 25% for plant fats, most being in the 10-15% range. The exceptions are tropical oils such as coconut and palm oil.

Monounsaturated fat

Studies have shown that monounsaturated fats (MUFAs) can reduce the risk of heart disease. Vegan dietary sources include olives and olive oil, rapeseed oil, nuts (such as almonds, cashews, hazelnuts, macadamias) and avocados. MUFAs should provide the main source of fat intake.

Polyunsaturated fat

The main dietary sources are vegetable oils, seeds, nuts, grains, legumes and other plant foods. Studies regarding their health effects are inconsistent, but when they replace saturated fats and trans fatty acids in the diet there is no doubt that they are beneficial. The two essential fatty acids are linoleic and alpha-linolenic acid. Linoleic acid is found in vegetable seeds and oils such as soya, corn, sunflower, safflower, walnuts and grains. Alpha-linolenic acid is found in linseed, rapeseed and walnuts. A high ratio of linoleic to alpha-linolenic acid inhibits the production of eicosapentaeonic acid (EPA) and docosahexaenoic acid (DHA), so it is important that vegans achieve a good balance of polyunsaturated fatty acids to ensure adequate levels of EPA and DHA.

Trans fatty acids (hydrogenated oils)

People believe that they are making healthier choices by changing from butter to margarine, but trans-fatty acids produced in the manufacture of margarine have been shown to be as harmful as saturated fat. Therefore, choose margarines which do not contain hydrogenated oils and avoid processed foods such as crackers, chips, biscuits, pastries and crisps.

PROTEIN

Protein provides the building blocks for new tissue and is vital for the growth and repair of all cells. It can also be used for energy production, if needed, or stored as fat. Protein is made up of 22 amino acids, the building blocks of protein; 8 of these are essential amino acids because the human body cannot make them, but they are easily supplied by plants. Plant sources can provide adequate amounts of essential and non-essential amino acids. Good sources of protein include nuts, seeds, grains (wheat, oats, rice, barley, buckwheat, millet, pasta, bread) and pulses (peas, beans, lentils).

Many people erroneously believe that animal protein is necessary for human health and that plant protein is inferior. Omnivores tend to have protein intakes above recommendations while vegan intakes meet the recommendations. Combining amino acids is unnecessary as they are stored in protein pools which can be drawn upon as needed.

Summary

- Use whole grains in preference to refined grains.
- Ensure a good balance of polyunsaturated fatty acids.
- Monounsaturated fatty acids should provide the main source of fat intake.
- Avoid hydrogenated oils.

VITAMINS

Vitamins are found in small quantities and are essential for normal body functioning. Fat soluble vitamins are A, D, E and K. Water soluble vitamins are B and C. With few exceptions, vitamins cannot be synthesised by the body and must be obtained from the diet. A vegan diet can provide all the vitamins necessary for good health. The following are of particular interest to vegans:

Vitamin C
Vitamin C is a powerful water soluble antioxidant, neutralising harmful reactions in the blood and the fluid inside the surrounding cells. Vegans and vegetarians are at a distinct advantage here and need to lead the way in the health revolution.

Vitamin D
Vitamin D3 is normally obtained from lanolin, which is derived from sheep's wool and not acceptable to vegans. Spending time outside reduces your need for foods fortified with vitamin D. When sun exposure is limited, a vitamin D supplement may be necessary. Vitamin D promotes the absorption of calcium and is essential for bones and teeth. Foods fortified with a vegan source of vitamin D (vitamin D2, ergocalciferol) include margarine, fortified cereals and some fortified non-dairy milks.

Vitamin B12

This vitamin is essential for the formation of red blood cells and a healthy nervous system. Some plant foods may contain vitamin B12 on their surface from soil residues, but this is not a reliable source. Much of the vitamin B12 present in spirulina, sea vegetables, tempeh and miso has been shown to be an inactive form rather than the active vitamin. So if you are not taking foods fortified with vitamin B12, ensure that you take a supplement. The UK government recommends 1.5 micrograms per day as sufficient to reliably prevent clinical deficiency, but higher intakes are required to avoid elevated homocysteine and associated increased mortality. The Vegan Society therefore recommends that all vegans get at least 3 micrograms of B12 every day to maximise the health benefits of their diet. (For further details, see www.vegansociety.com or contact The Vegan Society for a B12 information sheet.)

Summary

- Ensure regular exposure to sunlight for adequate vitamin D.
- Ensure a daily source of vitamin B12.

MINERALS

There are a number of minerals essential for health, but most are only needed in small amounts which come from a varied diet of whole grains, fruits, vegetables, nuts and seeds. The two main minerals needed in larger amounts which are of some interest to vegans are iron and calcium.

Calcium

Studies have found that vegan diets may be below current recommendations for calcium. Claims are commonly made that vegans require less calcium than omnivores, based on the lower acid production resulting from metabolism of plant proteins. This has not been resolved. Although oxalates, phytates and fibre in plant foods decrease calcium availability, research shows that absorption of calcium from many plant foods is excellent. Calcium absorption from low oxalate vegetables such as broccoli and kale is better than for cow's milk while absorption from beans, nuts and seeds is lower. Good vegan sources of calcium include dark green leafy vegetables such as spring greens and kale, calcium-set tofu, baked beans and fortified foods.

Iron

Vegan diets are higher in total iron content than omnivorous diets, but iron stores are lower in vegans because the iron from plant foods, known as non-haem iron, is less well absorbed than the haem iron found in meat. However, iron deficiency anaemia is no more common in vegans than in omnivores. Vitamin C and other organic acids commonly found in vegetables strongly enhance the absorption of non-haem iron. Vitamin C intakes of vegans are frequently high and this, in conjunction with generous levels of dietary iron, may compensate for the lower bioavailability of non-haem iron. Good iron sources include whole or enriched grains and grain products, iron-fortified cereals, legumes, green leafy vegetables and dried fruits.

Zinc

Diets of vegans and non-vegans often contain similar amounts of zinc. However, zinc from plant foods is less well absorbed as some plant foods contain phytate which interferes with zinc absorption. However, no reports of zinc deficiency in vegans have been found. Zinc is an essential component of a number of enzyme systems within the body and is widely distributed in plant foods. Good sources include nuts, seeds, beans and cereals.

Iodine

Iodine is needed by the thyroid gland to produce the thyroid hormone which regulates physical and mental development, including growth, reproduction and other essential functions. Iodine deficiency is rare in the UK. The main source of iodine in the UK is cow's milk, due to iodine supplemented cattle feed and the contamination of milk from teat dips containing iodophors as sterilising agents. Sea foods are rich sources of iodine, with dried seaweed being a popular choice for vegans. Two kelp tablets (with a declared iodine content between 150 and 250 micrograms) per week will ensure sufficient iodine; more than this is not desirable.

Summary

- Calcium absorption from low oxalate vegetables such as broccoli and kale is good.
- Vitamin C aids iron absorption.
- Good sources of zinc are nuts, seeds, beans and cereals.
- Seaweed is rich in iodine.

PHYTOCHEMICALS

It has been known for a long time that fruits and vegetables, grains, seeds, nuts and pulses are good for you, being rich in vitamins, minerals and fibre, but in the past few years there has also been interest in the phytochemicals, which have been shown to have many health benefits.

Some phytochemicals are strong antioxidants which mop up free radicals (active harmful molecules circulating in the body).

A special group of phytochemicals are the plant oestrogens, which block the deleterious action of the potent form of oestrogen either by competing with it for receptor sites or by reducing production of the potent form while increasing production of the less potent form, possibly reducing the risk of osteoporosis and certain types of hormone-dependent cancers. Concerns have been raised regarding the potential adverse effects of phytoestrogens in soya infant formulas, and the best food for babies is certainly breast milk. Nevertheless, where breast feeding is not possible there is a role for soya infant formulas, which have been used for many years without any reports of adverse effects other than occasional allergy. For children and adults, soya should be regarded as another healthy food to be added to the diet in moderation.

Another important group are the plant sterols - a type of fat which has been shown to protect against heart disease. There are no dietary recommendations for sterols, but plant sterols have been shown to be beneficial in lowering cholesterol; high levels of cholesterol in the blood can cause heart disease. The average Western diet contains 180 to 400mg plant sterols per day while the vegan diet contains 600 to 800mg per day.

Useful references

Davis B, Melina V (2000) Becoming Vegan: the complete guide to adopting a healthy plant-based diet, Book Publishing Co. Summertown.
Key TJ, Davey GK, Appleby PN (2001) *Health benefits of a vegetarian diet,* Proc Nutr Soc 58 271-275.
Walsh S (2003) *Plant Based Nutrition and Health*, The Vegan Society.

Sandra Hood is a State Registered Dietician and author of The Vegan Society's Raising your Vegan Infant - With Confidence. For more information, or to order your copy, go to www.vegansociety.com/shop or call 01424 427 393.

VEGAN NIUTRITION GUIDELINES

To ensure that vegans maintain good health it is important to:

- Eat plenty of brightly coloured fruit and vegetables, including dark green leafy vegetables.

- Eat plenty of wholefoods (brown bread, brown rice, etc).

- Include in your diet each day at least three micrograms of vitamin B_{12} from fortified foods or 10 micrograms from a supplement (no other vegan source of vitamin B_{12} has been shown to be reliably effective).

- Expose your face and arms to the sun for 15 minutes per day whenever you can (if your shadow is much longer than you, the sun is not strong enough). If your sun exposure is limited (for example in a British winter), or if you are dark skinned, make sure that you get 10 to 20 micrograms of vitamin D_2 each day from fortified food or a supplement.

- Ensure a source of iodine such as kelp or take a supplement. It is important to take neither too much nor too little iodine, since both overdose and underdose can be harmful. A good intake is 15 to 30 grams of kelp (kombu) *per year* or a daily supplement containing 100 to 150 micrograms of iodine.

- Try to get at least 500 mg per day of calcium from calcium rich foods or supplements.

- Consume a tablespoonful of ground flaxseed or a teaspoonful of (uncooked) flaxseed oil each day if possible, or consume other omega 3 rich oils. For example you could use two tablespoons of rapeseed oil (which does not have a strong taste) in place of other vegetable oils such as sunflower or corn oil.

FUTHER NUTRITION INFORMATION

The Vegan Society produces a free booklet, *Plant Based Nutrition,* which can be downloaded from our website at *www.vegansociety.com/resources/downloads.aspx* or contact the Vegan Society office for a copy. For more in-depth information on vegan nutrition, our comprehensive book *Plant Based Nutrition and Health* is only £7.95.

VEG 1

The Vegan Society's *VEG 1* supplement is a convenient source of vitamin B_{12}, vitamin D_2, iodine and selenium at a very low cost: £4.99 for three months adult supply or six months for a child under twelve. Other nutrients are generally well supplied from a varied intake of unrefined plant foods.

OTHER ETHICAL CONSIDERATIONS

To qualify for inclusion in the Animal-Free Shopper a product need only be free of animal ingredients and animal testing. However, whilst avoiding products that have direct animal involvement is a very positive and far-reaching ethical stance, many animal-free shoppers choose to make purchases on a range of additional ethical considerations for the sake of humans, animals and the environment — such as:

- **vegan ownership** Some shoppers prefer to support those companies which are wholly or partly owned by vegans (see **KEY**, page iii)
- **product range** Many companies manufacture or distribute both animal and non-animal products. Given the choice, many animal-free shoppers prefer to buy from those companies whose entire range is animal-free (see **KEY**, page iii)
- **company activities** A number of companies manufacturing or distributing animal-free (and animal) products are involved directly in animal abuse — such as the meat and dairy industries.
- **company connections** Some seemingly innocuous companies have parent, sister or subsidiary companies which are involved directly in animal abuse such as animal testing or the dairy and meat industry. See company details (page 373) for parent companies of listed brands.
- **company affiliations** Possible animal abuse affiliations include: The British Industrial Biological Research Association (BIBRA), Research Defence Society (RDS), Countryside Alliance, Game Conservancy.
- **company sponsorships & donations** Companies producing animal free products may donate to medical research charities involved in vivisection or may sponsor sporting events that involve animals.
- **organised boycotts** Even large multi-national companies have ceased an objectionable activity when threatened with, or subjected to, a boycott campaign. In some instances boycotts can result in a significant financial loss. Though not always successful, it is argued that boycotts are a useful means by which to heighten public awareness.
- **pesticide use** The excessive use of chemical pesticides and fertilisers damages the environment and kills wildlife. Many animal-free shoppers prefer to avoid contributing to the destruction of our countryside and instead chose organic products, we have printed organic products in bold and highlighted those companies whose entire product range is organic (see KEY page iii).
- **vegan organic farming** While organic farming is kinder to the environment and it's animal inhabitants compared to chemical farming, an increasing number of animal free shoppers are seeking fruits and vegetables that have been produced through vegan farming methods. Stock free organic systems avoid all chemical inputs, animal manure and slaughterhouse by-products such as blood powder, bone meal and fish meal etc

- **genetically-modified organisms** See **GENETICALLY-MODIFIED ORGANISMS**, (page 8 and **KEY**, page iii).
- **fair trade** As humans are animals too many animal free shoppers are choosing to by fairly traded products. The Fairtrade Foundation's Fairtrade mark ensure minimum standards related to pay, working conditions, and local and environmental sustainability are met

Recognising that human and animal rights are inextricably linked and that all life is dependent upon the well-being of the planet, the animal-free shopper might also wish to avoid companies involved in or with: cash crops, environmentally damaging practices, irresponsible marketing, land rights, low wages and poor conditions, and oppressive regimes.

As well as boycotting certain goods, many shoppers actively seek out products that promote a cleaner environment or seek to improve workers' rights. Organic and fair trade products are now available almost everywhere in the UK, with the number and variety of products increasing all the time. You can find contact details for organisations promoting these aspects of food production in the USEFUL ADDRESSES section, page 46.

FURTHER INFORMATION

The Ethical Consumer Research Association *www.ethicalconsumer.org*
0161 226 2929   Unit 21, 41 Old Birley St, Manchester M15 5RF

Publishes The Ethical Consumer: a magazine providing information on companies behind brand names across a range of ethical issues, including animal testing, factory farming, fair trade and environmental impact. Also publishes many reports on various issues on its website.

CONTACT NETWORKS

BUSINESS

- **Vegan Business Connection** www.veggies.org.uk/directory
  networking@veggies.org.uk 0845 458 9595
- **Vegan Village** postie@veganvillage.co.uk, www.veganvillage.co.uk

FAMILIES

- **Vegan Family House** www.veganfamily.co.uk
- **Vegan Society Families' List** *www.vegansociety.com* info@vegansociety.com
  0121 523 1730
- **Vegetarian and Vegan Families** lesley@vegan4life.org.uk 0208 941 8075

INTERNATIONAL

The Vegan Society has members all over the world and there are organised groups in most countries. Information about these groups can be found here: *www.vegansociety.com/about/international-organisations.aspx*

LOCAL CONTACTS AND GROUPS

In addition to our offices in Birmingham, The Vegan Society has a network of local contacts throughout the UK. These are members who have offered to act as a point of contact for people interested in the Society's work. So if you are interested in becoming more involved in local campaigning, or if you need advice on being vegan in your area, they are the people to speak to.

Details of Local Contacts and Local Groups are published on our website www.vegansociety.com/about/local-contacts.aspx, in *The Vegan* or are available on request. If you would like to become a local contact, please contact our Contacts Coordinators (UK and Éire) on cc@vegansociety.com or 0121 523 1738.

SOCIAL

- **London Lesbian Vegans** japope_1982@hotmail.co.uk,
  www.groups.yahoo.com/group/lvegangroup
- **Vegan Camp** www.vegancamp.co.uk gmforrest@tiscali.co.uk
- **Vegan Runners** www.veganrunners.makessense.co.uk
  veganrunners@talktalk.net 07967 589663
- **Veggie Snow** www.veggiesnow.org veggiesnow@makessense.co.uk
  0118 946 4858
- **Young Indian Veg*ans** www.youngindianvegetarians.co.uk
  animalahimsa@yahoo.co.uk 020 8681 8884

USEFUL ADDRESSES

ANIMAL EXPERIMENTS & ALTERNATIVES

- **British Union for the Abolition of Vivisection** www.buav.org 0207 700 4888
- **Dr Hadwen Trust for Humane Research** www.drhadwentrust.org 01462 436819
- **Safer Medicines Campaign** www.curedisease.net 0208 265 2880
- **FRAME** (Fund for the Replacement of Animals in Medical Experiments) www.frame.org.uk 0115 958 4740
- **Humane Research Trust** www.humaneresearch.org.uk 0161 439 8041
- **Lord Dowding Fund for Humane Research** www.ldf.org.uk/research/ 0207 630 3340
- **National Anti-Vivisection Society** www.navs.org.uk 0207 630 3340
- **Physicians' Committee for Responsible Medicine** www.pcrm.org
- **Uncaged** www.uncaged.co.uk 0114 272 2220

BLOODSPORTS

- **League Against Cruel Sports** www.league.uk.com

CIRCUSES & ZOOS

- **Captive Animals' Protection Society** www.captiveanimals.org 0845 330 3911
- **Born Free Foundation** http://www.bornfree.org.uk/ 01403 240 170

'DEVELOPING WORLD'

- **Help International Plant Protein Organisation** (HIPPO) *http://www.hippocharity.org.uk/* The Old Vicarage, Llangynog, Carmarthen SA33 5BS
- **Vegfam**, www.vegfamcharity.org.uk 01550 721197

GARDENING & GROWING

- **Garden Organic** www.gardenorganic.org.uk 02476 303517
- **Movement for Compassionate Living**
  http://www.iwvv.org.uk/indexMCL.htm mcl.ystalyfera@googlemail.com
- **Plants for a Future** www.pfaf.org
- **Stockfree Organic** http://www.stockfreeorganic.net/ 0845 223 5232
- **Vegan Organic Network** www.veganorganic.net 0845 223 5232

PRISONERS' SUPPORT (FOR ANIMAL RIGHTS/VEGAN PRISONERS)

- **Vegan Prisoners' Support Group** VPSG, BM 2107, London WC1N 3XX
  www.vpsg.org 0208 292 8325

47

RELIGIOUS

- **Anglican Society for the Welfare of Animals** www.aswa.org.uk 01252 843093
- **Catholic Concern for Animals** www.all-creatures.org/ca 15 Rosehip Way, Bishops Cleeve, Cheltenham, Glos, GL52 8WP
- **Christian Ecology Link** www.christian-ecology.org.uk 0845 4598460
- **Christian Vegetarian Association UK** www.christianvegetarian.co.uk 01428 723747
- **The Fellowship of Life** www.all-creatures.org/fol 43 Braichmelyn, Bethesda, Bangor, Gwynedd LL57 3RD
- **Humanist Vegetarian Group** www.humanist.veggroup.org 01803 858576
- **Islamic Concern** www.islamicconcerns.com
- **Kindness Unlimited** www.ivu.org/ku PO Box 188, Ross-On-Wye HR9 9DS
  Latter Day Saints Vegetarian/Vegan Support www.ldsveg.org
- **The Mary T and Frank L Hoffman Family Foundation** www.all-creatures.org/ff
- **The Methodist Animal Welfare Group**
  www.christianecology.org.uk/mawg.htm 32 Balderton Buildings, Balderton St, London W1Y 1TA
- **Quaker Concern for Animals** http://quaker-animals.co.uk/ 30 Sherry Lane, Arrowe Park, Wirral CH49 5LS
- **Vegan Pagans** http://veganpagans.tribe.net/
- **VeggieJews** http://groups.yahoo.com/group/VeggieJews/

SPORTS

- **Vegan Bodybuilding** www.veganbodybuilding.org
- **Vegetarian Cycling & Athletic Club** www.vcac.vegfolk.co.uk
- **Vegan Runners** www.veganrunners.makessense.co.uk 01908 503919

THEORY OF ANIMAL RIGHTS

- **Animal Rights FAQs** www.speciesism.com
- **Animal Rights: The Abolitionist Approach** (Prof. Gary Francione), www.abolitionistapproach.com
- **Culture and Animals Foundation** www.cultureandanimals.org

WILD ANIMALS

- **Badger Trust** www.nfbg.org.uk 0845 828 7878
- **Born Free Foundation** http://www.bornfree.org.uk/ 01403 240 170
- **British Hedgehog Preservation Society** www.britishhedgehogs.org.uk 01584 890801
- **Care for the Wild International**, www.careforthewild.com 01306 627900
- **Fox Project** www.foxproject.org.uk 01892 826222
- **Jenita Fox Rescue** Oak Tree Cattery, Main Rd, Colden Common, Winchester, SO21 1TL 02380 692309
- **Seal Sanctuary** www.sealsanctuary.co.uk 0871 423 2110
- **Tiggywinkle's** (Wildlife Hospital), www.sttiggywinkles.org.uk 01844 292292
- **The Wildlife Trusts** www.wildlifetrusts.org 01636 677711

SUGGESTED READING

There is now a wide range of literature related to vegan food and cookery, nutrition, vegan living, animal rights, activism and ethics. One of the roles of the Vegan Society is to provide resources to make vegan living as easy as possible. The Society provides information on a wide range of vegan topics including nutrition, parenting, recipes, becoming vegan and issues such as farmed animals, the environment and food security.

Information resources we provide include: our extensive website www.vegansociety.com; free information packs and fact sheets (available by email and post); leaflets and booklets for distribution; catering guides for restaurants, hospitals and care homes.

BOOKS

Some of the titles below are available from the Vegan Society. You can view the full range of products and purchase items on our online shop at *http://shop.vegansociety.com/*. Alternatively, contact the Sales department for product details or to buy over the phone on 0121 523 1730.

Note: The titles listed below may not have been written from an entirely animal free viewpoint but are included on the basis of their educational or practical value.

ACTIVISM

Campaign Against Cruelty Alex Bourke and Ronny Worsey, Scamp Media (2001)
Strategic Action for Animals Melanie Joy, Lantern Books (2009)
Striking at the Roots: A Practical Guide to Animal Activism Mark Hawthorne, O Books (2008)
The Animal Activist's Handbook Matt Ball and Bruce Friedrich, Lantern Books (2009)
The Lifelong Activist: How to Change the World Without Losing Your Way Hillary Rettig, Lantern Books (2006)

ADDITIVES

A Consumer's Dictionary of Food Additives Ruth Winter, Three Rivers Press (2004)
Animal Ingredients A-Z The EG Smith Collective, AK Distribution (2004)
Not on the Label: *What Really Goes into the Food on Your Plate* Felicity Lawrence, Penguin Book Ltd (2004)

ANIMAL CARE

Vegetarian Cats and Dogs James Peden, Harbingers of a New Age (1995)
The simple little vegan dog book: cruelty-free recipes for canines Michelle A. Rivera, Book Publishing Co. (2010)

ANIMAL EXPERIMENTS & ALTERNATIVES

Caught in the Act: *Feldberg Investigation* Melody MacDonald, Jon Carpenter (1994)
Sacred Cows and Golden Geese Jane Goodall & Dr C R Greek & J S Greek, Continuum International Publishing Group (2002)
Slaughter of the Innocent Hans Ruesch, Slingshot (2003)
Specious Science C Ray Greek & Jean Swingle Greek, Continuum (2003)
Vivisection or Science: An Investigation into Testing Drugs and Safeguarding Health Pietro Croce, Zed Books (2000)
Vivisection Unveiled: An Exposé of the Medical Futility of Animal Experimentation Dr Tony Page, Jon Carpenter (1997)
What Will We Do If We Don't Experiment On Animals? Medical Research for the Twenty-first Century Jean Swingle Greek, C. Ray Greek, Trafford Publishing (2006)

ANIMAL RIGHTS/ETHICS

Animal Century: A Celebration of Changing Attitudes to Animals Mark Gold, Jon Carpenter (1999)

Animal Liberation Peter Singer, Ecco (2001)

Animal Rights: A Very Short Introduction David DeGrazia, Oxford University Press (2002)

Animal Welfare: Limping Towards Eden John Webster, Wiley Blackwell (2005)

Animals as Persons: Essays on the Abolition of Animal Exploitation Gary L Francione, Columbia University Press (2008)

Animals, Politics & Morality: Second Edition Robert Garner, Manchester University Press (2005)

Animals, Property, and the Law Gary L. Francione, Temple University Press (1995)

Born to be Wild Juliet Gellatley, The Women's Press (2001)

Empty Cages: Facing the Challenge of Animal Rights Tom Regan, Rowman & Littlefield Publishers (2005)

Eternal Treblinka: Our Treatment of Animals and the Holocaust Charles Patterson, Lantern Books (2002)

Introduction to Animal Rights: Your Child or the Dog Gary L. Francione, Temple University Press (2000)

Making a Killing: The Political Economy of Animal Rights Bob Torres, AK Press (2008)

On Their Own Terms: Bringing Animal-Rights Philosophy Down to Earth Lee Hall, Nectar Bat Press (2010)

Rain Without Thunder: The Ideology of the Animal Rights Movement Gary L. Francione, Temple University Press (1996)

The Case for Animal Rights Tom Regan, University of California Press (2004)

The Dreaded Comparison: Human and Animal Slavery Marjorie Spiegel, Mirror Books (1997)

The Extended Circle: An Anthology of Humane Thought Jon Wynne-Tyson, Open Gate Press (2008)

The Face on Your Plate Jeffrey Moussaieff Masson, W. W. Norton & Co (2009)

The Pig Who Sang to the Moon: The Emotional World of Farm Animals Jeffrey Moussaieff Masson, Ballantine Books (2003)

The Savour of Salt: A Henry Salt Anthology George and Willene Hendrick, Open Gate Press (1989)

The Silent Ark Juliet Gellatley, HarperCollins (1996)

Why Animal Suffering Matters: Philosophy, Theology, and Practical Ethic Andrew Linzey, Oxford University Press (2009)

Why We Love Dogs, Eat Pigs and Wear Cows: An Introduction to Carnism Melanie Joy, Conari Press (2010)

BABIES & CHILDREN

Benji Bean Sprout Doesn't Eat Meat! Sarah Rudy, Sun King Pub and Graphics (2004)

Compassionate Kids: Raising Children the Vegan Way Helen Hewitt & Jacqulyn Edwards, Magpie House (2005)

Feeding your Vegan Infant – With Confidence Sandra Hood, The Vegan Society (2005)

Go Vegan Go! Seamus Brough, Magpie House (2006).

Happy, Caring, Healthy & Sharing – a book for young green vegans Graham Burnett, Land & Liberty (1991)

Raising Vegan Children in a Non-Vegan World Erin Pavlina, VegFamily (2003)

Raising Vegetarian Children Joanne Stepaniak & Vesanto Melina, Contemporary Books (2003)

The Amazing Adventures of Wonderpig Phil Tutton, Wonderpig Publishing (2007)

Vegan Eating for Kids Dana Villamagna & Andrew Villamagna, Alpha Books (2010)

Vegetarian and Vegan Mother and Baby Guide Rose Elliot, Viva! (2003)

CATERING

Profit From Emerging Dietary Trends John Hartley, Go Publish (2000)

CIRCUSES AND ZOOS

Animals in Circuses and Zoos – Chiron's World? Marthe Kiley-Worthington, Aardvark Publishing (1997)

Rattling the Cages: 50 Years of Campaigning for Animals Captive Animals Protection Society (2007)

The Rose-Tinted Menagerie William Johnson, Heretic Books (1994)

COOKERY BOOKS

Alternative Vegan: International Vegan Fare Straight from the Product Aisle Dino Sarma, Tofu Hound Press (2007)

Another Dinner is Possible Isy Morgenmuffel, Mike Home Brew, Anarchist Teapot & Active Distribution (2007)

A Vegan Taste of France Linda Majzlik, Jon Carpenter (2003)
A Vegan Taste of Greece Linda Majzlik, Jon Carpenter (2003)
A Vegan Taste of India Linda Majzlik, Jon Carpenter (2002)
A Vegan Taste of Italy Linda Majzlik, Jon Carpenter (2001)
A Vegan Taste of Mexico Linda Majzlik, Jon Carpenter (2002)
A Vegan Taste of North Africa Linda Majzlik, Jon Carpenter (2003)
A Vegan Taste of Thailand Linda Majzlik, Jon Carpenter (2004)
A Vegan Taste of the Caribbean Linda Majzlik, Jon Carpenter (2001)
A Vegan Taste of the Middle East Linda Majzlik, Jon Carpenter (2002)
Authentic Chinese Cuisine Bryanna Clark Grogan, Book Publishing Company (2000)
Cook Vegan Richard Youngs, Ashgrove Publishing (2001)
Easy Vegan Cooking: Over 350 Delicious Recipes for Every Occasion Leah Leneman, Thorsons (1998)
Fat-Free & Easy Jennifer Raymond, Heart & Soul Publications (1997)
Green Gastronomy Colin Spencer, Bloomsbury (1996)
Healing Foods Cookbook: The Vegan Way to Wellness Jane Sen, HarperCollins (2000)
Incredibly Delicious: Recipes for a New Paradigm M. Katz, Gentle World (2003)
Japanese Cooking Miyoko Nishimoto Schinner, Book Publishing Company (1999)
Kitchen Doctor – Vegan Cooking for Health Nicola Graimes, Southwater (2003)
La Dolce Vegan!: Vegan Livin' Made Easy Sarah Kramer, Arsenal Pulp Press (2007)
More Fabulous Beans Barb Bloomfield, Book Publishing Company (2003)
Nonna's Italian Kitchen Bryanna Clark Grogan, Book Publishing Company (1998)
Quick and easy vegan comfort food Alicia C. Simpson, The Experiment (2009)
Simple Treats Ellen Abraham, Book Publishing Company (2003)
Simply Vegan Debra Wasserman & Reed Mangels, Vegetarian Resource Group (US) (1999)
So What Do You Eat? Liz Cook (1999)
The Absolutely Animal-Free Cookbook Wendy Turner, The Book Guild (1997)
The Angelica Home Kitchen Leslie McEachern, Ten Speed Press (2003)
The Artful Vegan Eric Tucker with Bruce Enloe/desserts by Amy Pearce, Ten Speed Press (2003)
The Cake Scoffer Ronny, Vegan International Cake Engineers (2000)
The Everyday Vegan Dreena Burton, Arsenal Pulp Press (2003)
The Health Promoting Cookbook Alan Goldhamer, Book Publishing Company (1997)
The Joy of Vegan Baking: The Compassionate Cooks' Traditional Treats and Sinful Sweets Colleen Patrick-Goudreau, Fair Winds Press (2007)
The Passionate Way of Vegan Baking (e-book) Günter Eberwein, www.guntersvegancakes.com
The Joy of Vegan Cookery Amanda Grant, Metro Publishing Ltd (2002)
The Uncheese Cookbook Joanne Stepaniak, Book Publishing Company (2003)
The Vegan Cookbook Alan Wakeman and Gordon Baskerville, Faber & Faber (1996)
The Vegan Gourmet: Full Flavor and Variety with over 100 Delicious Recipes Susann Geiskopf-Hadler & Mindy Toomay, Prima Publishing (1999)
The Whole Foods Diabetic Cookbook Patricia Stevenson, Michael Cook & Patricia Bertron RD, Book Publishing Company (2003)

Vegan Tony Weston and Yvonne Bishop, Hamlin (2004)
Vegan Baking Linda Majzlik, Jon Carpenter (2000)
Vegan Barbecues & Buffets Linda Majzlik, Jon Carpenter (1999)
Vegan Cookies Invade Your Cookie Jar Isa Chandra Moskowitz & Terry Hope
Romero, Da Capo Press (2009)
Vegan Cooking: Recipes for Beginners Eva Batt, Thorsons (2002)
Vegan Cooking for Everyone Leah Leneman, HarperCollins (2003)
Vegan Cooking for One Leah Leneman, Thorsons (2000)
*Vegan Cupcakes take Over the World: 75 Dairy-free Recipes for Cupcakes
that Rule* Isa Chandra Moskowitz & Terry Hope Romero, Da Capo Lifelong (2008)
Vegan Dinner Parties Linda Majzlik, Jon Carpenter (1998)
Vegan Feasts Rose Elliot, Thorsons (2000)
Vegan Recipes Nicola Graimes, Southwate (2006)
Vegan Rustic Cooking for all Seasons Diana White, Vegan Organic Trust (2002)
Vegan Vittles: Second Helping: Down-Home Cooking for Everyone Joanne
Stepaniak, Book Publishing Company (2007)
Vegan with a Vengeance: Over 150 Delicious, Cheap, Animal-free Recipes
Isa Chandra Moskowitz, Grub Street (2007)
Veganomicon: The Ultimate Vegan Cookbook Isa Chandra Moskowitz & Terry
Hope Romero, Da Capo Lifelong (2008)
Vegan Yum Yum Lauren Ulm, Health Communications (2009)
Vice Cream: Gourmet Vegan Desserts Jeff Rogers, Celestial Arts (2004)

ETHICAL SHOPPING/LIVING

*The Good Shopping Guide: Certifying the UK's Most Ethical Companies
and Brands* Charlotte Mulvey, The Ethical Marketing Group (2010)
The Rough Guide to Ethical Living Duncan Clark, Rough Guides (2006)

FEMINISM & ANIMAL RIGHTS

Animals & Women: Feminist Theoretical Explorations CJ Adams & J
Donovan, Duke University Press (1995)
Feminist Care Tradition in Animal Ethics: A Reader Josephine Donovan &
Carol Adams, Columbia University Press (2007)
Neither Man Nor Beast: Feminism and the Defence of Animals Carol
Adams, Continuum International Publishing Group Ltd (2003)
The Pornography of Meat Carol Adams, Continuum International Publishing
Group (2003)
*The Sexual Politics of Meat: A Feminist-vegetarian Critical Theory: Tenth
Anniversary Edition* Carol Adams, Continuum International Publishing Group Ltd (2000)

FOOD

Food For Free Richard Mabey, Collins (2004)
Food Wars: The Global Battle for Mouths, Minds and Markets Tim Lang & Michael Heasman, Earthscan (2004)
Poison on a Plate: Dangers in the Food we Eat and How to Avoid them Richard Lacey, Metro Books (1998)
The Atlas of Food (2nd ed.) Erik Millstone & Tim Lang, Earthscan (2008)

GARDENING

All New Square Foot Gardening: Grow More in Less Space! Mel Bartholomew, Cool Springs Press (2006)
Forest Gardening Robert A de J Hart, Green Earth (1996)
Growing Green: Organic Techniques for a Sustainable Future Jenny Hall and Iain Tolhurst, Vegan Organic Network (2006)
How to Grow More Vegetables: And Fruits, Nuts, Berries, Grains, and Other Crops Than You Can Imagine John Jeavons, Ten Speed Press (2006)
Permaculture: A Beginners' Guide Graham Burnett, Land & Liberty (2000)
Plants for a Future Ken Fern, Permanent Publications (1997)
Sprout Garden Mark M Braunstein, Book Publishing Company (1999)
The Earth Care Manual: A Permaculture Handbook for Britain and Other Temperate Countries Patrick Whitefield, Permanent Publications (2004)
The Gaia Natural Garden: Gardening in Harmony with Nature Peter Harper, Jeremy Light & Chris Madsen, Gaia Books (2005)

MEAT/DAIRY INDUSTRIES

Animal Pharm: One Man's Struggle to Discover the Truth about Mad Cow Disease and Variant CJD Mark Purdey, Clairview Books (2007)
Cannibals, Cows and the CJD Catastrophe Jennifer Cooke, Random House USA Inc (2000)
Chew on This: Everything You Don't Want to Know About Fast Food Eric Schlosser, Puffin Books (2006)
Don't Worry (It's Safe to Eat): The True Story of GM Food, BSE and Foot and Mouth Andrew Rowell, Earthscan Publications (2003)
Fast Food Nation: What the All-American Meal is doing to the World Eric Schlosser, Penguin Books Ltd (2002)
Meat Market: Animals, Ethics, & Money Erik Marcus, Brio Press (2005)
Slaughterhouse: The Shocking Story of Greed, Neglect and Inhumane Treatment Inside the U.S. Meat Industry Gail A. Eisnitz, Prometheus Books (2006)
The Meat Business – Devouring A Hungry Planet Geoff Tansey & Joyce D'Silva (eds) Earthscan (1999)

NUTRITION & HEALTH

10 Days to Better Health Kirsten Hartvig & Dr Nic Rowley, Piatkus Books (2003)
Becoming Vegan Brenda Davis & Vesanto Melina, Book Publishing Company (2000)
Diet, Life Expectancy and Chronic Disease: Studies of Seventh-day Adventists and other Vegetarians Gary E Fraser, OUP (2003)
Dr Neal Barnard's Program to Reverse Diabetes Now MD Neal Barnard, Rodale (2007)
Feel-Good Food Susie Miller & Karen Knowler, The Women's Press (2000)
Foods That Fight Pain Neal Barnard, Bantam Books (1999)
Love Yourself, So Hate the Weight! Brother Craig, Woodbridge Press (1996)
Plant Based Nutrition and Health Stephen Walsh PhD, The Vegan Society (2003)
The Dietitian's Guide to Vegetarian Diets Virginia Messina, Reed Mangels and Mark Messina, Jones & Bartlett Publishers (2004)
The Vegan Diet as Chronic Disease Prevention: Evidence Supporting the New Four Food Groups Kerrie Saunders, Lo Scarabeo (2004)
Vegan Nutrition: Pure & Simple Michael Klaper MD, Book Publishing Company (1987)
Vegan + Sports: Vegan Nutrition and Endurance Sports Arnold Wiegand, (2006)

RAW FOOD

Becoming Raw Brenda Davis and Vesanto Melina, Book Publishing Company (2010)
Eat Smart Eat Raw: Detox Recipes for a High-Energy Diet Kate Wood, Grub Street (2002)
Naked Chocolate: Uncovering the Astonishing Truth About the World's Greatest Food Shazzie, Raw Creation Limited (2005)
Raw Food Made Easy Jennifer Cornbleet, Book Publishing Company (2005)
Raw Living: Detox Your Life and Eat the High Energy Way Kate Wood, Grub Street Publishing (2007)
Warming Up to Living Foods Elysa Markowitz, Book Publishing Company (1998)

TRAVEL

The New Spain – Vegan & Vegetarian Restaurants Jean-Claude Juston, available from www.vegetarianguides.co.uk
The Vegan Passport (3rd ed.) George Rodger (ed.), The Vegan Society (2010)
Vegan Guide to New York Rynn Berry, Chris Suzuki & Barry Litsky, Ethical Living (2005)
Vegetarian Britain Alex Bourke, Vegetarian Guides (2006)
Vegetarian Europe Alex Bourke, Vegetarian Guides (2000)
Vegetarian Guide to the Lake District Angie Greenaway, Viva! (2008)
Vegetarian Journal's Guide to Natural Foods Restaurants: In the U.S. and Canada Vegetarian Resource Group (2005)

Vegetarian London Alex Bourke, Vegetarian Guides (2008)
Vegetarian Visitor Annemarie Weitzel (2010)

VEGANISM

Abundant Living in the Coming Age of the Tree Kathleen Jannaway, MCL (1999)
Being Vegan Joanne Stepaniak, McGraw-Hill (2003)
Diet for a New America: How your Choices Affect your Health, Happiness & the Future òf Life on Earth John Robbins, H J Kramer (1998)
The Food Revolution: How your Diet can Help Save your Life and our World John Robbins, Conari Press (2001)
The Livewire Guide to Going, Being and Staying Veggie Juliet Gellatley, Trafalgar Square Publishing (1997)
The Vegan Sourcebook Joanne Stepaniak, McGraw-Hill Companies (2001)
Vegan Freak: Being Vegan in a Non-Vegan World (2nd ed.) Bob Torres & Jenna Torres, Tofu Hound Press (2010)
Vegan Stories Julie H Rosenfield (ed.), The Vegan Society (2002)
Vegan: The New Ethics of Eating Erik Marcus, McBooks Press (2003)
Why Vegan? Kath Clements, Heretic (1995)

VERSE

Explicit Vegan Lyrics: The Little Book of Vegan Poems Benjamin Zephaniah, AK Distribution (2001)
Talking Turkeys Benjamin Zephaniah, Puffin Books (1995)

MAGAZINES

Animal Action (youth magazine) and *Animal Life* (RSPCA) www.rspca.org.uk 0300 1234 555
Animal Times (PETA) www.peta.org.uk 020 7357 9229
Animals Defender & Campaigner (Animal Defender International) www.ad-international.org 020 7630 3340
Cook Vegetarian! http://www.cookveg.co.uk/ 0844 856 0648
Ethical Consumer www.ethicalconsumer.org 0161 226 2929
Farm Animal Voice (Compassion in World Farming) www.ciwf.org.uk 01483 521 950
Get Fresh (The Fresh Network) www.fresh-network.com/ 0845 833 7017
Green Futures (Forum for the Future) www.forumforthefuture.org.uk 01223 564334

Lifescape http://www.lifescapemag.com/
Outrage (Animal Aid) www.animalaid.org.uk 01732 364546
Resurgence www.resurgence.org 01237 441 293
The Ecologist www.theecologist.org 020 7422 8100
The Vegan (Vegan Society) www.vegansociety.com 0121 523 1730
The Vegetarian (Vegetarian Society) www.vegsoc.org 0161 925 2000
Vegan Views www.veganviews.org.uk
Veggie Health (Vegetarian and Vegan Foundation) www.vegetarian.org.uk
0117 970 5190
VegNews www.vegnews.com
Viva! Life - Viva! www.viva.org.uk 0117 944 1000
Wales Vegan / Figan Cymreig Bron yr Ysgol, Montpellier Park, Llandrindod,
LD1 5LW

VEGAN COMPANIES WHICH ARE TRADEMARK HOLDERS

Ace Outdoors
Adorn Mineral Cosmetics
Alexami Cosmetics
All Seasons Health
Alpro UK Ltd
amaZene
Anila's Authentic Sauces Ltd
Aqua Natural
Aquados Ltd
Arise and Shine Cosmetics Ltd
Aroma Comforts
Aromafoods
Aromatherapy Products Ltd
Aussie Mineral Makeup
Babycakes Direct
Beanie's Health Foods
Beauty Without Cruelty
Bellecare AG
Bernds Welt
BetterThanks Inc
Bio-D
Biofun bvba
Bourgeois Boheme
Brackencraft
Buckingham's Oativa
Cadaleah Home Bakers
Calder Valley Soap Co. Ltd
Clearspring
Cocada Fresco (UK) Ltd
Cosmetic Innovations Australia PTY Ltd
Cracker Drinks Co.
Cyberdyne Technologies Ltd, T/A Mama Shamba
Deva Nutrition LLC
Diet Freedom
Dipak Foods Ltd
Dolma
Earth Friendly products UK
Eau+ Ltd
EJs Conscious Chocolate
Empathy Skincare Ltd (Natural Empathy)

ESB Developments LTD
Essentially Yours Ltd
Eternity Designs International PTY Ltd
Excellart
Fauser Vitaquellwerk KG
First Grade International LTD
Five Star Foodies
Flex Enterprises Ltd
Freerangers
Fry Group Foods
Funk Bubble
Georgas Family
Green Valley Trading Co
Green Wych ltd
Halo Skincare Ltd
Happy Kitchen
Hedgecraft
Hemp Global Solutions Ltd
Hippy Heaven Natural Beauty
Honesty Cosmetics Ltd
Ilustre
Katharine Botanicals Ltd
Kitchen Buddy (Culinary Courses) Raw Chocolate
Konrad Haberberger Handels- und Consulting GmbH
Kuching Herbal Tea
Lifefood Czech Republic s.r.o.
Little Valley Brewery Ltd
Majik Blankit Skin Care
Manakedi Skincare
Mandala Mineral Cosmetics (Sircus)
Misshu Ltd T/A Lani-Jo
MJ Health(NZ) Ltd
Mooncup Ltd.
Ms. Cupcake
MuLondon
Mulu Chocolate Ltd
My Handmade Soaps
NAE, LDA
Naked Lunch .DA
Natural by Nature Oils
Nature Complete Ltd
Neuaura
NOHARM

NVS Ltd
Ole Hyvä Luonnontuote Oy
Organatural
Organic Connexion
Organic Soap Company
PharmaBrand USA LLC
Pitfield Brewery
Polar Sun Products Ltd
Pure Gaisha
QianNa Agricultural Products Ind & Trading Co. Ltd
Rare Natural Care, Inc.
Raw Alchemy Ltd
Raw Gaia
Raw Indulgence
Redwood Wholefood Company
Rimon Winery
Rosie's Gourmet Products (UK) Ltd
Sahfee Halal Care
Sant'Or
Scottish Herbal Supplies
Seagreens Ltd
Sensory Revolution, LLC
Shambhu's
Silver Wing Ltd
Simple System LTD
Skin Blossom Limited
Skinvac
Sophie's Kitchen
Source-Omega LLC
SpaRitual
Sunrise Granola
Talooza Inc
Tanjero
Tara Smith Limited
The Booja-Booja Company Ltd
The Green Superfood Company LLP
The Raw Chocolate Company Limited
The Raw Chocolatier
TOPAS
Treasured Earth Skincare
Truthful Co. Ltd (Purely Skincare)
Tunch Foods Ltd
Upcakes

Urban Jungle SARL
Vanilla Tree Natural Skin Care
Vegan Perfection
Veganline
Vegantisch
Vegetarians Choice
Violii
Visionary Soap Company
X35 Energy Ltd
XL Energy Marketing SP 200
Yaoh
Yozuna

VEGAN CATERERS AND EATERIES

222 Veggie Vegan Restaurant
Fairfoods
Gobble Green
Green Garden Cafe
Itadaki-Zen
MIAMO World Foundation for Wellbeing
Shambhu's
The Gentle Gourmet
Veggierose
Veggies Catering Campaign

VEGAN GUEST HOUSES

Fox Hall
The Barn
The Lodge

ANIMAL FREE SHOPS

The outlets listed below are run by vegans and only stock vegan products

- **Cardiff** *Pulse Wholefoods* 171 Kings Road, Cardiff CF11 9DE 029 2022 5873 www.pulsewholefoods.com
- **Derby** *Soundbites* 11 Morledge, Derby DE1 2AW 01332 291369 www.soundbitesderby.org.uk
- **Gwynedd** *Vegonia Wholefoods* 49 High Street, Porthmadog, Gwynedd, LL49 9LR 01766 515195
- **London** *Bourgeois Boheme* Hydrex House, Garden Road, Richmond TW9 4NR 0208 8788 388 www.bboheme.com
- **London** *FareShares food co-op* 56 Crampton Street, London SE17 3AE www.fareshares.org.uk
- **London** *Green Borders* 476 High Road, Leytonstone, London E11 3HN 020 8539 0941 www.greenborders.co.uk
- **London** *Vx* 73 Caledonian Road London N1 9BT 020 7833 2315 www.secretsocietyofvegans.co.uk/shop/
- **Manchester** *Unicorn* 89 Albany Rd, Chorlton, Manchester M21 0BN 0161 861 7675 www.unicorn-grocery.co.uk
- **Nantwich** *Vegonia Wholefoods* 8 Oatmarket Nantwich CW5 5AL 01270 618 647
- **Nottingham** *The Screaming Carrot* 42 Foxhall Road, Forest Fields, Nottingham NG7 6LJ 0115 910 3013 www.screamingcarrot.co.uk
- **Tyne and Wear** *Alternative Stores* Brunswick Industrial Estate, Tyne & Wear NE13 7BA www.alternativestores.com
- **West Midlands** *One Earth Shop* 54 Allison Street, Digbeth, Birmingham B5 5TH 0121 632 6909
- **Wirral** *Honest to Goodness* 33 Market Street, Hoylake, Wirral CH47 2BG 0151 6326516 www.honest-to-goodness.org.uk

FOX HALL VEGAN B&B
@ PRIZET STABLES,
Helsington, Kendal,
Cumbria, LA8 8AB

Tel:- Sylvia or Chris on 015395 61241
Email:- fox.hall@btinternet.com
Website:- www.fox.hall.btinternet.co.uk

We are 2 miles south of Kendal, South Lakes, 10 mins by car from M6 junction 36, 20 mins from Windermere on the A591 & 10 mins from Oxenholme railway station.

- ✓ *4 Guest Rooms, all en-suite*
- ✓ *Children very welcome*
- ✓ *Special Diets catered for*

- ✓ *Evening Meals available*
- ✓ *Organic food*
- ✓ *Vegan Cookery Courses*

Our nearest tourist attractions are Levens Hall & Sizergh Castle. There are good local walks along the Lancaster to Kendal Canal towpath, River Kent and into Levens Park as well as Scout Scar & The Helm.

Registered by the Vegan Society

"A no-smoking, vegan family home with organic food where children are always welcome"
Please visit our website for more up-to-date information on accommodation, availability, location, menus, cookery courses and much more!

FOOD

FOOD

BISCUITS

BILL'S NATUURBAKKERIJ ™
Cookies: **Almond Wholemeal Cookies, Cardamon Wholemeal Cookies, Coconut & Lemon Cookies, Kamut Cinnamon Cookies, Muesli Cookies, Oat Cookies, Organic Fruit Biscuits 50g, Organic Multigrain Biscuit 50g, Raisin Cookies, Raisin-filled cookies, Spiced Wholemeal Cookies, Wholemeal Cookies;** *Gluten Free Cookies:* **Coffee Gluten Free Cookies, Vanilla Gluten Free Cookies;** *Speculoos:* **Sesame Speculoos;** *Spelt Cookies:* **Apple & Cranberry Spelt Cookies, Ginger & Walnut Spelt Cookies, Spelt Sesame Cookies;** *Waffles:* **Wheatsyrup Waffles**

BIOFAIR
Spelt Brazil Nut Cantuccini Cookies

BIONA
Spelt Fruit Hearts; Sunflower Cookies

BLACKFRIARS BAKERY
Flapjacks: Apple & Raspberry, Apple & Sultana, Date & Walnut, Fruit, Original

BURTON'S FOODS LTD
Coconut Rings; Country Snapjacks; Rich Tea

CLIVE'S PIES ⊘
Flapjacks: Almond & Apple, Chocolate Chip, Original Oat, Sultana & Apple

DOVES FARM FOODS LTD ⊘
Chocolate Chip Cookies; Digestives; Double Chocolate Cookies; Fruity Oat Biscuits; Ginger & Brazil Nut Cookies; Hazelnut Cookies; Lemon Zest Cookies

ESSENTIAL TRADING CO-OPERATIVE LTD ™❶⊘✔
Organic Flapjacks: **Almond Fruit, Chocolate Chip + Brazil Nut, Date + Apricot, Vine Fruit**

GLUTEN FREE FOODS LTD
Barkat: Ice Cream Cones, Waffle Ice Cream Cones

GRANOVITA UK LTD ⊘✔
Organic Flapjack with LinuSprout: Apricot, Chocolate Chip, Cranberry, Ginger, Linseed & Raisin, Pumpkin & Sunflower Seed, Raisin, Apple & Cinnamon, Traditional Oat

HANDMADE FLAPJACK COMPANY LTD
Flapjack: Apricot, Brazil Nut Cluster, Cherry & Coconut, Date & Walnut, Fruit, Plain, Raspberry

HAPPY KITCHEN ™☺❶⊘✔
Cookie: **Fairly traded chocolate & raisin, Fairly traded ginger & nut, Gluten free granola**

IL MANGIARSANO S.P.A ™⊘✔
Mangiarsano Conventional Bakery Products : **Shortbread Biscuits**

KALLO FOODS ⊘
Thin Slice Slightly Salted Rice Cakes with Sesame

MCVITIES
Butter Puffs; Fruit Shortcake; Ginger Nuts; Lincoln; *Hob Nobs:* Original

ORGANICO ⊘ ✿
Break & Bil: Spelt Tea Biscuits

ORGRAN ☺
Biscotti: Amaretti, Choc Chip, Lemon & Poppy Seed; *Cookies:* Apricot & Coconut, Sultana & Cinnamon

PETER RABBIT ORGANICS ⊘ ✿
Organic Cookies: Appley, Orange & Raisin

QUINUA REAL BRASIL LTDA ™⊘
Cookie Flavour Cocoa; Cookie Flavour Vanilla; Granola Traditional

RJ FOODS LIMITED ™ ✔
Flapjacks: **Apple & Apricot, Cherry & Coconut, Cherry & Sultana, Date & Walnut, Fig, Fruit and Nut, Fruit Bar, Plain, Raspberry, Rum & Raisin, Rum & Raisin**

THE FOOD DOCTOR LTD ✔
Food Bar: Apple & Walnut, Apricot & Almond, Fig & Mango, Pineapple & Banana

TRAIDCRAFT PLC ⊘
Brazil Nut Cookies; Stem Ginger Cookies

TRIALIA FOODS AUSTRALIA ™
Eskal Noble Choice : **Scottish Chocolate Chip Shortbread, Scottish Shortbread**

UNITED BISCUITS LTD ⊘
Crawford's: Ginger Nuts, Morning Coffee

WHOLEBAKE LTD ⊘
Mixed Crisp Bars; *Flapjack Bites:* Cherry, Sultana & Apple; *Organic Flapjack:* Mixed, Original; *Wholebake Flapjacks:* Almond, Apple, Apricot, Banana, Berry, Cherry, Cranberry, Hazelnut, Mixed Fruit, Mixed Nut, Pecan, Pistachio, Premium Mixed, Sesame, Walnut

BREADS, ROLLS, PIZZA BASES ETC

ALLIED BAKERIES
Balmore: Balmore Batch Loaf; *Burgen:* Soya & Linseed Bread, Wholegrain and Cranberry Bread; *Country Maid:* White Bread; *Dayofresh:* White Bread

ALLINSON
Bread: Sunflower and Pumpkin Batch Bread, HiBran, Wholemeal Batch

AMISA
Hildegard Whole Spelt Bread; Hildegard Wholegrain Spelt Melba Toasts; *Crispbread:* Buckwheat Wholegrain, Corn & Rice

BIONA
Biodiet Gluten-Free Bread: Corn/Lupin, Four Grain Pizza Base, Millet, Rice, Rice & Sunflower Seed, Rice/Buckwheat Seed; *Long Life Bread:* Pumpernickel, Rye, Rye & Hempseed, Rye & Pumpkin Seed, Rye Amaranth, Rye Omega 3, Rye w Sunflower Seed; *Pizza Base:* Mini, Original, w Spelt Flour

CUISINE DE FRANCE

12"" Thin Crust Pizza Base; *Bagel:* Blueberry, Cinnamon & Raisin, Everything, Healthier Option, Multigrain, Plain, Poppy, Sesame; *Baguette:* Classic Demi, Demi, Granary Demi, Half, Malted Grain Demi, Plain, Poppy Seeds Half, Rusticata, Sourdough, Triple Grain, Triple Grain Demi; *Baps:* Granary, Kara Floured; *Batard:* Cross Cut, Small White; *Bloomer:* Granary, Malted Brown, Organic White, Plain, Poppy, White; *Bread:* 5 Grain Loaf, Almond/Apricot Loaf, Bouchon, Ciabattina Olive Bread, Country White Sourdough Oval, Cranberry, Cranberry & Rosemary, Golden Grain Seeded Tin Loaf, Granary Sandwich, Grand Rustique, Green Olive Focaccia, Harvester, Healthier Option White, Large Sun Dried Tomato Plait, L'Art Du Pain Parisienne, Longuet Rustic, Malted Brown, Malted Grain Petit Pain, Malted Grain Rusticata, Multigrain Shamrock, Olive Oval, Onion & Herb Loaf, Pain Complet, Pain du Couronne, Pain Rustique, Panini, Parisien, Pecan Raisin Oval, Petit Pain, Petit Pain Sandwich, Petite Parisienne, Plain Rusticata, Premium White Tin Loaf, Provencale Herbs Focaccia, Roasted Garlic Loaf, Rosemary Olive Oil Round, Rustic Flatbread, Rustic Sandwich Bread, Rustic Square, Seeded Rye Loaf, Seeded Tin Loaf, Small Bocata, Soft Grain, Split Tin Malted Brown, Split Tin White, Square Artic Flatbread, Stencilled Organic White Bread, Sundried Tomato Boutarde, Tear & Share, Triple Grain Loaf, Value French Stick, White Iced Fingers, White Loaf, White Petit Batard, Wholemeal Farmhouse Loaf, Wholemeal Tin; *Buns:* Plain Burger, Seeded Burger; *Ciabatta:* Mini, Plain, Rustica, Sandwich Roll, w Extra Virgin Olive Oil; *Doughnut:* Jam, Ring; *Rolls:* Brown, Classic Dinner, Cranberry & Rosemary Gourmet Rolls, Crusty Brown, Crusty White, Harvester Batched Crusty, Onion & Herb Gourmet Rolls, Rectangular Rustique, Rustic, Rustic Dinner, Sandwich, Seeded Classic Dinner Roll, Sun Dried Tomato Rolls, Triple Grain Roll, White Continental; *Wraps:* Plain, Tomato

DEES CARIBBEAN IMPORTS

HTB Jamaican Spiced Bun

DISCOVERY FOODS

Tortillas: Bakery, Garlic & Coriander, Gluten Free Corn, Plain Wheatflour

G. COSTA & CO ⊘

Granforno Breadsticks: Garlic Breadsticks, Plain Breadsticks, Sesame Breadsticks

GENERAL DIETARY

Pizza Bases; *Bread:* Brown Rice, Low-Protein Rice, Tapioca, White Rice; *Loaf:* Flax, Gluten-Free, High Fibre White, Raisin, Seattle Brown, Six Flour, Yeast-Free Rice; *Rolls:* Dinner, White Long, White Round

GLUTEN FREE FOODS LTD

Glutano: Wholemeal Sliced Bread, WM Sliced Bread Snack Pack

GR WRIGHT & SONS LTD ☺⊘

Bread Mixes: Ciabatta, Garlic & Rosemary Foaccia, Malty, Mixed Grain, Organic Stoneground Wholemeal, Premium White, Sunflower, Wholemeal

HOVIS
Best of Both; Classic Cut; Granary; Original Wheatgerm; Seeded Granary; White Farmhouse; White Half; White Square Cut; Wholemeal; Wholemeal Farmhouse

KINGSMILL
Gold Farmhouse Soft White Bread; Oatilicious Bread; Plain White Bread; Toastie White; *50 50:* (Note: 50 50 with Omega 3 is NOT vegan), Crusts Away, Medium 800g, Rolls, Thick 800g; *Crusts Away:* White Bread; *Gold Seeds & Oats:* Soft and Crunchy Bread, Wholesome and Nutty; *Great Everyday:* Sliced White Rolls, Soft White Bread, Soft White Rolls, Tasty Wholemeal Rolls, Wholemeal Bread; *Little Big Loaf:* Great Everyday White, Love to Toast White, Seeds and Oats Soft and Crunchy, Seeds and Oats, Wholesome and Nutty, Tasty Wholemeal; *Love to Toast:* 4 Muffins, 6 Crumpets, White Bread, Wholemeal Bread

LANSON VENTURES ™ ⊘ ⚓
Pappadum: **Black pepper, Coriander leaves & garlic, Madras masala, Madras plain, Mixed masala, Red Chilly flakes, Red Chilly powder**

MOTHERS PRIDE
Brown; White; White Danish

NEW YORK BAGEL CO. ⊘
Cinnamon & Raisin; Multi-seeded; Onion and Poppyseed; Plain; Seeded Bran; Sesame

NIMBLE
White; Wholemeal

ORGANICO ⊘ ✿
Rustic Classic Breadstick; Rustic Sesame Breadstick; Rustic Spelt Breadstick; Rustic Wholewheat Breadstick

ORGRAN ☺
Bread Mix; Pizza & Pastry Mix

PATAKS FOODS ⊘
Chapattis: Garlic & Herb, Plain; *Pappadums:* All varieties

PAUL'S TOFU ™ ⊘ ⚓ ✿
Breads: **Foccacia, Four Seed, Fruit Rye, Gluten Free Number One Sourdough, Gluten Free Number Three Sourdough, Gluten Free Number Two Sourdough, Light Rye, Melton Loaf, Olive Bread, Organic Herb Bread, Organic Individual Baguette, Organic Melton Loaf, Organic Rolls, Organic Sesame Rolls, Organic Tea Cakes, Organic Unbleached White, Organic Yeast Free Wheat Free Rye Bread, Organic Yeasted Bread, Organic Yeasted Malthouse, Organic Yeasted Mixed Seed, Organic Yeasted Spelt Bread, Organic Yeasted Stoneground Wholemeal, Pain de Campagne, Pane Basilicum, Rye & Sweetcorn Sourdough, Sechskorn, Sourdough 4 Seed Bread, Sourdough Bread Yeast Free, Sourdough Rice, Spelt Sourdough, Tsampa Sourdough, Unbleached White Bread, White Rolls**

REBECCA'S CAKES ™
Gluten and wheat free brown bread; Gluten and wheat free white bread; Vegan Pizza

SUNBLEST

Crumpets; Muffins; *Bread:* Brown, Danish White, Longlife White, Scottish Plain Batch Bread, White, Wholemeal; *Rolls:* Brown, Scottish Morning Rolls, White

WARBURTONS ⊘

12 Large Sandwich Rolls; 12 Sliced Fruity Teacakes; 12 Sliced Sandwich Rolls; 3 Seeded Sandwich Rolls; 3 Wholemeal Soft Sandwich Rolls; 4 Fruity Teacakes; 4 Large Sandwich Rolls; 4 Oven Bottom Muffins; 4 Sandwich Rolls; 4 Toasting Muffins; 6 Crumpets; 6 Grains & Seeds Lunch Rolls; 6 Round Potato Cakes; 6 Sliced Sandwich Rolls; 6 White Lunch Rolls; 6 Wholemeal Lunch Rolls; 6 Wholemeal Rolls; Fruit Loaf with Orange; Raisin Loaf with Cinnamon; *400g:* Crusty, Danish White, Half Loaf Stoneground Wholemeal Batch, Medium White, Seeded Batch, Soft White Farmhouse, Toastie White, Wholemeal Medium; *600g:* All in One, Tasty Grains & Seeds, Tasty White, Unsliced Tiger Brown, Unsliced Tiger White, Wholegrain Goodness; *800g:* Brown Farmhouse, Medium White, Our Thickest Slice White, Seeded Batch, Soft White Farmhouse, Stoneground Wholemeal Batch, Toastie White, Wholemeal Medium; *Weight Watchers:* Brown Danish, Malted Danish, Thick White, White Danish, Wholemeal Thick

BREAKFAST FOODS

ALARA WHOLEFOODS LTD

Gluten-Free Muesli: Everyday Delight, Goji Berries & Cranberries, Luxury; *Muesli:* Active, Branberry, Date with Cocoa, Fruit Seed & Spice, Goji Berries and Pineapple, Rich, Tropical, Very Berry; *Porridge:* OT Chocolate, OT Strawberry, OT Vanilla

AMISA

Hildegard Spelt Pops

BACHELDRE WATERMILL ORGANIC FLOWERS

Stoneground Fine Bran Flakes

BIOFAIR

Andean Muesli; Quinoa Pops

BIONA

Amaranth Fruit Muesli; Amaranth Popcorn

DOVES FARM FOODS LTD ⊘

Chewy Rice Pop & Chocolate Cakes; Corn Flakes; Tropical Cereal Bar; Whole Wheat Cereal Biscuits

ESSENTIAL TRADING CO-OPERATIVE LTD ™ ❶ ⊘ ◀

Essential Brand- Muesli (Organic & Conventional): **Cereal Base, Date + Apricot, Deluxe, Fine Organic, Fruit + Nut, Harvest, Organic, Organic Apple + Cinnamon Cereal, Organic Cereal Base, Organic Deluxe, Organic Fruit Crunch, Organic Strawberry + Cashew Crisp, Sultana**

Crunch, Sunflower, Super Hi-fibre, Tropical; *Essential Brand-Muesli (Organic & Conventional):* **Organic Date + Apricot**

GLUTEN FREE FOODS LTD

Barkat: Organic Chocolate Cornflakes, Organic Chocolate Rice Crunchies, Organic Muesli, Organic Porridge Flakes; *Glutano:* Cornflakes

GRANOVITA UK LTD ⊘ 🍂

Classic Flakes

GREENCITY WHOLEFOODS ❶⊘

Crunchy Muesli; De Luxe Muesli; Deluxe Muesli; Five Star Muesli; Gluten-Free Muesli; High Fibre Muesli; Highland Bramble Crunch; Muesli Base; No Coconut Muesli; Paradise Muesli; Super Muesli; Super Muesli No Coconut

HEMP GLOBAL SOLUTIONS LTD ™☺

Amaru: **HemPower**

IL MANGIARSANO S.P.A ™⊘ 🍂

Germinal Organic Bakery: **Bran stick, Cereal Mix and Fruit, Oat flakes, Whole Rusks**

JORDANS ⊘

DUO Strawberry; Multigrain Porridge; Natural Country Bran; Natural Wheatgerm; Organic Flakes & Berries; Organic Fruit & Fibre; Porridge: Raisin & Apple; Porridge: Sultana & Apricot; Superfoods Breakfast Flakes; Superfoods Porridge; *Country Crisp:* Chocolate (Export), Chocolate (France), Four Nut Combo, Luxury Raisin, Real

Strawberries, Whole Raspberries, Wild about Berries; *Country Crisp & Flakes:* Berries, Raisin & Hazel; *Crunchy:* Luxury Maple & Pecan, New Fruits Recipe, Raisin & Coconut; *Morning Crisp:* Maple & Pecan; *Muesli:* Light & Crispy, Ligne, Natural, Organic, Special, Special Fruit, Special Nut, Special Recipe Export, Superfoods Muesli

KALLO FOODS ⊘

Whole Earth: Cornflakes, Flakes with South Asian Exotic Fruit, Fruit & Fibre, Maple Frosted Flakes, North American Flakes with Blosson Berries, Puffed Rice Cereal Original, Swiss Style Muesli

KELLOGGS

Cornflakes; Fruit & Fibre; Just Right; Raisin Wheats; *Coco Pops:* Mega Muncher, Moon & Stars, Original; *Frosties:* Original; *Rice Krispies :* Multi-Grain Shapes, Original

NATURE'S PATH FOODS INC

Crispy Rice; Mesa Sunrise; Millet Rice Flakes; Oaty Bites; Optimum Power; *Envirokidz:* Gorilla Munch, Koala Crisp

ORGRAN ☺

Breakfast Cereals: Muesli Gluten Free, Rice Porridge

PERTWOOD ORGANIC CEREAL COMPANY ⊘✿

Maple Flakes; Muesli Delicious Fruits; Muesli Fruit and Seeds; *Organic barley crisp:* Barley Flakes

PETER RABBIT ORGANICS ⊘✿

Organic Cornflakes

73

the 100% natural vegetarian alternative

meat & egg free
dairy free
100% natural ingredients
no hydrogenated fats and oils
cholesterol free
soya based
GMO free
Ethical
Vegan

PORTER FOODS CO LTD
Lovedean Larder Granola: No.1, No.1 Lite, No.2 with Cranberries, No.3 Date and Apple

QUAKER OATS ⊘
Quaker Oat Crisp; Quaker Oat Crunch; Quaker Oat Hoops; Quaker Oats Simple Baked Apple Flavour; Quaker Oats Simple Blackberry & Apple Flavour; Quaker Oats Simple Fruit Muesli Flavour; Quaker Oats Simple Golden Syrup Flavour; Quaker Oats Simple Original; Quaker Puffed Wheat; Scott's Porage Oats Original; Scotts Old Fashioned Porage Oats; Scotts So Easy - Original

RYVITA ⊘
Crispbreads: Garlic & Rosemary; *Snack Packs:* Multi-Grain, Sesame; *Thins:* Cracked Pepper, Flatbread Multiseed, Flatbread Multiseed

SANITARIUM HEALTH FOOD CO ⊘
Granola; Lite-Bix; Puffed Wheat; Weet-Bix; Weet-Bix Kids; Weet-Bix Organic

SUMA WHOLEFOODS
™❶⊘✓ ⊛✄1985
Branflakes; Bransticks; *Muesli:* **Suma 4U Berries Muesli, Suma Omega, Suma Tropical Mix, Super Muesli;** *Organic Muesli:* **OG Suma Vine Fruit Mix, Organic Deluxe Muesli, Organic Muesli Base, Suma Org GF**

THE FOOD DOCTOR LTD ✓
Breakfast Cereals: Cereal Mix, Muesli Mix, Porridge Mix

TRAIDCRAFT PLC ⊘
Fruit & Nut Muesli

TROPICAL WHOLEFOODS
Tropical 5 Fruit Salad; Tropical Fruit Mix

WEETABIX LTD
Crunchy Bran; *Alpen:* Wheat Flakes; *Natures Own Organic:* Malt Wheat Squares; *Oatibix:* Bitesize, Original; *Ready Brek:* Original; *Weetabix:* Mini Crunch Fruit & Nut, Organic, Original

'BURGERS', 'SAUSAGES', 'MEAT' SLICES ETC

ALPRO UK LTD ☺❶⊘
Meat free: Tofu Mince, Tofu Pieces - Lightly Seasoned; *Provamel:* Soya Nuggets Organic 140g, Soya Peppered Schnitzel Organic 170g, Soya Tofu Plain Organic 2x200g; *Provamel Meat Free:* Organic lightly seasoned tofu pieces, Organic tofu burgers with vegetables, Organic tofu mince 180g

BEANIE'S HEALTH FOODS ™☺❶⊘
Vegetarian Chicken-style burgers; *Fry's Special Vegetarian Frozen Foods:* **Schnitzels, Spiced Burgers, Traditional Burgers, Traditional Sausages;** *Fry's Special Vegetarian Frozen Foods:* **Braai (BBQ) Sausages, Cutlets, Hot Dogs, Nuggets, Polony Slicing Sausage, Vegetarian Chicken-Style Strips, Vegetarian Mince, Wok and Stew Chunky Strips**

BIONA
Schnitzels in Crispy Breadcrumbs

FOOD

DALEPAK
Spicy Bean Burger; Spicy Veggie Burger; Vegetable Crispbake; Vegetable Grills; Vegetable Quarter Pounder

DIXIE DINERS CLUB
Chicken NOT fillets; Tuna NOT Salad

DRAGONFLY FOODS ⊘☼
Organic Soysage

FRY GROUP FOODS ™☺❶⊘
Fry's Special Vegetarian Frozen Foods: **Braai Flavour Sausages, Chunky Strips, Golden Crumbled Schnitzels, Mince, Original Hot Dogs, Polony, Spiced Burgers, Traditional Burgers, Traditional Sausages, Vegetarian chicken-style burgers, Vegetarian chicken-style nuggets, Vegetarian Chicken-Style Strips**

GOBBLIN WHOLEFOODS
Lentil Burger; Millet Burger

GOODLIFE FOODS ⊘
Fairtrade Nut Cutlet; Fruity Falafel Quarterpounders; Root Vegetable Roast; Spicy Bean Quarterpounders; Vegetable Burgers

JUST WHOLEFOODS ☺⊘
Organic Mixes: Banger, Burger

LINDA MCCARTNEY
Vegetarian Mince; Vegetarian Sausages

PAUL'S TOFU ™⊘◖☼
Savouries: **Five Grain Tofu & Herb Burgers, Five Grain Tofu & Nut Burgers, Ganmodoki Tofu Mock Goose, Organic Five Grain Tofu Bengal Burger, Organic Five Grain Tofu Mexican Chilli Burger**

REDWOOD WHOLEFOOD COMPANY ™☺❶⊘
Bio Curry Wurst; Fishless Steaks; Organic Coated Nuggets; Organic Coated Schnitzels; Organic Frankfurter Sausage; Organic Gyros Sausage; Organic Merguez Sausage; Scampi; Tuna; Vegetarian Breaded Fish-Style Fingers; Vegetarian Style Mince; *Cheatin':* **Chorizo Chunks;** *Cheatin' Chicken:* **Chicken Style Pieces;** *Cheatin' Roasts:* **Beef, Celebration, Turkey;** *Cheatin' Slices:* **Beef, Chicken, Garlic Sausage, Ham, Pepperoni, Sage & Onion, Turkey, Wafer Thin Chicken, Wafer Thin Ham, Wafer Thin Turkey;** *Organic:* **Frankfurter Style Sausages, Lincolnshire Style Sausages, Vegetarian Rashers;** *Rashers:* **Streaky-Style, Tempeh;** *Vegi-Deli:* **Boston Baked Bean Style, Oregano & Basil Sausages, Provencal Style, Ready to Eat Lincolnshire Sausage, Sage & Marjoram Sausages (Not Ready to Eat), Sage & Marjoram Sausages (Ready to Eat), Spicy Chilli Style, Spicy Thai Style, Thai Fish Style Cakes;** *Vegideli Organic Range:* **Organic Beef Style Slices, Organic Chicken style pieces, Organic Chicken Style Slices, Organic Ham Style Slices, Organic Pepperoni Style Slices, Organic Ready to Eat Lincoln Sausages, Organic Ready to Eat Pork Style Sausages, Organic Southern Fried Chicken Style**

Nuggets, Organic Vegetarian Rashers
SANITARIUM HEALTH FOOD CO ⊘
Lime and Ginger Sausages; Roast with
Mint and Rosemary Glaze; *Classic:* Hot
Dogs; *Deli:* Chicken Style Slices, Ham
Style Slices, Hencheon Luncheon,
Smoked Luncheon; *Traditional:* BBQ
Soya Sausages, Curried Sausages,
Homestyle Soya Sausages, Original Soya
Sausages, Soya Sausages, Vegie Soya
Sausages

SIMON HOWIE
Vegetarian Haggis

SUMA WHOLEFOODS
™❶⊘✔👁⚲–1985
Burger Mix; Sausage Mix; *Pre-Packs:*
**TVP Chunks, TVP Flavoured Chunks,
TVP Flavoured Mince, TVP Mince**

TAIFUN ☺⊘
Tofu Sausages: Grill Sausages, Herb
Sausages, Mini Wiener, Puszta-Wiener,
Rostbräterle, Sombreros, Tofu-
Bratgriller, Wiener

TOFURKY ☺
Deli Slices: "Philly Style" Steak,
Cranberry and Stuffing, Hickory
Smoked, Italian, Oven Roasted,
Peppered; *Holiday Products:* Cranberry
Apple Potato Dumplings, Feast, Giblet
and Mushroom Gravy, Roast; *Jurky:*
Original; *Pizza:* Pepperoni, Sausage;
Sausages: Beer Brats, Breakfast Links,
Chipotle, Italian, Kielbasa

TOPAS ™☺⊘✔✿
**Gran Chorizo; Vegan organic seitan
sausage "Krakow"; Vegan organic**
seitan sausage Bavarian style;
Vegan organic slices "Chorizo";
Spacebar: **Spacebar "Chorizo",
Spacebar Kur-Biss", Spacebar Pesto,
Spacebar Rosso;** *Tofu Slices:* **Tofu
slices leek, Tofu slices paprika, Tofu
slices smoky;** *Wheaty:* **Sausage
Frankenberger, Sausage Hot Dog,
Vegan Organic Rolls
"Cevapwheaty", Vegan Organic
Steak "Pizza", Wheaty Kebab
Doener, Wheaty Steaklets, Wheaty
ToRo;** *Wheaty Big Blocks For Slicing:*
**Vegan Organic Seitan Block, Vegan
Organic Seitan With Herbs Block,
Vegan Organic Slices "Salami" Bar,
Vegan Smoked Organic Seitan
Block;** *Wheaty Convenience:* **Vegan
Organic "Chilli con Wheaty", Vegan
Organic Wheaty "Stroganoff";**
Wheaty Kebabs (Big Packs): **Vegan
Organic "Hamburger Medallions",
Vegan Organic "Minced Meat" 2.5
kg, Vegan Organic "Vegoulash" 2.5
kg, Vegan Organic Greek Style
"Gyros" 2.5 kg, Vegan Organic
Kebab "Plain" 2.5 kg, Vegan
Organic Mexican Style Kebab
"Acapulco" 2.5 kg;** *Wheaty Roast:*
**Vegan Organic Roast With
Mushrooms;** *Wheaty Sausages:* **Vegan
Organic "Dwarf Wienies", Vegan
Organic "Wienies", Vegan Organic
Seitan Sausages "Country Style",
Vegan Organic Seitan Sausages "La
Rossa", Vegan Organic Seitan
Sausages Piquant With Marjoram,
Vegan Organic Seitan Sausages
With Herbs "Thuringen";** *Wheaty
Sausages & Snacks (Big Packs):*
**Spacebar "Hemp", Spacebar
"Hemp" Maxi Display, Spacebar**

"Pyrossi" Maxi Display, Spacebar "Red Hot Chilli Peppers" Maxi Display, Vegan Organic Seitan Sausages "Country Style", Vegan Organic Seitan Sausages With Herbs "Thuringen"; *Wheaty Slices For Frying:* Vegan Organic "Hamburger Medallions", Vegan Organic Schnitzel, Vegan Smoked Organic Seitan Steak, Vegan Thick Organic Slices For Frying; *Wheaty Slices For Frying (Big Packs):* Vegan Organic "Hamburger Medallions Piquant" Bar, Vegan Organic "Hamburger Medallions" Bar, Vegan Organic Seitan Slices Block, Vegan Organic Smoked Seitan Steak Block; *Wheaty Thin Slices:* Vegan Organic Seitan Slices, Vegan Organic Seitan Slices With Hemp, Vegan Organic Seitan Slices With Herbs, Vegan Organic Slices "Champion", Vegan Organic Slices "Red Bell Pepper", Vegan Organic Slices "Salami", Vegan Smoked Organic Seitan Slices; *Wheaty Vegan Kebabs:* Vegan Organic Greek Style Kebab "Gyros", Vegan Organic Indian Style Kebab "Jaipur", Vegan Organic Mexican Style Kebab "Acapulco", Vegan Organic Turkish Style Kebab, Vegan Organic Vegoulash; *Wheaty Vegetarian Salads:* Mixed Pack of Vegan Organic Salads: 2 x Meaty, Galina, KOsaken, Vegan Organic "Meat Salad" Meaty, Vegan Organic Salad "Galina", Vegan Organic Salad "Kosaken"

VEGAN PERFECTION ™☺❶◌✔
All products are vegan

VEGAN STORE ™☺❶◌✔
All products are vegan including tuna (not) salad, chicken (not) fillets, veggie ribs and seitan quick mix

VEGEFARM CORP ™☺❶◌✔
Vegefarm: Chicken-free Tender Chunks, Fish-free Steak, Hot Dog, Nuggets, Poultry-free Breast

VEGETARIANS CHOICE ™☺❶◌
Vegetable Protein: Burgers, Sausage Mix (400g tube), Sausages

VEGGIES CATERING CAMPAIGN ™☺❶◌✔✿
Burger Mix: Hemp-Seed, Veggies; *Burgers:* Chilli, Hemp, Veggies; *Sosage Mix:* Veggies; *Sosages:* Savoury, Tomato, Veggies

VIOLII ™☺
Cauliflower burger; Corn burger; Mushroom burger

WICKEN FEN
Sausages: Carrot and Coriander, Country Herb, Cumberland Style, Mediterranean Roasted Vegetable, Mushroom & Tarragon, Tomato & Garlic

CAKES & CAKE MIXES

AMANDA TRADING LTD T/A AFRICAN DELIGHTS ☺
Banana Rice Cake

THE NAUGHTIEST VEGAN CAKES IN TOWN...

WWW.MSCUPCAKE.CO.UK
INFO@MSCUPCAKE.CO.UK

BABYCAKES DIRECT ™☺❶
Apricot and Cashew Nut Cake (& 'Sweet Freedom' no added sugar alternative); Carrot and Cinnamon Muffins (& 'Sweet Freedom' no added sugar alternative); Coffee Muffins (& 'Sweet Freedom' no added sugar alternative); Cranberry and Almond Muffins (& 'Sweet Freedom' no added sugar alternative); Gluten- and Wheat-Free Carrot and Cinnamon Muffins (& 'Sweet Freedom' no added sugar alternative); Gluten- and Wheat-Free Chocolate Muffins (& 'Sweet Freedom' no added sugar alternative); Gluten- and Wheat-Free Spicy Apple Muffins (& 'Sweet Freedom' no added sugar alternative); *(& 'Sweet Freedom' no added sugar alternative):* **Spicy Apple Muffins;** *All available in 'sweet freedom' alternative:* **Apple Cake, Banana and coconut cake, Black**

Forest chocolate cake, Carrot and Cinnamon Cake, Carrot and raisin cake, Chocolate Cake, Chocolate Chip Muffins, Coffee Cake, Cranberry and Almond Cake, Date and Walnut Cake, Ginger and Pineapple Cake, Gluten- and Wheat-Free Carrot and Cinnamon Cake, Gluten- and Wheat-Free Chocolate Cake, Gluten- and Wheat-Free Spicy Apple Cake, Gluten free Banana, Coconut & Lime Cake Apple Cake, Gluten free carrot and raisin cake, Gluten free cranberry and almond cake, Lemon drizzle sponge, Rich Fruit Cake, Victoria Sponge; *No added sugar:* **No added sugar carrot and raisin cake, No added sugar coconut, date and banana cake, No Added Sugar Fruit Cake**

DIXIE DINERS CLUB
Brownie Mix; Choc Chip Cookie Mix; Fudge Mix

ESSENTIAL TRADING CO-OPERATIVE LTD ™❶⊘✔
Midnight mix; Paradise Mix

GOBBLIN WHOLEFOODS
Apricot & Cinnamon Flapjack; Apricot Slice; Banbury Cake; Barmbrack; Black Cherry Slice; Date Slice; Eccles Slice; Fig Slice; Fruit & Nut Sesame Slice; Seville Coconut Slice; *Organic:* Apricot Slice, Date Slice

HAPPY AND HEALTHY FOODS ☺❶
Cherrybrook Kitchen: Chocolate Cake, Chocolate Chip Cookies, Chocolate Frosting, Sugar Cookies, Vanilla Frosting, Yellow Cake

HAPPY KITCHEN ™☺❶⊘✔
Cake: **Cherry & Almond, Damson wine poached pear, English apple & fairly traded cinnamon, English strawberry & fairly traded vanilla, Fairly traded chocolate & (fruit), Gluten free carrot & coconut, Gluten free fairly traded banana brownie, Omega seed mix & sweet orange oil, Plum roast pumpkin**

MRS CRIMBLE'S ⊘
Dutch Apple Cake; Dutch Fruit Loaf; Stem Ginger Cake

NATURALLY ME INC ☺
Apple Muffins; Blueberry Muffins; Cherry Muffins

ORGRAN ☺
Gluten-free Pancake Mixes: Apple & Cinnamon, Buckwheat

PAUL'S TOFU ™⊘✔☼
Cakes: **Apple Strudel, Fruit Pie with Kuzu**

RAW ALCHEMY LTD ™☺❶⊘✔
Raw: **Handmade Raw Chocolate Brownies**

REBECCA'S CAKES ™
Blueberry Waffles; Fruit Loaf Cake; Apple cinnamon pancakes; Apple Pies; Bakewell tarts squares; Banana blueberry muffins; Banana cupcakes; Banana loaf cake; Banana peanut butter; Banana pecan pancakes; Banana Raspberry Layer Cake; Banana split cupcakes; Banoffee Cake Layer Cake; Black and White Cupcakes; Blackberry almond loaf cake; Blueberry cupcakes; Bread pudding tray bake squares; Brownie; Butterfly cupcakes; Capuccino Cupcakes; Carrot cake tray bake squares; Carrot cupcakes; Cherry almond loaf cake; Chocolate "Honey" Cupcakes; Chocolate Brownie Cheesecake; Chocolate cherry cupcakes; Chocolate chunk cookies; Chocolate Dipped Fruit; Chocolate fudge cupcakes; Chocolate orange cupcakes; Chocolate Sponge Layer Cake; Chocolate syrup loaf cake; Chocolate syrup muffins; Cinnamon apple muffins; Coconut Cake Layer Cake; Coconut cupcakes; Coconut lime cupcakes; Coconut pancakes; Coffee cupcakes; Coffee Layer Cake; Coffee walnut loaf cake; Cola float cupcakes; Fruit Cake Cupcakes; Fruit Loaf Cake; Ginger ginger ginger cupcakes; Gingerbread Scones; Half

and half cupcakes; Health Crunch Muffins; Hummingbird cupcakes; Jaffa orange drizzle loaf cake; Jam tarts; Kids Birthday Cake Layer Cake; Lemon almond loaf cake; Lemon Cheesecake; Lemon cranberry muffins; Lemon drizzle loaf cake; Lemon kiss cupcakes; Lemon pistachio cupcakes; Lemon poppyseed loaf cake; Lemon Sponge Layer Cake; Lemon Victoria Sponge Layer cake; Lime drizzle loaf cake; Lime poppyseed loaf cake; Macadamia and white chocolate muffins; Mango passion cupcakes; Maple banana walnut; Maple pecan cupcakes; Maple streusel muffins; Mini bakes doughnuts; Mint chocolate chip cupcakes; Orange drizzle loaf cake; Orange poppyseed loaf cake; PB&J cupcakes; Peach pecan muffins; Peanut butter; Peanut butter loaf cake; Pineapple allspice loaf cake; Pink vanilla cupcakes; Plain scones; Plum and almond loaf cake; Pumpkin Cheesecake; Pumpkin cupcakes; Pumpkin Loaf Cake; Pumpkin Pie; Pumpkin-walnut waffles; Raspberry Almond cake tray bake squares; Raspberry almond loaf cake; Raspberry almond squares; Raspberry cupcakes; Red velvet cupcakes; Rum and raisin cupcakes; Sour cherry yogurt loaf cake; St Paddy's Day Chocolate stout cake; Sticky ginger loaf cake; Sticky toffee cupcakes; Sticky Toffee Pudding; Strawberries and cream cupcakes; Tiramisu; Vanilla Cheesecake; Vanilla Cheesecake Brownie; Vanilla Layer Cake; Vanilla loaf cake; Vegan cheese and chive muffins; Vegan chocolate cake mix; Vegan Gingerbread Squares; Vegan Marble Cake Squares; Victoria Sponge Layer Cake

SUNBLEST
Hot Cross Buns; Teacakes

UPCAKES ™☺❶◐⃠ ⃥
Chocolate Brownie: **Chocbites**

VEGAN STORE ™☺❶◐⃠ ⃥
All Products are vegan including brownie, pancake, muffin, cake and cookie mix

'CHEESE' & 'CHEESE' SPREADS

ALPRO UK LTD ☺❶⃠
Provamel: Soya Alternative to Spreadable Cheese Plain 150g

BIOFUN BVBA ™✿
Blocks- olivio; Blocks- original; Blocks- pomodori; Blocks-greek style; Fleur de Soja; Spread- basil; Spread- chive; Spread- fine herbs; Spread- horseradish; Spread- original; Spread- provencale; Young Ripened-herbs; Young Ripened- original

BUTE ISLAND FOODS LTD ™☺❶⃠
Creamy Sheese: **Cheddar Flavour Creamy Sheese, Chives Flavour Creamy Sheese, Garlic and Herb Flavour Creamy Sheese, Mexican Flavour Creamy Sheese, Original**

Flavour Creamy Sheese; *Sheese:* **Blue Flavour, Cheddar Style, Cheddar with Chives, Cheshire Style, Edam Style, Gouda Style, Medium Cheddar style, Mozzarella Style, Smoked cheddar Style**

DIXIE DINERS CLUB
Cheese NOT Sauce Mix

HAPPY AND HEALTHY FOODS ☺❶
Road's End Organics: Alfredo Style Gluten Free Chreese Mix, Cheddar Style Chreese Mix, Cheddar Style Gluten Free Chreese Mix, Mozzarella Style Chreese Mix, Nacho Chreese - Mild Dip, Nacho Chreese - Spicy Dip

KERRY FOODS LTD ™⊘
Pure: **Soya Dairy Free Cheddar Style Slices, Soya Dairy Free Creamy Triangles, Soya Dairy Free Spread**

MH FOODS ™⊘✔
Florentino: **Parmazano;** *Life Free From:* **Cheddareese**

REDWOOD WHOLEFOOD COMPANY ™☺❶⊘
Cheezly: **Cream Style – Garlic & Herb Flavour, Cream Style - Original, Cream Style – Sour Cream & Chive Flavour, Feta Style, Garlic & Herb Flavoured, Greek Style, Mature Cheddar Style, Mature Cheddar Style w Cranberries, Nacho Style, Red Cheddar Style, Smokey Style w Added Bacon Style Pieces;** *Cheezly Melting:* **Cheddar Blocks, Cheddar Slices, Edam Blocks, Gouda Blocks, Mozzarella Blocks, Mozzarella Slices**

TOFUTTI ☺❶⊘
Creamy Smooth Slices: Cheddar, Mozzarella; *Soft Cheese:* Creamy Smooth Country Vegetable, French Onion, Garlic & Herb, Herb & Chives, Original

CHOCOLATE

ALTERNATIVE STORES ☺
All products are vegan

ANIMAL AID ™☺❶⊘✔☂1976
Boxed Chocolates: **Coffee Creams 120g, Marzipan Assortments, Orange Cremes, Pecan Parfaits, Peppermint Fondant Cremes, Stem Ginger, Vegan Selection Boxes**

BENDICKS OF MAYFAIR
Bittermints

BIONA
Dark Chocolate Bar; Dark Chocolate Cranberry Bar; Plain Chocolate Covered Brazils

CELTIC CHOCOLATES ⊘
Freefrom: Dairy Free Chocolate Bar, Dairy Free Chocolate Selection, Dairy Free Easter Egg, Dairy Free Mint Crisps

CHOCAID
Tiru: Fairtrade Organic Dark Chocolate 70% Cocoa

D & D CHOCOLATES ☺
Dark Couverture: Animal Shapes, Bar, Dinosaur Shapes, Flower Shapes,

Lemon Fondant Creams, Peppermint Fondant Creams, Plain Chocolate Chips for Cooking/Eating, Praline Hearts, Strawberry Fondant Creams

DARK SECRETS CHOCOLATE ☺
Easter Eggs; Kentucky Orange Truffles; Mint & Rosemary Truffles; Noir Tuffles; Peanut Butter Truffles; Vanilla Truffles

DARTMOOR CHILLI FARM ™❶⊘✔
Dartmoor Dark Chocolate: **Chilli Dark Chocolate, Chilli Dark Chocolate with Almonds, Chilli Dark Chocolate with Apricot, Chilli Dark Chocolate with Coffee, Chilli Dark Chocolate with Ginger, Chilli Dark Chocolate with Hazelnut & Cranberry, Chilli Dark Chocolate with Orange, Chilli Dark Chocolate with Peppermint**

DIETARY NEEDS DIRECT
Advent Calendar Inserts; Santa Lollies; Santa Lollies with No Added Sugar; Snowmen Lollies with No Added Sugar; Animal Faces; Bite Size Mr & Mrs Santa; Chocolate Money; Christmas Shapes; Farm Animals; Hearts; Hollow Easter Egg; Snowmen Lollies; Stars; *Chocolate / Mint Chocolate / Orange Chocolate:* Easter Eggs on Lolly Sticks, Rabbits on Lolly Sticks; *Mint Chocolate:* Mint Chocolate Christmas Shapes, Mint Mr & Mrs Santa, Mint Presents, Mint Santa Lollies, Mint Stars, Mint Swirls, Mint Turtles, Rudolf Mint Lollies; *Orange Chocolate:* Orange Christmas Shapes, Orange Santa Lollies, Orange Stars, Orange Turtles

DIVINE CHOCOLATE ⊘
70% Dark Mini Eggs; 70% Dark; 70% Dark Cho colate Hearts; 70% Mint Dark; After Dinner Mints; Divine Delights

FOOD

EJS CONSCIOUS CHOCOLATE
TM☺❶◎✓

Berry Christmas; Cherry Christmas; Chili Hot; Chocha Mocha Magic; Citrus Zest; Fiery Hazelnut; Fruit Fantasy; Goji & coconut; Lovepotion No 9; Merry Christmas; Mint; Nicely Nutty; Orange; Plain; Spiced up & fruity; Sunny Easter Feast; Superfood; Yummy Mummy

ELIZABETH SHAW
Dark Chocolate Mint Crisp; Dark Chocolate Orange Crisp; Mint Cream Chocolates

HOTEL CHOCOLAT
72% Dark Chocolate Engraved Easter Egg; Chocolate for Anything 72% Dark; Serious Dark Fix Egg

HUMDINGER LTD TM◎✓
Cooking chocolate; Dairy Free Easter Bunny; Dairy Free Rice Crackle Bar; Dairy Free White Buttons; Dairy-Free Chocolate Block 100g; Dairy-Free Chocolate Buttons

KITCHEN BUDDY (CULINARY COURSES) RAW CHOCOLATE
TM☺❶◎✓☼

Deluxe Chocolates & Truffles Selection Boxes: **Florentines, Ginger, Marzipan Truffles, Mint, Orange;** *Raw:* **Chocolate Halva**

LIFEFOOD CZECH REPUBLIC S.R.O. ☺❶◎✓☼
Life food: Organic Raw Chocolate 80% cacao, Organic Raw Chocolate with Hemp Seeds, Organic Raw Chocolate with Orange

LINDT & SPRUNGLI ◎
Excellence: 70% Cocoa, 85% Cocoa, 99% Cocoa; *Excellence Origins:* Cuba, Ecuador, Madagascar

LYME REGIS FINE FOODS LTD ◎
Kidz Break: Chocolate; *Marzipan Bar:* Organic Orange Marzipan, Organic Plain Choc Coated Original, Plain Chocolate Coated

MCKEITH ☺
Cacao Bean Bar; Cacao Nibs; Cacao Powder

MISS BELLASIS ☺
Amour de Tita Chocolate

MONTEZUMAS CHOCOLATES
Dark Chocolate Tubby Teddy; *3175 Series:* Box; *Bar:* Dark with Chilli, Very Dark Foundation; *Bars:* Orange & Geranium, Vera - Dark Chocolate with Pistachio; *Choco-Block:* Cocoa Nibs, Dark Brazil, Date, Walnut & Pecan; *Dainty Dollops:* Bergamot, Mandarin, Peppermint; *Emperor Bar:* Chilli, Orange & Geranium; *Fruit and Nuts:* Dark Chocolate Ginger, Dark Chocolate Mango, Dark Chocolate Orange, Dark Dusted Dates, Grand Marnier Apricots, Kirsch Cherries, Madeira Prunes; *Single Origin:* Ecuador, Papua New Guinea, Peru; *Speciality Bar:* Gourmet Gorilla, Orangutang, Spice it Up; *Truffles:* Cheers III, Famous Five, Nut Case, Quick Fix, Scurvy, Sunrise; *Turtles:* Turtely Nuts

MOO FREE CHOCOLATES TM◎✓
Milk Alternative Caramelised Pralines; Milk Alternative Chocolate Drops; Milk Alternative Hearts; Milk Alternative Squares; Orange Alternative Squares

MULU CHOCOLATE LTD ™☺⊘✿
Dark Bar; Dark Individual
Chocolates; Dark with Cacao Nibs
Bar; Dark with Cacao Nibs
individual chocolates; Silk Bar; Silk
Individual Chocolates

ORGANIC MELTDOWN
Swiss Organic Dark Chocolate:
Cinnamon & Chilli, Indian Spice, Plain,
Rooibos & Raspberry

**ORGANIC SEED
& BEAN CO LTD** ™⊘✦✿
85g Handmade Chocolate Bars: 66%
Cocoa; Coconut & Raspberry
Chocolate Bar, 70% Cocoa; Sea Salt
Chocolate Bar, 72% Cocoa;
Pumpkin & Hemp Chocolate Bar,
72% Cocoa; Extra Dark Chocolate
Bar

PLAMIL ☺❶⊘
Dairy Free Alternative to Milk
Chocolate; Dairy Free Chocolate Drops;
Dairy Free Mint Chocolate; Dairy Free
Orange Chocolate; Dairy Free Plain
Chocolate; Fairtrade Alternative to Milk
Chocolate; Fairtrade Alternative To Milk
Chocolate Catering Pack Large; Free
From' Baking Chocolate Catering
Drops; Free From' Baking Chocolate
Catering Pack Large; No Added Sugar
Alternative to Milk Chocolate; No
Added Sugar Chocolate; No Added
Sugar Chocolate Catering Drops; No
Added Sugar Chocolate Catering Pack
Large; No Added Sugar Chocolate
Snack Bar; No Added Sugar Chocolate
with Shelled Hemp; No Added Sugar
Mint Chocolate; No Added Sugar

Organic Chocolate; No Added Sugar
Organic Chocolate Catering Drops; No
Added Sugar Organic Chocolate
Catering Pack Large; Organic
Alternative To White Chocolate
Catering Drops; Organic Alternative To
White Chocolate Catering Pack Large;
Organic Cayenne Chocolate; Organic
Chocolate; Organic Dark Chocolate;
Organic Dark Chocolate (87% Cocoa);
Organic Dark Chocolate with White
Mint; Organic Fairtrade Baking
Chocolate Catering Drops; Organic
Fairtrade Baking Chocolate Catering
Pack Large; Organic Ginger Chocolate;
Organic Luxury Chocolate Catering
Drops; Organic Luxury Chocolate
Catering Pack Large; Organic Mint
Chocolate; Organic Orange Chocolate;
Organic Orange Chocolate with
Cranberries; Organic Rich Chocolate
Catering Drops; Organic Rich Chocolate
Catering Pack Large; Organic Rich
Chocolate Orange Catering Drops;
Organic Rich Chocolate Orange
Catering Pack Large; Organic Rum and
Raisin Chocolate

RAW ALCHEMY LTD ™☺❶⊘✦
Raw: Handmade Raw Chocolate

RAW LIVING ™☺❶⊘✦
Be The Change; Buddha of Bliss;
Bullet Ride Power Bar; Lucky Me;
Whoosh; *Hi:* Hi-Crunch, Hi-Lovers

RAWCREATION LTD ™☺❶⊘✦
Cacao Nibs; Christmas Love Bar;
Desire Chocolate Bar; Empress;
Goddess Chocolate Bar; I Love u;
Intacta Chocolate bar; Raw Cacao

FOOD

Liquor; Raw Organic Cacao Butter; Raw organic chocolate powder; Raw Shelled Cacao Beans; Raw Whole Cacao Beans; Temptress Chocolate Bar; The Siren Chocolate Bar

RITTER SPORT ⊘
Dark Chocolate 71%; Marzipan; Peppermint; Plain 50%

ROCOCO CHOCOLATES ⊘
Ciociolato Nocciole Piemonte (Dark Chocolate with Crunchy Hazelnuts); Cocoa Dusted Scorched Almonds; Cocoa Powder; *Dark Chocolate Bars:* Chocolate Amer 70%, Extra Brut 85%, Grenada Chocolate 60%, Grenada Chocolate 71%, Organic Dark 65%, Plus Noir Que Noir 100%, Sugar Free 56%, Valrhona 64%, Valrhona 66%, Valrhona 70%; *Dark Chocolate Flavoured Bars:* Arabic Spices, Basil & Lime, Black Pepper, Caramelized Almond, Cardamom, Chilli, Cocoa Nibs, Crystallised Ginger, Earl Grey, Fine Mocha, Geranium, Lavender, Morello Cherry, Orange & Geranium, Peppered Mint, Pink Peppercorn; *Dark Chocolate Mini Bars "Bee Bars":* 65%, Chilli, Earl Grey, Ginger, Lavender, Orange & Geranium; *Hot Chocolate:* Plain, Spiced with Cardamom Nutmeg & Cinnamon; *Loose English Creams:* Brazil Nut, Coffee, Dark Banana, Dark Raspberry, Dark Strawberry, Geranium, Lavender, Lemon, Marzipan, Orange, Passion Fruit, Rose, Stem Ginger, Violet; *Loose House Selection:* Cherry in Cognac, Dark Nut Cluster, Dipped Apricot, Dipped Orange Slices, Dipped Orange Sticks, Ginger Slices, Ginger Sticks, Lubecker Almond Marzipan

SJAAK'S ORGANIC CHOCOLATES
Almond Butter Bites; Dark Chocolate Bar; Dark Chocolate with Almonds; Dark Chocolate with Creamy Caramel; Dark Chocolate with Espresso Bar; Dark Chocolate with Raspberry Bar; Extra Dark 70% Chocolate Bar; Extra Dark Bites; Peanut Butter Bites; Vegan European Assortment; Vegan Nuts & Chews Assortment; Vegan Truffle Assortment

SUPERNUTRIENTS LTD ™☺⊘✔
Cacao: **Organic cacao Butter, Organic Cacao Powder**

THE BOOJA-BOOJA COMPANY LTD ™☺⊘✔✿
Raw Truffles: **Dark Ecuadorian chocolate truffles, Raspberry Ecuadorian chocolate truffles;** *Truffles:* **Around Midnight Espresso Truffle, Champagne Truffle, Flambeed Banana Truffle, Ginger Wine Truffle, Hazelnut Crunch Truffle**

THE CHOCOLATE ALCHEMIST ⊘✿
Choc Chunks with Brazilnuts & Sultanas; Choc Chunks with Ginger; Choc Chunks with Walnuts & Dates; Chunky Bar with Brazilnuts & Sultanas; Chunky Bar with Walnuts & Apricots; Dark Chocolate Big Buttons; Dark Chocolate Fruity Bar with Blackcurrant; Dark Chocolate Nutty Slab ; Dark Chocolate Spicy Bar with Chilli; Dark Chocolate Spicy Bar with Nutmeg; Plain Dark Chocolate Bar; *Fruit Spice & All Things Nice :* Mango in Dark Chocolate with Orange & Nutmeg; *Wo Wo's Favourite Food:* Dark Chocolate Alphabets, Dark Chocolate Big Buttons

FOOD

THE FAMOUS
CHOCOLATE HOUSE 1657
Loose Chocolates: Coffee and Pecan (Plain), Coffee Creme with Bean (Plain), Firm Bittermint (Plain), Stem Ginger (Plain), Strawberry Creme (Plain)

THE GORGEOUS
CHOCOLATE HEART CO
Raw Chocolate Balls: BerriBall, Lovebite Ball, SpiraBall

THE ORGANIC PHARMACY
Glamour Food: Organic Chocolate Goji Acia & Blueberry

THE RAW CHOCOLATE
COMPANY LIMITED ™☺❶⊘✔
Midnight; Pitch Dark; Raw GO!; Twilight; Vanoffe

TRAIDCRAFT PLC ⊘
After Dinner Mints; Swiss Plain Chocolate

TRIALIA FOODS AUSTRALIA ™
Eskal Noble Choice : **Mint Crunch Dark Chocolate;** *Eskal Noble Choice:* **Rice Crisp Dark Chocolate;** *Eskal Noble Choice :* **Rich Dark Chocolate, Semi Sweet Choc Chip, Raspberry Dark Chocolate, Toasted Almond Dark Chocolate**

VALRHONA
Cocoa Powder; *Dark Chocolate Bar:* Abinao 85%, Ampamakia, Araguani, Cao Grande Noir, Caraibe, Gran Couva 2006, Guanaja, Palmira 2006; *Dark Chocolate Couvertures:* Manjari

VEGANTISCH ™☺❶⊘✔ ✿
Chocolate Bars: **Plain chocolate, Plain chocolate almond, Plain chocolate amaranth, Plain chocolate apple, Plain chocolate apricot, Plain chocolate banana, Plain chocolate blueberry, Plain chocolate cashew, Plain chocolate cherry, Plain chocolate coconut, Plain chocolate coffee, Plain chocolate cranberry, Plain chocolate date, Plain chocolate fig, Plain chocolate hazelnut, Plain chocolate hemp, Plain chocolate lemon, Plain chocolate mulberry, Plain chocolate orange, Plain chocolate peanut, Plain chocolate pear, Plain chocolate pepper, Plain chocolate pineapple, Plain chocolate pistachio, Plain chocolate raisin, Plain chocolate strawberry, Plain chocolate walnut, Rice milk chocolate, Rice milk chocolate almond, Rice milk chocolate amaranth, Rice milk chocolate apple, Rice milk chocolate apricot, Rice milk chocolate banana, Rice milk chocolate blueberry, Rice milk chocolate cashew, Rice milk chocolate cherry, Rice milk chocolate coconut, Rice milk chocolate coffee, Rice milk chocolate cranberry, Rice milk chocolate date, Rice milk chocolate fig, Rice milk chocolate hazelnut, Rice milk chocolate hemp, Rice milk chocolate lemon, Rice milk chocolate mulberry, Rice milk chocolate orange, Rice milk chocolate peanut, Rice milk chocolate pear, Rice milk chocolate pepper, Rice milk chocolate**

pineapple, Rice milk chocolate pistachio, Rice milk chocolate raisin, Rice milk chocolate strawberry, Rice milk chocolate walnut, Solidarity Bar for Criminalised Activists in Austria, Soy milk chocolate; *Chocolate Muesli Bar:* **Plain chocolate muesli bar, Rice milk chocolate muesli bar;** *Chocolate Popcorn:* **Plain chocolate popcorn, Rice milk chocolate popcorn;** *Chocolate Spreads:* **Almond chocolate spread, Coconut chocolate spread, Hazelnut chocolate spread, Nougat chocolate spread;** *Filled Chocolates:* **Nougat clogs plain chocolate, Nougat clogs rice milk chocolate, Nougat hearts plain chocolate, Nougat hearts rice milk chocolate, Nougat whirls plain chocolate, Nougat whirls rice milk chocolate;** *Message-Platelets:* **Plain Chocolate, Rice milk chocolate**

VENTURE FOODS UK LTD ™⊘
Chocolate couverture bar; Dark chocolate bar; Dark chocolate bar with cocoa nibs (Food of the Gods); Dark chocolate with cinder toffee; Swiss Chocolate couverture with Raisins & Almonds; Swiss Chocolate Marrakesh; Swiss Chocolate Tangiers; Swiss Dark Chcolate with Hazelnut; Swiss Dark Chocolate with Cranberries; Swiss Plain Chocolate with Mint; Swiss Vegan Diets White Bar

VIVA! ☺❶⊘✓
Giant Buttons

CONFECTIONERY & SWEET SNACKS

AUSTRALIAN NOUGAT COMPANY ™⊘
Macadamia Bliss Nougat with Pistachio

BIONA
Bio Smarties; Cola Bottles; Fruit Lollies; Peppermints; Pineapple Chews; Tutti Frutti Wine Gums; *Jelly Bears:* Licorice; *Jelly Bears :* Tutti Frutti

BLACK OPAL INTERNATIONAL AUSTRALIA
Soft-Eating Liquorice: Black, Raspberry

CADALEAH HOME BAKERS ™☺
Twisted doughnut: **Etwist / Koeksuster**

CADBURY TREBOR BASSETT
Trebor Soft Fruits; *Bassett's:* Mint Creams, Pear Drops; *Trebor Extra Cool:* Peppermint, Spearmint; *Trebor Soft Mints:* Peppermint, Spearmint

CEDAR HEALTH LTD
Castus Fruit Bars: Apricot, Banana, Fig, Stawberry; *Panda Licorice:* Bar, Bear, Comfits, Cuts, Raspberry Bar

CLEARSPRING ™☺❶⊘✓☻
Ginger Rice Malt Sweets; Lotus Rice Malt Sweets; Lotus Rice Malt Sweets; Peppermint Rice Malt

Sweets; Sour Plum Rice Malt
Sweets; Vanilla Rice Malt Sweets;
Organic Snack Bars: **Almond, Sesame,
Sesame and Raisin**

D & D CHOCOLATES ☺
Siesta : Carob Animal Shapes, Carob
Bar (Original/Orange/Mint), Carob
Dinosaur Shapes, Carob Drops; *Siesta:*
Carob Flakes for Cooking; *Siesta :*
Carob Flower Shapes
(Original/Orange/Mint), Carob Orange
Fondants, Carob Peppermint Fondants,
Carob Strawberry Fondants

DIETARY NEEDS DIRECT
Pineapple Chunks; Pineapple Pear
Drops; *Fudge:* Chocolate Fudge, Vanilla
Fudge; *Sweets:* Carob Mixed Christmas
Shapes, Carob Santas, Carob
Snowmen, Mint Humbugs, Strawberry
& Peach Delights, Strawberry & Peach
Fruit Pear Drop, Strawberry Humbugs,
Treacle Toffee

DOVES FARM FOODS LTD ⊘
Apple & Sultana Flapjack; Chocolate &
Crispy Rice Bar; Low Fat Fruity Oat Bar

FTF SWEETS LTD ™❶⊘ᶜ
Goody Good Stuff Wine Gums: **Cola
Breeze, Sour Fruit Salad, Sour Mix &
Match, Summer Peaches**

GOBBLIN WHOLEFOODS
Coconut Flapjack; *Organic:* Coconut
Flapjack

GOVINDA NATUR GMBH ™⊘
Confectionery: **Almond Magic, Choco
Ginger, Choco Light, Choco Nuts,
Chocolate Bites, Date Coconut Orbs,
Energy Orbs, Ginger Cubes, Ginger
Joy, Mango Apricot Orbs, Mango
Orbs Confectionery, Paradiso,
Pineapple Orbs, Sahara, Sweet
Chestnut**

GRANOVITA UK LTD ⊘ᶜ
Castus Date & Apricot Fruit Bar;
Coconut Bars: Almond, Cherry, Mango,
Original, Pineapple, Strawberry; *Organic
Oskri Snack Bar:* Quinoa, Sesame with
Date Syrup, Sesame with Date Syrup &
Black Cumin, Sesame with Date Syrup
& Fennel; *Taste of Nature Organic
Snack Bars:* Argentina Peanut Bar,
Brazilian Raisin & Nut Bar, California
Sesame, Almond & Raisin Bar, Niagara
Oat, Apple & Cinnamon Bar

GUARANA COMPANY LTD ™
**Blueberries; Cranberries; Goji
Berries; Sun Dried Inca Berries; Sun
Dried Mango Strips**

HAPPY KITCHEN ™☺❶⊘ᶜ
Flaxjack: **Gluten free & (fruit or
chocolate) flaxjack, Rhubarb flaxjack;**
Slice: **Gluten free raspberry bakewell**

HOTEL CHOCOLAT
Turkish Delight

IL MANGIARSANO S.P.A ™⊘ᶜ
Germinal Organic Bakery: **Apple
Snack, Apricot Stuffed Bar, Apricot
Stuffed Bar, Blueberry Stuffed Bar,
Blueberry Stuffed Bar, Wildfruits
Snack**

JORDANS ⊘
Multigrain bar: Cranberry & Raspberry;
Frusli: All Fruit bar: Apple &
Passionfruit, All Fruit bar: Apple &
Strawberry

JUST WHOLEFOODS ☺☺⊘
VegeBears: Frooty Fruits, Fruit Jellies

KALLO FOODS ⊘
Flapjacks; Raisin Flapjacks

KELLOGGS
Strawberry Fruit Winders

**KITCHEN BUDDY (CULINARY
COURSES) RAW CHOCOLATE**
™☺❶❶✦☼
Raw: **Almafi Bliss, Chocolate Maca
Brownie, Etoile d'Or, Halva, Little
Cubes of Superfood**

LARABAR ☺
Apple Pie; Banana Cookie; Cashew
Cookie; Cherry Pie; Chocolate Coconut
Chew; Cinnamon Roll; Cocoa Mole;
Ginger Snap; Key Lime Pie; Lemon Bar;
Pecan Pie; Pistachio

**LIFEFOOD CZECH
REPUBLIC S.R.O.** ☺❶⊘✦☼
Life food: Organic Poppy Seed Balls;
Life food: Cashew and Date Balls,
Jakonella Bio, Lifeballs Brazil Mix,
Lifeballs Choco, Lifebar Cherry, Lifebar
Chocolate, Lifebar Fig, Organic Apple
Cinnamon Flax Rolls, Organic Cacao
and Date Flax Rolls, Organic Coconut
Balls, Organic Figs and Spices Flax Rolls,
Organic Ginger Lemon Flax Rolls,
Organic Raw Cacao Buckwheaties,
Organic Raw Cacao Dream Deluxe,
Organic Raw Chocolate Nuts &
Cherries, Organic Raw Chocolate with
Raw Cashews, Organic Vanilla
Buckwheaties

LYME REGIS FINE FOODS LTD ⊘
Fruit 4 U: Apple, Cherry, Raspberry;
Fruit Break: Banana, Date & Fig, Plum &
Apricot; *Kidz Break:* Blackcurrant,
Raisin; *Kidz Organic Fruit Bars:* Apple,
Blackcurrant, Strawberry; *La Fruit:*
Apricot, Blackcurrant, Raspberry;
Organic Fruitus Bars: Apple, Apricot,
Mixed Berry, Sultana & Hazelnut;
Organic Seven Seeds & Nut Bar:
Cranberry, Orginal

MA BAKER ☺
Obars: All

MARS
Starburst: Fruity Chews, Smoothies,
Sour Chews, Strawberry Mix

MASTERFOODS ⊘
Aquadrops: Apple

MCKEITH ☺
Goji Berry Bar; Goji Berry Bar Bites;
Living Food Energy Cookie Bites; Living
Food Energy Love Bites; Raw Hemp
Seed Bar; *Living Food Bar:* Energy, Love,
Vitamin C

MUNCHY SEEDS ™☺⊘
Vanilla Pumpkin

NATURKRAFTWERKE ™
**Energy 1 bar with Spirulina &
Banana; Energy 2 bar with
Chlorella; Energy 3 bar with
Weizengras; Energy 4 bar with
Gruentee & Zitrone; Energy 5 bar
with Guarana & Kakao; Energy 6
bar with Acerola**

NESTLÉ
Jelly Tots; *Polo:* Original, Spearmint,
Sugar Free, Xtra Strong

ORGANICO ⊘☼
Break & Bil: Spelt Apricot Delizia Bars,
Spelt Blueberry Delizia Bars

ORGANIX BRANDS PLC ⊘☼
Cereal Bars: Apple & Orange,
Blackcurrant, Carrot Cake, Cocoa &
Raisin, Munch Bar, Raspberry & Apple

ORGRAN ☺
Gluten-free Fruit Bars: Apricot,
Blueberry-Filled, Choc Cherry,
Chocolate Hazel Bars

PETER RABBIT ORGANICS ⊘☼
Organic 100% Fruit Bar; Organic Fruit
& Oat Bar

PLAMIL ☺❶⊘
Carob; Carob Catering Drops; Carob
Catering Pack Large; Carob No Added
Sugar; Carob No Added Sugar Catering
Drops; Carob No Added Sugar Catering
Pack Large

RAW ALCHEMY LTD ™☺❶⊘♟
Raw: **Handmade Raw Fruit Leathers**

RAW LIVING ™☺❶⊘♟
Bullet Ride; Incan berries; Magic Mix;
Mulberries; Yacon Root; *Hi:* Hi-Trail

REBECCA'S CAKES ™
**Flapjack; Vegan Flapjack; Vegan
Flapjack Fruit crumble Squares**

RENK'S INDUSTRIAL LTDA ™⊘☼
bi02: **Banana & Acai, Banana &
Cinnamon;** *eBar:* **Acerola Cherry,
Banana & Acai, Cupuacu, Pineapple
& Apple**

RJ'S
Natural Licorice: Soft Eating Raspberry;
Natural Licorice Logs: Chocolate
Orange, Raspberry

SCIENCE IN SPORT
SMART1 Gel; *GO Bars:* All Flavours; *GO
Gels:* All Flavours

SUPERNUTRIENTS LTD ™☺⊘♟
Cacao: **Organic cacao nibs;** *Organic:*
Organic goji berries

SWIZZELS MATLOW LTD ⊘♟
Climpies; Mr Fruits; Rainbow Drops;
Refresher bar lemon mega; *Deposited
Crystal:* Barley Sugar, Crystal Fruits,
Licorice; *Lolly:* Fruity Pops, Fruity Pops
Sour, Ice Cream Pops, Swizz Kid Fruity

**THE BOOJA-BOOJA
COMPANY LTD** ™☺⊘♟☼
**Organic, Raw Cacao Beans 50g &
200g; Organic, Raw Cacao Nibs 50g
& 200g**

THE SUNRISE GRANOLA COMPANY LLC ™☺⊘
Granola Snack Bar: **Apricot Almond Solgaia Bar, Cranberry Almond Solgaia Bar, Mango Coconut with Almonds Solgaia Bar**

THORNTONS ⊘
Fruit Jellies; Single Ice Cream Cone

TRAIDCRAFT PLC ⊘
Mixed Fruit Sweets

TRIDENT
Soft: Peppermint, Spearmint, Strawberry Smoothie, Tropical Twist

TROPICAL WHOLEFOODS
Tropical Fruit Bar

TUNCH FOODS LTD ™☺⊘ ✔
Pack Tunch: **Apple & Cinnamon Healthy Snack Bar, Lemon & Lime Healthy Snack Bar, Pineapple & Coconut Healthy Snack Bar**

VEGAN PERFECTION ™☺❶⊘ ✔
All products are vegan

VEGAN STORE ™☺⊘ ✔
All products are vegan including fudge, marshmallows, golden crunch, boxed chocolates and after dinner chocolates; *Chocolate bars: new name & Vegan, same taste:* **Buccanneer Bar, Golden Crunch 100g, Jekerz Bar, Mahalo Bar, Twilight Bar**

VENTURE FOODS UK LTD ™⊘
Vegan Dark Chocolate & Coconut;

Vegan Dark Chocolate & Hazelnut Nougat

VIMTO
Fizzy Centred Lollipops

WHOLEBAKE LTD ⊘
Hemp Flapjack

WILLIAM SANTUS & CO. LTD ™⊘
Uncle Joe's: **Mintballs**

WINNING WAYS FINE FOODS LIMITED ™
Coconut Ice

WRIGLEY ☺⊘ ✔
Doublemint; Juicy Fruit; *5:* Cobalt, Electro, Pulse; *Airwaves:* Black Mint, Cherry Menthol, Green Mint, Menthol & Eucalyptus; *Extra:* Chewy Mints, Cool Breeze, Cool Breeze Bottle, Fusion Orange Mango, Fusion Pineapple Banana, Fusion Raspberry Blackcurrant, Fusion Strawberry Peach, Ice, Ice Bottle, Ice Mints Roll Pack, Ice Peppermint Tin, Ice Spearmint Tin, Peppermint, Peppermint Handy Box, Spearmint, Spearmint Bottle, Spearmint Handy Box, Spearmint Roll Pack; *Hubba Bubba:* Atomic Apple, Cool Cola, Seriously Strawberry, Snappy Strawberry, Sour Double Berry, Strawberry and Watermelon, Triple Treat; *Orbit Complete:* Freshmint, Lemon & Lime, Peppermint, Spearmint, Strawberry, Strong Mint; *Tunes:* Blackcurrant, Cherry, Strawberry

COOKING AIDS - SAVOURY

A. VOGEL
Herbamare: All Varieties

AMISA
Bouillon

BIONA
Gluten-Free Breadcrumbs; Gomasio

BLUE DRAGON
Panko Breadcrumb Mix; Rice Flour Pancakes; Spring Roll Wrappers; Stem Ginger in Syrup; Tamarind Paste; Tempura Batter Mix; *Sushi ingredients:* Sushi Ginger, Wasabi Paste

CLEARSPRING ™☺❶⊘✔👁
Johsen Shoyu; Kuzu; Shiso Condiment; Tamari Soya Sauce; Ume Puree; *Organic:* Sesame Sea Salt - Gomasio, Shoyu Soya Sauce, Soya Sauce, Sushi Rice Seasoning, Sushi Rice Seasoning, Sushi Sauce, Tamari Soya Sauce, Teriyaki Sauce

ESSENTIAL TRADING CO-OPERATIVE LTD ™❶⊘✔
Organic Yeast Extract; Yeast Extract; *Essential Brand- Flours:* All (Organic & Conventional); *Essential Brand- Herbs:* All (Organic & Conventional); *Soya Sauce:* Organic Shoyu, Organic Tamari, Shoyu, Tamari

GEETA'S FOODS LIMITED ™✔
Geeta's Curry Creations: Geeta's Curry Night - Goan, Geeta's Curry Nights - Madras, Geeta's Hara Masala Curry Creation, Geeta's Kashmiri Curry Creation, Geeta's Tandoori Curry Creation; *Geeta's Spice and Stir:* Geta's Dhansak Spice and Stir, Geta's Jalfrezi Spice and Stir, Geta's Karai Bhuna Spice and Stir, Geta's Madras Spice and Stir

GILCHESTERS ORGANICS LTD ™⊘✿
Stoneground Organic 100% Spelt; Stoneground Organic 100% Wholemeal Flour; Stoneground Organic Farmhouse Flour; Stoneground Organic Pizza Ciabatta Flour; Stoneground Organic Unbleached White

GLUTEN FREE FOODS LTD
Barkat: Baking Powder

GOURMET CLASSIC LTD ™
Cooking Spirits: Cooking Brandy, Cooking Calvados, Cooking Gin, Cooking Whisky; *Cooking Wines:* Cabernet Sauvignon Cooking Wine, Chardonnay Cooking Wine, Cooking Madeira, Cooking Marsala, Cooking Port, Italian Red Cooking Wine, Italian White Cooking Wine

GREEN'S
Dumpling Mix

HIGHER NATURE LTD
Omega Excellence: Cold Milled Flax Seeds, Organic Cold Milled Flax Seeds, Organic Sprouted Flax Seeds

HOLISTIX HERBAL PRODUCTS ❶
Dried Herbs: All

JUS-ROL
Filo Pastry; Pastry Cases; Puff Pastry; Shortcrust Pastry

JUST WHOLEFOODS ☺⊘
Organic Sprouting Mix; Organic Wholemeal Breadcrumbs; VegeRen; *Organic Stuffing Mixes:* Apple & Sage, Cranberry & Orange, Sage & Onion

KITCHEN GARDEN
Curry Flavour TVP

KNORR
Paste Bouillon: Mediterranean Vegetable, Rich Vegetable, Vegetable

MARIGOLD
Engevita: Nutritional Yeast Flakes

MCKEITH ☺
Hemp Sauce

NATURKRAFTWERKE ™
Zhug

ODYSEA
Tomato Perasti; Vine Leaves

ORGRAN ☺
All Purpose Gluten-Free Crumbs

POLAR SUN PRODUCTS LTD ☺⊘
Vegan Soya Flours: Soya flour

QIANNA AGRICULTURAL PRODUCTS IND & TRADING CO. LTD ™☺
Roasted Black Bean; Roasted Green Soybean; Roasted Soybean

QUINUA REAL BRASIL LTDA ™⊘
Quinoa Flour

RAWCREATION LTD ™☺❶⊘✴
Crushed Purple Corn; Organic Hemp Powder from Canada; Organic Maca; Purple Corn Flour; Purple Corn Powder; Raw Black Himalayan Salt - Course; Raw Black Himalayan Salt - Fine; Raw Organic Pumpkin Seeds; Raw Pink Himalayan Fine-Ground Salt; Raw Pink Himalayan Rock Salt; Shelled Hemp Seeds; Whole Hemp Seeds

SEAGREENS LTD ™☺⊘
Seagreens- Medium Granules: **Catering Ingredient, Culinary Ingredient**

THE FOOD DOCTOR LTD ✴
Salad Boost: Herb Seed Mix; *Soup Boost:* Omega Seed Mix; *Stir Fry Boost:* Spicy Seed Mix

VENTURE FOODS UK LTD ™⊘
Essential: **Coarse Sea Salt, Fine Sea Salt;** *Geo Organics:* **Atlantic Sea Salt, Atlantic Sea Salt Shaker, Bagged Sea Salt, Balti Curry Paste, Cranberry Sauce, Korma Curry Paste, Madras Curry Paste, Thai Green Curry Paste, Thai Pine Nut Satay Paste, Thai Red Curry Paste, Thai Yellow Curry Paste, Tikka Masala Curry Paste, Tomato Relish, Tomato Sauce;** *The Raintree:* **Fleur de Sel**

WHITWORTHS LTD ⊘
Sage & Onion Stuffing

COOKING AIDS - SWEET

BIRD'S
Bird's: Original Custard Powder

CLEARSPRING ™☺❶◌◌◐
Japanese Brown Rice Malt Syrup;
Organic: **Barley Malt Syrup, Corn and
Barley Malt Syrup, Rice Malt Syrup**

CUISINE DE FRANCE
Assorted Sugar Strands

DIET FREEDOM ™☺❶◌◌
*Natural honey alternative and
sweetener:* **Sweet Freedom Natural
Sweetener (Mild), Sweet Freedom
Natural Syrup (Rich)**

DOVES FARM FOODS LTD ◌
Plain Chocolate Drops

DR OETKER
Angelica; Chocolate Flavour Strands;
Cream of Tartar; Glycerine; Ready to
Roll Regalice; *Bread Crumbs :* Golden,
Wholemeal; *Colours and Flavours :* All,
Except Natural Red; *Easyice:* Chocolate,
Vanilla; *Marzipan :* Golden, Natural;
Select Vanilla Pods: Extract, Powder

**ESSENTIAL TRADING
CO-OPERATIVE LTD** ™❶◌◌
Coconut milk

G. COSTA & CO ◌
Royal ascot: Stem ginger in syrup

GENERAL DIETARY
Xanthan Gum

GOURMET CLASSIC LTD ™
Cooking Spirits: **Cooking Dark Rum**

**GREEN VALLEY
TRADING CO** ™☺❶◌
Yaoh: **Organic Hemp Protein Powder**

GREEN'S
Lemon Pie Filling; Quick Gel

HIGHER NATURE LTD
ZyloSweet

JIF
Lemon Juice: Bottled, Squeezy; *Lime
Juice:* Bottled

JUS-ROL
All except Sweet Dessert products

JUST WHOLEFOODS ☺◌
All Natural Custard Powder

KALLO FOODS ◌
Multigrain Rice Cakes; Traditional Grissini
Breadsticks; *Rice Cakes:* Corn Cakes

MAXIM MARKETING COMPANY ™
Weikfield - Jelly Crystals: **Banana,
Cherry;** *Weikfield- Jelly Crystals:*
**Mango, Orange, Pineapple,
Raspberry, Strawberry**

MERIDIAN FOODS ◌
Malt Extract; Mince Pie Filling; *Natural
Sweeteners:* Malt Extract, Mince Pie
Filling

NESTLÉ
Dessert Sauce: Caramel, Chocolate

PHARMABRAND USA LLC ™☺⊘✔
Cid Botanical's: **Stevia**

RAW LIVING ™☺❶⊘✔
Agave Nectar; Chocolate Powder; Lucuma powder; Mesquite powder; Vanilla powder; Yacon flour; Yacon syrup

RAWCREATION LTD ™☺❶⊘✔
Acai Powder (raw & organic); Agave Syrup; Carob Powder; Dark Agave Syrup; Hempini (hemp seed butter); Mulberries (raw & organic); Organic Lucuma; Organic Yacon Slices; Raw Apricot Kernels; Raw Carob Nectar; Raw Incan Berries; Raw Organic Mesquite Meal; Raw Whole Carob Pods; Shazzie's Whole Almond & Cacao Spread; Tahini; White Almond Butter; Whole almond butter; Yacon Syrup

SAUCES OF CHOICE
Sauces to Dine For: Black Cherry with Kirsch

SUPERNUTRIENTS LTD ™☺⊘✔
Natural Sweetener: **Organic Agave Nectar**

SWEETBIRD ⊘
Syrups: English Toffee, Hazelnut, Vanilla

THE BEST OF TASTE COMPANY
Jewelled Fruits in Madeira; *Coulis:* Apricot, Black Cherry with Kirsch, Blackberry, Blackcurrant, Cranberry & Orange with Cointreau, Damson with Sloe Gin, Mango and Passionfruit, Raspberry, Strawberry, Summer Fruit, Tipsy Plum, Wild Blueberry

CRACKERS, CRISPBREADS ETC

ARTISAN BISCUITS
Bread: 3 Seed; *Millers:* Damsels Wheat Wafers, Organic Damsels Wheat Wafers; *Mondovino Crackers:* Black Olive, Spicy Seed & Nut; *Wheat Wafers:* Charcoal, Oat, Organic 3 Seed, Organic Spelt, Organic Wheat, Rye, Sour Dough, Spelt, Wheat

BIONA
Corn Cakes; *Rice Cakes:* Dark Chocolate Coated, No Salt, With Amaranth, With Quinoa, With Salt

BLUE DRAGON
Rice crackers: Chilli Flavour, Nori Flavour, Original Flavour

BURTON'S FOODS LTD
Cream Cracker

CLEARSPRING ™☺⊘✔👁
Brown Rice Wafers - Sesame; Japanese Rice Cakes - Black Sesame; Japanese Rice Cakes - Black Sesame; Japanese Rice Cakes - Miso; Japanese Rice Cakes - Tamari Garlic; Japanese Rice Cakes - Tamari Garlic; Japanese Rice Cakes - Teriyaki; Japanese Rice Cakes- Sea Vegetable; Rice Snacks -

Black Sesame; Rice Snacks - Quinoa; Rice Snacks - Quinoa; Rice Snacks - Sea Vegetable; Rice Snacks - Sea Vegetable; Rice Snacks - Whole Sesame; *Organic:* **Puffed Rice Cakes - Plain, Puffed Rice Cakes - Multigrain with Spelt, Puffed Rice Cakes - Salted, Rice Cracker - Olive Oil and Salt, Rice Crackers - Olive Oil and Salt, Rice Crackers - Tamari**

DEES CARIBBEAN IMPORTS
Homemade Special Cream Water Crackers; HTB Crackers

G. COSTA & CO ⊘
Pagen Krisprolls: Cranberry & Blueberry Krisprolls, Golden Krisprolls, Wholegrain Krisprolls; *Pop pan:* Spring Onion crackers

GEO ORGANICS ⊘
Toasted Croutons

GLUTEN FREE FOODS LTD
Glutano: Crispbread

JACOB'S ⊘
Cornish Wafer; Cream Cracker; Cream Cracker Light; High Bake Water Biscuits; High Fibre Cream Crackers; Hovis Cracker; Oat Cracker; Rosemary & Sea Salt Thins; Salk & Cracked Black Pepper Bakes; Savours Assortment Carton; Sesame & Roasted Onion Thins; Sweet Chilli Thins; Table Cracker

KALLO FOODS ⊘
High Fibre Oat and Rice Cakes; Low Fat Lightly Salted Rice Cakes; No Added Salt Rice Cakes; No Added Salt Rice Cakes with Sesame; Original

Breadsticks; Rice Cake Bites With Sea Salt; Rice Cake Bites With Yeast Extract; Rosemary Crackers; Savoury Rice Cakes; Slightly Salted Rice Cakes with Sesame; Thin Slice No Added Salt Rice Cakes; Thin Slice Slightly Salted Rice Cakes with Sesame; Wholemeal Rye Crispbread; *Grains and Seeds:* Khorosan and Sorghum Corn Cakes, Quinoa and Amaranth Corn Cakes, Quinoa and Amaranth Rice Cakes; *Primo D'Oro Torinesi:* Original Breadsticks, Pepper Breadsticks

LIFEFOOD CZECH REPUBLIC S.R.O. ☺❶⊘✔✿
Life food: Organic Flax Onion Crackers, Organic Garlic Marjoram Flax Crackers, Organic Tomato Chilli Flax Crackers

MARMITE
Breadsticks; Ricecakes

ORGRAN ☺
Gluten-Free Corn Cakes; *Gluten-free Crispbreads:* Corn, Rice, Rice & Cracked Pepper, Rice & Garden Herb, Salsa Corn; *Organic Rice Cakes:* Salted, Sesame Salted, Sesame Unsalted, Sunsalted; *Rice Cake Thins:* Salted, Unsalted

RAW ALCHEMY LTD ™☺❶⊘✔
Raw: **Raw Crackers**

RYVITA ⊘
Crispbreads: Dark Rye, Multigrain, Original, Pumpkin and Oat, Sesame, Sunflower and Oat, Tomato & Basil

SUMA WHOLEFOODS
™❶⊗✔☜⚓1985
Japanese Rice Crackers

THE FOOD DOCTOR LTD ✔
Organic Spelt Crackers

UNITED BISCUITS LTD ⊗
Carr's - Table Water: Cracked Black Pepper, Large, Small, Toasted Sesame Seed

VENTURE FOODS UK LTD ™⊗
Geo Organics: **Toasted Salted Croutons;** *The Raintree:* **Garlic Soup Croutons**

CREAM REPLACERS

ALPRO UK LTD ☺❶⊗
Chilled Dairy Free Alternative to single cream 250ml; Culinaire Soya Dairy Free Alternative to Single Cream 1 litre; Dairy Free Alternative to single cream + screw top 250ml; *Provamel:* Soya Dairy Free Alternative to Single Cream

GRANOVITA UK LTD ⊗✔
Organic Cremo Vita - alternative to dairy whipping cream

RAW ALCHEMY LTD ™☺❶⊗✔
Raw: **Handmade Raw Chocolate Sauce**

DESSERTS

ALPRO UK LTD ☺❶⊗
Dairy Free Custard Calcium 525g; Fruits of the Forest; *Pot Desserts:* Caramel, Caramel Dessert Calcium 4x125g, Chocolate Calcium 4x125g, Dark chocolate Calcium and Vitamins 4x125g, Vanilla Calcium 4 x125g; *Pot Desserts Provamel :* Organic mocha 4x125g; *Provamel:* Organic chocolate custard 525g, Organic vanilla custard 525g; *Provamel Pot Desserts:* Organic caramel 4x125g, Organic Chocolate 4x125g, Organic Vanilla 4x125g

BRITISH SUGAR PLC
Silver Spoon - Treat Toppings: Dark Chocolate, Monster Crackin'

CLEARSPRING ™☺❶⊗✔☜
Organic: **Brown Rice Amazake, Fruit puree - Apple/Apricot, Fruit Puree - Apple/Plum, Fruit puree - Apple, Fruit Puree - Apple and Pineapple, Fruit puree - Apple/Blueberry, Fruit puree - Apple/Pineapple, Fruit puree - Apple/Strawberry, Fruit Puree - Pear, Fruit Puree - Pear and Banana, Fruit Puree - Pear/Banana, Millet Amazake, Oat Amazake, Pear Fruit Purée**

CUISINE DE FRANCE
7"" Plate Rhubarb Pie; 7/"" Plate Apple Pie; Apple & Blackberry Lattice; Apple & Blackberry Pie; Apple & Cinnamon Strudel; Apple & Cranberry Lattice; Apple Lattice; Apple Puff; Apple Tart;

Apple Turnover; Deep Fill Apple Pie; Delicious Apple & Blackberry Pie; Delicous Apple Pie; Delicous Rhubarb Pie; Everyday Apple & Blackberry Tart; Everyday Bramley Apple Tart; Everyday Rhubarb Tart; Hero Apple Pie; Hero Premium Apple Tart; Lattice Rhubarb Tart; Mini Apple Pie; Rhubarb Tart

ESSENTIAL TRADING CO-OPERATIVE LTD ™❶⊘✔
Canned mango chunks; Canned pineapple chunks; Canned tropical fruit mix; *Essential Brand- Canned Fruit:* **Organic Canned Papaya in Juice**

JUST WHOLEFOODS ☺⊘
Jelly Crystals: Lemon, Raspberry, Strawberry, Tropical

LYONS
Lyons: Lattice Treacle Tart, Treacle Tart

NATURALLY ME INC ☺
Cherry Pie; Chocolate Mousse Pie; Gourmet Apple Cranberry Pie; Gourmet Apple Struesel Pie; Gourmet Blueberry Struesel Pie; Pie Shells; Pumpkin Pie

NATURGREEN
Almond Dessert; Hazelnut and Chocolate Dessert; Hazelnut Dessert

ORGANICO ⊘✿
Coteaux Nantais: Apple and Blueberry Desserts, Apple and Cherry Desserts, Apple and Rhubarb Desserts, Apple and Strawberry Desserts, Magic Apricot Compote, Magic Nectarine Compote, Magic Plum Compote

REBECCA'S CAKES ™
Apple and Blackberry Crumble; Banoffee Trifle; Fruit Pies; *Mini Desserts/Petit Fours:* **Chocolate Dipped Seasonal Fruit, Mini Chocolate Cupcakes, Peanut Butter and Chocolate Squares, Scones with Cream and Strawberries, Caramel Trifle Shots with Kahlua, Cherry Gallettes, Chocolate and Nut Dipped Frozen Bananas, Chocolate Brownie Squares with Raspberries, Cocoa Dusted Truffles, Fruit Patisserie Tarts, Mini Vanilla Cupcakes with Pink Icing and White Piped Initials:, Pecan Pies, Rocky Roads, Victoria Sponges with Cream and Berries**

DIPS & DRESSINGS

ANILA'S AUTHENTIC SAUCES LTD™☺
Sweet chilli dipping sauce

BEAN THINKING
Humous; *Patés:* Satay Sauce

DARTMOOR CHILLI FARM ™❶⊘✔
Dartmoor Chilli: **Chilli Salad Dressing**

DISCOVERY FOODS
Ranch Style Salsa: Hot, Medium

G. COSTA & CO ⊘
Casa fiesta: Guacamole flavour dip

FOOD

GOBBLIN WHOLEFOODS
Houmous; *Organic:* Houmous

GRANOVITA UK LTD ⊘ ✔
Mayola! Egg Free Mayonnaise: Garlic, Lemon, Original

HELLMANN'S
Classic Vinaigrette; Dry Vinaigrette Classic; Dry Vinaigrette Raspberry; Dry Vinaigrette Sun Dried Tomato; Fat Free Vinaigrette; Garlic & Herbs; Olive Oil & Balsamic Vinegar; Raspberry Flavour Vinegar & Mustard

JETHROS
'Spirits of Summer' Vinaigrettes: Cranberry Pepper & Vodka, Irish Whiskey & Grain Mustard, Orange & Bourbon

KITCHEN GARDEN
Salad Oil: Oregano, Piri Piri

MA BAKER ☺
Al'fez: Tahini dressing 200ml

MH FOODS ™⊘ ✔
Life: **Mayonnaise Style Sunflower Oil Dressing - Egg Free**

ODYSEA
Meze: Aubergine, Roasted Red Pepper, Sun-Dried Tomato

PATCHWORK TRADITIONAL FOOD COMPANY
Pate: Brown Lentil with Hazelnuts, Brown Lentil with Mushrooms

PHILEAS FOGG
Chunky Salsa Dip; Sweet Chilli Dip

PLAMIL ☺❶⊘
Chilli Mayonnaise; Egg Free Mayonnaise Catering Pack; Egg Free Mayonnaise Garlic Catering Pack; Garlic Mayonnaise; Organic Egg Free Mayonnaise Catering Pack; Organic Egg Free Rice Mayonnaise Catering Pack; Organic Lemongrass Mayonnaise; Organic Plain Mayonnaise; Organic Rice Mayonnaise; Plain Mayonnaise; Tarragon Mayonnaise

RAW ALCHEMY LTD ™☺❶⊘ ✔
Raw: **Raw Hummus**

SOURCE FOODS ☺✿
Organic Miso Mustard

THE ENGLISH PROVENDER CO. ⊘
Hot Chilli Marinade; Smokey Barbecue Marinade; Thai Lime & Coriander Dressing

EGG REPLACERS

GENERAL DIETARY
Egg Replacer

ORGRAN ☺
No Egg - Egg Replacer (Gluten-Free)

GRAVIES & STOCKS

A. VOGEL
Kelpamare; Plantaforce

BISTO
Favourite Gravy Granules (Reduced Salt); Favourite Gravy Granules; Onion Gravy Granules; Original Gravy Powder

HAPPY AND HEALTHY FOODS ☺❶
Golden Gravy Mix; Savoury Herb Gravy
Mix; Shiitake Mushroom Gravy Mix

KALLO FOODS ⊘
French Onion Stock Cubes; Garlic &
Herbs Stock Cubes; Low Salt Vegetable
Stock Cubes; Mushroom Stock Cubes;
Tomato & Herb Stock Cubes; Vegetable
Stock Cubes; Vegetable Stock Powder;
Yeast Free Vegetable Stock Cubes; *Just
Bouillion:* Vegetable Concentrate; *Just
Bouillion:* Vegetable Gravy Granules,
Vegetable Stock Cubes

KNORR
Simply Stock; Simply Stock - Vegetable;
Touch of Taste - Vegetable; Vegetable
Stock Cubes

MARIGOLD
Gravy Mix; Marigold Liquid Aminos;
Bouillon Cubes: Low Salt, Regular, Yeast
Free; *Instant Miso Bouillon Powder:*
Organic; *Swiss Vegetable Bouillon
Powder:* Organic, Organic Reduced Salt,
Reduced Salt

ORGRAN ☺
Gluten-Free Gravy Mix

**REDWOOD WHOLEFOOD
COMPANY** ™☺❶⊘
Cheatin': **Vegan Gravy Powder**

SUMA WHOLEFOODS
™❶⊘ ✔ ☞⚒1985
Bouillon Stock: **Reduced Salt/Vegan
Vegetable Bouillon**

HAMPERS

MANNA GIFTS ™⊘✔
Kosher & Vegan Hampers: **Dark Magic,
Organic Black Magic, Vegan Heaven,
Vegan Rosh Hashanah**

RIPE GIFTS ™⊘✔
Vegan Hampers: **Natural Temptation
Hamper, The 'V' Hamper, The New
Year Resolution, Vegan Christmas
Hamper, Vegan Easter Hamper,
Vegan Valentine Hamper**

'ICE CREAMS', SORBETS ETC

BEN & JERRY'S
Sorbets: Jamaican Me Crazy, Mango
Berry Swirl

B'NICE ™☺
**Non Dairy Rice Cream Chocolate;
Non Dairy Rice Cream Strawberry;
Non Dairy Rice Cream Vanilla**

COCADA FRESCO (UK) LTD ™☺❶⊘✔
No nuts just coconuts

**ESSENTIAL TRADING
CO-OPERATIVE LTD** ™❶⊘✔
Organic Fruit Lollies

SANITARIUM HEALTH FOOD CO ⊘
So Good Bliss Ice Cream: All Flavours

RAW VEGAN 'ICE CREAM'

www.nonutsjustcoconuts.com

email: sales@nonutsjustcoconuts.com

Coco+Mango Coco+Pineapple
Coco+Cacao Coco+Coco

SWEDISH GLACE ☺
Smooth Vanilla Lollies with Chocolate Flavoured Coating; *Non Dairy Frozen Dessert:* Juicy Raspberry, Neapolitan, Rich Chocolate, Smooth Vanilla, Wild Blueberry

THE BOOJA-BOOJA COMPANY LTD ™☺⊘ 🦴 ☼
Stuff In A Tub: **Coconut Hullabaloo, Feisty Winjin Ginger, Hunky Punky Chocolate, Keep Smiling Vanilla M'Gorilla, Pompompous Maple Pecan**

TOFUTTI ☺❶⊘
Non Dairy Dessert: Strawberry, Vanilla; *Non Dairy Frozen Soya Organic Desserts:* Chocolate, Mango & Passionfruit; *Rock & Roll:* Cakes, Cones; *Sour Supreme :* Soya Alternative to Sour Cream

WORTHENSHAWS ™
Frozen Dessert: **Coconice- all flavours**

MARGARINES, FATS, OILS ETC

BIONA
Omega 3 Oil Enriched Spread; Organic Vegetable Margarine; *Olive Extra:* Extra Virgin Olive Oil Margarine, Reduced Fat Extra Virgin Olive Oil Spread

BRAHAM & MURRAY LTD ™ 🦴
Oils: **Good Oil Mild+Light, Good Oil Original**

CLEARSPRING ™☺❶⊘🦴👁
Toasted Sesame Oil; *Organic:* **Hazelnut Oil, Italian Extra Virgin Oil, Olive Oil, Omega Oil, Rapeseed Oil, Safflower Oil, Sesame Oil, Soya oil, Styrian toasted pumpkin seed oil,**

Sunflower frying oil, Sunflower oil, Toasted sesame oil, Walnut oil

COOKEEN
Solid Vegetable Fat: Cookeen

ESSENTIAL TRADING CO-OPERATIVE LTD ™❶⊘✔
Essential Brand- Organic Oils: **All**

FAUSER VITAQUELLWERK KG ™
Vitaquell Extra Margarine: **Extra Omega 3 Organic 250g;** *Vitaquell Margarine:* **Organic 500g**

GLASGOW HEALTH SOLUTIONS ™
Lignan Flax Oil

HIGHER NATURE LTD
Coconut Oil; Essential Balance Oil; Flax Seed Oil; Organic Omega 3:6:9 Balance Oil; *Omega Excellence:* Garlic-Chilli Flax Seed Oil, Hemp Seed Oil, Omega Excellence, Organic Coconut Butter, Organic Flax Seed Oil, Organic Garlic-Chilli Flax Seed Oil, Organic Hemp Seed Oil, Organic Omega 3:6:9 Balance Oil, Organic Virgin Coconut Butter, Virgin Coconut Oil, Virgin Hemp Seed Oil

KERRY FOODS LTD ™⊘
Pure: **Soya Spread, Sunflower Spread**

KONRAD HABERBERGER HANDELS-UND CONSULTING GMBH ™☺
Pro Oleic: **High oleic sunflower oil deodorised**

LIFEPLAN PRODUCTS LTD ™⊘✔👁
Wheatgerm Oil; *Oils:* **Flaxseed Oil**

MH FOODS ™⊘✔
Fry Light- Cooking Non-Stick Spray: **Extra Virgin Olive Oil, Sunflower Oil**

MUNCHY SEEDS ™☺⊘
Mixed Seed Oil: **Roasted Sunflower & Pumpkin Seed Oil**

OLEADOR UG (HAFTUNGSBESCHRÄNKT) ™
Argan Oil Basic; Argan Oil Classic; Argan Oil Light

PANACEA APS ™
Udo's Choice-: **Ultimate Oil Blend**

RAKUSEN'S ™☺⊘✔
Tomor: **250g Block Margarine, Sunflower Tub 250g**

ROSIE'S GOURMET PRODUCTS (UK) LTD ™☺⊘✔
Extra Virgin Olive Oil

SMILDE ™⊘
Sunflower Spread

SUMA WHOLEFOODS
™❶⊘✔👁⚒1985
Suma Spreads: **100% Sunflower – 2kg, Low Fat – 500g, Organic Sunflower 500g, Soya – 2kg & 500g**

SUPERNUTRIENTS LTD ™☺⊘✔
Organic: **Organic Coconut Oil**

THE FOOD DOCTOR LTD ✔
Salad Oil: Omega Oil; *Spreads:* Omega Nut Butter, Omega Seed Butter

WHITE MARK MARKETING UG ™
Oleador: **Argan Oil Classic, Argan oil pure**

YAOH ™☺❶⊘✔
Hemp Oil 250ml; Hemp Oil 500ml

PASTRY

BABYCAKES DIRECT ™☺❶
Cheeseley and chive scones; Choc chip scones; Original scones; Sun dried tomato and olive scones

CUISINE DE FRANCE
Medium Vol Au Vent Cases; Puff Pastry Sheets

IL MANGIARSANO S.P.A ™⊘✔
Gaia Organic Bakery Products: **Apricot Tart, Blueberry Tart, Strawberry Tart;** *Germinal Organic Bakery:* **Apple Puff Pastry, Apple Puff-Pastry, Apple Snack, Apricot Tart, Blueberry kamut puff-pastry, Blueberry Tart, Wild Fruit Tart, Wild Fruits Snack**

JUS-ROL
Frozen: Filo Pastry Sheets, King Size Puff Pastry Cases, Medium Size Puff Pastry Cases, Party Size Puff Pastry Cases, Puff Pastry Blocks, Puff Pastry Sheets, Shortcrust Pastry Blocks, Shortcrust Pastry Sheets

REBECCA'S CAKES ™
Maple pecan Danish pastries

PICKLES, SAUCES, VINEGARS ETC

ANILA'S AUTHENTIC SAUCES LTD ™☺
Aubergine Pickle; Carrot & Date Pickle; Chilli Chutney; Chilli Pasta Sauce; Chilli pickle; Fruity Mild Korma Curry Sauce; Goan green curry sauce; Hot Lime Pickle; Hot Mango Pickle; Hot Methi Curry Sauce; Lemon Pickle; Mild Korma Curry Sauce; Shredded Mango Chutney; Spicy Apple Chutney; Spicy Hot Curry Sauce; Spicy Korma Curry Sauce; Spicy Medium Curry Sauce; Spicy Mild Curry Sauce; Sweet Lime Pickle; Sweet Mango Chutney; Sweet Mango Pickle; Tamarind & Date Chutney; Tindori (Mini Gherkin) Pickle

ASPALL ⊘✔
Vinegar: All

BAXTERS ⊘
Beetroot: Baby Beetroot, Beetroot in Redcurrant Jelly, Beetroot Pickle, Crinkle Cut Beetroot, Rosebud Beetroot, Sliced Beetroot; *Chutney:* Albert's Victorian Chutney, Apple Cider & Fig, Crushed Pineapple and Sweet Pepper, Fire roasted Pepper, Spiced Fruit, Sweet Cherry Tomato & Peppadew, Tomato; *Condiments:* Cranberry Jelly, Cranberry Sauce, Mint Jelly, Mint Sauce, Redcurrant Jelly

BERTOLLI
Family Pasta Sauce: Basil, Garlic, Original, Spicy; *Pasta Sauces:* Chilli and Peppers, Grilled Vegetable, Mushroom and Roasted Garlic, Red Wine and Shallots, Sundried Tomato and Oregano, Tomato and Basil; *Rustico Pasta Sauce:* Mediterranean Veg, Mushroom, Garlic & Oregano, Sweet Chilli and Red Onion, Sweet Red and Yellow Peppers

BIONA
Hot Pepper Sauce; Tomato Ketchup; Worcestershire Sauce; *Anti Pasti:* Black

www.currytree.co.uk

Olive Pate, Capers in Extra Virgin Olive Oil, Pesto; *Mustard:* Dijon, Horseradish, Wholegrain; *Passata:* Original, Rustica, With Basil; *Pasta Sauce:* Arrabbiata Hot & Spicy, Basilico Tomato & Basil, Peperona Tomato & Sweet Pepper, Toscana Tuscan Style; *Relish:* Harrissa Chilli, Horseradish; *Vinegar:* Balsamic, Cider, Red Wine, White Wine

BLUE DRAGON
Chilli Sauces: Chilli & Garlic Sauce, Hot Chilli Sauce, Sweet & Sour Chilli Sauce, Sweet Chilli Sauce; *Condiment sauces:* Japanese Rice Vinegar, Mirin, Rice Vinegar, Sushi Su Rice Vinegar; *Cooking sauces:* Plum, Satay, Spring Roll, Teriyaki Marinade; *Dips:* Hot Chilli Dipping Sauce, Sweet Chilli & Mango, Sweet Chilli & Pineapple Dipping Sauce, Sweet Chilli Dipping Sauce, Sweet Chilli with Kaffir Lime; *Pestos:* Coriander & Kaffir Lime, Satay & Sweet Chilli; *Premium stir fry sachets:* Black Bean with Roasted Garlic & Chilli, Sticky Plum, Sweet & Sour with Coriander, Sweet Chilli & Kaffir Lime, Sweet Soy & Roasted Red Chilli; *Soy Sauce:* Dark, Garlic Infused, Japanese, Light, Mushroom Infused, Premium; *Stir fry sachets:* Black Bean, Chow Mein, Hoi Sin & Garlic, Peking Lemon, Sweet & Sour, Sweet Chilli & Garlic, Sweet Soy with Garlic & Ginger, Szechuan Tomato, Teriyaki; *Stir fry sauces:* Black Bean, Hoi Sin, Hot Chilli, Plum, Sweet & Sour, Sweet Chilli, Szechuan Tomato

BUITONI ☺
Sauces: All

CALEDONIAN CURRY CO. ™⊘
Beetroot & Chilli Relish; Hot Rhubarb & Chilli Relish; Red Pepper & Chilli Relish; Tomato & Chilli Relish

CLEARSPRING ™☺❶⊘✔👁
Brown Rice Vinegar; Miso relish; Sushi cucumber pickle; Sushi Cucumber Pickle; Sushi Daikon Pickle; Sushi ginger pickle; Takuan (Pickled Daikon Radish); Tsuyu; Ume concentrate; Umeboshi puree; Wasabi; *Organic:* **Apple balsamic vinegar, Balsamic vinegar, Balsamic vinegar - Vintage Red, Brown Rice Vinegar, Chuno Dipping Sauce, Mikawa mirin, Miso Dipping Sauce, Red wine vinegar, Umeboshi plums, White wine vinegar**

COLMAN'S
Colmans: Bramley Apple Sauce, Classic Mint Sauce, Double Superfine Mustard Powder, Fresh Garden Mint; *Colmans Mustard:* Dijon, English, Mild, Wholegrain

CUISINE DE FRANCE
Chilli Sauce; Red Onion Relish; Red Pepper Dressing; Sweet Chilli & Garlic Sauce

CURRY SLIM
Curry Slim Cooking Sauces: Jalfrezi

DARTMOOR CHILLI FARM ™❶⊘✔
Dartmoor Chilli: **Apache Chilli, Apple & Mango Chutney, Beast of Dartmoor Chilli Sauce, Bhut Jolokia Chilli Flakes, Bhut Jolokia Chilli Powder, Carrot & Habanero Orange Chilli Chutney, Cider & Jalapeno Chilli Chutney, Devils Hound Chilli Puree, Extreme Apple Chilli Chutney, Fireball Pickled Onions, Hot Fire Chilli Sauce, Hot Mango &**

FOOD

Ginger Chilli Chutney, Mango & Ginger Chilli Chutney, Rhubarb & Ginger Chilli Chutney, Sweet Chilli Chutney, Sweet Chilli Sauce, Sweet Pepper & Tomato Chilli Chutney, Thai Spiced Chilli & Apple Jelly, Tomato Chilli Salsa

DISCOVERY FOODS
Sliced Jalapenos; *2-Step:* Chilli Con Carne, Texan Fajita Sauce; *Sauce:* Buffalo Wings, Enchilada, Hot & Smoky BBQ, Mexican, New Orleans Creole

DOLMIO
Chunky Sauces for Bolognese: Mediterranean Vegetable, Roasted Garlic & Onion, Summer Vegetable, Sweet Pepper; *Microwaveable Sauce Pouches:* Chilli, Sun Ripened Tomato & Basil; *Pasta Bake:* Roasted Mediterranean Vegetable; *Sauce for Bolognese:* Extra Mushroom, Extra Onion & Garlic, Extra Spicy, Organic, Original, Original Light, Red Lasagne; *Stir in Sauce:* Spicy Tomato & Sweet Onion, Sun Dried Tomato Light; *Taste of Sauces for Pasta:* Sicily - Tomato, Basil & Garlic, Tuscany - Tomato & Chianti

ESSENTIAL TRADING CO-OPERATIVE LTD ™ ❶ ⊘ ✔
Wholegrain mustard; *Essential Brand-Bottled, Jarred, Canned:* **Organic Dijon Mustard**

G. COSTA & CO ⊘
Curry club: Madras sauce, Mild curry paste, Sweet mango chutney, Tandoori paste; *Elsenham:* Apple & Pear Sauce with Calvados, Country Mint Sauce, Cumberland Berry Sauce, Fresh Mint & Rosemary Jelly, Hot English Horseradish Sauce, Luxury Cranberry Sauce, Spiced Orchard Chutney, Three Apple Sauce, Wild Cranberry Sauce; *Elsenham Mustard:* English Ale Mustard, Hot English Mustard, Irish Whiskey Mustard, Tewkesbury Mustard; *Frenchs:* Deli Mustard, Frenchs American Mustard, Frenchs American Mustard Squeezy; *Go tan:* Java's spicy indonesian crackers, Ketjap manis, Nasi goreng meal kit, Sambal oelek, Satay kit, Satay manis; *Grey Poupon:* Dijon Mustard, Wholegrain Mustard (A l'ancienne); *Ken Holm sauces:* Black bean with orange and lime, Chilli and garlic with jalapeno peppers, Sweet and sour with Passion fruit; *La Favorite:* Coarsegrain Mustard, Dijon Mustard, Hot English Mustard; *Maille:* Bearnaise, Dijon Mustard Dressing, Dijon Original Mustard, Dijonnaise, Hollandaise, Wholegrain Mustard; *Old Ranch House:* Bar-B-Bar Caribbean Calypso BBQ Sauce, Caribbean Calypso BBQ Sauce; *Old Ranch House :* Coln Valley Dill Sauce, Geo Watkins Mushroom Ketchup, OK Fruity Sauce; *Old Ranch House Cattlemen's BBQ Sauces:* Classic BBQ Sauce, Smokehouse BBQ Sauce; *Old Ranch House Lorenz Snack World:* Crunchips X Cut Paprika Crisps, Crunchips X Cut Salted Crisps, Saltletts Classic Sticks; *Rajah:* Balti sauce, Vindaloo sauce; *S & B:* Wasabi paste; *S& B:* Wasabi powder; *Tabasco:* Chipolata Sauce, Green Sauce, Habanero Sauce, Red Sauce, Red Sauce Minis, Red Travel Pack; *Tabasco :* Spicy Manzanilla Olives; *Tabasco:* Spicy Pepper Jelly; *Tabasco :* Spicy Stuffed Olives; *Vincotto:* Aceto di vincotto,

Mild pepper sauce, Vincotto originale; *Zest:* Coriander,Basil & hazelnut pesto sauce, Hot & spicy pasta sauce, Mexican chilli sauce, Mushroom & green garlic sauce, Organic tomato & herb pasta sauce, Sundried tomato paste, Vegan pesto

GEETA'S FOODS LIMITED ™ ⊘ ℐ
Geeta's Aubergine Pickle; Geeta's Chilli Pickle; Geeta's Garlic Pickle; *Geeta's Chutney:* **Geeta's Lime & Chilli Chutney, Geeta's Mango & Chilli Chutney, Geeta's Mango & Ginger Chutney, Geeta's Onion Chutney, Geeta's Papaya & Orange Chutney, Geeta's Pineapple Chutney, Geeta's Premium Mango Chutney, Geeta's Squeezy Premium Mango Chutney, Geeta's Squeezy Spicy Lime Chutney, Geeta's Squeezy Tomato and Onion Chutney, Geeta's Tamarind Chutney;** *Geeta's Regional Sauces:* **Geeta's Goan Cooking Sauce, Geeta's Mumbai Cooking Sauce**

GEO ORGANICS ⊘
Apple, Apricot & Ginger Chutney; Balti Curry Paste; Black Bean Cooking Sauce; Brinjal Pickle; Brown Sauce; Fairtrade Mango Chutney; Garlic Pickle; Korma Curry Paste; Lime Pickle; Madras Curry Paste 180g; Mango Chutney in Apple Juice; Mexican BBQ Sauce; Mexican Salsa; Mexican Tomato Fajita Sauce; Picalilli; Spicy Tomato Chutney; Sweet & Sour Cooking Sauce; Sweet Chilli Sauce; Sweet Pickle; Szechuan Stir Fry Sauce; Thai Green Curry Paste; Thai Red Curry Paste; Thai Satay Paste with Pine

Kernels; Thai Yellow Curry Paste; Tikka Masala Curry Paste; Tomato & Apple Chutney; Tomato Sauce; Veggie Relish; Worcestershire Sauce; *Pasta Sauce:* Tomato & Basil; *Pasta Sauce :* Tomato Mushroom, Tomato Pepper

GEORGAS FAMILY ™☺❶⊘ℐ✲
Vinegar: **Wine vinegar**

GRANOVITA UK LTD ⊘ℐ
Organic Brown Sauce

HEINZ
Baby Beetroot in sweet vineagr; Crinklecut Beetroot in Sweet Vinegar; Pickled Onions in Vinegar; Red cabbage in sweet vinegar; Silverskin Onions in Vinegar; Sweet Silverskin Onions in Vinegar; *Heinz Condiments:* Hot Tomato Dipping Sauce; *Heinz Sauces:* English Mustard, Exoctic Sweet and Sour Sauce, Hot n Spicy BBQ sauce, Original Barbecue Sauce, Rich Salsa Sauce, Sundried Tomato Sauce, Tangy Curry Sauce; *HP:* (Mexican) Chilli, BBQ Classic, BBQ Spicy, Brown Sauce, Fruity Sauce, Hot Sauce - Jalapeno Pepper & Lime, Hot Sauce - Smokey Chilli, Indian Sauce, Reduced Salt & Sugar Brown Sauce, Steak sauce; *Pickles:* Mild Mustard Pickle, Piccalilli Pickle, Ploughmans Pickle, Tangy Sandwich Pickle, Tangy Tomato Pickle

HENDERSONS ☺
Hendersons Relish

HIGHER NATURE LTD
Omega Excellence: Organic Apple Cider Vinegar

JEREMY'S SOUPS ⊘ 🖟
Sauce: BBQ, Tomato & Chilli, Tomato & Garlic

JETHROS
Glazes - for Roast & Grill: Balsamic Ginger, Blackcurrant Chilli; *Marinades:* Amadou Barbecue Sauce, Cajun Lime & Jalapeno, Lemon Bay & Rosemary, Lemon Chilli & Coriander, Lime Chilli & Oregano, Orange Chilli & Cumin, Pineapple Chilli & Basil; *Sauces - for Dipping & Basting:* 12 Days of Christmas, Ginger & Orange, Ginger Chilli, Ginger Lime, Green Chilli & Coriander, Red Chilli & Garlic

KALLO FOODS ⊘
Whole Earth: Tomato Sauce

KITCHEN GARDEN PRESERVES 🖟
Chutney: Autumn Apple, Beetroot, Christmas, Hot Mango, Ploughmans Pickle, Plum & Cranberry, Red Pepper & Chilli Relish, Spiced Apple with Mint, Spiced Apricot & Orange, Spiced Tomato & Apple, Sweet Mustard Pickle, Sweet Onion Relish, Sweet Plum & Date, Tomato; *Cranberry Sauce:* Non-organic, Organic; *Jelly:* Apple with Mint, Organic Redcurrant, Redcurrant; *Organic Chutney:* Spiced Apricot & Orange

KNOBBLY CARROT FOOD COMPANY
Pasta Sauce: Luxury Vegetable, Spicy Tomato w ithPepper & Ginger, Sun Dried Tomato & Pesto

KNORR
Curry Granulated Sauce; Provencale Sauce; *Beef Tonight Sauces:* Ale & Mushroom, Goulash; *Chicken Tonight Sauces:* Chasseur, Spanish Chicken, Stir Fry Tomato and Vodka; *Indian Collection Pastes:* Biryani, Jalfrezi, Madras, Masala, Rogan Josh, Tandoori, Tikka, Tikka Masala, Vindaloo; *Indian Collection Sauces:* Jalfrezi, Madras, Paltia, Rogan Josh, Vindaloo; *Mediterranean Range - Sauces:* Bolognese, Cacciatora, Napoli Tomato & Basil, Spicy Arrabbiata, Tuscan Bean, Vegetale; *Oriental Collection - Pastes:* Black Bean, Hoi Sin, Szechuan, Thai Green; *Oriental Collection - Sauces:* Beijing Five Spice, Cantonese Sweet & Sour, Shanghai Black Bean, Spicy Szechuan, Sweet & Sour, Sweet Vietnamese Chilli; *Ragu Sauces:* Basil & Oregano, Bolognese Original Sauce, Onion & Roasted Garlic, Red Lasagne Sauce, Red Wine & Herb, Spicy, Sweet Red Pepper, Traditional; *Sausage Tonight Sauces:* Cumberland, Ranch BBQ, Red Wine & Onion; *Sizzle & Stir Sauces:* Balti, Chilli Con Carne, Stir Tikka Bhuna, Sweet & Sour; *Standard Sauce Mix:* Chasseur, Curry, Demi Glace, Sweet & Sour; *Stir It Up Pastes:* Bejing 5 Spice, Chinese 5 Spice, Fajita, Jamaican, Jamaican Jerk, Mexican Fajita; *Taste of Americas - Pastes:* Cajun, Hickory Smoked BBQ, Jamaican Jerk, Salsa; *Taste of Americas - Sauces:* Cajun, Chilli, Salsa, Sweet Hickory BBQ

LYME BAY WINERY
Cider Vinegar

MA BAKER ☺
Al'fez: Spice & sauce garlic & ginger 142g

MERIDIAN FOODS ⊘
Cool Salsa; French Dressing; *Free From:* Creamy Mushroom and White Wine Sauce; *Free From :* Creamy Sundried Tomato Sauce; *Free From:* Garlic & Herb Sauce, Hot Salsa, Korma Sauce, Tikka Masala Sauce, Tomato Ketchup; *Free From Range:* Creamy Tomato & Herb, Dopiaza Sauce, Garlic and Herb, Green Thai Sauce, Madras Sauce; *Pasta Sauces:* Mushroom; *Pasta Sauces :* Red Chilli & Pepper, Spanish Olive, Sundried Tomato, Tomato & Basil, Tomato & Chilli, Tomato & Herb; *Salad Dressing - Organic:* French; *Soya Sauces:* Shoyu, Tamari

MH FOODS ™⊘ ⬢
Life: **Fish Free Worcestershire Sauce**

ODYSEA
Aged Corinthian Vinegar

ORGANICO ⊘ ✿
Mushroom & Red Wine Pasta Sauce; Olives, Capers & Chilli Sauce; Red Pepper and Balsamic Vinegar Sauce; Tomato & Aubergine Sauce; Tomato & Basil Sauce; Tomato & Zucchini Sauce; Veggie Bolognese Pasta Sauce; *Danival:* Bolognese Sauce with Seitan, Bolognese Sauce with Tofu, Chilli with Seitan, Ketchup Squeezy Bottle, Ratatouille, Ravioli Stuffed Seitan

PASTA KING (UK) LTD ™
Arrabiata; Arriba Arriba; Basilico; Cajun Quinoa; Hoisin Sauce; Kari Veg; Mediterranean Vegetables; Mushroom Thyme; Peperonata; Pomodoro; Ratatouille; Tuscan Bean;

Veg Sweet and Sour; Vegetable Chilli; Veggie-Bol; Zingy Peppers; *Enriched products:* **Enriched Basilico**

PATAKS FOODS ⊘
Canned cooking sauces: Balti Medium, Madras, Rogan Josh, Vindaloo; *Chutney:* Hot Mango, Major Grey, Sweet Mango; *Cooking sauces in jars:* Balti, Jalfrezi, Madras, Rogan Josh, Vindaloo; *Curry pastes:* Balti, Bhuna, Biryani, Extra Hot Curry, Garam Masala, Jalfrezi, Kashmiri Masala, Korma, Madras Curry, Mild, Rogan Josh, Tandoori, Tikka, Tikka Masala, Vindaloo; *Meena's Accompaniments:* Sweet Lime Pickle, Tomato & Onion Relish; *Meena's Sauces:* Balti, Jalfrezi; *Pickle:* Brinjal, Chilli, Garlic, Hot Lime, Hot Mango, Lime Med/Hot, Mango Medium, Mixed

PETER RABBIT ORGANICS ⊘✿
Organic Garden Vegetable Sauce; Organic Italian Sauce; Organic Ketchup; Tomato and Basil Sauce

PORTER FOODS CO LTD
Classic Thai Sauces: Peanut Satay, Sriracha, Sweet and Sour, Sweet Chilli; *Dress Italian Pesto:* Artichoke & Almond, Aubergine & Black Olive, Pistachio & Fennel, Red Pepper & Walnut, Sun Ripened Tomato; *Italian Pasta Sauces:* Basil & Onion, Red Hot Chilli, Sun Dried Tomato, Sweet Cherry Tomato; *PET Range:* Red Hot Chilli Sauce

REAL ORGANIC FOODS ⊘
Organic Barbeque Sauce: Spicy Mexican; *Organic Indian Sauce:* Jalfrezi, Rogan Josh; *Organic Pasta Sauce:*

Arrabbiata, Sicilian Tomato & Olive, Tomato, Pepper & Herb; *Organic Thai Sauce:* Green Curry, Red Curry, Yellow Curry

ROSIE'S GOURMET PRODUCTS (UK) LTD ™☺⊘ ⁌

Basil Pesto; Black Olive Tapenade; Fresh Tomato Bruschetta Topping; Hot Red Chilli Relish; Mediterranean Sundried Tomatoes With Herbs; Mushroom Bruschetta Topping; Olive Bruschetta Topping; Roasted Pepper Bruschetta Topping; Spicy Sundried Tomatoes Paste; Sun Dried Tomato Pesto; *Pasta Sauce/ Pizza Base:* **Courgettes Sauce, Italian Mushroom Sauce, Neopolitan Sauce, Wild Rocket Sauce;** *Pasta Sauce/Pizza Base:* **Aubergine Sauce, Basil Sauce, Olive Sauce**

SACLA

Dallaglio by Sacla Pasta Sauce: Bolognese Pasta Sauce, Diavola Pasta Sauce; *Italian Ingredients:* Artichokes Antipasto, Char-Grilled Peppers Antipasto, Italian Oven Roasted Tomatoes with Chilli, Mixed Beans with Mushrooms Antipasto, Peperonata Antipasto, Sun-Dried Tomato Intense Paste, Sun-Dried Tomatoes Antipasto, Tomato & Chilli Intense Paste, Wild Mushroom Antipasto; *Pesto:* Char-Grilled Aubergine Pesto; *Stir-Through Sauces for Pasta:* Italian Tomato & Olive, Sun-Dried Tomato & Garlic, Vine-Ripened Tomato and Chilli Pepper; *Whole Cherry Tomato:* Whole Cherry Tomato & Basil, Whole Cherry Tomato & Chilli, Whole Cherry Tomato & Roasted Vegetables

SANCHI ⊘

Ume Su plum Vinegar; *Sauces:* Mirin, Organic Shoyu, Organic Tamari, Shoyu Soy Sauce, Tamari Reduced Sugar, Tamari Soy Sauce, Teriyaki; *Vinegar:* Organic Brown Rice, Ume Su Plum

SAUCES OF CHOICE

Balsamic & Garlic Sauce; Lemon & Dill Vinaigerette; Sweet Chilli Sauce; *Chutneys:* Apricot & Orange, Caramelised Onion, Mango, Spicy Fruit, Tomato & Red Pepper; *Cook in Sauces:* Bolognese Sauce, Chilli Con Carne, Coconut Lime & Coriander, Creamy Peppercorn, Red Pepper & Sun Dried Tomato, Sweet 'n' Sour; *Curry Sauces:* Balti, Green Thai, Jalfrezi, Korma, Madras, Red Thai, Rogan Josh, Tikka Masala; *Kids Sauces:* BBQ, Bolognese, Mild Chilli, Sweet and Sour, Tomato and Herb; *Sauces to Dine For:* Mediterranean Tomato & Olive

SEDLESCOMBE ORGANIC VINEYARD ™☺⊘ ⁌ ✿

Organic Vinegar: **Organic Cider Vinegar**

SEEDS OF CHANGE

Pasta Sauces: Bolognese, Mediterranean Vegetable, Tomato & Basil, Tomato & Chilli, Tomato & Garlic; *Sauces:* Balti, Chilli, Jalfrezi, Sweet & Sour; *Stir-in Pasta Sauces:* Roasted Red Peppers, Sun Dried Tomato & Basil

SOMA ORGANIC ☺⊘ ⁌ ✿

Nomato: Chilli, Ketchup, Pasta Sauce

THAI KITCHEN

Curry Paste: Green, Red; *Sauces:* Peanut Satay, Spicy Thai Chili, Sweet Red Chili

THE BEST OF TASTE COMPANY
Wild Bilberry Dessert Sauce

THE ENGLISH PROVENDER CO. ⊘
Cumberland Sauce; Dill Mustard Sauce;
Hot Chilli Relish; Hot Horseradish; Mint
Sauce with Balsamic Vinegar; Moroccan
Spiced Chutney; Organic Spicy Onion
Chutney; Organic Sweet Tomato &
Chilli Chutney; Organic Wild Cranberry
Sauce; Ploughmans Plum Chutney;
Sweet Pickle; Wild Cranberry Sauce

UNCLE BEN'S
Cajun Mexican Sauce; Thai Sweet Chilli
Sauce; *Indian Sauces:* Balti, Jalfrezi,
Medium Curry; *Oriental Sauces:* Black
Bean, Hoi Sin, Lemon Chicken, Sweet &
Sour Extra Pineapple, Sweet & Sour
Light, Sweet & Sour Original, Szechuan
Chilli; *Stir Fry Sauces:* Cantonese Soy &
Sesame, Soy & Black Bean, Sweet &
Sour Aromatic, Sweet Spicy Chilli

VEGEFARM CORP ™☺❶⊘✔
Vegefarm: **Beijing Spicy Orange
Sauce, Black Pepper Sauce, Original
Black Bean Sauce, Original Sweet &
Sour Sauce, Sweet Lemon Sauce,
Teriyaki BBQ Sauce**

VENTURE FOODS UK LTD ™⊘
Geo Organics: **Brown Sauce, Faitrade
Mango Chutney, Mango & Apple
Juice Chutney, Sweet Chilli Sauce,
Veggie Relish, Worcestershire Sauce**

PIES & PASTIES

BABYCAKES DIRECT ™☺❶
**Broccoli, mushroom and tofu tart;
Butterbean, sun dried tomato and
cashew nut tart; Pizza tart**

CLIVE'S PIES ⊘
Vegetable Chilli Pasty; *Organic Gluten
Free Pies:* Aloo Gobi, French Cassoulet,
Lentil & Olive, Minty Chickpea, Vegetable
Chilli; *Organic Pies:* Aloo Matar Curry,
Arabian Chickpea, Chestnut Cassoulet,
Creamy Mushroom, Greek Olive & Lentil,
Hungarian Goulash, Mexican Chilli

FRY GROUP FOODS ™☺❶⊘
Fry's Special Vegetarian Frozen Foods:
Veg Express Cottage Pie

PAUL'S TOFU ™☺✔✿
Savouries: **Mushroom & Nut Parcels,
Organic Mushroom & Tofu Pie, Tofu
Arame Pasty, Tofu Vegetable Pasty**

REBECCA'S CAKES ™
**Vegan Cornish Pasties; Vegan Pies;
Vegan Vegetable Pasties**

SAVOURIES - CANNED/BOTTLED

BIONA
Baked Beans in Tomato Sauce; Plain
Tofu in Jars; Sauerkraut

CLEARSPRING ™☺❶⃠ ✔ 👁
Takuon

DISCOVERY FOODS
Refried Beans; Spicy Refried Beans

**ESSENTIAL TRADING
CO-OPERATIVE LTD** ™❶⃠ ✔
**Borlotti beans; Cannellini Beans;
Green soya edamame beans;**
Essential Brand- Bottled, Jarred, Canned:
**Organic Apples, Organic Apricots,
Organic Baby Carrots, Organic
Blackberries, Organic Blackeye
Beans, Organic Button Mushrooms,
Organic Cherries, Organic Chickpeas,
Organic Chopped Peeled Tomatoes,
Organic Chopped Tomatoes, Organic
Cranberries, Organic Forest Fruits,
Organic French Beans, Organic
Gherkins - Sour, Organic Grapefruit
Segments, Organic Green Peas,
Organic Green Peas + Carrots,
Organic Green Peas + Mint, Organic
Haricot Beans, Organic Mango
Chunks, Organic Mixed Beans,
Organic Passata, Organic Peach
Slices, Organic Pineapple, Organic
Plums, Organic Prunes, Organic Puy
Lentils, Organic Raspberries,
Organic Red Kidney Beans, Organic
Sauerkraut, Organic Spinach,
Organic Strawberries, Organic
Sweetcorn, Organic Tomato Puree,
Organic Tropical Fruits, Organic
Whole Tomatoes**

GRANOVITA UK LTD ⃠ ✔
Nut Luncheon; Vegetable Hotpot

HEINZ
Baked Beans in Tomato Sauce; Baked
Beans with Hidden Veg; BBQ Beans;
Curried Beans; HP Baked Beans; Organic
Baked Beans in Tomato Sauce; Reduced
Sugar and Salt Beans; Smokey BBQ
Beanz; Snap Pot Baked Beans in
Tomato Sauce; Sweet Chilli Beanz;
Weight Watchers Baked Beans in
Tomato Sauce; *Big Eat:* Veg & Tomato
Hotpot; *Pasta:* Spaghetti in Tomato
Sauce, Weight Watchers Spaghetti in
Tomato Sauce with Parsley

KALLO FOODS ⃠
Whole Earth: Baked Beans

ODYSEA
Karyatis: Artichokes, Atlas Green Olives,
Baked Gigantes Beans, Bruschetta Meze,
Colossal Green Olives, Garlic Stuffed
Olives, Green Olive Meze, Green Organic
Olives, Jumbo Kalamata Olives, Jumbo
Natural Black Olives, Kalamata Olive
with Capers, Kalamata Olives, Kalamata
Organic Olives, Mixed Hot Chillies, Mixed
Olives, Roasted Red Peppers, Stuffed Vine
Leaves; *Olives:* Green Cracked with Lemon,
Hot Spiced Natural Black, Kalamata &
Green; *Olives Relish:* Sweet Kalamata;
Rovies: Almond Stuffed Green Olives,
Almond Stuffed Green Organic Olives,
Garlic Stuffed Green Olives, Green Olives,
Green Organic Olive Paste, Green
Organic Olives, Kalamata Olives,
Kalamata Organic Olive Paste, Kalamata
Organic Olives, Lemon Stuffed Green
Olives, Mixed Olives, Natural Black
Olives, Pimento Stuffed Green Olives,
Pimento Stuffed Green Organic Olives;
Stuffed Green Olives: Almond, Chilli,
Garlic, Jalapeno, Pimento

ORGANICO ⊘ ✻
Danival: Lentils Meal with Tofu

ORGRAN ☺
Gluten-Free Tinned Spaghetti

SOMA ORGANIC ☺⊘ ✔ ✻
Nomato: Baked Beans

SUMA WHOLEFOODS
™❶⊘✔ ☞✕1985
Cannellini Beans; *Organic Soups:* **Suma Organic Tuscan Bean Soup;** *Organics:* **Suma Organic Cherry Tomatoes**

VENTURE FOODS UK LTD ™⊘
Geo Organics: **Baked beans with agave syrup, Bombay Potatoes, Chickpea and Lentil Dahl, Hearty thick vegetable hot pot, Saag Aloo, Spiced thick vegetable stew**

WESTLER FOODS LTD ⊘
Chesswood : Vegetable Curry; *Chesswood:* Chilli No Carne; *Chesswood :* Organic Baked Beans, Organic Vegetable Chilli; *Chesswood:* Organic Vegetable Hot Pot, Vegetable Chilli; *Wayfarer:* Spicy Vegetable Rigatoni; *Westlers BIGMEX:* Chips & Dips Box, Salsa Pots

SAVOURIES - CHILLED/FRESH

ARABESQUE ™
Olive & walnut potato bites; Potato kibbeh; Pumpkin kibbeh; Rice Kibbeh

AROMAFOODS ™☺✔
Greek Spinach Falafel; Lime and Coriander Aloo; Masala Veget-Apple Pakora; Mexican Bean Burger; Sesame Falafel; Spinach & Onion Bhajia; Sweetcorn & Pineapple Bhajia

BEAN THINKING
Empanadillas; Kachoris; Thai Spring Rolls; *Pasties:* Curried Vegetable, Fresh Vegetable, Mediterranean

BIONA
Energy Mini Burgers; Lucky Stars with Pumpkin Tofu & Ginger; Provancale Style Ballini; Spelt & Almond Cutlets; *Fresh Filled Pasta:* Fresh Gnocchi, Spelt Tortellini with Green Spelt and Vegetables, Tortellini Tri Colore with Tofu & Spice; *Spring Rolls:* Mini, Original, Spicy Mexicana, Thai

BUCKINGHAM'S OATIVA ™✔
Protein food: **Jaipur Oativa, Mediterranean Oativa, Mushroom Oativa, Original Oativa, Thai Oativa**

CAULDRON ⊘
Chickpea & Spinach Balti; Mexican chilli & rice

CHIMANS ™☺❶⊘✔
Cauliflower & Spinach Bhaji; *Organic:* **Cauliflower & Spinach Bhaji**

CLEARSPRING ™☺❶⊘✔ ☞
Mikawa Mirin; Rice Mirin

CLIVE'S PIES ⊘
Soya Roll

CUISINE DE FRANCE
Battered Onion Rings; Chilled Chips; Croquettes; Fruity Rice Salad; Mediterranean Vegetable Salad; Mild Curry Fries; Mini Vegetable Spring Rolls; Pierres Spicy Wedges; Savoury Rice; Seasoned Wedges; Spanish Style Salad; Stealth Fries; Sweet Chilli Potato; Traditional Roast Potatoes; Vegetable & Salsa Burritos; Vegetable Samosa; Vegetable Spring Rolls

DESIBOX INDIAN CUISINE ™ ✔
Ready Meals: **Desi Potato Ready Meal, Mixed Bean Curry Ready Meal, Mixed Vegetable Curry Ready Meal;** *Snacks:* **Onion Bhajis**

DIPAK FOODS LTD ™☺❶⊘✔
Dal Kachori; Mixed Vegetable Spring Rolls; Onion Bhaji; Peas Kachori; Peas Petis; Soya Chunks Curry; Soya Mince Curry; Spinach Bhaji; Spinach Pakora; Sunder Curry Sauce; Vegetable Curry Sauce; *Samosas:* **Mixed Vegetable, Soya**

GOBBLIN WHOLEFOODS
Aduki Shepherds Pie; Curry Pastie; Onion Bhaji; Pinto Pie; Samosa; Savory Roll; Savory Vegetable Pastie; Spiced Pastie; Spinach Pakora; Spring Roll; Vegetable Tofu Pie; *Organic:* Lentil Samosa, Pinto Pie, Vegetable Tofu Pie

MACSWEEN OF EDINBURGH
Haggis: Vegetarian

MEDITERRANEAN FOODS (LONDON) LTD ☺
Aubergine Salad; Couscous Salad; Dolma (Stuffed Vine Leaves); Teboula

NAKED LUNCH .DA ™☺⊘✔
Norway boxed salads: **Bulgur Salad, Chickpeas, Celery Roots, & Apple Salad, Red Pesto Whole Wheat Pasta Salad**

PAUL'S TOFU ™☺✔ ✿
Savouries: **Tofu & Vegetable Samosa**

PICK ME
Punchy Pad Thai; Rainbow Curry; Vegalicious Masala; Vegetable Chilli

QIANNA AGRICULTURAL PRODUCTS IND & TRADING CO. LTD ™☺
Mushroom buckwheat instant noodle; Soba Instant Noodle

RAW ALCHEMY LTD ™☺❶⊘✔
Raw: **Raw Hemp Pesto**

RAWCREATION LTD ™☺❶⊘✔
Peruvian Olives

REBECCA'S CAKES ™
Cheddar and chive muffins; Herb muffins; Low sugar banana, cinnamon and maple tea bread cake; Mozzarella, basil and sun dried tomato muffins; Spinach and cream cheese muffins

REDWOOD WHOLEFOOD COMPANY ™☺❶⊘
Vegi-Deli: **Falafel**

ROSIE'S GOURMET PRODUCTS (UK) LTD ™☺⊘✔
Truffles: **Sliced Truffles, Truffle Paste, Whole Summer Truffles, Whole Winter Truffles**

TAIFUN ☺☺
Falafel; Mexico-Sticks; Pizza-Pizza Tofu
Filets; Thai-Sticks; *Pan Ready Tofu:*
Spelt-Sunflower Cutlets, Tofu Filets
Japanese style, Tofu-Hazelnut Cutlets,
Tofu-Rice Cutlets Corn-Pepper, Tofu-
Rice Cutlets Curry-Pineapple

SAVOURIES - DRIED

BEAN THINKING
Herb and Onion Stuffing

BLUE DRAGON
Dry Noodles: Dried Soba Noodles, Dried
Udon Noodles, Express Instant Noodle
Multi Pack, Medium Rice Noodles,
Wholewheat Noodles; *Quick Wok
Noodles:* Chilli Infused, Coriander
Infused, Medium Wheat, Medium
Wholewheat, Wide Wheat

CLEARSPRING ™☺❶⊘☣👁
**Bifun Rice Noodles; Lotus root
slices; Maitake mushrooms; Shiitake
mushrooms; Shredded Daikon; Sushi
Rice;** *Organic:* **Brown rice udon
noodles, Lomein noodles(wheat),
Mochi -Brown Rice, Mochi -Mugwort,
Soba Noodles - 100% Buckwheat
(Salt Free), Soba noodles - 100%
buckwheat(salt free), Soba Noodles
- Jinenjo (Mountain Yam), Soba
noodles(with wheat), Soba noodles-
Jinenjo(Mountain yam), Sushi
Brown Rice, Sushi rice, Udon
noodles(with wheat)**

DISCOVERY FOODS
Traditional Tacos Shells; *Kit:* Cajun
Fajita, Chinese Dinner, Gluten Free,
Mexican Fajita, Nachos; *Wrap & Roll:*
Healthy 'n' White, Original, Wholemeal

**ESSENTIAL TRADING
CO-OPERATIVE LTD** ™❶⊘☣
Essential Brand- Pastas: **Organic Fusilli,
Organic Lumache, Organic Spaghetti,
Organic Stoneground Fusilli, Organic
Stoneground Penne, Organic
Stoneground Spaghetti, Organic
Tortiglioni;** *Essential Brand- Pre Packs
(Organic & Conventional):* **Apple Rings,
Apricots, Cereals Flakes & Grain Meals,
Cranberries, Crystallised Ginger,
Currants, Dates, Figs, Flours (All),
Fruit Salad, Grains (All), Herbs +
Spices (All), Mango Slices, Mixed
Fruit, Nuts, Papaya, Pear Halves,
Pineapple Rings, Prunes, Pulses +
Beans, Raisins, Rice (All), Seeds (All),
Sugars (All), Sultanas, Tomatoes
(All);** *Essential Brand-Pre Packs (Organic
& Conventional):* **Textured Vegetable
Protein - Plain**

FLEX ENTERPRISES LTD ™☺⊘☣
Seed: **Flaxseed Organic,
Pumpkinseed Organic, Sesameseed
Organic, Sunflowerseed Organic**

G. COSTA & CO ⊘
Casa fiesta: Ambient flour tortillas,
Green sliced jalapeno, Natural tortilla
crisps, Refried beans, Taco shells

GLUTEN FREE FOODS LTD
Barkat: Buckwheat Pasta Penne,
Buckwheat Pasta Spirals

GRANOSE
Falafel Mix; Meat Free Burger Mix; Meat Free Chicken Style Roast Mix; Meat Free Lincolnshire Sausage Mix; Meat Free Sausage Mix; Mixed Nut Roast Mix; Soya Mince; Sunflower Seed & Vegetable Mix

GREENCITY WHOLEFOODS ❶⊘
Broth Mix; Chickpea Noodles

HAPPY AND HEALTHY FOODS ☺❶
Road's End Organics: 123'z and Chreese, Mac & Chreese - Brown Rice Alfredo Style, Mac & Chreese - Whole Wheat Elbow Macaroni Style, Penne & Chreese, Shells & Chreese

HIGH BARN OILS ™
Linseed Flour

JUST WHOLEFOODS ☺☺
Organic World Mixes: Biryani, Chow Mein, Cous Cous with Lentils, Falafel, Hummus

NATURKRAFTWERKE ™
Blinis; Falafel with black cumin oil; Latkes; Tabouleh

ORGANICO ⊘✿
Serrra Rica: Mediterranean Chestnut Stuffing with Couscous, Traditional Chestnut Stuffing with Breadcrumbs

ORGRAN ☺
Falafel Mix; *Biscotti:* Pasta & Sauce

PAUL'S TOFU ™⊘⥀✿
Savouries: **Organic Nut Roast**

PAXO
Sage & Onion Stuffing

POLAR SUN PRODUCTS LTD ☺⊘
Vegan Soya Food: Soya Bolognese, Soya Burger Mix, Soya Chunks, Soya Flakes, Soya Goulash, Soya mince brown, Soya Mince Neutral, Soya Strips, Soya Tex-Mex Mix

QIANNA AGRICULTURAL PRODUCTS IND & TRADING CO. LTD ™☺
Barley leaves noodle; Black Bean Spaghetti; Brown Rice Noodle; Carrot Ginger Instant Noodle; Carrot noodle; Corn Noodle; Garlic & Pepper Instant Noodle; Green tea buckwheat noodle; Green Tea Noodle; Mung Bean Noodle; Rice Noodle; Roasted chestnut kernel; Soba; Soba (Buckwheat Noodle); Soyabean Chicken; Soybean Fish; Soybean Noodle; Soybean Sausage; Soybean Spaghetti; Spinach Instant Noodle; Spinach noodle; Tomato Instant Noodle; Tomato noodle; Udon; Vegetable Instant Noodle; Whole Wheat Noodle

QUINUA REAL BRASIL LTDA ™⊘
Organic Quinoa; Quinoa Flakes; Spaghetti

ROSIE'S GOURMET PRODUCTS (UK) LTD ™☺⊘⥀
Dried Porcini Mushrooms

SANCHI ⊘
Noodles: Organic 40% Soba, Organic Brown Rice Udon, Organic Cup, Organic Green Tea, Organic Thai Rice,

Organic Udon, Somen; *Organic Noodles:* 40% Soba, Green Tea, Someh, Thai Rice; *Organic Ramen Noodles :* Ginger; *Organic Ramen Noodles:* Mushroom; *Organic Ramen Noodles :* Seaweed; *Organic Udon Noodles:* Brown Rice; *Soba Noodles:* 100% Buckwheat

THAI KITCHEN
Jasmine Rice Mixes: Jasmine, Roasted Garlic & Chili; *Noodle Carts:* Pad Thai, Roasted Garlic, Thai Peanut, Toasted Sesame; *Stir-Fry Rice Noodle Meal Kit:* Lemongrass & Chili, Thai Peanut, Toasted Sesame; *Take-Out Boxes:* Tangy Sweet & Sour, Thai Peanut

THE FOOD DOCTOR LTD ✔
Easy Grains: Cereals and beans, Cereals pulses and beans, Quinoa, Spelt

SAVOURIES - FROZEN

BEAN THINKING
Chilli Bean Casserole; Savoury Vegetable Crumble; Vegetable & Hazelnut Wellington; Vegetable Hotpot

BEANIE'S HEALTH FOODS ™☺❶⊘
Fry's Special Vegetarian Frozen Foods:
Veg Express Cottage Pie, Veg Express Sausage Rolls

CALEDONIAN CURRY CO. ™⊘
Aloo Choley (Minted Potato & Chickpea); Baigan Nariyal (Hot Aubergine & Chilli); Baigan Tamatar

(Spiced Aubergine & Tomato); Bombay Potato; Caledonian Chickpea; Channa Dhal Masala; Highland Beetroot Curry; Palak Choley (Spinach & Chickpea Curry); Saag Aloo; Tarka Dal

DALOON FOODS ⊘
Indian Classics: Mini Samosas, Mini Samosas & Onion Bhajis, Onion Bhajis, Vegetable Onion Bhajis; *Indian Snacks :* Onion Bhajis; *Oriental Classics :* Mixed Vegetable Spring Rolls; *Oriental Snacks:* Mini Spring Rolls

DRAGONFLY FOODS ⊘✿
Organic beany

FRY GROUP FOODS ™☺❶⊘
Fry's Special Vegetarian Frozen Foods:
Veg Express Sausage Rolls

G. COSTA & CO ⊘
Tipiak: Potato fecule

LINDA MCCARTNEY
Chilli Non Carne; Chilli with potato wedges; Cornish Pasties; Country Pies; Sausage Rolls

MCCAIN ⊘
5% Fat Roasts; 5% Fat Wedges; Baby Potatoes with Oven Roasted Tomatoes and Garlic; Chippy Chips; Crispy French Fries; Groovy Wedges; Hash Brown Bites; Hash Browns; Home Roasts; McCain Gold; Nicely Spiced Wedges; Quick Chippy Chips; Sea Salt & Cracked Black Pepper; Seasoned Curly Fries; Southern Fries; Steak Fry Chips; Super Value Chunky; Super Value Crinkle Cut; Super

Value Straight Cut; Super Value Thin Fries; Traditional Roasts; *Home Fries:* Chunky, Crinkle Cut, Straight Cut, Thin & Crispy; *MicroChips:* Crinkle Cut, Straight Cut; *Oven Chips:* Crinkle Cut, Rustic, Straight Cut

SILVER WING LTD ™☺⊘ ✔
Nut Burger: **NutBurg Chilli, NutBurg Curry, NutBurg Original, NutBurg Sundried Tomato**
TOFURKY ☺
Pizza: "Cheese"

WESTLER FOODS LTD ⊘
Wayfarer: Vegetable Curry

SEASONAL FOODS

D & D CHOCOLATES ☺
Carob: Chuckling Bunny Shapes, Hollow Easter Egg, Solid Hearts, Solid Mini Eggs; *Dark Couverture:* Chuckling Bunny Shapes, Hollow Easter Egg, Solid Mini Eggs

DIVINE CHOCOLATE ⊘
70% Dark Chocolate Advent Calendar; Dark Chocolate Easter Egg

KINNERTON LTD
Childrens Dairy Free Easter Eggs; Luxury Dark Chocolate Easter Egg

KP
Luxury Roasted Pistachios (Xmas); Seasonal Fruit and Nut Mix (Xmas); *Big Nuts:* Red Hot Chilli Flavour

PAUL'S TOFU ™⊘ ✔ ☼
Breads: **Organic Hot x Buns;** *Cakes:* **2 Organic Mince Pies with Miso & Kuzu, 2 Organic Mince Pies with Miso & Kuzu (Gluten Free), Gluten Free Christmas Cake, Gluten Free Christmas Pudding, Gluten Free Mince Pies, Organic Christmas Cake, Organic Christmas Pudding**

VIVA! ☺❶⊘ ✔
Selection of Easter Eggs

SEAWEED & SEAVEG

BLUE DRAGON
Roasted Nori Seaweed Leaves; *Sushi ingredients:* Sushi Nori

CLEARSPRING ™☺❶⊘ ✔ ☀
Agar agar flakes(gelling agent); Arame; Dulse; Green nori sprinkle (flakes); Hijiki; Instant wakame flakes; Kombu; Nori flavoured strips; Nori sheets; Nori sushi toasted sheets; Sea salad(dulse, sea lettuce,nori); Sea vegetable salad - Japanese; Wakame

QUALITY SEA VEG ☺
Irish Carragheen; Irish Dulse; Irish Mixed SeaVeg; Irish Nori; Irish Sea Spagetti; Irish Spirulina; Irish Wakame; Sea Spice; Sea Tangle; Smoked Dulse and sugar kelp; Sweet Tangle

SANCHI ⊘
Seaweed: Kombu, Nori, Sushi Nori, Wakame

SEAGREENS LTD ™☺⊘
Seagreens: **Dulse Granules, Liquid Ascophyllum;** *Seagreens- Pelvetia Pieces:* **Salad Condiment**

SOURCE FOODS ☺✿
Herbs of The Sea; Nori; Sushi Sheets; Wakame

SNACKS - SAVOURY

AJITAS VEGE CHIPS
Deli Chips: Original; *Grain Chips:* Natural; *Vege Chips:* BBQ, French Onion, Herbs & Garlic, Lime Chilli, Natural, Sea Salt & Vinegar, Sweet & Sour; *Vege Crisps:* Rosemary & Garlic

BAXTERS ⊘
Chunky: Carrot, Butterbean & Coriander, Country Vegetable; *Deli inspired:* Root Vegetable & Butternut Squash; *Favourites:* Minestrone; *Healthy:* Autumn Vegetable with Mild Spices, Carrot, Onion & Chickpea, Italian Bean & Pasta; *Vegetarian:* Carrot & Butterbean, Mediterranean Tomato, Tomato & Butterbean

BIOFAIR
Quinoa Snack w Oregano; Quinoa Snack with Onion; Rice Quinoa Crunchies

BLUE DRAGON
Noodle Town: Beef & Black Pepper, Chicken & Chilli, Chow Mein, Crispy Duck, Mushroom, Won Ton; *Noodle*

Wok: Oriental Chicken, Spicy Thai, Sweet Chilli Chicken

CLEARSPRING ™☺❶⊘✔◉
Instant Wakame Flakes; Roasted Seeds & Soya with Cranberry Snack; Tamari Roasted Sicilian Almonds; *Organic:* **Roasted seed and soya snack, Roasted seeds and soya with cranberry snack, Roasted Snack Mix, Roasted Styrian pumpkin seeds, Tamari roasted Sicilian almonds**

CRIPS ☺
Salt & Pepper; Salt & Vinegar; Sea Salt

DISCOVERY FOODS
Gluten Free Tortilla Chips; Tortilla Chips

ESSENTIAL TRADING CO-OPERATIVE LTD ™❶⊘✔
Essential Brand- Mixes: **Fruit Salad, Organic Fruit + Nut Mix, Organic Fruit Salad**

G. COSTA & CO ⊘
Old Ranch House Lorenz Snack World: Ready Salted Chipsletten (Stackers)

GENERAL DIETARY
Pretzels: Rings, Sesame

GOLDEN WONDER ⊘
Crisps: Pickled Onion Flavour, Quite Hot Curry Flavour, Ready Salted, Ready Salted Flavour, Salt and Vinegar Flavour, Sausage + Tomato Flavour, Smokey Bacon Flavour, Tomato Ketchup Flavour; *Crunchy Fries:* Salt and Vinegar Flavour; *Ringos:* Pickled Onion Flavour, Salt and Vinegar Flavour

GREENCITY WHOLEFOODS ❶⊘
Bombay Mix; Chilli Rice Crackers; Garlic Sticks; Japanese style Rice Cracker Mix; Seaweed Peanut Crackers

HULA HOOPS
Hula Hoops: Original, Original Stars & Hoops Xmas Tub, Salt & Vinegar Flavour, Smoky Bacon Flavour

JACOB'S ⊘
Twiglets: Original

JONATHAN CRISP
Black Olive & Garlic; Jalapeno Pepper; Lightly Salted; Parsnip Beetroot and Sweet Potato; Parsnip Crisps; Sea Salt & Black Pepper; Sea Salt & Malt Vinegar; Sundried Tomato & Basil

KALLO FOODS ⊘
Whole Earth: SO Crispy Sea Salt and Balsamic Vinegar, SO Crispy Smoky Paprika

KETTLE CHIPS
Ridge crisps: Flamed steak flavour, Salt and malt vinegar; *Sharing bags:* Lightly salted, No added salt, Roasted tomato and basil, Sea salt and balsamic vinegar, Sea salt with crushed black peppercorns, Sweet red pepper salsa; *Small bags:* Lightly salted, Sea salt and balsamic vinegar, Sea salt with crushed black peppercorns; *Vegetable chips:* Golden parsnip, sweet potato and beetroot

KP
Big Nuts: Char Grilled Steak Flavour, Hickory Smoked BBQ Flavour; *Brannigans Peanuts:* Dry Roasted, Roasted Salted; *Crisps:* Beef, Ready

Salted, Salt & Vinegar, Worcester Sauce; *Jumbo Salted:* Peanuts; *KP:* Bombay Mix; *Original Salted:* Peanuts; *Peanuts:* Dry Roasted, Salt & Vinegar, Spicy Chilli; *Roast Salted:* Cashews, Pistachios

LIFEFOOD CZECH REPUBLIC S.R.O. ☺❶⊘ 🖊 ✿
Life food: Organic Bite-sized Pizza Crackers, Organic Bugs Chilli, Organic Bugs Curry, Organic Bugs Provensal, Organic Carrot Crackers, Organic Indian Cashews, Organic Raw Italian Crispbread, Organic Raw Rosemary Crispbread, Organic Raw Tomato pitta Crispbread, Organic Teriyaki Almonds, Organic Wild Garlic Flax Crackers

MCCOY'S
Potato chips: Lamb and mint flavour, Mexican chilli flavour, Salt and malt vinegar flavour, Salted, Thai sweet chicken; *Ridged tortilla chips:* BBQ chicken flavour

MEDITERRANEAN FOODS (LONDON) LTD ☺
Falafel; Falafel Meal with Couscous Salad; Falafel Meal with Taboula; Falafel Sandwich; Mixed Vegetable Kebab; Mixed Vegetable Kebab Sandwich; Spinach Kebab; Spinach Kebab Sandwich

MUNCHY SEEDS ™☺⊘
Seed mix: Cajun Mix, Chilli Mix, Naked Mix, Omega Mix, Original Mix, Pumpkin Mix; Snack Packs: Chilli Bites, Crunchy Bites

NATURKRAFTWERKE ™
Mumbai mix

FOOD

ORGANIX BRANDS PLC ◐ ✿
Carrot Stix; Saucy Tomato Noughts &
Crosses; Spicy Stars; *Rice Cakes:* Apple
Rice Cakes, Orange Rice Cakes, Plain
Rice Cakes

PHILEAS FOGG
Indian Red Chilli Poppadoms; Mexican
Sweet Chilli Flavour Crisps; Salsa with
Mexican Chilli Flavour Tortillas; Sea Salt
with Indonesian Black Peppercorn
Flavour Crisps

PORTER FOODS CO LTD
Fruit Pyramid: Apricot & Pistachio, Fig &
Almond, Pear & Hazelnut

POT NOODLE
Beef and Tomato; Bombay Bad Boy;
Doner Kebab; Lamb Hot Pot; Southern
Fried Chicken; Sweet & Sour Flavour

QUAKER OATS ◐
New Quaker Oats Bar Mixed Berry
Flavour; New Quaker Oats Bar Original
Golden Syrup Flavour; Quaker Jumbo
Snack-Jacks Caramel Flavour; Quaker
Seasons Lime & Coriander Flavour

RAW ALCHEMY LTD ™◐❶◐✔
Raw: **Raw Chips, Raw Super Carob
Crunch Bars, Raw Tortilla**

RAW LIVING ™☺❶◐✔
**Buckwheaties; Macadamia nuts;
Oats groats; Oats rolled; Raw
Cashew Nuts**

SANCHI ◐
Brown Rice Chips; Brown Rice Crackers;
Chilli Crackers; Hot and Spicy Wasabi

Chips; Quinoa & Tamari Arare; Sanchi
Nippers; Sea Vegetable Chips

SEABROOK POTATO CRISPS LTD ◐
Crisps: Canadian Ham, Canadian ham
crinkle cut, Pickled Onion, Salt &
Vinegar, Sea Salt, Sea Salt & Black
Pepper, Sea Salt Original, Smokey
Bacon, Tomato, Unsalted

SUMA WHOLEFOODS
™❶◐✔☻⚘1985
**Bhusu; Bombay Mix; Dehli Mix;
Garlic Sticks; Organic Bombay Mix;
Spiced Roast Chick Peas; Spicy
Noodles; Spicy Sticks**

THE FOOD DOCTOR LTD ✔
Seed Mix: Dry Roasted Bean mix, Dry-
Roasted Soy Nuts, Essential Omega
Seed Mix, Mixed Herb; *Seed Mix :*
Original; *Seed Mix:* Spicy Mix

TOPAS ™☺◐✔✿
Spacebar: **Spacebar Chorizo,
Spacebar Nuts, Spacebar Tofu;**
Wheaty Snack Bars: **Spacebar
"Hemp", Spacebar "Pyrossi",
Spacebar "Red Hot Chilli Peppers"**

TRAIDCRAFT PLC ◐
Bombay Mix; Savoury Snacks Variety
Pack; Spicy Plantain Chips

UNITED BISCUITS LTD ◐
Brannigans - Peanuts: Dry Roasted,
Roasted Salted; *Crunchies:* Prawn
Cocktail Flavour; *Discos:* Salt &
Vinegar; *Frisps:* Ready Salted, Salt &
Vinegar; *Go Ahead Crinkle Cut Crisps:*
Lightly Salted, Salt & Vinegar; *Mini*

Chips: Beef, Salt & Vinegar; *Nik Naks:* Pickle N Onion, Rib N Saucy; *Space Raiders:* Pickled Onion; *Wheat Crunchies:* Worcester Sauce Flavour

WALKERS SNACK FOODS
Sunbites Original; *Baked:* Mango Chilli, Ready Salted; *Crisps:* BBQ Rib, Chilli & Lemon, Pickled Onion, Prawn Cocktail, Ready Salted, Roast Gammon, Salt 'n' Shake, Sweet Cumberland Sausage, Worcester Sauce; *Doritos:* Chilli Heatwave, Lightly Salted; *French Fries:* Ready Salted, Salt & Vinegar; *Lights:* Simply Salted; *Potato Heads:* Ready Salted; *Quavers :* Prawn Cocktail; *Quavers:* Salt & Vinegar; *Sensations:* Caramelised Onion & Sweet Balsamic Vinegar, Gently Infused Lime & Thai Spiced Flavour, Lime and Coriander Chutney Flavour Poppadom Bites; *Smiths Chipsticks:* Ready Salted, Salt 'n' Vinegar; *Squares:* Ready Salted, Salt & Vinegar; *Wotsits:* Flamin' Hot Flavour

YAOH ™☺❶⊘ɪ
De-Hulled Hemp Seeds; Whole Hemp Seeds

SOUPS

BLUE DRAGON
Spicy Red Curry Soup; Won Ton Soup

CLEARSPRING ™☺❶⊘ɪ☜
Instant miso soup - Heart red with sea vegetables; Instant miso soup - mellow white with tofu; *Organic:*

Instant miso soup - brown rice with sea vegetables, Instant Miso Soup - Brown Rice with Sea Vegetables

ESSENTIAL TRADING CO-OPERATIVE LTD ™❶⊘ɪ
Essential Brand- Soups: **Concentrated Organic Clear Vegetable Broth, Concentrated Organic Mediterranean Vegetable Bouillon with Organic Olive Oil, Organic Lentil & Pumpkin Soup, Organic Lentil Soup, Organic Pea Soup**

HEINZ
Big Soups: Big Soup Chunky Vegetable, Big Soup Spicy Mixed Bean; *Instant Soup:* Vegetable Cup Soup; *Ready to serve soups:* Autumn Lentil & Vegetable, Carrot & Lentil, Lentil Soup, Spring Vegetable, Vegetable Soup, Winter Vegetable Broth; *Real Soups:* Homestyle Minestrone, Tuscan Tomato; *Weight Watchers from Heinz:* Carrot & Lentil Soup, Country Vegetable Soup, Hearty Vegetable Broth Soup, Mediterranean Tomato & Lentil Soup, Mediterranean Tomato & Vegetable Soup, Mexican Spicy Bean Soup, Moroccan Tomato And Chickpea Soup, Roasted Red Pepper & Tomato Soup, Root Vegetable and Bean Soup, Spiced Lentil & Potato Soup, Tangy Tomato and Rice Soup, Tomato & Red Pepper Soup, Vegetable Soup

JEREMY'S SOUPS ⊘ɪ
Soup: Chickpea & Harissa, Curried Parsnip, Gazpacho, Lentil, Minestrone, Red Pepper, Black Olive & Tomato, Sweetcorn & Chilli

JUST WHOLEFOODS ☺⊘
Organic Soup in a Mug: Carrot & Coriander, Leek & Potato, Minestrone, Tomato & Basil, Vegetable

KNOBBLY CARROT FOOD COMPANY
Broccoli; Celery & Apple; Courgette & Lemon; Leek & Potato; Minestrone; Mushroom & Garlic; Spicy Tomato; Tomato & Orange

KNORR
Florida Spring Vegetable Packet Soup; French Onion; Highland Lentil; Highland Vegetable; Leek; Minestrone; Moroccan Chickpea; Spring Vegetable; *Soup:* Florida Spring Vegetable, Italian Tomato & Basil, Tomato & Pepper

ORGANICO ⊘✿
Danival: Barley Miso, Japanese Pumpkin Cream, Miso Cubes, Miso Soup Powder, Rice Miso; *Serrra Rica:* Chesnut and Carrot with Ginger, Chesnut and Tomato, Gazpacho, Red Pepper and Toasted Almond, Tomato and Basil

ORGRAN ☺
Garden Vegetable Soup Mix

SANCHI ⊘
Miso Soup: Instant with Seaweed, Organic, Organic Miso Soup with Mushroom

SANITARIUM HEALTH FOOD CO ⊘
John Tickell's 12 Vegetable Soup; Vegetable & Minestrone

SOMA ORGANIC ☺⊘✎✿
Nomato: Soup

SUMA WHOLEFOODS
™❶⊘✎☀1985
Broth Mix; *Organic Soups:* **Carrot & Coriander, Italian Tomato and Basil Soup, Minestrone, Pea, Spicy Lentil, Thick Vegetable, Tomato, Tomato & Red Pepper**

THAI KITCHEN
Instant Rice Noodle Soup: Garlic & Vegetable, Spring Onion; *Rice Noodle Soup Bowls:* Hot & Sour, Mushroom, Roasted Garlic, Spring Onion

SOYA AND OTHER 'MILKS'

ALPRO UK LTD ☺❶⊘
Ambient Milk: Light Calcium and Vitamins 1 Litre, Original Calcium and Vitamins 1 Litre/500ml/3x250ml, Soya Soleil Unsweetened Calcium and Vitamins 1 Litre; *Chilled milk:* Chocolate shake calcium and vitamins 1 Litre, Chocolate Shake Calcium and Vitamins 500ml, Light Unsweetened Calcium and Vitamins 1 Litre, Organic 1 Litre, Unsweetened 1 litre; *Provamel Ambient Soya Milks:* Organic sweetened plus calcium; *Provamel Flavoured soya milk:* Organic banana flavour shake 3 x 250ml, Organic chocolate drink 1 litre, Organic chocolate flavour shake 3x 250ml, Organic strawberry flavour shake 3 x 250ml, Organic vanilla drink 1litre, Organic vanilla flavour shake 3 x 250ml; *Provamel Organic Soya Milk:*

Guaranteed free from flatulent cows and belching factories.

The soya plant is a relatively planet friendly producer of protein. As is our soya plant. From the time our organic soya beans enter the factory to the time they exit, the process is carbon neutral.

From Holland & Barrett and independent Health Food stores.

LOVE YOUR FUTURE

Organically grown. *Ethically* sourced. *Sustainably* produced. *Lovingly* made.

Original Calcium and Vitamins 1 litre, Original Calcium and Vitamins 250ml, Original Organic 1 litre, Unsweetened Calcium and Vitamins 1 litre, Unsweetened Calcium and Vitamins 500ml; *Provamel OY! Flavoured Soya Milk:* Banana, Chocolate, Strawberry, Vanilla; *Provamel Rice Drink:* Organic 1 litre, Rice drink Calcium + Vitamins 1 litre; *Provamel soya milk:* Organic chocolate drink 1 litre, Soya with Omega 3 1 litre; *Soya Milk:* Organic Sweetened, Sweetened Calcium and Vitamins for Coffee 1 litre, Unsweetened 1 litre, Unsweetened 250ml; *Soya Soleil:* Sweetened Calcium and Vitamins 1 litre, Unsweetened

BRAHAM & MURRAY LTD ™ ☝
Milks: **Good Hemp**

DIXIE DINERS CLUB
Moo NOT

FIRST GRADE INTERNATIONAL LTD ™☺⊘☝
Coconut milk: **Kara Dairy Free Original + Calcium**

GRANOVITA UK LTD ⊘ ☝
Soya Drink: Calcium Enriched, Organic Sugar Free

HOLLAND AND BARRETT RETAIL LTD ☝
Soya Alternative to Milk: Sweetened, Unsweetened

KALLO FOODS ⊘
Thin Slice Slightly Salted Rice Cakes

OATLY
Healthy Oat Alternative to Cream; Healthy Oat Organic

PLAMIL ☺❶⊘
Organic Soya Milk

RICE DREAM ☺
+ Calcium Chilled; Chocolate + Calcium; Hazelnut & Almond; Original + Calcium; Original Organic; Vanilla Organic

SANCHI ⊘
"Bonsoy" Soya Milk

SANITARIUM HEALTH FOOD CO ⊘
So Good Soya Milk: All Soya Milk including Active & Essential

SPIRAL FOODS
Original Bonsoy

VEGAN STORE ™☺❶⊘☝
Tam Tov: **Coffee Creamer**

SPICES

CHIMANS ™☺❶⊘☝
Aloo Gobi; Balti Pasta; Bean Curry; Bombay Potatoes; Dal; Spicy Chick Peas; Spicy Vegetable Soup; *Organic:* **Aloo Gobi, Bean Curry, Bombay Potatoes, Dal, Spicy Chick Peas, Spicy Vegetable Soup**

DISCOVERY FOODS
Seasoning Mix: Cajun, Fajita, Taco

HOLISTIX HERBAL PRODUCTS ❶
Mulled Wine Spice Powder; Mulled Wine Spice Whole

FOOD

PURITY TRADING LTD ™☺✔
Biryani; Butter Chicken; Chicken Achari; Chicken Curry; Chicken Karahi; Chicken Madras; Chicken Tikka Masala; Chicken with capsicum & Onion; Chickpeas Curry; Chutney Chicken; Fish Fry; Goan Fish Curry; Jalfrezi; Lamb Curry; Rogan Josh; Tandoori Chicken; Vindaloo

SCOTTISH HERBAL SUPPLIES ™❶⊘✔
Dried Organic Herbs

SEASONED PIONEERS ⊘✔
Africa: Berbere, Harissa Spices, South African Curry Powder, Tsire Powder, Tunisian Five Spice, Tunisian Tabil, West African Pepper Seasoning, Zanzibar Curry Powder; *Balti:* Garam Masala; *Cajun:* Cajun Blackening, Cajun Spice Blend, Creole Spice Blend; *Caribbean:* Adobo Rub Caribbean, Caribbean BBQ Jerk Rub, Poudre de Colombo, Virgin Islands Spiced Salt, West Indian Curry Powder; *China:* Chinese Five Spice; *India:* Bombay Masala, Cardamom Masala, Char Masala, Chat Masala, Garam Masala, Gujarati Masala, Kashmiri Masala, Madras Curry Powder, Panch Phoran, Punjabi Masala, Rose Petal Masala, Tandoori Masala; *Indonesia:* Seven Seas Curry Powder; *Japan:* Gomashio, Shichimi Tagarashi; *Mediterranean:* Quatre-Épices, Spice Parisienne; *Mexico:* Achiote Paste Spices, Adobo Rub Mexican; *Middle East:* Advieh (Iranian Rice Seasoning), Bahar (Kuwait), Baharat, Dukkah (Egypt), Hawaj (Yemen), Kabsa (Saudi), Sabzi Ghormeh (Iran), Zahtar (Za'atar); *Morocco:* La Kama, Ras-el-Hanout;

Mulling Drink Spices: Cajun Cafe Brulot Rum Spices, Caribbean Sorrel Rum Spices, Hot Toddy Spices, Mulled Cider Spices; *South India:* Sambhar Masala, Sri Lankan Curry Powder; *Worldwide:* Aliño (Chile), Celery Salt, Khmeli-Suneli (Georgia), Malay Curry Powder (Malaysia), Massalé (Mauritius), Mixed (pudding) Spice, Pickling Spice

SPREADS - SAVOURY

AROMAFOODS ™☺✔
Cajun Butternut Squash; Chilli Bean Spread; Coronation Spinach with Omega 3 seeds Sandwich Filling; Provencale Roast Veg; Roast Veg Houmus

BEAN THINKING
Patés: Cajun Red Pepper, Carrot & Ginger, Curried Lentil, Mushroom & Hazelnut, Pepper and Pumpkin Seed, Zucchini and Dill

BIONA
Black Olive Pate; Horseradish Relish; *Daily Balance Spread:* Country with Wild Garlic, Mexico with Corn Tomato & Cayenne Pepper, Styria with Pumpkin Seed, Tuscana with Olive Tomato & Basil

BUTE ISLAND FOODS LTD ™☺❶⊘
Vegan Mayonnaise: **Curry Flavour Island Mayo, Garlic Flavour Island Mayo, Mexican Flavour Island Mayo, Original Flavour Island Mayo, Tartar Flavour Island Mayo**

ESSENTIAL TRADING CO-OPERATIVE LTD ™❶⊘♨
Fairtrade tahini(light+ dark);
Essential Brand: **Tahini (Organic & Conventional);** *Essential Brand- Peanut Butters:* **All (Organic & Conventional)**

GRANOVITA UK LTD ⊘♨
Mushroom Savoury Pate in Chubb Pack; *Organic Ready Spready:* Garlic & Herb, Herb, Mushroom, Original; *Organic Tofu Pate:* Spicy Mexican (Yeast Free), Tomato (Yeast Free); *Ready Spready:* Herb Provence, Mushroom, Original; *Savoury Pate in Tin:* Mushroom, Olive, Vegetable

HIGHER NATURE LTD
Omega Excellence: Organic Pumpkin Seed Butter

MARMITE
Spread; Squeezy

MEDITERRANEAN FOODS (LONDON) LTD ☺
Black Olive Houmus; Houmus; Plain Houmus; Red Pepper Houmus; Red Pepper Houmus

MERIDIAN FOODS ⊘
Free From: Creamy Tomato & Herb Sauce, Dopiaza Sauce, Green Pesto, Green Thai Sauce, Madras Sauce; *Free From :* Red Pesto

MH FOODS ™⊘♨
Florentino- Pesto: **Basil - Cheese Free, Red - Cheese Free**

NATURKRAFTWERKE ™
Jars: **Poppy Seed Mush, Pumpkin Seed Mush**

ORGANICO ⊘✿
Nate: Carrot and Paprika Pate, Garlic and Basil Pate, Hazelnut Pate, Provincial Herbs Pate, Shii-take Mushroom Pate; *Serrra Rica:* Artichoke Spread, Aubergine and Garlic Spread, Caramelised Onion Spread, Roasted Red Pepper Spread, White Bean & Capers Spread

REAL ORGANIC FOODS ⊘
Province of India Chutneys: Mango with Ginger & Roasted Cumin, Spicy Tomato with Caramelised Onion, Tangy Eastern

REDWOOD WHOLEFOOD COMPANY ™☺❶⊘
Beanfeast Pate; Smoked Salmon Pate; *Cheatin' Pate:* **Forestier Pate, Provencal Pate;** *Vegideli Organic Range:* **Organic Beanfeast Pate, Organic Brussels Pate**

SANITARIUM HEALTH FOOD CO ⊘
Yeast Extract; *Peanut Butter:* All Varieties

SUMA WHOLEFOODS ™❶⊘♨☻☀-1985
Organic Tomato Paste; *Organic Pate:* **Herb, Mushroom;** *Organic Peanut Butter:* **Crunchy, Crunchy - No Salt, Smooth, Smooth - No Salt;** *Organic Pesto:* **Green, Red**

FOOD

SUN-PAT
Creamy Crunchy Peanut Butter; Creamy Smooth Peanut Butter; Original Crunchy Peanut Butter; Original Smooth Peanut Butter

TOPAS ™☺⊘ⓘ☼
Pate: **Gourmet Pate Soya Spread with marjoram, Gourmet Pate soya spread with mushrooms, Gourmet Pate Soya Spread with Red Bell Pepper, Gourmet Pate soya spread with wild garlic, Pate Wild Garlic**

TYRRELLS POTATO CHIPS
Crisps: Lightly Sea Salted, Naked/No Salt, Sea Salt & Black Pepper, Sea Salt & Cider Vinegar, Spicy Jalapeno Chilli & Lemon, Sweet Chilli & Red Pepper

SPREADS - SWEET

BIONA
Apple & Cranberry Compote; Dark Chocolate Spread; Pear & Apple Spread

CLEARSPRING ™☺ⓘ⊘ⓘ☜
Organic: **Apricot fruit spread, Blackcurrant fruit spread, Blueberry fruit spread, Peach Fruit Spread, Peach fruit spread, Prune fruit spread, Sour cherry fruit spread, Strawberry fruit spread**

CUISINE DE FRANCE
Seedless Raspberry Jam

DARTMOOR CHILLI FARM ™ⓘ⊘ⓘ
Dartmoor Chilli: **Chilli Jam, Hot Strawberry Jam, Lemon & Ginger Chilli Marmalade, Lime Chilli Marmalade, Orange & Ginger Chilli Marmalade, Seville Orange Chilli Marmalade, Three Fruit Chilli Marmalade Medium Cut, Three Fruit Chilli Marmalade Thick Cut**

ESSENTIAL TRADING CO-OPERATIVE LTD ™ⓘ⊘ⓘ
Fruit Spreads: **Organic Cherry, Organic Four Fruit, Organic Raspberry, Organic Strawberry, Organic Wild Bilberry;** *Spreads:* **Organic Apricot, Organic Blackberry, Organic Blueberry**

FRANK COOPER ☺
All Jams & Marmalades

KALLO FOODS ⊘
Whole Earth: Apple and Raspberry, Apricot, Blueberry, Cherry, Forest Fruits, Orange Thick Cut, Orange Thin Cut, Raspberry, Strawberry

KITCHEN GARDEN PRESERVES ⓘ
Jams: Blackberry & Apple, Blackcurrant, Gooseberry & Orange, Kiwi & Gooseberry, Mango & Papaya, Plum, Raspberry, Rhubarb, Strawberry, Summer Berry; *Marmalade:* Grapefruit, Lime, Orange & Cranberry, Orange with Lavender, Seville Orange, Three Fruit; *Organic Chutney:* Beetroot, Country Fruit, Piccalilli; *Organic Jams:* Apricot & Almond, Blackcurrant, Blueberry & Apple, Plum, Raspberry, Rhubarb, Strawberry; *Organic Marmalade:* Grapefruit, Seville Orange, Three Fruit

LYME BAY WINERY
Chutney: Apple with Elderflower Wine, Black Beer with Raisin Wine, Spicy Tomato with Jack Ratt Cider; *Extra Preserve:* Blackcurrant with Elderberry Port Liqueur, Strawberry with Summer Fruit Liqueur; *Marmalade:* Lyme Bay Sunrise with Apricot Brandy Liqueur, Red Onion with Damson Gin Liqueur, Vintage with Whisky & Ginger Liqueur

MERIDIAN FOODS ⊘
Fruit Spread: Apricot, Blackcurrant, Blueberry, Breakfast Seville Orange, Cherries/Berries, Cherry, Cranberry, Cranberry & Orange, Grapefruit Breakfast, Grapefruit Breakfast Spread, Morello Cherry, Pineapple & Ginger, Raspberry, Strawberry, Tropical, Wild Blueberry; *Fruit Spread - Organic:* Apricot, Blackcurrant, Blueberry, Cherries/Berries, Cherry, Cranberry

NATROL ✔
Mango Chutney

ORGANICO ⊘✿
Coteaux Nantais: Magic Apricot Jam, Magic Cherry Jam, Magic Raspberry Jam, Magic Strawberry Jam; *Serrra Rica:* Clementine Marmalade, Lemon Marmalade, Membrillo - Quince Paste, Seville Orange Marmalade, Valencia Orange Marmalade

PLAMIL ☺❶⊘
Organic Chocolate Spread; Organic Orange Chocolate Spread

REAL ORGANIC FOODS ⊘
Organic Conserve: Apricot, Blueberry, Raspberry with a hint of Citrus, Strawberry & Blackberry, Summer Fruits; *Organic Marmalade:* Seville Orange

ROBERTSONS ☺
All Jams & Marmalades

TRAIDCRAFT PLC ⊘
Exotic Fruit Mix; Orange Marmalade; Strawberry Jam; Tropical Fruit Mix

TOFU, TEMPEH, MISO ETC

BLUE DRAGON
Firm Silken Tofu

CAULDRON ⊘
Tofu: Block, Marinated Pieces

CLEARSPRING ™☺❶⊘✔👁
Tekka(miso condiment); Ume Concentrate; *Organic:* **Barley Miso, Brown Rice Miso, Hatcho miso, Sweet white miso**

DRAGONFLY FOODS ⊘✿
Organic Tofu: Deepfried, Natural, Smoked

MARIGOLD
Braised Tofu

ORGANICO ⊘✿
Danival: Ravioli Stuffed Tofu

R&R TOFU INTRODUCE:

Tofu
CLEAR SPOT

Opening a whole new world of nutritious cooking

organic **vegan**

R&R Tofu Ltd, Unit 5, Rye Close
York Road Industrial Estate, Malton,
North Yorkshire YO17 6YD
Tel: 01653 690235

Cpt. Beancurd recommends you find a CLEAR SPOT product!

PAUL'S TOFU ™⊘✶
Savouries: **Abura Age Marinated Tofu, Nigari Tofu, Tempeh**

R & R TOFU ™☺⊘
Marinated Tofu; Naturally Smoked Tofu; Organic Tofu; Tofu Sea Cakes; Tofu Sesame Burgers; Tofu with Mixed Herbs

SANCHI ⊘
Miso: Genmai (Brown Rice), Hatcho (Soya Bean), Mugi (Barley), Organic Genmai (Brown Rice), Organic Mugi (Barley), Organic Unpasteurised Barley (Mugi), Shiro

SOURCE FOODS ☺✶
Low Sodium Rice & Soy Organic Miso:
Mellow Brown, Sweet Brown; *Ohso Miso:* Yummo Sesame; *Ohso Miso - Organic Instant Soup:* Original; *Organic Instant Soup:* Beetroot, Ginger, Spirulina; *Organic Miso:* Field Bean Barley, Ginger, Hemp, Mellow Barley, Mellow Brown, Mex Chilli, Sweet Brown

TAIFUN ☺⊘
Pan Ready Tofu: Tofu filets Wild Garlic, Tofu Rösti; *Smoked Tofu:* Demeter, Smoked, With Almonds and Sesame Seeds; *Tofu:* Basil, Demeter, Kinugoshi; *Tofu:* Natural; *Tofu:* Nigari, Silken; *Tofu Terrine:* Graffiti

TOPAS ™☺⊘✶
Finest Smoked Tofu; *Wheaty:* **Vegan Organic Seitan "Classic"**

134

'YOGURTS'

ALPRO UK LTD ☺❶⊘
Alpro Dairy Free Alternative to Yogurt
Raspberry & Vanilla Flavour; Alpro Dairy
Free Chocolate Flavoured Custard +
Calcium; Exotic Fruits; Forest Fruits;
Peach; Strawberry; *Organic Yofu:*
Peach/Mango, Plain, Red Cherry,
Summer Fruits; *Provamel Yoghurts:*
Organic Blueberry 500g; *Provamel
Yogurts:* Organic Bluberry 4x125g,
Organic blueberry and peach 4X125g,
Organic cherry 4x125g, Organic forest
fruits 500g, Organic peach and mango
4x125g, Organic Plain 500g, Organic
strawberry 500g, Organic Vanilla 500g;
Yofu Junior: Peach & Pear, Strawberry &
Banana; *Yogurts:* Forest Fruits Calcium
and Vitamins 500g, Organic Red
Cherry/Peach & Mango 4x125g, Peach
Calcium and Vitamins 4x125g,
Peach/Pear & Strawberry/Banana
Calcium and Vitamins 4x125g

GRANOVITA UK LTD ⊘ 🥄
Deluxe Soyage: Banana, Black Cherry,
Mango, Peach & Apricot, Plain,
Raspberry, Strawberry, Tropical; *Organic
Soyage:* Fruits of the Forest, Peach &
Apricot, Strawberry

NOTES

■ **Banana chips** may be dipped in
honey, check the ingredients.

■ **Bread:** a few pre-packed loaves
contain either skimmed milk powder
or vitamin D3. Most large producers
use vegetable-based emulsifiers
(E471, E472 etc). When buying bread
from local bakers check ingredients
and type of fat used to grease tins.

■ **Breakfast cereals and margarines**
fortified with vitamin D may contain
the animal-derived D3.

■ **Chocolate:** unfortunately, plain
chocolate is not always animal-free
and may contain milk powder. All of
the chocolate products listed in the
Animal Free Shopper have been
made without animal-derived
ingredients or processing aids, but
may have been produced on the
same lines as milk chocolate
products, see **contamination**,
below.

■ **Contamination:** the *Animal Free
Shopper* only lists products that we
have been informed meet our
ANIMAL-FREE CRITERIA. However,
many of the foods listed will have
been produced on the same lines as
products containing animal-based
ingredients. Although health and
hygiene, and product quality,
requirements mean that machines
are cleaned thoroughly between

different products, there is sometimes a slight risk of contamination. This means, for example, that some listed products may not be suitable for dairy or egg allergy sufferers.

■ **Crisps** may contain lactose or whey or animal derived additives.

■ **Fruit,** mainly citrus fruits or some apples, may be glazed with animal (commonly beeswax or shellac), vegetable (usually carnauba) or mineral waxes. Contact manufacturers for further details as information changes regularly (according to season, supplier, etc). Fruit is not waxed under organic standards.

■ **Gelatine carrier:** beta-carotene and vitamin D2 may be 'carried' in gelatine to maintain stability e.g. orange coloured drinks may contain beta-carotene held in a gelatine suspension (see DRINK NOTES, page 163). In the case of beta-carotene, vegetable oil carriers are available and are generally animal-free.

■ **Natural Flavourings** may be animal derived

■ **Processing aids** may be animal derived. There is no statutory requirement for these to be listed on products.

■ **Salt** is usually vegan, some low salts may contain a milk derivative.

■ **Sugar:** bone char is sometimes used as a decolourant in sugar production. However, the largest suppliers of sugar to companies in the UK - British Sugar, Tate & Lyle and Billington - do not use any animal-derived ingredients (except for Tate & Lyle Traditional Royal Icing, which contains dried egg white powder). Most supermarkets' own-brand sugars are made for them by one of these companies.

WILL POWER

Vegans have it.

We rely on will power even though we've been doing it for over 60 years. Leaving a charity a donation in your will is an excellent way to continue to provide support.

You will be helping to secure our future - for people, animals and the environment.

We are an educational charity and since 1944 have promoted a healthful, compassionate lifestyle, encouraging the growth of veganism worldwide.

It is only with the help of people like you that we can continue to succeed.
Please phone 0845 45 88244 (local rate) and request our free will and legacy pack.

It's that easy.

Thank you for all your help

- The Vegan Society

THE Vegan SOCIETY

DRINK

DRINK

BEERS

ANHEUSER-BUSCH
Ascent 54; Bare Knuckle Stout; Busch Ice; Busch Light; Busch; Czechvar; Demon's Hop Yard IPA; Grolsch Amber Ale; Grolsch Blonde Lager; Grolsch Light Lager; Grolsch; Harbin Lager; Hurricane High Gravity; Hurricane Ice; Hurricane Malt Liquor; King Cobra; Kirin Ichiban; Kirin Light; Mule Kick Oatmeal Stout; Natural Ice; Natural Light; Ray Hill's American Pilsner; Redbridge; Rolling Rock; Tarpon Spoon; Tequiza; Tiger Beer; Tilt; ZiegenBock Amber; ZiegenBock; *Bacardi Silver:* All; *Seasonal Beers:* Beach Bum Blonde Ale, Jack's Pumpkin Spice; *Specialty Organic Beers:* Stone Mill Pale Ale, Wild Hop Lager

ANHEUSER-BUSCH INBEV ⊘ ✦
Beck's; Beck's Blue; Beck's Vier; Brahma; Leffe; Staropramen; Stella Artois 4%

ARTISAN BRASSEUR
Antidote; Calixte-Peloquin; Dorimene; Flambee 64; Jos-les-Boeufs; Lile de Grace; Maisouna; Saison du Loup

BLACK SHEEP BREWERY PLC ⊘ ✦
Bottled Ales: Black Sheep, Emmerdale, Golden Sheep Ale, Monty Python's Holy Grail, Riggwelter Strong

BRAKSPEAR'S
Bottled: Oxford Gold Organic Beer

BUDWEISER
Bud Dry; Bud Extra; Bud Ice; Bud Ice Light; Bud Light; Budweiser; Budweiser Select

CALEDONIAN BREWING CO ⊘
Bottled Beers: Caledonian 80 (500ml bottle), Deuchars IPA (500ml bottle), Golden Promise Organic (500ml bottle)

CARLSBERG UK LTD ⊘ ✦
Carlsberg; Carlsberg Edge; Carlsberg Elephant Beer; Carlsberg Export; Carlsberg Special Brew

CROPTON BREWERY
Balmy Mild; Endeavour; King Billy; Monkman's Slaughter; Scoresby Stout; Two Pints; Uncle Sam's; Yorkshire Moors Bitter; *Seasonal:* Haunting Hanks, Rudolph's Revenge

DANIEL THWAITES
Kaltenberg; Warsteiner

EVERARDS BREWERY
Hazy Daze

FREEDOM BREWERY LTD ™☺❶⊘
Freedom Organic Dark Lager; Freedom Organic Lager; Freedom Pilsner

FULLERS
Bottled & Keg (NOT Draught): All except Honey Dew

GEORGE BATEMAN & SON ™⊘✦
ALDI Specially Selected Range: **ALDI - Golden Ale, ALDI - India Pale Ale, ALDI - XB Ale;** *Bottled Beers:* **Combined Harvest Multigrain Beer, Dark Lord Premium Ale, M & S Lincolnshire Best Bitter, Mr. George's**

Ruby Porter, Organic Hop Bine
Bitter, Rosey Nosey Premium Ale,
Spring Breeze, Summer Swallow,
Triple XB, Victory Ale, XXXB Classic
Bitter

GROLSCH
Lager

HALL & WOODHOUSE LTD
Badger: Blandford Fly, First Gold, Fursty
Ferret, Golden Champion, Golden
Glory, Poacher's Choice, Pumpkin Ale,
Stinger, Tanglefoot

HEINEKEN
Lager: Pilsener

HOLSTEN
Holsten Export; Holsten Pils; Holsten
Super

KELTEK BREWERY
Natural Magik

**LANCASTER
BREWERY LTD** ™☺◌ℹ
Lancaster Amber; Lancaster Black;
Lancaster Blonde; Lancaster Red

LITTLE VALLEY BREWERY LTD ™
Bottle Conditioned: **Cragg Vale Bitter,
Fairtrade Organic Ginger Pale Ale,
Hebden's Wheat, Moor Ale,
Stoodley Stout, Tod's Blonde,
Withens IPA**

MICHELOB
Michelob; Michelob AmberBock;
Michelob Golden Draft Light; Michelob
Golden Draft; Michelob Light; Michelob

Ultra; Michelob Ultra Amber; *Seasonal
Beers:* Michelob Bavarian-Style Wheat,
Michelob Ultra Fruit Infused

PITFIELD BREWERY ™◌ℹ☼
Bottled Beers: **Amber Ale, Black
Eagle, Dark Ale, East Kent Goldings,
Eco Warrior, Hoxton Heavy, Imperial
Stout, India Pale Ale, London Porter,
Mild Ale, N1 Organic Wheat Beer,
Pitfield Organic Lager, Pitfield
Original, Red Ale, Shoreditch Stout,
XXXX Stock Ale**

**ROBERT CAIN
& COMPANY LIMITED** ◌ℹ
Bottled Beers: 2008 Culture Beer, Bock
Beer, Dragonheart Ale, FA Ale, Finest
Lager, Organic Wheat Beer, Raisin Beer;
Canned: Dark Mild, FA Ale, Finest Bitter,
IPA beer, Liverpool Lager; *Keg:* Bitter,
Finest Lager, IPA, Liverpool Lager, Mild

SAMUEL SMITH ™◌ℹ
**Alpine Lager; Celebrated Oatmeal
Stout; Extra Stout; Famous Taddy
Porter; Imperial Stout; India Ale;
Nut Brown Ale; Old Brewery Pale
Ale; Organic Best Ale; Organic
Cherry Fruit Beer; Organic Lager;
Organic Raspberry Fruit Beer;
Organic Strawberry Fruit Beer;
Organic Wheat Beer; Pure Brewed
Lager; Sovereign Bitter; Taddy
Lager; Winter Welcome Ale**

SKOL
Skol (Cans); Skol Special; Skol Super

SPECTRUM BREWERY
Bottled: 42, Bezants, Black Buffle, Capt.

Scarlet, Dark Fantastic, Light Fantastic, Old Stoatwobbler, Solstice Blinder, Spring Promise, Trip Hazard, Wizzard, XXXX, Yule Fuel; *Cask:* Black Buffle, Dark Fantastic, Old Stoatwobbler

STROUD BREWERY LTD ™⊘✔☼
Ales: **Budding Organic Pale Ale (bottled), Ding Dong Organic Spiced Porter (bottled), Tom Long Organic Amber Bitter (bottled), Woolsack Organic Porter (bottled)**

THE DURHAM BREWERY LTD
Bottle-Conditioned: Benedictus, Cloister, Evensong, St Cuthbert, Temptation

THE HOP BACK BREWERY
Entire Stout: Bottles, Cask

THE INNIS & GUNN BREWING COMPANY ⊘
Blonde Oak Aged Beer; Original Oak Aged Beer; Rum Cask Oak Aged Beer

TRADITIONAL SCOTTISH ALES
Bottled Ales: Bannockburn, Ben Nevis, City of Stirling, Glencoe Stout, Lomond Gold, Shefiffmuir, Stirling Brig, William Wallace

VINTAGE ROOTS ⊘☼
Freedom; Prospect pale ale; Vintage roots organic beer; *Brakspear:* Brakspear bottle conditioned organic beer; *Caledonian:* Golden promise; *Duchy:* Duchy originals organic ale; *Dupetit:* Cannabia; *Hall & woodhouse:* River cottage stinger ale; *Hartsfelder:* Vintage roots organic lager; *Hepworth*

brewery: Cool blonde lager; *Lammsbrau:* Lammsbrau organic pilsner; *Little valley brewery:* Stoodley stout, Withens ipa; *Ridgeway brewery:* Ridgeway rob; *Riedenburger:* Reidenburger low alcohol, Riedenburger organic lager, Riedenburger wisse wheatbeer; *Westons:* Westons organic cider

WELLS & YOUNG'S
Wells Banana Bread Bear: Canned Bottled and Keg Varieties (Not Cask); *Wells Bombardier:* Canned Bottled and Keg Varieties (Not Cask); *Wells Eagle IPA:* Canned Bottled and Keg Varieties (Not Cask); *Wells John Bull:* Canned Bottled and Keg Varieties (Not Cask); *Youngs Bitter:* Canned Bottled and Keg Varieties (Not Cask); *Youngs Special:* Canned Bottled and Keg Varieties (Not Cask)

WESTERHAM BREWAERY CO LTD
British Bulldog; Little Scotney Best Bitter; Little Scotney Pale Ale; William Wilberforce Freedom Ale

WIBBLER'S ☺
All Bottled Beers

WYCHWOOD BREWERY
Circlemaster

CHAMPAGNE

MOET & CHARDON ☺
Brut Imperial; Grand Vintage; Nectar Imperial; Rose Imperial

SMITHFIELD WINE
Vegan Champagne: Th. Blondel Rosé Brut Premier Cru, Thierry Blondel Premier Cru

THOMAS LOWNDES & CO
Champagne Brut NV (Rosé) 12%; Champagne Brut NV 12%; Marc de Champagne 60%

VINTAGE ROOTS ⊘ ✿
Duval-leroy: AOC Authentis cumieres 2001; *Faust:* AOC Carte d'or

CIDERS & PERRIES

A'BECKETT'S VINEYARD
All

ASPALL ⊘ ✔
Cyder: All

DUNKERTON'S CIDER COMPANY ☺⊘✔✿
Black Fox; Perry; Premium Organic; *Still Blended:* Dry, Med, Med Sweet; *Still Blended:* Sweet

GWYNT Y DDRAIG CIDER
Cider: Black Dragon, Orchard Gold

LUSCOMBE ORGANIC DRINKS ☺⊘✔✿
Organic Devon Cider

LYME BAY WINERY
Cider: Jack Ratt Scrumpy, Jack Ratt Vintage, Lyme Bay Sparkling Cider

MERRYDOWN ☺⊘
All

PITFIELD BREWERY ™⊘✔✿
Fred's Perry; *Bottled Cider:* **Hoxton Farmhouse Dry Cider**

SAMUEL SMITH ™⊘✔
Cider Reserve; Organic Cider

SEDLESCOMBE ORGANIC VINEYARD ™☺⊘✔✿
Speciality Cider: **Dry Cider**

SHEPPY'S CIDER ⊘✔
Bullfinch; Goldfinch; Oakwood Supreme; Organic Dry; Organic Medium; *Draught Cider:* Dry, Medium, Sweet; *Gold Medal Vintage Cider:* Dry, Medium, Sweet; *Oakwood Draught Cider:* Dry, Medium; *Oakwood Special:* Dry, Medium, Sparkling; *Single Variety Ciders:* Dabinett, Kingston Black, Taylor's Gold, Tremlett's Bitter

SOMERSET CIDER BRANDY COMPANY & BURROW HILL CIDER ☺
Ciders: All

VINTAGE ROOTS ⊘✿
Cinq autels: Normandy cider; *Dunkertons:* Black fox cider, Premium organic cider, Vintage cider 2004/05; *Sheppy's:* Sheppy's organic cider

WESTON & SONS LTD ☺⊘
Oak Conditioned Cider: Henry Westons Vintage Reserve, Medium Sweet, Strong Extra Dry, Strong Medium Dry, Vintage Cider; *Organic Cider:* Draught Vintage, Westons Organic; *Perries:* Herefordshire Country, Original;

DRINK

Scrumpy Cider: 1st Quality Cider, Extra Strong Scrumpy, Old Rosie Scrumpy, Traditional Scrumpy Cider; *Speciality Ciders:* 1880 Anniversary Cider; *Stowford L.A.:* Low Alcohol; *Stowford Press Cider:* Dry, Export, Medium Dry, Medium Sweet, Supreme

'HOT'

A. VOGEL
Bambu

CADBURY TREBOR BASSETT
Bournvita

CLEARSPRING ™☺❶⊘✔👁
Hasucha Lotus Tea; Hasucha Lotus Tea; Mu Tea -16 herbs; *Organic:* **Genmaicha Green Tea/Roasted Rice - Bags, Genmaicha Green Tea/Roasted Rice - Loose, Hojicha Roasted Green Tea - bags, Hojicha Roasted Green Tea - Bags, Hojicha Roasted Green Tea - Loose, Hojicha Tea bags, Kukicha Roasted Twig Tea - bags, Kukicha Roasted Twig Tea - loose, Sencha Green Tea - loose, Sencha Green Tea bags**

ESSENTIAL TRADING CO-OPERATIVE LTD ™❶⊘✔
Essential Brand- Organic Coffee: **All;**
Essential Brand- Organic Demeter Teas: **All**

GUARANA COMPANY LTD ™
Hot Guarana Punch

HERBS HANDS HEALING LTD ™⊘✔
Herbal Tea Blends & Single Herb Teas: **Basil, Burdock Root, Cassia Split Bark, Catnip, Dandelion Coffee, Dandelion leaf, Fennel Seeds, Hibiscus Flower, Lavender Flowers, Lift and Calm, Liquorice root, Marigold Flowers, Marjoram, Mellissa, Oregano, Parsley, Pau d'arco, Peppermint, Sage, Spearmint, St. John's Wort, Thyme, Uva Ursi, White Willow Bark, Wild Cherry Bark**

HOLISTIX HERBAL PRODUCTS ❶
Herb Blends: Calm Tea, Detox Blend, English Garden

KALLO FOODS ⊘
Whole Earth: No Caf, Wake Cup

KITCHEN GARDEN
SoyCaf

KUCHING HERBAL TEA ☺⊘✔
Loose Tea Leaves: Kuching Herbal's Premium Java Tea

MONTEZUMAS CHOCOLATES
Drinking Chocolate: Omacati Dos, Omacati Uno

NATROL ✔
Laci Le Beau Teas: All

OPTIMAH ⊘✔🦅1995
Vital Health Foods: Organic Rooibos Tea Bags

RAW ALCHEMY LTD ™☺❶⊘✔
Raw: **Hot Chocolate Elixir**

RAWCREATION LTD ™☺❶⊘✔
Olive Leaf Tea; Pau D'arco Tea; Yerba Mate Tea

REDBUSH TEA CO
Redbush: Apple, Finest, Lemon, Spiced, with Lemon Oil

SIMPLY SOAPS
Gift Sets: Yogi Tea 'Calming' Gift Box, Yogi Tea 'Detox' Gift Box, Yogi Tea 'Harmony' Gift Box

THE CHOCOLATE ALCHEMIST ⊘✿
Dark Drinking Chocolate: Plain, with Chilli, with Nutmeg

TRAIDCRAFT PLC ⊘
Drinking Chocolate

LOW & NON-ALCOHOLIC

LUSCOMBE ORGANIC DRINKS ☺⊘✔✿
Organic Ginger Beer: Cool, Hot

SHANDY BASS ☺
Shandy

SOFT

7UP ☺
7UP: Cherry, Free, Regular

A'BECKETT'S VINEYARD
Juices: All

AME ☺
Elderberry and Lemon; Grape and Apricot; Orange and Grape; Raspberry and Blackberry

ARCIM HYPOGEEN B.V.
Hypo-Fit Direct Energy for Diabetics

ASPALL ⊘✔
Apple Juice

BELVOIR FRUIT FARMS ☺⊘
Cordials: Elderflower, Ginger, Gooseberry & Mint, Lime & Lemongrass, Passion Fruit & Mango, Pomegranate & Raspberry, Raspberry & Rose Cordial, Spiced Winter Berries, Summer Berries; *Organic Cordials:* Blackcurrant, Blood Orange & Mandarin, Blueberry, Cranberry, Elderflower, Ginger

BETTERTHANKS INC ™☺
Cordia: **Organic Fruit Extract, Organic Grape Juice;** *Royale:* **Organic Fruit Extract, Organic Pear Juice**

BRITVIC
American Ginger Ale; Bitter Lemon; Blackcurrant Cordial; Indian Tonic Water; Lime Cordial; Low Calorie Tonic Water; Orange Cordial; Soda Water; *Britvic 55:* Apple, Apple Raspberry and Cranberry, Orange; *J2O:* Apple and Mango, Apple and Melon, Apple and Raspberry, Orange and Passionfruit, Orange and Pomegranate

CHEGWORTH VALLEY JUICES ☺
Certified Organic Juices: Bramley Apple, Cox Apple, Discovery Apple, Pear; *Classic Apple Juices:* Bramley, Cox & Bramley, Discovery, Discovery & Bramley, Russet, Worcester & Bramley; *Pear Juice & Special Variety Juices:* Apple & Beetroot, Apple & Blackberry, Apple & Blackcurrant, Apple & Cranberry, Apple & Elderflower, Apple & Raspberry, Apple & Rhubarb, Apple & Strawberry, Pear

COCA-COLA
Aqua & Grapefruit; Aqua & Lime; Berry & Tropical; Burn; Caffeine-Free diet Coke; Cherry Coke; Citrus Punch; Coca-Cola; Coco-Cola with Lime; Deuce Cranberry & Raspberry; Diet Coke; Diet Coke with Cherry; Diet Coke with Lemon; Diet Coke with Lime; Diet Ginger Ale; Diet Lemonade; Dr Pepper; Dr Pepper Z; Froot Refresh Apple & Mango; Froot Refresh Red Grape & Raspberry; Fruit Twist; Fusion Berry & Elderflower; Fusion Vanilla & Passion Fruit; Ginger Ale; Ginger Beer; Hi-Juice 66; Icy Lemon; Icy Lemon Z; Kiwi and Watermelon; Lemon & Grapefruit; Lemon Ice Tea; Lemon Lime Light; Lemonade; Lemonade Shandy; Lime Cordial; Low Calorie Lemonade; Mango; Mixed Fruit; NAS Mixed Fruit; NAS Pear & Blackcurrant; Orange Juice with Juicy Bits; Orange Juice with Juicy Bits and Multi-Vitamins; Orange Squash; Pear & Blackcurrant; Pink Grapefruit; Red Fruits Ice Tea; Russchian; Slimline Bitter Lemon; Smooth Orange; Smooth Orange and Raspberry with Zinc; Smooth Orange with Multi-Vitamins; Sparkling Blackcurrant; Sparkling Lemon; Sparkling Orange & Lemon; Sprite; Sprite 3G; Sprite Z; Summer Fruits; Summer Fruits Light; Summer Fruits Z; Summer Punch Lemonade; Sweetened Grapefruit; Tomato Juice Cocktail; Zero; *Cordial:* Blackcurrant Cordial, Lime Cordial, Peppermint Cordial; *Five Alive:* Berry Blast, Berry Blast Five Fruit Splash, Berry Whirl, Citrus Burst, Cranberry Splash, Tropical Hit; *Oasis:* Blackcurrant Apple; *Powerade:* Cherry; *Schweppes:* American Ginger Ale, Bitter Lemon; *Tonic Water:* Indian Tonic Water, Indian Tonic Water with a hint of lemon, Slimline Tonic Water, Slimline Tonic Water with a hint of lemon

CRACKER DRINKS CO. ™☺
Apple and raspberry juice drink; Apple, strawberry and cranberry juice drink; Blueberry and blackberry juice drink; Mango and passion fruit juice drink; Pineapple, guava, lime juice drink

ELLA DRINKS ☺⊘✔
Bouvrage: Blaeberry Drink, Raspberry Drink

ESSENTIAL TRADING CO-OPERATIVE LTD ™❶⊘✔
Essential Brand: **Organic Apple Juice, Organic Beetroot Juice, Organic Carrot Juice, Organic Vegetable Juice**

FENTIMANS LTD ☺⊘
Curiosity cola; Dandelion & Burdock; Mandarin and Seville Orange Jigger; Traditional Brewed Shandy; Traditional Ginger beer; Victorian Lemonade

G & G VITAMINS
Aktiv Ingredient Energy Drink

GEORGAS FAMILY ™☺❶⊘◢☼
Fruit Juice: **Grape Concentrate,
Red/White Grape Water, White/Red
Grape Juice**

GERBER JUICE COMPANY
Libby's: Apple C Juice Drink,
Blackcurrant C Juice, NAS Tropical
Drink, Orange C Juice Drink, Tomato
Juice with Vitamins C and E, Um
Bongo; *Ocean Spray:* Cranberry &
Blackcurrant Juice Drink, Cranberry &
Blueberry Juice Drink, Cranberry &
Mango Juice Drink, Cranberry &
Orange Juice Drink, Cranberry &
Raspberry Juice Drink, Cranberry and
Acerola Juice Drink, Cranberry Juice
Drink - Classic; *Scooby Doo:* Tropical
Juice Drink; *Sunpride:* Cranberry Juice
Drink, Exotic Juice Drink, Mango Juice
Drink; *Thomas the Tank Engine:* Apple
& Blackcurrant Juice Drink, Orange
Juice Drink; *Welch's:* Grape & Mango
Juice Drink, White Grape & Peach Juice
Drink, White Grape & Pear Juice Drink,
White Grape, Pear & Apple Juice Drink

GUARANA COMPANY LTD ™
Cold Guarana Punch

IDRIS ☺
Fiery Ginger Beer; Red Devil

KALLO FOODS ⊘
Whole Earth: Sparkling Cola, Sparkling
Cranberry, Sparkling Elderflower,
Sparkling Ginger, Sparkling Lemonade

KNORR
Vie Shots: Apple, Carrot & Strawberry,
Kiwi, Pumpkin & Banana, Orange,
Carrot & Banana

LIPTON
Lipton Ice Tea: Lemon, Mango, Peach

**LUSCOMBE ORGANIC
DRINKS** ☺⊘◢☼
Organic Apple & Apricot Juice; Organic
Apple & Pear Juice; Organic Apple Juice;
Organic Apple with Elderflower; Organic
Apple with Ginger; Organic Elderflower
Bubbly; Organic Lime Crush; Organic
Raspberry Lemonade; Organic Sicilian
Lemonade; Organic St. Clements;
Organic Strawberry Lemonade

LYME BAY WINERY
Dorset Ginger Cordial

MCKEITH ☺
Organic Juice: Berry Chi, Cherry Chi,
Peach Chi; *Organic Smoothie:* Groovy
Guava, Mango Mania, Veggie Vitality

MERIDIAN FOODS ⊘
Fruit Juice Concentrates: Apple, Apple
& Blackcurrant, Organic Apple, Pear

ORGANICO ⊘☼
The Organic Collection: Blueberry
Sparkle Juice, Raspberry Sparkle Juice

PENNARD ORGANIC WINES & CIDER
Pennard Organic: Apple Juice

PENNINE SPRING ☺
Pennine Spring: Citrus Mineral Water,
Orange & Peach, Strawberry Mineral Water

147

PEPSI ☺
Diet; Max; Raw; Regular

PURDEY'S ☺
Multi Vitamin Juice Drink

PURELY WICKED SHAKES LIMITED
Soya Fruit Milkshakes - All Flavours

R WHITES ☺
Diet Lemonade; Premium Lemonade

RED BULL ☺⊘
Red Bull: Energy Drink, Natural Cola, Stimulation, Sugar Free

RELENTLESS
All flavours except Inferno

RIBENA
Juice Drink Concentrate: Blackcurrant Juice Drink Concentrate; *Ready to Drink:* Apple, Blackcurrant, Orange, Strawberry; *Really Light No Added Sugar Juice Drink Concentrate:* Berry Burst, Blackcurrant, Blueberry; *Really Light No Added Sugar Ready to Drink:* Blackcurrant, Blueberry; *Sparkling:* Blackcurrant

ROBINSONS
Barley Water : Lemon, Orange; *Be Natural:* Apple & Strawberry, Blackcurrant & Pear; *Be Natural:* Orange & Passionfruit; *Fruit & Barley:* Apple and Blackcurrant, Orange, Peach, Pink Grapefruit, Strawberry and Kiwi, Summer Fruits; *Fruit Shoot:* Apple, Blackcurrant and Apple; *Fruit Shoot H2O:* Apple, Blackcurrant, Orange; *Fruit Shoot My-5:* Apple & Blackcurrant, Apple & Pear, Orange & Pineapple; *Fruit Shoot No Added Sugar:* Apple, Blackcurrant and Apple, Orange,

Summer Fruits, Tropical; *Fruit Squash:* Apple and Blackcurrant, Orange, Orange and Pineapple, Summer Fruits; *No Added Sugar:* Apple and Blackcurrant, Lemon, Orange, Orange and Pineapple, Summer Fruits; *Select:* Apple & Blueberry; *Select:* Orange Mandarin & Peach, Red Grape Pomegranate & Raspberry; *Select (No Added Sugar):* Orange Mandarin & Peach

ROCKS ORGANIC CORDIALS ⊘✿
Juice Drinks: Bella Blackcurrant; *Organic Cordials:* Blackcurrant, Cranberry, Elderflower, Fruit Punch, Ginger, Lemon, Lime, Summer Fruit; *Squashes:* Lizzy Lemon, Olly Orange

RUBICON DRINKS LTD.
Sparkling Juice Drinks: Guanabana, Guava, Lychee, Mango, Passion, Pomegranate, Tropical; *Still Juice Drinks:* Coconut Water, Guanabana, Guava, Guava Berry, Lychee, Mango, Mango Apple, Papaya, Passion, Pomegranate, Blueberry & Cranberry, Tropical

SCIENCE IN SPORT
GO Electrolyte: All Flavours; *PSP22:* All Flavours; *REGO Recovery:* All Flavours

SEDLESCOMBE ORGANIC VINEYARD ™⊘⊘ ⚓ ✿
Luxury Fruit Juice: **Apple Juice, Blackberry & Apple Juice, Bramley Apple Juice, Cox Apple Juice, Grape Juice, Pear Juice**

SOMA ORGANIC ☺⊘ ⚓ ✿
Lemonade; Original; *Pure Fruit Smoothies:* Blackberry & Blueberry,

Mango & Passionfruit, Peach & Strawberry, Raspberry & Blackcurrant; *Super smoothies:* Blueberry Bliss, Fruity Roots, Jungle Juice, Tropical Twist

TANGO ☺
Apple; Cherry; Citrus; Diet Orange; Orange

THE HIBISCUS DRINKS COMPANY LIMITED ™
Hibiscus & Grape; Hibiscus & Peppermint; Hibiscus Classic; Hibiscus Cordial

THE REALLY WILD DRINKS CO ☺
The Really Wild Drinks Co: Apple and Blackcurrant Still, Apple Blackcurrant Sparkling, Apple Blackcurrant Still, Orange and Pineapple Sparkling, Orange and Pineapple Still

VIMTO
Cordial: Apple, No Added Sugar, Orange, Original; *Fizzy:* No Added Sugar, Original; *Ready to Drink:* No Added Sugar, Original

VINCEREMOS ORGANIC WINES ⊘ ❦ ✿
Rocks: Blackcurrant squash 74cl, Lemon squash 74cl, Orange squash

X35 ENERGY LTD ☺
X35 Body Fuel- energy drink- 250ml and 500ml sizes.

SPIRITS & APÉRITIFS

ABSOLUT ☺
100; Apeach; Citron; Kurant; Mandrin; Mango; Pears; Peppar; Raspberry; Ruby Red; Vanilia; Vodka

ARCHERS
Schnapps: All

BARON WINE CELLARS LTD T/A TISHBI ESTATE WINERY ™☺❶⊘❦
Barbera-Zinfandel; White Brandy

CLEARSPRING ™☺❶⊘❦☻
Shizengo Sake; Tamaki Sake

COCKBURN'S
Special Reserve: Port 20%

COURVOISIER
V.S. : Cognac 40%, Cognac 60%; *V.S.O.P.:* Cognac 40%

FONSECA
Ports: All Vintage, Terra Prima Oganic Reserve

GLENFIDDICH ⊘
Glenfiddich Scotch Whisky: All

GORDON'S ☺
Gin & Tonic; Sloe Gin; Special Dry London Gin

GOURMET CLASSIC LTD ™
Eaux de Vie: **Kirsch, Peach, Pear William, Plum, Strawberry**

GRAND MARNIER
Liqueur 40%

HARVEYS
Orange 17.5%; *Bristol Cream:* Sherry
17.5%

JIM BEAM
Black Bourbon Whiskey 43%; White
Bourbon Whiskey 50%

JOHNNIE WALKER
Whisky: Black Label, Blue Label, Gold
Label, Green Label, Red Label

LAMBS NAVY
Rum 60%

LAPHROAIG
Single Islay Malt Scotch Whisky 40%

LYME BAY WINERY
Fruit Liquers: Apricot Brandy, Blackcurrant
Rum, Damson, Elderberry & Port, Plum,
Sloe, Summer Fruit, Whisky & Ginger;
Somerset Cider Brandy Company: 10
Years Old Cider Brandy, 3 Years Old
Cider Brandy, 5 Years Old Cider Brandy,
Eau de Vie Cider Brandy, Kingston Black
Aperitif Cider Brandy

MALIBU
Coconut

PENNARD ORGANIC WINES & CIDER
Pennard Organic: Ginger Liquor,
Raspberry Liquor

**SEDLESCOMBE ORGANIC
VINEYARD** ™☺⊘✦✿
Speciality Liqueur: **Blackberry Liqueur,
Organic Bramley Apple Liqueur,**

**Organic Raspberry Apple Liqueur,
White Grape Liqueur**

SMIRNOFF ☺
& Cola; Black; Black Ice; Blue; Ice; Lime
& Soda; Norsk; Penka; Red

**SOMERSET CIDER BRANDY
COMPANY & BURROW HILL CIDER** ☺
Eau De Vie; Kingston Black Apple
Aperitif 18%; Somerset Pomona 20%;
Brandy: Somerset Alchemy, Somerset
Five Year Old, Somerset Royal, Somerset
Ten Year Old

TEACHERS
Calvados 40%; Kirsch 50%; Scotch
Whisky 60%

**THE ORGANIC SPIRITS
COMPANY** ☺⊘✦✿
Highlands Harvest: Organic Scotch
Whisky; *Juniper Green:* Organic Gin;
Papagayo: Organic White Rum; *UK5:*
Organic Vodka; *Utkins:* Fairtrade White
Rum

THOMAS LOWNDES & CO
Amaretto 50%; Coconut Liqueur
Extract 50%; Coffee Liqueur Extract
50%; Creme de Menthe Extract 60%;
Culinary French Brandy 40%; Culinary
Jamaican Rum 40%; Culinary Malt
Whisky 60%; French Dry White Tolosan
11.5%; Marsala Superiore 18%;
Medium Dry Amontillado Sherry
18.5%; Oloroso Cream Sherry 17.5%;
Peach Schnapps 50%; Rich Ruby Port
20%; Single Speyside Malt Whisky (6
year old) 40%; Vodka 40%

VINCEREMOS ORGANIC WINES ⊘ ◢ ✿
Casal dos Jodoes (Portugal): Majara Finest Reserve Port Quinta da Esteveira; *Highland Harvest:* Highland Harvest organic whisky; *Utkins:* Fairtrade white rum

VINTAGE ROOTS ⊘ ✿
Benromach: Speyside single malt whisky; *Beucher:* Calvados; *Da mhile:* Da mhile blended whisky, Da mhile highland whisky; *Dwersteg:* Amaretto liqueur; *Organic spirit company:* Highland harvest whisky, Juniper green organic london dry gin, Papagayo organic spiced golden rum, Utkins fairtrade premium single estate white rum, Utkins uk5 organic vodka; *Pinard:* Cognac napoleon, Cognac VSOP, Cognac***; *Saoubis:* Bas Armagnac; *Verdet:* Creme de cassis (blackcurrant), Creme de framboise (raspberry), Creme de mure (blackberry), Creme de peche (peach)

SPORTS DRINKS

GATORADE
Gatorade: Lemon, Orange

WINES

A'BECKETT'S VINEYARD
All

BARON WINE CELLARS LTD T/A TISHBI ESTATE WINERY ™☺❶⊘◢
Tishbi: **Tishbi Junior, Vineyards Shiraz**

CLEARSPRING ™☺❶⊘◢👁
Shizengo Sake; Tamaki Sake

CONSTELLATION WINES
Counry Manor: All; *Rougemont:* All

DELAFORCE
Vintage Ports: All

EMILIANA ORGANICO ⊘✿
Colchagua Valley 2003; Coyam Colchagua Valley 2004/2005; *Winemakers Selection:* Novas Casablanca Valley Syrah Sauvignon 2005, Novas Colchagua Valley Mourvedre 2004/2005, Novas Colchagua Valley Syrah 2004/2005

NIEPOORT
Ports: All Vintage

NO COWS ☺
Mixed Case: Connoisseurs' Organic Selection, Friends For Dinner Mixed Selection, MIxed case of 12 Organic Wines

SMITHFIELD WINE
Casa Verde Rueda; Finca de Altura range; Septima range; Vivallis range; Welmoed Range

DRINK

WINES - FRUIT

BROUGHTON PASTURES ⊘ ✔ ☼
Elderflower; Ginger (Fairtrade);
Sparkling Elderflower

LYME BAY WINERY
Apricot; Birch; Blackbeer & Raisin;
Blackberry; Blackberry & Apple;
Blackcurrant; Cowslip; Cranberry;
Damson; Dandelion; Dry Damson; Dry
Gooseberry; Elderberry; Elderflower;
Ginger; Gooseberry; Parsnip; Peach;
Plum; Raspberry; Raspberry & Apple;
Rhubarb; Sloe; Strawberry; Strawberry
& Apple

PENNARD ORGANIC WINES & CIDER
Pennard Organic: Apple, Elderberry,
Folly, Ginger, Gooseberry, Plum,
Raspberry, Tayberry

RIMON WINERY ™☺
Rimon: **Pomegranate dessert wine,
Pomegranate dry wine**

**SEDLESCOMBE ORGANIC
VINEYARD** ™☺⊘ ✔ ☼
Speciality wine: **Black Cherry Wine,
Blackberry Wine, Elderberry Wine,
Elderflower Wine, Ginger Wine,
Golden Apple Wine, Old Vine
Organic Wine, Plum Wine**

VINTAGE ROOTS ⊘ ☼
Irjimpa: DO La mancha caballero de
mesarrubbias 2005/06; *Pinol:* DO Terra
alta sacra natura 2005/06

WINES - RED

SANT'OR ™☺❶⊘ ✔ ☼
Red Wine

**BARON WINE CELLARS LTD T/A
TISHBI ESTATE WINERY** ™☺❶⊘ ✔
Dessert wine: **Jonathan Tishbi
Special Reserve Red Muscat;**
Jonathan Tishbi Special Reserve Series:
**Cabernet Sauvignon Blend (Sde
Boker), Cabernet Sauvignon Gush
Etzion, Merlot;** *Oak aged:* **Estate
Old Carignan, Estate Organic Sirah,
Estate Petit Sirah;** *The Vineyards:*
**Cabernet Sauvignon, Carignan,
Merlot, Red Dessert Muscat, Ruby
M;** *Tishbi:* **Cabernet Petite Syrah;**
Tishbi Estate: **Cabernet Sauvignon,
Merlot, Pinot Noir, Shiraz**

EMILIANA ORGANICO ⊘ ☼
Adobe Carmenere 2005/2006; Adobe
Colchagua Valley Syrah 2005/2006;
Novas Central Valley Cabernet Merlot
2005; Novas Central Valley Cabernet
Sauvignon 2005; Novas Colchagua
Valley Cabernet Sauvignon 2005;
Novas Colchagua Valley Carmenere
2005

GEORGAS FAMILY ™☺❶⊘ ✔ ☼
Wines: **Red Wine**

HARBOURNE VINEYARD ☺⊘ ✔
2002 Harbourne

MAJESTIC WINE WAREHOUSE LTD
Vergelegen Mill Race Cabernet
Sauvignon Merlot 2005 Stellenbosch;
Agramont Crianza 2004 Navarra; Aloxe
Corton 1er Cru 2005 Domaine
Chevalier Père et Fils; Aloxe-Corton
2004 Domaine Maillard; Beaune Rouge
2004 Domaine Maillard Père et Fils;
Bonterra Vineyards Zinfandel 2005
Mendocino; Bourgogne Côte
Chalonnaise Les Gorgères 2005 Michel
Sarrazin; Bourgogne Pinot Noir 2006
Cave Co-op de Buxy; Bourgogne Rouge
2005 Domaine Sarrazin; Caracol
Serrano 2005 Jumilla; Carmen
Winemaker's Reserve 2002 Maipo
Valley; Castillo Rioja 2006 Bodegas
Palacio; Cavas de Weinert Merlot 2002
Mendoza; Chapoutier Organic Tricastin
2006 Côteaux du Tricastin; Château
Batailley 2001 Pauillac, 5ème Cru
Classé; Château Bel Air 2003 Haut
Médoc, Cru Borgeois; Château du Cray
Bourgogne Rouge 2003/2004 Côte
Chalonnaise; Château Guiot 2006
Costières de Nîmes; Château Haut
Franquet 2002 Bordeaux; Château
Potensac 2002 Médoc Cru Borgeois
Exceptionnel; Chénas 2005 Cave du
Château de Chénas; Chianti Classico
Riserva Carpineto 2000/2003 DOCG;
Clos d'Yvigne Le Petit Prince 2005
Côtes de Bergerac; Clos d'Yvigne Le
Rouge et Le Noir 2004; Collection
Privée de l'Oratoire 2006 Vin de Pays
de Vaucluse, Léonce Amouroux;
Corbières La Combe des Oliviers 2005;
Cuvée de Richard Red 2006 Vin de Pays
de l'Aude; Domaine de l'Amauve
Séguret Rouge 2006 Côtes du Rhône
Villages; Domaine Delubac 'Les
Bruneau' 2005 Côtes du Rhône Villages

Cairanne; Fairhills Fairtrade Pinotage
Cabernet 2006 Western Cape; Gevrey
Chambertin 2005 Domaine Chevalier
Père et Fils; IIIB Merlot, Jean-Claude
Mas 2006 Vin de Pays d'Oc; King's
River Shiraz 2006 Robertson; La
Chapelle de Pitray 2005 Côtes de
Castillon; La Motte Shiraz 2005
Franschoek; Ladoix Rouge 1er Cru
'Clou d'Orge' 2005 Domaine Chevalier
Père et Fils; Ladoix Rouge 2005
Domaine Chevalier Père et Fils; Les
Fontanelles Cabernet Sauvignon 2006
Vin de Pays d'Oc; Les Fontanelles
Merlot 2006 Vin de Pays d'Oc; Mâcon
Rouge 2006 Les Vignerons des Grandes
Vignes; Martin Sarmiento 2004 Bierzo;
Paul Mas Cabernet de Cabernet 2006
Vin de Pays d'Oc; Pinot Noir Domaine
de Valmoissine 2005 Louis Latour, Vin
de Pays des Côteaux du Verdon;
Pommard 'La Chanière' 2004 Domaine
Maillard Père et Fils; Sablet Le Rêve de
Marine 2004 Domaine de Piaugier;
Sancerre Rouge 2006 Paul Thomas;
Saumur Rouge 2005 Réserve des
Vignerons; Savigny-Lès-Beaune Rouge
2004 Domaine Millard Père et Fils; Spy
Mountain Pinot Noir 2006
Marlborough; Swartland Winery
Pinotage 2006; Tatachilla Foundation
Shiraz 2003 McClaren Vale; Tempranillo
La Serrana 2006 Vino de la Tierra
Castilla y León; Vergelegen Cabernet
Sauvignon 2004 Stellenbosch; Vino
Nobile di Montepulciano 'La Ciarliana'
2004; Yering Frog Cabernet Shiraz
2006 Yarra Valley; Yering Frog Pinot
Noir 2006 Yarra Valley; Yering Station
Pinot Noir 2004/2005 Yarra Valley;
Yering Station Shiraz/Viognier 2005
Yarra Valley

DRINK

NO COWS ☺
Aroa Tempranillo 2004; Camino Los
Robles - Tempranillo Roble; Can
Vendrell Tempranillo Garnatxa; Chateau
Grolet La Coccinelle 2003; Chateau
Grolet Le G 2003; Compte Cathare -
Domaine Maris La Touge; Compte
Cathare Maris Grenache 2002; Compte
Cathare Syrignan; Domaine Majelus
Merlot; L'Esprit de Valeriane; Novas
Carmenere Cabernet; Pech-Roc
Cabernet 2005

OLIVERHILL WINERY ™☺❶⊘✓ ✿
Blended: **Red Silk;** *Sauvignon:*
Cabernet Sauvignon; *Shiraz:*
**Clarendon Shiraz, Jimmy Section
Shiraz, Mount Benson Shiraz;** *Sirah:*
Petite Sirah

PETER LEHMANN
All Red Wine

RIMON WINERY ™☺
Rimon: **Pomegranate port style wine**

SEDLESCOMBE ORGANIC
VINEYARD ™☺⊘✓ ✿
Speciality English wine: **Regent Dry
Red English Wine**

SMITHFIELD WINE
Azcunaga Semi Crianza; Bodegas
Palacio de Villachia 4T; Casa Viva Pinot
Noir; Casas del Bosque Pinot Noir
Reserva; McGuigan Bin 2000 Shiraz;
Palandri Estate Chardonnay; Poco Mas
Cabernet Sauvignon; Poco Mas Merlot;
Rincon Privada Cabernet Sauvignon;
Rincon Privado Malbec; Rosario
Carmenere Reserva; Rosario Merlot;
Santa Luisa Malbec; Santa Luisa Merlot;
Santa Luisa Syrah; *Australian Wines:*
Jarrah Ridge Red, McGuigan Bin 4000
Cabernet Sauvignon, McGuigan Black
Label Merlot, McGuigan Black Label
Shiraz; *French Wines:* Chateau Leon,
Chateau Taillefer, Chateauneuf du Pape
La Roche, Cotes du Rhone Caves St-
Pierre, Cotes du Rhone Village, Dom.
de la Garelle, Cote du Luberon Cuvee
Pere Antoine Rouge, Domaine de La
Garelle Merlot VDP de Vaucluse,
Domaine de La Garelle Syrah VDP de
Vaucluse, Domaine de la Garelle, Cote
du Luberon Cuvee Speciale; *Israeli
Wines:* Dalton Merlot, Tishbi Cabernet
Petit Syrah, Tishbi Special Reserve
Merlot, Tishbi Vineyards Cabernet
Sauvignon, Tishbi Vineyards Merlot;
New Zealand Wines: Springbank Pinot
Noir; *South African Wines:* Cape Bay
Mellow Red, Cape Bay Pinotage, Neil
Joubert Pinotage, Peaks View Pinotage;
Spanish Wines: Bodega Palacio de
Villachica 5T, Bodegas 1877 Arx
Crianza, Bodegas 1877 Arx Negro
Tempranillo/Merlot, Bodegas Bilbainas
La Vicalanda Gran Reserva, Bodegas
Bilbainas La Vicalanda Reserva, Bodegas
Bilbainas Vina Pomal Reserva, Bodegas
Entrecepas Crianza, Bodegas Irius
Absum Varietales Tempranillo Merlot,
Bodegas Valdevinas Tinar Crianza,
Castillo Viejo Catamayor Merlot,
Castillo Viejo Catamayor Merlot Tannat,
Cune Crianza, Cune Reserva, Imperial
Gran Reserva, Imperial Reserva,
Montalvo Wilmot, Mynus+ Tinto,
Palaciego Rioja Red, Rioja Palaciego
Crianza DOC, Rioja Valsarte Crianza
DOC, Rioja Valsarte Reserva,
Vallformosa Cabernet Sauvignon,

Vallformosa Val Reserva, Vina Real Crianza, Vina Real Gran Reserva, Vina Real Reserva; *Spansi Wines:* Bodegas Bilbainas Viña Pomal Crianza

TRAIDCRAFT PLC ⊘

Argentinian Shiraz; Chilean Cabernet Merlot; South African Cabernet Sauvignon Merlot; South African Pinotage

VINCEREMOS ORGANIC WINES ⊘ ♦ ✿

Iberum Tinto DO Navarra 2005&2006; Paul Giboulot (France); *Albet i Noya (Spain):* Can Vendrell Tinto; *Boira:* Pinot Grigio, Sangiovese; *Bon Cap:* Syrah - Cabernet 'The Ruins' 2005; *Bon Cap Winery (South Africa):* 'The Ruins' Pinotage; *Bucaro:* Montepulciano d'Abruzzo Riserva; *Chatelaine Stephanie:* VDT rouge- 10 litres bag in box; *Domaine de Clairac:* Cuvee des Cinq Filles, French Organic Red, Joubio Rouge, Marsanne, Syrah, Vin de Pays de l'Herault, Cabernet- Merlot 2004&2005; *Domaine Richeaume (France):* Côtes de Provence, Cuvée Columelle Côtes de Provence, Syrah; *Domaine St. Michel (France):* Cabernet Sauvignon Vin de Pays d'Oc, Merlot Vin de Pays d'Oc, Syrah-Malbec Vin de Pays d'Oc; *Dominio Basconcillos:* Ribera del duero DO 2005; *Eden Collection Wines (Spain):* Tempranillo; *Era (Italy):* Inzolia, Montepulciano, Nero D'Avola, Primitivo, Sangiovese; *Jacques Frelin (France):* Crôzes Hermitage, Cuvee Olivier Vin de Table Rouge (10L Box), Merlot Cuvée la Marouette, Vin de Pays du Gard; *La Nature:* Barbera Argentina, Merlot Vin de Pays d'Oc, Rhone Valley

Red, Shiraz/Cabernet Sauvignon Australia, Vin de Pays d'Oc, Vin de Pays Rouge; *La Nature Wines (France):* Cabernet Sauvignon; *Los Pinos (Spain):* Crianza, Dominio los Pinos Barrica, Seleccion Tinto; *Ottomarzo (Italy):* Bardolino Classico, Schaffer (Italy) Barbera 'Solo per Laura', Valpolicella Classico; *Perlage (Italy):* Cabernet del Veneto, Corte del Giano, Merlot del Veneto, Solatio Rosso; *Pircas Negras (Argentina):* Torrontes Barbera Malbec Syrah; *Richmond Plains (New Zealand):* Escapade Nelson, Pinot Noir Nelson, Reserve Pinot Noir Nelson; *San Michele (Italy):* Chanti Classico Riserva, Chianti Classico, Chianti Colli Fiorentini; *San Vito (Italy):* Chianti, Chianti Vigna la Reina, Fior di Selva Barrique; *Ventura:* Pinot Noir 2006; *Vignoble Saint Frédéric (France):* Gigondas; *Volpi (Italy):* Era Montepuiciano d'Abruzzo, Era Nero d'Avola, Era Sangiovese; *Wilhelm Zähringer (Germany):* Baden, Spätburgunder, Spätburgunder Spätlese Baden; *Wilkie Estate (Australia):* Cabernet Merlot

VINTAGE ROOTS ⊘✿

Albet i noya: DO penedes tempranillo col.leccio 2000/01; *Azul y garanza:* DO Navarra 2006, DO Navarra series 2004/05; *Barra:* Zinfandel 2005/06; *Basconcillos:* DO Ribera del duero roble 2005; *Beausejour:* Puisseguin St Emilion 2004/2005, Puisseguin St Emilion Petit Beusejour Tradition 2005; *Bioghetto:* de l'Herault RN13 Vin de Pique-nique Rouge 2005; *Blanchard:* AOC Pineau des charenes; *Brau:* Cabardes 2004/2005, Cabardes Cuvee Exquise 2004/2005, Cite de Carcassonne

Meditation Syrah/Egiodola 2004/2005, de l'Aude 2005, de l'Aude 'Pure' Cabernet Sauvignon 2006, de l'Aude 'Pure' Pinot Noir 2006, d'Oc Cuvee Gabriel Merlot 2005/2006; *Buis Rond:* Beaujolais 2006; *Casal dos jordoes Fortified Wine:* Finest Reserve Port, Tawny Port, Vintage port 2004; *Chapoutier:* AOC Coteaux du tricastin 2006; *Clos Plince:* Pomerol 2003; *CLVD:* d'Oc WWF Element Terre Merlot/Cabernet Sauvignon 2005; *Combebelle:* St Chinian Syrah/Grenache 2006; *Comte Cathare:* Minervois Domaine Maris La Touge Syrah 2004/2005; *Couronneau:* Bordeaux Superieur 2005/2006, Bordeaux Superieur Cuvee Pierre de Cartier 2005/2006, Bordeaux Superieur L'Ecuyer de Couronneau 2005; *Fasoli gino:* IGT La calle merlot 2004/05, IGT Rosso veronese pinot noir sande 2005; *Ijalba:* DO Rioja crianza 2003/04, DO Rioja dionisio ruiz ijalba 2004, DO Rioja graciano 2004, DO Rioja livor 2006/07, DOC Rioja genoli 2006/07; *Irjimpa:* DO Lamancha shiraz 2006; *Javillier:* Pommard Premier Cru 2005, Volnay Premier Cru 2004/2005; *Joliette:* AOC Muscat de rivesaltes 2005/06, Cotes du Roussillon Cuvee Andre Mercier 2003/2004, Cotes du Roussillon Villages Cuvee Romain Mercier 2002/2003; *La raia:* DOCG Gavi la raia 2006/07, DOCG Gavi la raia pise 2006/07; *Mas igneus:* DO Priorato Costers De Mas Igneus 2001, DO Priorato FA206 2004; *Moulin de Cadet:* St Emilion Grand Cru Classe 2004; *OVA:* Five Plots Merlot/Ruby Cabernet/Cabernet Sauvignon 2004/2005, Jamberoo Cabernet Sauvignon/Merlot 2003, Jamberoo Shiraz/Cabernet Sauvignon 2004/2005; *Palacios duque:* DOC Rioja buradon 2005, DOC Rioja padus 2004; *Pech-Latt:* Corbieres Selection Vielles Vignes 2005; *Perrini:* IGT Salento primitvo 2004/05; *Purisma:* DO Yecia Cerro Campana Old Vine Nonastrell 2006; *Quinta do coa:* Quinta do coa branco; *Richard:* Bergerac 2006, Bergerac Les Charmes Merlot/Cabernet Franc 2006, Bergerac Rouge 2006; *Rizzotti:* DOCQ Chianti san donato a lucardo 2005/06; *Robinvale:* Shiraz/Cabernet Sauvignon/Merlot 2005/2006; *San polino:* DOC Brunello di montalcino 2001, DOC rosso di montalcino 2004; *St Paul:* d'Oc Viognier 2006; *Stellar:* Cabernet sauvignon 2006/07, Heaven-on-earth sweet muscat, Live-a-little really ravishing red 2005, Live-a-little really revealing rose 2006/07, Merlot 2006/07; *Tsantali:* Merlot 2004/05; *Viberti:* DOC Barbera d'alba 2004, DOC Barolo 2001, DOC Langhe nebbiolo 2003/04; *Vintage Roots Own-label:* Organic rouge, Organic Tinto

VIVA! ☺❶⊘✔
All

WINES - ROSÉ

HARBOURNE VINEYARD ☺⊘✔
2001 Dry Rosé Pinot Meunier

MAJESTIC WINE WAREHOUSE LTD
Lawson's Dry Hills Pinot Noir Rosé 2006 Marlborough; Pinot Grigio Rosé 2006

DRINK

Cantina Beato Bartolomeo di Breganze; Puig Ventos Garnacha 2005 Terra Alta

MEINKLANG
Pinot Noir Frizzante 2005/2006; Pinot Noir Frizzante 2006

NO COWS ☺
Camino Los Robles - Rosado; Pech-Roc Syrah

SEDLESCOMBE ORGANIC VINEYARD ™☺⊘ ◀ ✿
Speciality English wine: **English Wine**

SMITHFIELD WINE
South African Wines: Peaks View Pinotage Rose; *Spanish Wines:* Mynus+ Rose 2007, Vallformosa Gran Reserva

VINCEREMOS ORGANIC WINES ⊘ ◀ ✿
La Mancha Blanco; *Bon Cap:* Pinotage rose 'The Ruins' 2006; *Domaine de Clairac:* Cabernet Sauvignon Rosé, Joubio Rosé; *Ventura:* Carmenere Rose 2006

VINTAGE ROOTS ⊘ ✿
Albet i noya: DO Penedes Pinot Moir/Merlot Classic Rosat, Penedes Pinot Noir/Merlot Classic Rosat 2006/2007; *Azul y garanza:* DO Navarra rosa 2006/07, Navarra Rosa; *Bassac:* Organic Rose; *Bettili:* Serenel Vivace Rosato 2006/2007; *Bioghetto:* de l'Herault, de l'Herault RN13 Vin de Pique-nique Rose 2006/2007, Vin de Pique-nique Rose 2006/2007; *Brau:* de l'Aude Brau Rose 2006/2007; *Emiliano Organico:* Touchstone Rose; *Fabril Alto

Verde: Buenas Ondas Syrah Rose 2006/2007; *Jas d'esclans:* AOC Cotes de provence cru classe 2006/07; *Jas d'Esclans:* Cotes de Provence Cru Classe 2006/2007; *Meinklang:* Pinot Noir Frizzante 2006/2007; *Stellar:* Live-a-little rather revealing rose 2006/07, Live-a-Little Rather Revealing Rose; *Vintage Roots Own-label:* Organic rose, Organic Rosso

WINES - SPARKLING

LIMNEY ☺⊘ ◀ ✿
Quality Sparkling Wine 2004

NO COWS ☺
Albet I Noya - Classic Xarel.lo K; Can Vendrell Cava; Canals Brut Nature Rosat; Limney Estate Sparkling

SEDLESCOMBE ORGANIC VINEYARD ™☺⊘ ◀ ✿
Speciality English wine: **Cuvee Bodiam Brut English Sparkling Wine, Cuvee Pinot Noir Regent Brut Rosé English Sparkling Wine 2002;** *Speciality wine:* **Elderflower Sparkling Wine**

SMITHFIELD WINE
Palandri Solora Sauvignon Blanc; *Israeli Wines:* Tishbi Estate Chardonnay; *Spanish Wines:* Vallformosa Winery Cava Brut; *Vegan Sparkling Wines:* Old Acres Cava brut/rose

VINCEREMOS ORGANIC WINES ⊘ ✴ ✿

Achard Vincent (France): Clairette de Die Brut, Clairette de Die Tradition; *Albet i Noya (Spain):* Cava Brut 21 Can Vendrell, Cava Can Vendrell; *Domaine du Jas (France):* Blanquette de Limoux, Cremant de Limoux; *Perlage (Italy):* Prosecco Frizzante, Prosecco Spumante de Valdobiaddene

VINTAGE ROOTS ⊘ ✿

Albet i noya: DO Cava brut 21, DO Cava brut reserva, DO Cava brut rosat, DO Cava can vendrell; *Mont'albano:* IGT Prosecco; *Naturian:* Ffizz! Organic brut; *Vintage Roots Own-label:* Organic bianco; *Zuccardi:* Santa julia organica sparkling chardonnay 2004

WINES - WHITE

SANT'OR ™☺❶⊘✴ ✿
Dry White Wine

BARON WINE CELLARS LTD T/A TISHBI ESTATE WINERY ™☺❶⊘✴
Jonathan Tishbi Special Reserve Series: **Chardonnay;** *Sparkling wine:* **Jonathan Tishbi Special Reserve Brut;** *The Vineyards:* **Dry French Colombard, Emerald Riesling, Sauvignon Blanc;** *Tishbi:* **Chenin Blanc, Estate Gewurztraminer, French Riesling, Muscat Alexandroni, Semi Dry French Colombard;** *Tishbi Estate:*

Chardonnay, Riesling Late Harvest, Sauvignon Blanc, White Riesling

EMILIANA ORGANICO ⊘✿
Adobe Casablanca Valley Sauvignon Blanc 2007; Novas Casablanca Valley Chardonnay 2005/2006; *Winemakers Selection:* Novas Casablanca Valley Chardonnay 2004/2006, Novas Casablanca Valley Marsanne 2004/2006, Novas Casablanca Valley Viognier 2004/2006

GEORGAS FAMILY ™☺❶⊘✴ ✿
Wines: **White Wine**

HARBOURNE VINEYARD ☺⊘✴
1995 Harbourne Medium Dry; 1999 Harbourne Seyval Blanc; 1999 Harbourne Ortega/Regner Dry; 2000 Harbourne Ortega/Muller Thurgau Unfiltered Dry; 2002 High Halden Estate Dry; 2003 Seyval Blanc; Harbourne High Halden Medium Dry

LEOPARD'S LEAP
Lookout White

LIMNEY ☺⊘✴ ✿
Horsmonden Dry 2006/2007

MAJESTIC WINE WAREHOUSE LTD
Lirac Blanc 2006 Château d'Aquéria; Marc Ducournau Grand Heron 2006 Vin de Pays des Côtes de Gascogne; Yering Frog Chardonnay 2006 Yarra Valley; Argento Chardonnay 2006 Mendoza; Argento Pinot Grigio 2007 Mendoza; Bonterra Vineyards Chardonnay 2005 Mendocino; Chablis 2006 Domaine Servin; Cheverny Le

Vieux Clos 2006 Emmanuelle Delaille; Chorey-Lès-Beaune Blanc 2004 Domaine Maillard Père et Fils; Clos d'Yvigne Princesses de Clèves 2006 Bergerac Blanc Sec; Clos d'Yvigne Cuvée Nicolas 2006 Bergerac Sec; Corton-Charlemagne Grand Cru 2005 Domaine Chevalier Père et Fils; Coulée d'Argent Vouvray Sec 2006 Bourillon-Dorléans; Crios Torrontes 2007 Susana Balbo; Cuvée Elise Demi Sec 2006 Vin de Pays du Comté Tolosan; Domaine Begude Chardonnay 2006 Vin de Pays d'Oc; Domaine Caillaubert Sauvignon 2006 Vin de Pays des Côtes de Gascogne; Drylands Sauvignon Blanc 2006 Marlborough; Finca Las Moras Viognier 2007 San Juan; Five Rivers Chardonnay 2005 Monterey County; Grechetto di Todi 2006 Franco Todini; Greco di Tufo 2006 Vesevo; Grüner Veltliner 2006 Weingut Pfarre Weissenkirchen; Kangarilla Road Viognier 2006 Mclaren Vale; King's River Chardonnay 2006 Robertson; King's River Pinot Grigio 2006 Robertson; King's River Viognier 2007 Robertson; Klein Constantia Chardonnay 2005 Constantia; La Nuit Blanche' Roussanne 2006 Domaine Sainte Rose; La Serrana Chardonnay 2006 Vino de la Tierra Castilla y León; 'Le Vent du Nord' Roussanne Chardonnay 2005 Domaine Sainte Rose, Vin de Pays d'Oc; Meursault 2005 Domaine Vincent Bouzereau; Montagny 1er Cru 2004 Cave de Buxy; Montagny 1er Cru 2005 Domaine Vincent Bouzereau; Montes Limited Selection Sauvignon Blanc 2007 Leyda Valley; Muscadet 2006/2007 Jacques Arnoult;

Muscadet de Sèvre et Maine Sur Lie 2006 Domaine de la Tourmaline; Paulett's Riesling 2006 Polish Hill River, Clare Valley; Pinot Grigio 'Punggl' Single Vineyard 2006 Alto Adige, Nals & Margreid; Pinot Grigio Superiore 2007 Cantina Breganze; Pouilly-Fumé 'Les Ferrées' 2006 Marcel Sautejeau; Robert Mondavi Winery Fumé Blanc 2005 Napa Valley; Robertson Winery Chenin Blanc 2007; Sancerre Blanc 2005 Thauvenay Masson Blondelet; Sancerre Vielles Vignes 2005 Domaine Paul Cherrier et Fils; Saumur Blanc 2006 Réserve des Vignerons; Sauvignon de Touraine 2006 Domaine de La Prévôté; Sauvignon Les Fumées Blanches 2006 J&F Lurton, Vin de Pays d'Oc; St Clair Estate Selection Sauvignon Blanc 2007 Marlborough; St Clair Pioneer Block 6 Sauvignon Blanc 2006/2007 Marlborough; St-Véran 2006 Les Vignerons des Grandes Vignes; Vasse Felix 'Adams Road' Chardonnay 2006 Margaret River; Vergelegen Chardonnay 2006 Stellenbosch; Vergelegen Sauvignon Blanc 2007 Stellenbosch; Vignes de Nicole Chardonnay Viognier 2006 Vin de Pays d'Oc; Viognier Collection 2006 Gérard Bertrand, Vin de Pays d'Oc; Yering Station Chardonnay 2005 Yarra Valley; Zonda Chardonnay Chenin 2007 Mendoza; Zondernaam Sauvignon Blanc 2007 Stellenbosch

MEINKLANG
Burgenland White 2005/2006; Eiswein 2003; Gruner Veltliner 2006/2007

DRINK

NO COWS ☺
Borghi Pinot Grigio; Camino Los Robles
- Airen; Chianti Majnoni; Domain
Majelus Chardonnay Rousane; Domaine
Begude Sauvignon Blanc; Horsmonden
2006; M Chapoutier - Mirabel Viognier;
Pech-Roc Sauvignon Blanc; Rolly
Gassman - Reisling

OXFORD LANDING
Sauvignon Blanc

PENNARD ORGANIC WINES & CIDER
Pennard Organic: Dry White English
Table Wine

SANCHI ⊘
Sake

SEDLESCOMBE ORGANIC
VINEYARD ™☺⊘✦☼
Speciality English wine: **Bodiam
Harvest English Wine, Dry White
English Wine, Reserve English Wine**

SMITHFIELD WINE
Casa Viva Sauvignon Blanc; Casas del
Bosque Sauvignon Blanc; Domaine de
la Garelle Chardonnay VDP de
Vaucluse; McGuigan Black Label
Chardonnay; Mynus + Blanco ; Palandri
Chardonnay; Palandri Riesling; Palandri
Sauvignon Blanc; Palandri Solora
Chardonnay; Poco Mas Chardonnay;
Poco Mas Sauvignon Blanc; Rincon
Privada Torrontes; Rosario Chardonnay;
Rosario Chardonnay Reserva; Rosario
Sauvignon Blanc; Santa Luisa
Chardonnay; Vistamar Chardonnay;
Vistamar Sauvignon Blanc; *Australian
Wines:* Jarrah Ridge Colombard
Chardonnay, McGuigan Black Label

Chardonnay, McGuigan Estates Bin
7000 Chardonnay; *Chilean Wines:* Los
Robles Sauvignon Blanc; *Israeli Wines:*
Carmel Vineyard Select Sauvignon
Blanc, Dalton Canaan White, Dalton
Fume Blanc, Dalton Safsufa Sauvignon
Blanc, Tishbi Emerald Riesling, Tishbi
Special Reserve Chardonnay, Tishbi
Vineyards Sauvignon Blanc; *New
Zealand Wines:* Tohu Sauvignon blanc;
South African Wines: Neil Joubert
Chenin Blanc, Peaks View Chenin
Blanc, Peaks View Sauvignon Blanc;
Spanish Wines: Bodegas Irius Absum
Varietales, Castillo Viejo Catamayor
Chardonnay, Vallformosa Chardonnay

TRAIDCRAFT PLC ⊘
Chilean Chardonnay; South African
Chenin Blanc; South African Sauvignon
Blanc

VINCEREMOS ORGANIC
WINES ⊘✦☼
Albet i Noya (Spain): Can Vendrell
Blanco, Lignum Blanc; *Aquis Celenis DO
Rias Baixas:* Albarino 2004; *Bonterra
(USA):* Chardonnay, Muscat,
Roussanne, Viognier; *Ch de Barradis
(France):* La Balance Bergerac,
Monbazillac; *Chatelaine Stephanie:* La
Mancha Blanco, 10 litres bag in box;
Clos St Martin (France): Muscat de
Rivesaltes, Muscat Sec Vin de Pays des
Pyrenées Orientales; *Dom Garreliere
(France):* Chenin Blanc Touraine,
Sauvignon Blanc Cuvée Cendrillon
Touraine, Sauvignon Blanc Touraine;
Domaine de Clairac: Joubio Blanc;
Domaine de Farlet (France):
Chardonnay Vin de Pays des Collines de

la Moure, Viognier Vin de Pays des Collines de la Moure; *Domaine de la Parentiere:* French Organic White, Muscadet de Sevre et Maine sur lie; *Domaine Richeaume (France):* Blanc de Blanc Côtes de Provence, Viognier Côtes de Provence; *Domaine St. Michel (France):* Chardonnay Vin de Pays d'Oc, Entre Deux Mers, Sauvignon Blanc Vin de Pays d'Oc; *Eden Collection Wines (Spain):* La Mancha Blanco; *Eugène Meyer (France):* Gewurztraminer, Pinot Blanc, Sylvaner; *Frick (France):* Gewurztraminer Cuvée Precieuse, Pinot Blanc Cuvée Classique, Pinot Blanc Cuvée Precieuse, Pinot Gris Cuvée Precieuse, Sylvaner Cuvée Classique; *Guy Bossard (France):* Domaine de la Parentière Muscadet de Sèrvre et Maine Sur Lie, Gros Plant Sur Lie Vin de Pays Nantais, Hermine d'Or Muscadet de Sèrvre et Maine Sur Lie, Muscadet de Sèrvre et Maine Sur Lie; *Jacques Frelin (France):* Château Petit Roubie Picpoul de Pinet, Cuvée de Marouette Sauvignon Blanc Vin de Pays de l'Aude, Cuvee Olivier La Mancha Blanc (10L Box), Domaine de Petit Roubie Vin de Pays des Côtes de Thau, Joubio Blanc Domaine de Clairac Vin de Pays l'Herault, Marsanne Vin de Pays de l'Herault; *Jean Goulley (France):* Chablis, Petit Chablis; *Klaus Knobloch (Germany):* Bacchus Kabinett Rheinhessen, Ortega Spätlese Rheinhessen; *La Nature:* Chardonnay Vin de Pays d'Oc, Chardonnay/Sauvignon Blanc Australia, La Mancha Blanco Spain, Sauvignon Blanc Vin de Pays d'Oc, Torrontes Argentina; *Millton (New*

Zealand): Chardonnay Barrel Fermented Gisborne, Chardonnay Gisborne, Chenin Blanc Barrel Fermented Gisborne, Opou Reisling Gisborne, Viognier Tietjen Gisborne; *Paul Giboulot (France):* Bourgogne, Hautes Côtes de Nuits; *Perlage (Italy):* Chardonnay, Solatio Bianco; *Podere Canneta (Italy):* La Luna e Le Torri, Vernaccia di San Gimignano; *Richmond Plains (New Zealand):* Chardonnay Nelson, Sauvignon Blanc Nelson; *San Vito (Italy):* Bianco Colli dell'Etruria Centrale, Verdiglio, Vin Santo; *Ventura:* Chardonnay 2006, Sauvignon blanc 2006; *Volcanic Hills (Hungary):* Dry White Neszmély, Irsai Oliver Neszmély; *Weingut Stefan Sander:* Kerner Kabinett Lieblich, Riesling Kabinett Trocken, Riesling Spatlese Trocken; *Wilkie Estate (Australia):* Verdelho

VINTAGE ROOTS ◐✿

Organic blanc; *Albet i noya:* DO Penedes cabernet suavignoncol.leccio 2000/01, DO Penedes can vendrell petit albet chardonnay/xarel.lo 2006/07, DO Penedes can vendrell petit albet tempranillo/garnacha 2006/07, DO Penedes lignum blanc 2006/07, DO Penedes lignum negre 2003/05, DO Penedes reserva marti 1998, DO Penedes syrah col.leccio 2000, DO Penedes tempranillo classic 2006, DO Penedes xarel.lo classic 2006/07; *Andre:* AOC Chateauneuf-du-pape 2001/03; *Barra:* Pinot noir 2005/06; *Bettili:* IGT Veneto frizzante 2006/07, IGT Veneto pinot grigio 2006/07, IGT Veneto serenael vivace rosato 2006/07, Veneto

Frizzante 2006/2007; *Bioghetto:* de l'Herault RN13 Vin de Pique-nique Blanc 2006; *Bonterra:* Chardonnay 2005/06; *Bossard:* AOC Muscadet de servre et maine sur lie, AOC Muscadet de sevre et maine, VDP Du jardin de la France cabernet franc 2005/06; *Boudonno:* DOCG Chianti classico 2005/06, DOCG Chianti classico riserva 2003/06; *Bousquet:* Chardonnay 2006; *Brau:* d'Oc Blanc de Brau Chardonnay/Roussanne 2006/2007, d'Oc Chardonnay Finement Boise 2005/2006; *Brocard:* Chablis Jean-Marc Brocard 2005; *Cantine bricco:* IGT Sicilia inzolia bricco al sole 2006, IGT Sicilia nero d'avola bricco al sole 2005; *Casale mattia:* DOC Frascati superiore 2006/07; *Chapoutier:* VDP Des coteaux de l'ardeche domaine des granges de miribel viognier 2006; *Clos du caveau:* AOC Vacqueras 2004; *Clos du joncuas:* AOC Gigondas 2000; *CLVD:* d'Oc WWF Element Terre Chardonnay 2006; *Cossentino:* IGT Sicilia gadi catarratto 2006, IGT Sicilia nero d'avola 2005; *Couronneau:* Bordeaux Superieur 2006; *Dauny:* AOC Sancerre 2006/07; *Fabril alto verde:* Buenas ondas chardonnay 2006/07, Buenas ondas malbec 2006/07, Buenas ondas syrah rose 2006/07, Semental gran reservado 2005; *Fasoli gino:* DOC Soave borgoletto 2006/07, DOC Soave pieve vecchia 2004/05, DOC Valpolicella 2006/07, DOC Valpolicella amarone alteo 2001/03, DOC Valpolicella amarone la corte del pozzo 2004, DOC Valpolicella classico la corte del pozzo 2005/06, DOCG Recioto di soave san

zeno 2004/05, Grappa di chardonnay; *Ferraton:* AOC Hermitage blanc le miaux 2006, AOC Hermitage le miaux 2004; *Foraci:* IGT Sicilia sollatio rosso 2005/06; *Gaudry:* AOC Sancerre le tournebride 2006, AOC Sancerre melodie de vieilles vignes 2006; *Giol:* Prosecco Frizzante; *Goulley:* Chablis 2006/2007, Chablis Premier Cru Montmains 2002/2003, Petit Chablis 2005/2006; *Guillemot Michel:* Macon-Villages Quintaine 2005; *Guyot:* Puligny Montrachet 2006/2007; *Jasci:* DOC Montepulciano d'abruzzo barrique domino 2006, DOC Monttepulciano d'abruzzo 2006/07, DOC Trebbiano d'abruzzo 2006, IGT Atteso pecorino 2006; *Javillier:* Meursault Les Tillets 2005/2006, Meursault Poruzot Premier Cru 2005/2006; *Jeandeau:* Pouilly-Fuisse Les Progues 2004/2006; *Knobloch:* QMP Rheinhessen riesling 2006/07; *La fourmente:* AOC Cotes du rhone 2005/06; *Longchamp:* VDP des bouches du rhone 2004/06; *Maisons brulees:* AOC touraine sauvignon blanc 2006/07; *Mant'albano:* DOC Friuti grave pinot grigio 2006/07; *Moncaro:* d'Oc Verdicchio Dei Castelli Di Jesi 2006/07; *Mont'albano:* IGT Delle venezie pinot bianco/pinot grigio 2006/07; *OVA:* Five Plots Semillon; *Pajot:* Des Cotes de Gascogne 2006/2007; *Passavant:* AOC Anjou sec 2006; *Plouzeau:* AOC Chinon chateau de la bonneliere 2005, AOC Touraine sauvignon blanc chateau de la bonneliere 2006; *Pulmary:* Cuq 2004/06; *Richard:* Bergerac Sec 2006/2007, Bergerac Sec Les Charmes

Semillon/Sauvignon Blanc 2006/2007,
Saussignac Coup de Coeur 2004,
Saussignac Cuvee Noble 2003;
Richmond plains: Nelson sauvignon
blanc 2006/07; *Robinvale:* Cabernet
Sauvignon/Cabernet Franc/Merlot/Ruby
Cabernet 2005/2006,
Chardonnay/Chenin Blanc/Sauvignon
Blanc 2006/2007; *Sedlescombe:* Dry
White 2005/2006; *Sonop:* Organic
terroir chardonnay 2007, Organic
terroir shiraz 2007; *St Paul:* d'Oc
Sauvignon Sur Lie 2006; *St ursula:* QBA
St ursula ornament 2006; *Stellar:* Stellar
sauvignon blanc 2007; *Stentz:* Alsace
Gewurztraminer 2006, Alsace
Gewurztraminer Grand Cru Steingruber
2004, Alsace Pinot Blanc 2005; *Tulbagh
mountain:* Syrah/mourvedre 2003/04,
Theta 2003; *Vida buena:* Vida buena
red, Vida buena white; *Vintage Roots
Own-label:* Organic Blanco; *Zuccardi:*
Santa julia organia torrontas 2006/07,
Santa julia organica bonarda/sangiovese
2006, Santa julia organica chenin
blanc, Santa julia organica tempranillo
2006/07

VIVA! ☺❶⊘✔
All

NOTES

- **Beers:** As a general rule traditional,
cask-conditioned beers ('real ales')
are usually clarified (cleared) with
isinglass finings (see GLOSSARY OF
ANIMAL SUBSTANCES page 10).
The addition of the finings speeds
up a process that would otherwise
occur naturally. Keg, canned, beers
and some bottled beers are usually
filtered without the use of animal
substances. Lagers are generally
chill-filtered but some may involve
the use of isinglass. Keg beers may
contain the foam-control agent
Glyceryl Monostearate (E471), which
can be animal-derived; alternatives
are available and are widely used.

- **Fruits** used for producing fruit
juices are not normally coated with
shellac. However some fruits
coated with shellac and originally
destined for sale as whole fruit may
be used to produce juices (see
FOOD NOTES, page 135).

- **Soft drinks and alcopops** may
contain animal-derived colourings
such as cochineal / carmine (see
GLOSSARY OF ANIMAL SUBSTANCES
page 10). Orange coloured drinks
may contain beta-carotene held in a
gelatine suspension. For example,
some Coca-Cola products use gelatine
as a stabiliser for beta-carotene;
these ARE Lilt, Lilt Zero, Kia-Ora
Orange, Powerade Orange, Schweppes
Deuce and Relentless Inferno.

An up to date list can be found at
www.coca-cola.co.uk/faq or
telephone 0800 22 77 11. Also see
FOOD NOTES, page 135.

- **The production of spirits** does not
  usually involve the use of animal
  substances; however, some red
  drinks may contain cochineal /
  carmine as a colouring agent.

- **Wines** may be fined using one of
  the following: blood, bone marrow,
  chitin, egg albumen, fish oil,
  gelatine, isinglass, milk or milk
  casein (see GLOSSARY OF ANIMAL
  SUBSTANCES page 10). Non-animal
  alternatives include limestone,
  bentonite, kaolin and kieselguhr
  (clays), plant casein, silica gel, and
  vegetable plaques.

- Co-op labels those wines that are
  suitable for vegans and declares all
  processing aids used in their
  manufacture. Sainsbury's also label
  some of their wines as vegan.
  Increasing numbers of online wine
  sellers have vegan wine categories
  or allow buyers to search for vegan
  wines.

ACT NOW

A sow lies thrashing and screaming on the killing room floor, in agony from the electric shock that is meant to stun her humanely, but doesn't.

A ewe is stunned while her terrified lamb suckles her. As her unconscious body is dragged to the killing rig, the poor lamb follows.

Our investigator filmed this cruelty secretly. He videoed terror-stricken animals trying to escape the slaughter they were seeing – some so desperate they even tried to climb the walls to get away.

British law demands that animals be humanely killed – what we saw showed that slaughterhouses routinely ignore the law and brutalise animals.

And they get away with it, because there is no effective monitoring system.

We need CCTV in every abattoir to prevent this terror. The RSPCA and even the government's own Food Standards Agency (FSA) support our demand, but there is much work needed to make the FSA's verbal commitment a reality.

Please will you help?
Send a donation to help our battle to make life and death less cruel for farmed animals.

Yes! I want action! Here is my donation to help your work to stamp out brutality to animals. I enclose a cheque payable to Animal Aid for:

£5 ☐   £10 ☐   £15 ☐   £25 ☐   Other £_____

Mr/Mrs/Miss/Ms (delete as appropriate)

Name

Address

Postcode

Please return this with your donation to: **Animal Aid, The Old Chapel, Bradford St, Tonbridge, Kent TN9 1AW.**

To make your gift by credit card, or to learn more about this campaign, visit **www.stopthebrutality.com** or call **01732 364546.** *Thank you so much.*

Please send an information pack ☐

Data Protection: Please tick here if you do not want us to make your name available to chosen sympathetic organisations. ☐

Registered in the UK as Animal Abuse injustice and Defence Society. Company no. 1787309

TOILETRIES & COSMETICS

AFTERSHAVE

ANIMAL AID ™☺❶❷⊘✔⚡1976
Aftershave Lotion

AUBREY ORGANICS
Mens Stock: Northwoods Aftershave

BRONNLEY & CO LTD ✔
Eau do Toilette

DOLMA ™☺❶⊘✔👁⚡1976
Especially For Men: **Freedom,
Imagine, Kwame, Sirius**

ESSENTIALLY NATURAL ™
Sandalwood Aftershave (Organic)

FLORIS ☺✔
Elite; JF; No 89

**SOLARAY NUTRITIONAL
SUPPLEMENTS**
Northwoods

VERDESATIVA S.R.L. ™☺❶❷⊘✔☼👁
**Dopobarba Canapa (Aftershave
Hemp); Dopobarba Canapa e Menta
(Aftershave Hemp and Mint)**

BATH & SHOWER

ABSOLUTE AROMAS ™⊘✔
Ord River: **Bath & Shower Gel 250ml**

AGE VERT LYNX INDUSTRIES
Passion Fruit & Guava Bath Soak

AKAMUTI
Himalayan Salts; *Bath Salts:* Fragrant
Tranquility, Tropical Zest

ALTERNATIVE STORES ☺
All products are vegan

ALVIN CONNOR LIMITED ™☺⊘
Natural Balance: **Natural Bath Soak,
Unscented Bath Soak**

AMAZENE ™☺❶⊘✔☼
**Avocado & Andiroba Bath & Shower
Gel; Avocado & Andiroba Bath Soak;
Cocoa & Copaiba Bath & Shower Gel;
Cocoa & Copaiba Bath Soak; Coconut
& Buriti Bath & Shower Gel; Coconut
& Buriti Bath Soak; Mango &
Murumuru Bath & Shower Gel;
Mango & Murumuru Bath Soak;
Papaya & Acerola Bath & Shower
Gel; Papaya & Acerola Bath Soak;
Passion Fruit & Guava Bath & Shower
Gel; Passion Fruit & Guava Bath Soak;**
Amazon Bath & Body- Shower Gel:
**Esfoliante Buriti com Sementes de
Apricot;** *Natural Company- Bath Foam:*
**Ervas, Floral, Lavanda & Laranja,
Marine, Silvestre;** *Natural Company-
Bath Salts:* **Ervas, Floral, Lavanda &
Laranja, Marine;** *Natural Company-
Bath Salts:* **Silvestre;** *Phytophilo
Aromatherapy Range- Bath and shower
gels:* **Cocoa & Cupuacu, Green Tea,
Aloe Vera & Anise, Lavender,
Calendula & Primrose, Papaya,
Passion Fruit & Acerola, Strawberry
n Cream;** *Phytophilo Aromatherapy*

Range- Bath Salts: **Cocoa & Cupuacu, Green Tea, Aloe Vera & Anise, Lavender, Calendula & Primrose, Papaya, Passion Fruit & Acerola, Strawberry n Cream;** *Phytophilo Aromatherapy Range- Fizz Balls:* **Cocoa & Cupuacu, Green Tea, Aloe Vera & Anise, Lavender & Calendula, Papaya, Passion Fruit & Acerola, Strawberry n Cream;** *Phytophilo Aromatherapy Range- Gift Sets- 2 piece:* **Cocoa & Cupuacu, Green Tea, Aloe Vera & Anise, Strawberry n Cream;** *Phytophilo Aromatherapy Range- Gift Sets- 4 piece:* **Cocoa & Cupuacu, Green Tea, Aloe Vera & Anise;** *Phytophilo Aromatherapy Range- Gift Sets-2 piece:* **Lavender, Calendula & Primrose, Papaya, Passion Fruit & Acerola;** *Phytophilo Aromatherapy Range- Gift Sets-4 piece:* **Lavender, Calendula & Primrose, Papaya, Passion Fruit & Acerola, Strawberry n Cream**

ANIMAL AID ™☺❶⊘🐰🐾←1976
Violet & Almond Foaming Bath Oil; *Body Wash:* **Amber Body Wash, Woodspice Body Wash;** *Foam Bath:* **Calendula & Vanilla, Vanilla & Passion Flower Foam Bath;** *Shower Gel:* **English Rose, Tropical**

ANNEMARIE BORLIND 🐾
Bodyvital Body Crème Scrub; *Anne Lind:* Cranberry Body Scrub, Shower Gels (All); *Body Lind:* Shower Gel; *Body Lind Sportiv:* Shower Gel; *For Men:* Revitalizing Shower Gel

ARBONNE 👁
f.y.i: It Shines Lip Gloss, Wash & Wear Body Wash; *NutriMin C RE9:* REfresh Foaming Body Wash; *SeaSource Detox Spa:* Fortifying Hair Mask, Purifying Sea Soak

AROMA COMFORTS ™☺⊘
Anti Stress Body&Bath Oil

AROMATHERAPY PRODUCTS LTD ™☺
Accessories: **Spa bathing mitt, Spa bathing pad, Spa bathing strap;** *Bath and shower oil collection:* **Rebalance, Relax, Revive;** *Bath Care:* **Awaken Shower Gel, Indulge Bath Soak, Indulge Soap, Mind Unwind Bath Oil, Muscle Ease Bath Oil, Refresh Bath Soak, Refresh Soap, Rejuvenate Shower Gel, Relax Bath Soak, Relax Soap;** *Clear Breathe:* **Clear Breathe Bath Oil;** *Lavender Products:* **Lavender Bath Soak, Lavender Bath Soak, Lavender cream body wash;** *Wash, bath and shower:* **Essential oil Rich Awaken Shower and Bath Gel, Essential oil Rich Indulge Bath Soak, Essential oil Rich Rejuvenate Shower and Bath Gel, Essential oil Rich Relax Bath Soak, Tea tree and Grapefruit skin wash, Tea tree and Lime cream body wash**

AUSTRALIAN TEA TREE
Hand & Body Wash

BAREFOOT BOTANICALS ☺⊘✍
SOS : Bodyguard Soothing Body Wash, Lifesaver Moisturising Bath Oil

BEAMING BABY ™
Organic Lavender Shampoo and Body Wash

BEAUTY NATURALS ✍
Gently Exfoliating Seaweed Body Scrub; *Bath Oil:* Citrus Refreshing, Lavender Relaxing, Rose Geranium Harmonising, Seaweed Therapeutic; *Body Wash:* Citrus Refreshing, Lavender Relaxing, Rose Geranium Harmonising, Seaweed Therapeutic; *Martha Hill:* Citrus Refreshing Body Wash, Lavender Relaxing Bath Oil; *Martha Hill:* Lavender Relaxing Body Wash; *Martha Hill:* Rose Geranium Harmonising Body Wash

BELLECARE AG ™
Body and Hair Shampoo

BL COSMETICS
Silvan Fayre Bath Gel; White Musk Bath and Shower Gel; *Bath & Shower Foam:* Flower Power, Very Fruity; *Bath Cake:* Blueberry Pie, Heart of Fire, Satsuma Angel Cake, Star Crazy, Sweetness; *Bath Creamer:* Banana Colada, Bling, Candy Flowers, Devils, Pink Passion, Rose & Geranium, Rosehip, Satsuma, Sweet Violet, Vanilla & Coffee Bean; *Bath Fizzer:* Aromantics, Bath Bomb, Citrus Sensation, Cocobanana, Depth Charge, Floral Fizz, Freshly Squeezed, Glam Rocks, Great Balls of Fire, Green Mist, Lets Get Fizzy Cool, Mini Hearts, Nice & Spicy, Night Time, Smoothy, Stress Buster, Sweet Heart, Think Plink Fizz, Watermelon Fizzer, Wonder Ball; *Bath Melts:* Asleep, Chocolate, Lavender, Seventh Heaven; *Bath Salts:* Rosehip, Satsuma; *Bath Truffles:* Calendula, Chocolate, Coconut, Larkspur, Rose, Safflower; *Bubble Bath:* Heather & Patchouli, Rosehip, Satsuma; *Scrubs:* Orange, Pumice Soap Ball, Salt, Strawberry Body Polish, Sweet Feet; *Solid Bubble Bath:* Bubble Bath Confetti, Bubble Bath Crumble, Fantastic Flowery

Tub, Fruity Tub, Pineapple, Satsuma, Violet, Watermelon

BONANO GMBH ™⊘
Alviana Feuchtigkeit: **Duschgel;** *Alviana Rose:* **Duschgel;** *Alviana Sensitiv:* **Pflegedushe**

BRACKENCRAFT ™☺❶⊘⚘
Lemon & Lime Bath bombs; Peppermint and cinammon; Vanilla Bath Bombs; *Bath Bomb:* **Dried Blackcurrant Powder Bath Bombs, Festival Bath Bombs, Geranium and Orange Bath Bombs;** *Bath Bombs:* **Cinnamon and lemon, Cinnamon, patchouli, orange and lemon, Floral, Geranium and patchouli, Ginger and lime, Lavender, Lemon and lime, Lemongrass, Orange, Patchouli and orange, Rose, Vanilla;** *Fizzing Bath Melts:* **Floral, Lavender, Lemon and lime, Orange and grapefruit, Vanilla;** *Lip balms:* **Vanilla;** *moisturiser:* **Patchouli and orange, Vanilla**

BRONNLEY & CO LTD ⚘
Bath & Shower Gel: Africa, Asia, Caribbean, Europe, India, Mediterranean; *Bath Foam:* Apricot & Almond, English Fern, Lavender, Orchid, Pink Bouquet, White Iris; *Bath Gel:* Bird of Paradise, Tulip; *Bath Relaxant:* Passion Flower, Rose; *Body Care for Men:* Bath Relaxant, Hair & Body Wash; *Body Scrub:* Bird of Paradise, Tulip; *Royal Horticultural Society - Bath Relaxant:* Passion Flower, Rose; *Royal Horticultural Society - Bath Seeds:* Passion Flower,

Rose; *Royal Horticultural Society - Bath Soak:* Gardener's; *Royal Horticultural Society - Shower Gel:* Gardener's, Passion Flower, Rose; *Shower Gel:* Apricot & Almond, English Fern, Lavender, Orchid, Pink Bouquet, White Iris

BURT'S BEES ⊘⚘👁
All-In-One Wash; Therapeutic Bath Crystals; *Face & Body:* Vitamin E Body & Bath Oil

CAURNIE SOAPERIE ☺⊘⚘⚒1976
Marigold Shower Gel

CAWARRA COSMETICS LTD ™
OrganicSpa: **Body Salt Scrub**

CEBRA ETHICAL CHIC ™⊘⚘
Cebra- ethical skin care: **Calm Me Down Body Wash, Make Me Smile Body & Hair Wash, Me Time Bath Fizzies, Total Detox Bath Salt**

DESERT ESSENCE ⊘⚘⚒1985
Organics Body Wash: Italian Red Grape, Red Raspberry, Green Apple & Ginger

DIRK ROSSMANN GMBH ™
Alterra: **Duschcreme Granatapfel Aloe Vera, Duschgel Aprikose Zitronengras, Duschgel Blaubeere Vanille, Duschgel Pfirsich Litschi, Duschpeeling Cranberry Feige, Waschgel Wasserminze**

DOLMA ™☺❶⊘⚘👁⚒1976
Aromatic Body Shampoos: **Antiseptic, Deep Relaxing, Invigorating, Relaxing, Relaxing & Refreshing**

DR HAUSCHKA ⊘ ⓭
Bath: Lavender, Lemon, Rose, Rosemary, Sage, Spruce

DR ORGANIC
Aloe Vera: Body Wash; *Lavender:* Body Wash; *Pomegranate:* Body Wash; *Tea Tree:* Body Wash; *Vitamin E:* Body Wash

ECO COSMETICS GMBH & CO. KG ™⊘ ⓭ ✿
Shower Gel

EMPATHY SKINCARE LTD (NATURAL EMPATHY) ™☺ ⓭
Botanical Body Wash; *All in one:* **Hair And Body Wash For Men;** *Bathing beauty:* **Nourishing Bath Milk**

ESSENTIAL CARE
Bath Products: Aloe Vera Bodywash, Lavender Hand & Bodywash, Lemongrass Hand & Bodywash, Ylang Ylang & Orange Bodywash

ESSENTIALLY NATURAL ™
Bath Oils: **Calming, Reviving, Soothing**

ESSENTIALLY YOURS LTD
Fragrance Free Range: FF5 Fragrance Free Shampoo & Body Wash; *LYB Range:* LYB002 Grapefruit & Kiwi Shower Gel, LYB003 Eucalyptus & Juniper Bath Shower Gel, LYB004 Patchouli & Lavender Shower Gel, LYB010 Luxury Orange & Sandalwood Bath Oil, LYB011 Relaxing Orange & Lavender Bath Oil, LYB012 Sandalwood & Neroli Bath/Shower Gel, LYB105 Orange and Ginger Shower Gel, LYB108 Rose & Lavender Foam Bath;

Therapeutics Range: NE034 Therapeutic Bath Oil, NE037 Therapeutic Body Wash

FAITH PRODUCTS LIMITED ™⊘ ⓭ ☜ ⚘ 1988
Aloe Vera Shower Gel / Foam Bath 400ml / 5 Ltr; Chocolate Shower Gel / Foam Bath 400ml / 5 Ltr; Hemp and Meadowfoam Shower Gel / Foam Bath 400ml / 5 Ltr; Lavender and Geranium Shower Gel / Foam Bath 400ml / 5 Ltr; Mum's relaxing bath oil; Purifying Face and Body Scrub 150ml; Seaweed Shower Gel / Foam Bath 400ml / 5 Ltr; Tea Tree Shower Gel / Foam Bath 400ml / 5 Ltr

FLORI ☺ ⓭
Concentrated Bath Essence: Edwardian Bouquet, Florissa, Lily of the Valley, Rose Geranium, Seringa, Stephanotis; *Foaming Bath & Shower Gel:* Elite, JF, Santal; *Moisturising Bath & Shower Gel:* Cefiro, China Rose, Edwardian Bouquet, Fleur, Florissa, Lily of the Valley, Night Scented Jasmine, No 89, Rose Geranium, Seringa Moisturising, Stephanotis, White Rose; *Natural Benefits:* Energising Body Wash, Invigorating Body Polish

FOREVER LIVING PRODUCTS
Aloe Bath Gelee

FREERANGERS ™☺ ⓭
Arnica Bath Soak; Power Shower Gel; Stress-Less Bath Soak; *Free Spirit Organics:* **Bath melts**

FUNK BUBBLE ™☺

Bath&Body Melts: **Blueberry, Cherry, Chocolate/orange, Coconut, Rose;** *Bubble Bath:* **Lavender/Geranium, Tea Tree;** *Fizzers and Bath Bombs:* **Chocolate Bath Bomb, Coconut Bath Bomb, Lavender, Mango Bath Bomb, Orange/Grapefruit, Rose, Strawberry, Vanilla Bath Bomb, Vanilla Fizzer;** *Organic Bubble Bath:* **Aloe Vera, Chocolate;** *Organic Shower Wash:* **Aloe Vera, Chocolate;** *Shower Wash:* **Lavender/Geranium, Tea Tree**

GEO ORGANICS ⊘
Atlantic Bath Salt with Aloe Vera 250g

GREEN PEOPLE CO. ™⊘✓
Shower wash: **C003 Aloe Vera Shower Gel, C016 Vitamin Shower Wash, C045 Exfoliating Shower Wash, F014 Kids Bath & Shower Lavender, F019 Kids Bath & Shower Citrus & Aloe Vera, H006 Organic Base Shower Bath, M005 Cool Style - Hair & Body Wash, M006 Vitamin Boost - Hair & Body Wash, R011 Exfoliating Spa Shower Wash**

GREEN WYCH LTD ™☺❶⊘✓
Bath Fizzer: **Therapeutic Bath Fizzers - Bergamot, Therapeutic Bath Fizzers - Geranium, Therapeutic Bath Fizzers - Lavender, Therapeutic Bath Fizzers - Lemongrass, Therapeutic Bath Fizzers - Sweet orange;** *Natural Bath Salts:* **Bergamot, Geranium, Lavender, Orange**

HEALTHQUEST LIMITED ™⊘✓
Organic Blue: **Body Scrub;** *Organic*

Blue- Body Care: **Shower Gel;** *Organic Blues - Mens:* **Bath Soak, Hair & Body Wash, Shower Scrub;** *Pure Adore:* **Chamomile Bubblebath, Lavender Bubblebath, Mandarin Bubblebath**

HEDGECRAFT ™☺⊘
Bath Bomb Range: **Groovy Grapefruit, Muscle Ease, Orange and Patchouli, Simply Lavender, Simply Rose, White Chocolate, Ylang Ylang and Orange**

HEMP GARDEN ™
Hand & Body Wash; *Bath Oil:* **Sensual, Soothing, Stimulating**

HERBS HANDS HEALING LTD ™⊘✓
Organic Bitter Orange Body Oil; Organic Lavender and Mint Bodywash

HIGHER NATURE LTD
Alka-Bathe (Powder); Special Sea Soak

HIPPY HEAVEN
NATURAL BEAUTY ™☺⊘✓
Mens energy face and body wash

HOLISTIX HERBAL PRODUCTS ❶
Bath Salts - 580g Kilner Jar: All

HONESTY COSMETICS LTD ™☺❶⊘✓⚘↝1976
Foam Bath: **Orange Geranium & Lavender;** *Honesty Essential Range:* **Mandarine, Ginger & Ylang Ylang Shower Gel, Orange, Geranium & Lavender Foam Bath, Rose Shower & Bath Gel;** *Honesty Fruit Range:* **Apple & Mint Shower & Bath Gel,**

Green Tea & Citrus Shower & Bath Gel, Strawberry & Papaya Shower & Bath Gel; *Shower Gel:* Apple & Mint, Mandarine Ginger & Ylang Ylang, Strawberry & Papaya

I AM NATURAL ™❶⊘✔☼
Shower Gel: **Organic Lavender & Chamomile, Organic Mint & Rosemary, Organic Tea Tree & Ginger**

INNGINNI LIMITED (OHSOBO) ™☺
Ohsobo: **Shower Gel - Citrus Medley, Shower Gel - Orange Tree, Shower Gel - Rose & Lavender Burst, Shower Gel - Skin Bliss, Shower Gel - Tropical Sunset**

ITS ELIXIR (UK) LIMITED ™⊘✔👁
Body scrubbing gel; Bright Shower Gel; Cold Ease Bath Foam; Ginger and Lime Shower Gel; Head Clear Bath Foam; Head Clear Bath Oil; Head Clear Shower Gel; Relaxing Bath Foam; Sensuous Bath Foam; Sensuous Bath Oil; Skin Nourishing Bath Oil

JASON NATURAL PRODUCTS
Satin Shower Body Wash: Aloe Vera, Apricot, Chamomile, Citrus, Herbal Extracts, Lavender, Mango, Rosewater, Tea Tree

JR LIGGETT ☺
Body Scrub: Lemon & Lime, Unscented, Western Slope, White Sage

JUST SOAPS ™
Lavender Bath Salts; Lavender &

Rose Bath Salts; Patchouli Bath Salts

KISS MY FACE
Organic Foaming Soap: C-Weed; *Organic Shower Gel:* C-Weed, In the Pink, Rough Seas, Sports Complex; *Shower and Bath Gel:* Active Athletic, Anti Stress, Cold & Flu, Early to Bed, Early to Rise, Peaceful Patchouli, Rough Thyme, Silky Soft

LAVERANA GMBH & CO. KG ™✔
Lavera Body Spa: **Body Lotion Apricot-Almond Blossom, Body Scrub Orange-Sea Buckthorn, Body Wash Exfoliating Vervain-Lime, Shower & Bath Cream Orange-Sea Buckthorn, Shower & Bath Cream Wild Rose, Shower & Bath Gel (Citrus), Shower & Bath Gel (Lavender/AloeVera), Shower & Bath Gel (Orange/Sea Buckthorn), Shower & Bath Gel (Vanilla/Coconut), Shower & Bath Gel (Vervain/Lemon), Shower & Bath Gel (Wild Rose), Shower & Bath Gel Apricot-Almond Blossom;** *Lavera Body Spa Bath Oil:* **Exclusive pampering wild rose, Fruity revival Orange-Sea Buckthorn, Refreshment Vervain-Lime, Relaxation Lavender-Aloe Vera, Warmth Vanilla-Coconut;** *Lavera Body Spa Sea Bath Salts:* **Exclusive pampering Wild Rose, Fruity revival Orange-Sea Buckthorn, Refreshment Vervain-Lime, Relaxation Lavender-Aloe Vera, Warmth Vanilla-Coconut;** *Men SPA:* **Shower Shampoo, Shower Shampoo - Aqua Fresh, Shower Shampoo - Cool Lime, Shower Shampoo - Relaxing Santal**

LIZ EARLE ⓥ
Deep Cleansing Mask Sponges; Energising Body Wash; Orange Flower Botanical Body Wash; Vital Oils for the Bath

LUSH ™⊘ ⓥ
Satsumo Santa; *Bath Ballistics:* **Absolute Delight, Avobath, Big Blue, Blackberry Bath Bomb, Bon Bain Bonnard, Bon Bomb, Butterball, Butterfly Ball, Christmas Party, Cinders, Fairy Jasmine, Fizzy O'Therapy, Fox in the Flowers, Geophyzz, Gingerman, Haagenbath, Harvey Bath Ballistic, Hippy Chick Bath Ballistic, Honey Bun Bath Ballistic, Hot Java, Ickle Baby Angel, Ickle Baby Baff, Ickle Baby Bot Bath Ballistic, Ickle Baby Devil, Jacko, Jingle Spells, Keep it Fluffy – Orange Bath Ballistic, Keep it Fluffy – Purple Bath Ballistic, Kiss Me Klimt, Lemon Days and Ginger Beer, Luverly, Mr Butter Ball, Ne Worry Pas Bath Ballistic, Rainbow Worrier, Sakura, Sex Bomb, Sicilian, So White, Softy, Space Girl Bath Ballistic, Supernova, The Happy Pill, Think Pink Bath Ballistic, Tisty Tosty, Uluru, Vanilla Fountain, Waving Not Drowning, World Piece;** *Bath Melts:* **Happy Blooming Bath Melt, Karma Bath Melt, Something Wicked This Way Comes, Star, Want to Believe;** *Body Scrubs:* **Sugar scrub;** *Bubble Bar Slices:* **A French Kiss, Amandapondo, Auntie Pamela, Aura Suavis, Bathos, Blue Skies and Fluffy White Clouds, Elixir, Flosty Gritter, Ice Hotel, It's a Date, Ma Bar, Marzibain, Melomint, Playdoze, Pleasure Dough, Pop In The Bath Bubble Bars, Psychodelic,** **Something Wicked This Way Comes, Sunnyside, The Comforter, The Phoenix, Two Timing Tart;** *Bubble Bars:* **Candy Cane, Christmas Eve, Creamy Candy Bath Bubble Bars, Dorothy Bubble Bar, Fabulous Mrs Fox, Happy Bubble Bar, No Name, Ruby slippers, Temple Of Truth, The Phoenix, The Wuss, Turbo Bubble;** *Emotibombs:* **Double fast luck, Sex in the Shower, Too Drunk, Up The Wooden Hill, Up You Gets;** *Karma Products Bubble Bars:* **Karma Bubble Bar;** *Luxury Bath Melts:* **Ceridwen's Cauldron, Dreamtime, Floating Island, Melting Marshmallow Moment, You've Been Mangoed Bath Melt;** *Sauna:* **A Token To The Forest Gods Sauna Tabs;** *Shower:* **13 Rabbits, Brimstone Shower Cubicle, Chai, Freeze, Glorious Mud Shower Cubicle, Grass Shower Gel, Narcotick;** *Shower Gels:* **Ghost, Glogg Shower Gel, Happy 4 Sad Shower Gel, Happy Hippy, Rub Rub Rub Shower Gel, Smaragadine, Snow fairy, Sonic Death Monkey, The Olive Branch, Tramp;** *Shower Jellies:* **Deep Sleep, Party On, Snow showers, Strawberry Santa, Sweetie Pie, The Joy Of Jelly;** *Shower Soap:* **Turkish Delight;** *Smoothie Shower Soaps:* **Creamed Almond and Coconut Smoothie, Dreamwash, Lush Lime Smoothie;** *Valentines:* **Love Soap, XFactor Bath Ballistic;** *Valentines Bubble Bars:* **Magic Mushroom Bubble Bar**

MAJIK BLANKIT SKIN CARE™☺ ⓥ
Comfrey Root Shower Jelly; Lavender and roman chamomile sensitive shower jelly

TOILETRIES & COSMETICS

MISSHU LTD T/A LANI-JO ™☺❶✔
Essential: **Bath Fizzer, Body Gel, Body Scrub, Body Wash;** *Healing:* **Bath Fizzer, Bath Gel, Body Scrub, Body Wash;** *Heaven:* **Bath Fizzer, Bath Gel, Bath Lotion, Body Scrub, Body Wash;** *Sensual:* **Bath Fizzer, Bath Gel, Body Scrub, Body wash**

MONTAGNE JEUNESSE ⊘✔
Eucalyptus & Camphor Anti Cold Bath; *Bath:* Dead Sea Aches-Away

MY SKINCARE LTD ™☺⊘✔
Bath Oils: **Anti-Cellulite Bath Oil, Deeply Relaxing Bath Oil, Pre Labour Bath Oil, Stress Buster Bath Oil;** *Bath Wash & Shampoo:* **Sleepeeze Bath Wash & Shampoo**

NATURA ORGANICS ⊘✔✿
Shower Gel: Nourishing with Aloe Vera, Vitamin E and Soft Almond Oil, Revitalising with Vitamin E, Lemon and Mandarin

NATURAL BY NATURE OILS ☺
Organic Blend Bath Oils: Jasmine, Lavender, Meditation, Rose, Seduction, Tranquility

NATURAL SENSE
Himalayan Bath Salts; Luxury Bath Oil

NATURE'S GATE
Organics - Advanced Care: Natural Results Acne Body Wash; *Organics - Fruit Blend Body Washes:* Grapefruit & Wild Ginger, Mandarin Orange & Patchouli, Persimmon & Rose Geranium; *Organics - Fruit Blend Liquid Soaps:* Asian Pear & Red Tea; *Organics - Herbal Blend Body Washes:* Chamomile & Lemon Verbena, Cucumber & Mint, Lavender & Aloe, Lemongrass & Clary Sage

NEAL'S YARD REMEDIES ⊘✔👁✂1998
Aromatic Foaming Bath; Baseline Bath & Shower Gel; Baseline Bath Oil; English Lavender Foaming Bath Oil; Exotic Bath Oil; Frankincense & Mandarin Shower Cream; Geranium & Orange Bath Oil; Geranium & Orange Shower Gel; Lavender & Tea Tree Shower Gel; Lavender (Nourishing) Shampoo; Lavender Bath Salts; Mothers Bath Oil; NYR Men Invigorating Body Wash; Rose & Geranium Shower Gel; Rose & Pomegranate Bath Oil; Silver Birch Bath Oil; Soothing Bath Oil

NEW SEASONS
Hair & Body Wash; *Neutral & Toiletry Bases:* Foam Bath Base, Shower Gel Base

NOTHING NASTY ✔
Bath Salts: Lavender & Calendula, Rose & Calendula

OPTIMAH ⊘✔✂1995
Raw Aloe: Shower Gel with Tea Tree & Citrus Oils

POTIONS AND POSSIBILITIES ⊘ ✿

Bath & Shower Gels: ...And To Sleep, Anti-fatigue, Detox, Divinity, English Garden, English Lavender, English Rose, Relax & Unwind, Serenity Perfume, Sleepy Prince, Sleepy Princess, Traditional Lavender; *Bath Sizzlers & Bath Salts:* Bath Salt Pouch Lavender, Bath Salt Pouch Rose, Bath Salts Cook, Bath Salts Gardener, Bath Salts Golfer, Champagne Message Bombs, English Garden Bath Salts Pouch, English Lavender Bath Salts Pouch, English Rose Bath Salts Pouch, Heart Shaped Sizzler In Net, Luxury Bath Sizzler Cracker (Energizing), Luxury Bath Sizzler Cracker (Relaxing), Therapeutic Bath Salts, Therapeutic Bath Salts Joint & Muscle, Therapeutic Bath Salts Stress Ease, Tudor Sleep Parcels; *Clinical Bath Oils:* All; *Luxury Bath Oils:* All

PURATY LTD ☺ ✿

Balancing Shower Wash; Refreshing Shower Wash

PURE GAISHA ™☺❶ ✿

Fragrant Shower Gel; Kindred Spirit Bath Soak; Tranquility Bath Soak

PZ CUSSONS UK LTD ™⊘ ✿

Original Source Skin Food Shower: **Watermint & Lemongrass;** *Original Source Bath:* **Vanilla Bean & Cocoa Bath Milk, White Tea & Grapefruit Bath Tea;** *Original Source Bath Foam:* **Basil & Lemongrass, Mandarin & Sandalwood, Rose & Geranium, Tea Tree & Lavender, Ylang Ylang & Patchouli;** *Original Source Core Shower:* **Dragon Fruit and Capsicum,** **Lavender & Tea Tree, Lemon & Tea Tree, Mint & Tea Tree, Pure Lime;** *Original Source Deep Soak Foam Bath:* **Fir and Juniper, Rose and Aloe, Ylang and Neroli;** *Original Source Men's Shower:* **Eucalyptus & Lime Basil, Norwegian Sea Kelp & Rock Salt body wash, Orange & Ginger;** *Original Source Scrubs:* **Bitter Orange & Crushed Sweet Almond Body Scrub, Detoxifying, Moisturising, Regenerating;** *Original Source Shower:* **Rose & Geranium, Spearmint & Lavender, Ylang and Neroli;** *Original Source Shower Gel:* **Australian Wildberry, Blackpepper & Cardamom, Cassis & Cranberry, Chocolate & Mint, Lime & Sweet Chilli, White Pear & Avocado, XXX Mint;** *Original Source Shower Season Editions:* **Black Pepper & Cardamom, Cocoa & Vanilla, Goji Berry & Mallow, Grapefruit & Gingerlily;** *Original Source Skin Food Bath:* **Almond and Coconut Bath, Mango & Macadamia;** *Original Source Skin Food Shower:* **Pomegranate & Fig**

QUINESSENCE AROMATHERAPY ☺⊘ ✿ ◉

Bath Base; Relaxing Bath Soak; Shower Gel Base

REN ⊘

High Altitude Lavender Body Wash; Moroccan Rose Otto Bath Oil; Moroccan Rose Otto Body Wash; Multi Vitamin Apricot Shower Wash; Neroli and Grapefruit Body Wash; Rhassoul and Moroccan Rose Thalassotherapy Bath Soak; Seaweed and Sage Body Wash

RJ MINERAL COSMETICS INTERNATIONAL PTY LTD ™ 🐰

Body: **BSG Body Bath & Shower Gel - Firestarter, BSG Body Bath & Shower Gel - Floral Moods, BSG Body Bath & Shower Gel - Icy Blast, BSG Body Bath & Shower Gel - Knight Moods, BSG Body Bath & Shower Gel - Moonlight, BSG Body Bath & Shower Gel - Sunshine, BSG Body Bath & Shower Gel - Twilight, BSG Body Bath & Shower Gel - VanillaSyn**

SAAF INTERNATIONAL LIMITED ™
Pure Shower Gel

SAHFEE HALAL CARE ™☺⊘🐰

Halal products - Shower Gels: **Ladies' shower gel - Damen douchegel;**
Halal products - Shower Gels: **Gents' shower gel - Heren douchegel**

SENSORY REVOLUTION, LLC ™☺⊘🐰

Bath Salts: **Sensational Salts- various fragrances**

SHANTI PRODUCTS ⊘🐰

Bath Bombs: Bath Truffles, Mini Fizzers, Relaxing, Uplifting

SIMPLE 🐰

Moisturise Bath Cream; Refreshing Shower Gel; Relax Bath Soak; Soothe Bath Milk; Soothe Shower Cream; *Body Polish:* Energise; *Body Wash:* Exfoliate, Moisturise, Nourishing, Relax

SIMPLY SOAPS

Bath Oils: Invigorating & Detoxifying, Love, Relax; *Bath Salts:* Citrus, Love,

Relax, Woodland Calm; *Gift Sets:* Citrus, Decadence, Relax, Woodland; *Hedgerow Herbals:* Aaag Bath Bag, Grrr Bath Bag, Mmm Bath Bag, Oooo Bath Bag, Oww Bath Bag, Scrumptious Bath Bar Treats, Zzzzz Bath Bag; *Hedgerow Herbals-Queen of Sheba:* Bath Herb Tea Bags; *Salt Scrub:* Aphrodisia, Exfoliating, Invigorating, Stimulating

SKIN BLOSSOM LIMITED ™☺⊘🐰✿

Body Wash: **Body Wash**

SOLARAY NUTRITIONAL SUPPLEMENTS
Rosa Mosquesta Bath & Shower Gel

STELLA MCCARTNEY
Stella: Soft Bath Oil; *Stella in Two:* Exfoliating Shower Gel

SUPERDRUG
Naturals: Mango & Papaya Bath Essence, Olive & Bergamont Shower Cream

THE HIGHLAND SOAP COMPANY ⊘
Bath Bombes: Citrus Delight, Highland Lavender, Mango Butter, Rose & Patchouli, Rose & Ylang Ylang, Scottish Heather, White Jasmine; *Bath Salts:* Highland Lavender, Rose&Patchouli, Rose & Ylang Ylang, Scottish Heather, White Jasmine; *Body Wash:* Ginger & Lemongrass, Rosemary & Wild Nettle, Wild Nettle & Heather; *Bubble Bath:* Highland Lavender, Mango Butter, Rose & Patchouli, Rose & Ylang Ylang, Scottish Heather, White Jasmine; *Dead Sea Salt Scrubs:* Ginger & Lemongrass, Rosemary & Wild Nettle, Ylang & Ylang Patchouli

TREACLE MOON ☺
Lovely Mind Story: Bath and Shower Gel; *My Coconut Island:* Bath and Shower Gel, Body Scrub; *That Vanilla Moment:* Bath and Shower Gel, Body Scrub; *The Ginger Morning:* Bath and Shower Gel, Body Scrub; *The Raspberry Kiss:* Bath and Shower Gel, Body Scrub; *Those Lemonade Days:* Bath and Shower Gel, Body Scrub

TRUTHFUL CO. LTD (PURELY SKINCARE) ™☺⊘
Purely Skincare: **Shower/bath wash- female variant, Shower/bath wash- male variant, Shower/bath wash- refreshing variant, Shower/bath wash- sensitive variant**

URTEKRAM
Shower Gel: All

VERDESATIVA S.R.L. ™☺❶⊘✓✿👁
Bagno Doccia Canapa e Agrumi (Bath and Shower Gel Hemp and Citrus Fruit); Bagno Doccia Canapa e Lavanda (Bath and Shower Gel Hemp and Lavender); Bagno Doccia Canapa, Vetiver e Arancia (Bath and Shower Gel Hemp, Vetiver and Orange); Shampoo Doccia Canapa e Ylang Ylang (Shampoo and Bath/Shower Gel Hemp and Ylang Ylang); Shampoo Doccia Frutti e Fiori (Shampoo & Bath/Shower Gel Hemp Fruits and Flowers)

VISIONARY SOAP COMPANY ™☺
Bath Melts: **Geranium Rose, Lavender, Lemongrass, Patchouli and Ylang Ylang, Peppermint**

Orange; *Bath Salts:* **Lemon Lavender, Orange Geranium, Recuperate, Rejuvenate, Relax, Romance;** *Body Oils:* **Lemon Lavender**

WELEDA ⊘✓🐾1985
Chestnut Toning Bath Soak; Citrus Creamy Body Wash; Citrus Refreshing Bath Milk; Lavender Creamy Body Wash; Lavender Relaxing Bath Milk; Pine Reviving Bath Milk; Rosemary Invigorating Bath Milk; Sea Buckthorn Creamy Body Wash; Wild Rose Creamy Body Wash

BRUSHES ETC

ABSOLUTELY PURE
Vegan Kabuki Brushes

ALEXAMI COSMETICS ™✓
Bamboo handle vegan kabuki brush

AROMATHERAPY PRODUCTS LTD ™☺
Accessories: **Sisal back brush, Sisal body brush, Sisal foot brush**

BEAUTY NATURALS ✓
Complexion Massage Brush; *Cosmetic Brushes:* All

ESSENTIALLY NATURAL ™
Cotton Exfoliating Face Cloths

HOLISTIX HERBAL PRODUCTS ❶
Body Brush / Massager; Facial Loofah; Pumice; Terry / Loofah Palm Pad; Wooden Massager; *Gift bags:* Jute Display Bag

INIKA TM ✎
Eyeshadow Brush; Kabuki Brush

QUALITY SEA VEG ☺
Sea Bath and Skin pads

URBAN DECAY
Make-Up Brushes: Big Buddha Brush, Big Buddha Brush Set, Blender Brush, Blush Brush, Brow Brush, Crease Brush, Liner Brush, Little Buddha Brush Set, Powder Brush, Shadow Brush, Wonder Brush

CONDITIONERS & HAIR CARE

ABSOLUTE AROMAS TM ⊘ ✎
Ord River: **Conditioner 250ml**

AKAMUTI
Hair Care Products: All

ALOE PURA ✎
Organic Aloe Vera Herbal Shampoo Dry/Damaged Hair

ALTERNATIVE STORES ☺
All products are vegan

ANIMAL AID TM☺⊘⊘✎ ✂ 1976
Coconut Conditioner

ANNEMARIE BORLIND ✎
Ceramide Cream Rinse; Vital Hair Care Fluid

ARBONNE 👁
Intelligence: Daily Self-Adjusting Conditioner, Thermal Fusion & Scalp Revitalizer

AROMATHERAPY PRODUCTS LTD TM☺
Tea tree, Lemon and Rosemary conditioner; *Accessories:* **Spa cosmetic band;** *Head and hair care:* **Essential oil rich 3 in 1 Shampoo;** *Lavender Products:* **Lavender and Mint conditioning shampoo;** *Tea Tree Products:* **Tea Tree Lemon & Rosemary Conditioner, Tea tree, Lemon and Eucalyptus headlice repellent, Tea Tree, Lemon and Rosemary Balancing Conditioner, Tea tree, Lemon and Rosemary shampoo**

AUBREY ORGANICS
Camomile Luxurious: Conditioner; *Green Tea:* Finishing Cream Rinse; *Honeysuckle Rose:* Moisturising Conditioner; *Jojoba and Aloe Desert Herb:* Revitilising Conditioner; *Mens Stock:* Ginseng Biotin Hair Repair; *Rosa Mosqueta Rose Hip:* Conditioner; *Swimmers:* Conditioner

AUSTRALIAN TEA TREE
Conditioner

AVEDA
Be Curly: Conditioner; *Brilliant:* Conditioner; *Color Conserve:* Conditioner, Strengthening Treatment; *Damage Remedy:* Intensive Restructuring Treatment, Restructuring Conditioner; *Dry Remedy:* Conditioner, Treatment Masque; *Smooth Infusion:* Conditioner

BAREFOOT BOTANICALS ☺⊘✦
SOS: Intensive Care Dry Scalp
Conditioner

BEAUTY NATURALS ✦
Conditioner: Deep Moisturising; *Martha Hill:* Conditioning Hair Gel; *Martha Hill Purely Natural Haircare Conditioner:* Mild & Gentle, Moisturising, Reconstructive, Treatment

CAWARRA COSMETICS LTD ™
OrganicSpa: **Conditioner For Dry Hair, Conditioner For Normal Hair, Conditioner For Treated Hair;** *Sanctum:* **Conditioner - Dry, Conditioner - Normal**

CEBRA ETHICAL CHIC ™⊘✦
Cebra- ethical skin care: **Make Me Shine Conditioner**

DESERT ESSENCE ⊘✦⚓1985
Organics: Green Apple & Ginger, Italian Red Grape, Lemon Tea Tree, Red Raspberry

DOLMA ™☺❶⊘✦👁⚓1976
Hair Preparations: **Cedarwood & Cypress Hair Conditioner, Lavender & Jojoba Hair Conditioner, Rosemary Nettle & Marigold Hair Lotion**

DOME ☺
Extensions: Monofibre Hair Extensions: Free from glues, chemicals and acetones, Prolin Hair Enhancers

DR HAUSCHKA ⊘✦
Neem Hair Lotion; Neem Hair Oil

ECO COSMETICS GMBH & CO. KG ™⊘✦✿
Conditioner

EMPATHY SKINCARE LTD (NATURAL EMPATHY) ™☺✦
Natural Zing Shampoo; Pure Luxury Conditioner

ESSENTIAL CARE
Skincare: Hair Lice Therapy Oil

ESSENTIALLY YOURS LTD
Fragrance Free Range: FF6 Fragrance Free Conditioner; *Wish Range:* W11 Aloe Vera & Lime Conditioner, W5 Jojoba & Ylang Ylang Conditioner, W8 Rosewood & Bergamot Conditioner, W9 Lemongrass & Ginger Conditioner

FAITH PRODUCTS LIMITED ™⊘✦👁⚓1988
Aloe Vera 400ml / 5 Ltr; Chocolate conditioner; Gingko Biloba 400ml / 5 Ltr; Hemp and Meadowfoam; Jojoba 400ml / 5 Ltr; Lavender and Geranium 400ml / 5 Ltr; Rosemary 400ml / 5 Ltr; Seaweed 400ml / 5 Ltr; Tea Tree 400ml / 5 Ltr

FOREVER LIVING PRODUCTS
Aloe Jojoba Conditioner

FUNK BUBBLE ™☺
Conditioner: **Jojoba, Lavender/Geranium, Tea Tree;** *Organic Conditioner:* **Aloe Vera, Chocolate**

GREEN PEOPLE CO. ™⊘✦
Conditioner: **C002 Aloe Vera Conditioner, C005 Rosemary**

Conditioner, C015 Vitamin Conditioner, C031 Intensive Repair Conditioner, C039 Moisturising Conditioner, F017 Kids Conditioner Lavender, H005 Organic Base Conditioner, R023 Nourishing Spa Conditioner

HEALTHPOL ⊘ ✔
Herbacet Herbal Hair Balsam

HEALTHQUEST LIMITED ™⊘✔
Organic Blue- Body Care: **Conditioner**

HEMP GARDEN ™
Conditioner: **For all hair types**

HERBSGO LIMITED T/A CLIVE FOOT ☺
Clive Foot: Sunflower and Tea Tree Conditioner

HONESTY COSMETICS LTD ™☺❶⊘ ✔ ☻⅄ 1976
Conditioner: **Coconut & Avocado, Jojoba & Peach;** *Honesty Essential Range:* **Nettle, Lavender and Olive Conditioner;** *Honesty Fruit Range:* **Coconut & Avocado Conditioner, Jojoba & Peach Conditioner**

I AM NATURAL ™❶⊘ ✔ ✿
Organic Lavender & Geranium Hair Conditioner; Organic Lime & Rosemary Hair Conditioner; Organic Tea Tree & Neem Conditioner

INNGINNI LIMITED (OHSOBO) ™☺
Ohsobo: **Anti-Dandruff Conditioner, Conditioner - Original Formula**

ITS ELIXIR (UK) LIMITED ™⊘✔👁
Hair treatment oil dandruff; Hair treatment thinning; Normal Hair Cream

JASON NATURAL PRODUCTS
84% Pure Aloe Vera Conditioner, Damage Control Creme Conditioner, Hemp Super Moisturizing Conditioner, Henna Hi-lights Conditioner, Incredible Thin-to-Thick™ Revitalizing Scalp Elixir, Lavender Conditioner – 70% Organic, Natural Apricot Conditioner, Natural Biotin Conditioner, Natural Sea Kelp Conditioner, Pro-Vitamin Thin-to-Thick™ Conditioner, Rosewater Conditioner – 70% Organic, Scalp Balancing Natural Jojoba Conditioner, Swimmers & Sports™ Revitalizing Conditioner, Tall Grass™ High-Protein Conditioner, Tea Tree Scalp Normalizing Conditioner, Vitamin E with A & C Conditioner; *All Natural Color Enhancing Temporary Shampoos:* Color Sealant Conditioner; *Natural Salon Hair Care:* Kiwi & Apricot Root Boot, Kiwi & Apricot Volumizing Conditioners, Mint & Rose Intense Moisture Treatment, Plumeria & Sea Kelp Moisturizing Conditioners, Plumeria & Sea Kelp Moisturizing Leave-In Conditioning Spray, Rosewater & Chamomile Normalizing Conditioners

KEY SUN LABORATORIES PTY LTD™⊘
Key Sun: **Conditioner**

KISS MY FACE
Big Body; Miss Treated; Whenever; *Organic Hair Care:* Whenever

LAVERANA GMBH & CO. KG ™ ◊
Lavera HAIR: **Mango Milk Care Conditioner, Mango Milk Care Treatment, Rose Milk Repair Conditioner**

LIVE NATIVE ™ ☺
Deep Hair Repair

LUSH ™ ◊ ◊
Hair Moisturisers: **Dr Peppermint, Irresistible Bliss, Jasmin and Henna Fluff-Eaze, Marilyn, R&B Hair Moisturiser, Reincarnate, The Strokes;** *Liquid Conditioner:* **Veganese;** *Solid Conditioners:* **Jungle**

MONTAGNE JEUNESSE ◊ ◊
Miracle Hair: Frizz Pink Grapefruit, Lime Oil Reconstructer, Seville Orange Emergency Repair

MORROCCO METHOD
Euro Organic Oil Hair & Scalp Conditioning Therapy; Zen Detox Hair & Scalp Therapy; *Instant Hair Conditioner:* Chi, Diamond Crystal Mist

NATURA ORGANICS ◊ ◊ ✿
Nourishing with Shea Butter, Vitamin E and Orange

NATURE'S GATE
Aloe Vera Moisturizing Conditioner; Awapuhi Volumizing Conditioner; Biotin Strengthening Conditioner; Chamomile Replenishing Conditioner; Hemp Nourishing Conditioner; Henna Shine Enhancing Conditioner; Herbal

Daily Conditioner; Jojoba Revitalizing Conditioner; Pomegranate Sunflower Conditioner; Tea Tree Calming Conditioner; *Masques:* Aloe Vera Moisturizing, Chamomile Replenishing, Herbal Hair Hydrating, Jojoba Revitalizing; *Organics - Fruit Blend:* Asian Pear & Red Tea, Grapefruit & Wild Ginger, Mandarin Orange & Patchouli, Persimmon & Rose Geranium; *Organics - Herbal Blend:* Chamomile & Lemon Verbena, Lavender & Aloe, Lemongrass & Clary Sage, Tea Tree & Blue Cypress

NEAL'S YARD REMEDIES ◊ ◊ ◉ ✄ 1998
Chamomile & Jojoba Conditioner; Lavender (Nourishing) Conditioner; Orange Flower (Revitalising) Conditioner; Rose (Nurturing) Conditioner; Rosemary & Cedarwood Hair Treatment

NEW SEASONS
Neutral & Toiletry Bases: Conditioner, Conditioning Shampoo Base

OPTIMAH ◊ ◊ ✄ 1995
Raw Aloe : Medicated Shampoo

ORGANIX SOUTH INC
Thera Neem: Conditioner

PZ CUSSONS UK LTD ™ ◊ ◊
Original Source Conditioner: **Mint & Tea Tree, Almond & Coconut, Lime and Guarana, Rose & Aloe, Tangerine & Bergamot, White Pear and Avocado**

QUINESSENCE AROMATHERAPY ☺⊘♨👁
Protein Conditioner

REN ⊘
Conditioners: Manketti Conditioner, Monoi Conditioner, Phytokeratin Volumising Conditioner, Tomato Bioferment Conditioner

RJ MINERAL COSMETICS INTERNATIONAL PTY LTD ™♨
Hair: HC Hair Conditioner - Sandalwood & Ylang Ylang, HC Hair Conditioner - Unscented

SAAF INTERNATIONAL LIMITED ™
Organic Enriching Hair Oil

SIMPLE ♨
Conditioner: Colour Protect, Frequent, Intensive

SIMPLY SOAPS
Hair Care: Conditioning Oil, Strengthening Oil

SKIN BLOSSOM LIMITED ™☺⊘♨☼
Organic: **Complete Care Conditioner**

SOLARAY NUTRITIONAL SUPPLEMENTS
Ginseng Biotin Hair Repair; Green Tea Finishing Cream Rinse; Mandarin Gingko & Ginseng Moisturising Jelly; Primrose Tangle-Go Hair Conditioner; White Camelia & Jasmine Conditioner Spray; *Hair Conditioner:* Calaguala Fern Texturising Leave-In Treatment, Camomile Luxurious Volumising, Honeysuckle Rose, Jojoba & Aloe Desert Herb, Rosa Mosqueta Rose Hip, Swimmers

SUKI PURE SKIN CARE
Clean Balance with Horsetail Yerba Lavender & Rosemary

TARA SMITH LIMITED ™☺⊘♨👁
Tara Smith: **Base Coat Serum, Big Baby Conditioner, C Curl Hair Conditioner, Feed The Root Conditioner, Serum, Straight Away Conditioner, Top Coat Glosser**

THE HIGHLAND SOAP COMPANY ⊘
Conditioner: Rosemary & Wild Nettle, Wild Nettle & Heather

TINTS OF NATURE ⊘♨
Conditioner; Natural Scalp Treatment; Seal & Shine Conditioner

TRUTHFUL CO. LTD (PURELY SKINCARE) ™☺⊘
Purely Skincare: **Hair Conditioner - (normal/oily variant), Hair Conditioner (smooth and sleek variant), Hair Conditioner- (sensitive variant), Hair Conditioner (volumising variant)**

URTEKRAM
Conditioner: All

VANILLA TREE NATURAL SKIN CARE ™☺♨
Nourishing Conditioner; Nourishing Shampoo

VERDESATIVA S.R.L. ™☺❶⊘✔☼👁
Balsamo (Hair Conditioner);
Revitalizing Hair Conditioner

WELEDA ⊘✔☘1985
Calendula and Chamomile Conditioner;
Lemon Balm and Orange Blossom
Conditioner; Rosemary and Ginger
Conditioner; Rosemary Hair Lotion

WHITE LOTUS COSMETIC
ACUPUNCTURE ™❶⊘✔
Herbal: **White Lotus Herbal Hair**
Spray

YAOH ™☺❶⊘✔
Conditioner

DEODORANTS
& ANTIPERSPIRANTS

A. VOGEL
Deodorant: Crystal Spring

ALTERNATIVE STORES ☺
All products are vegan

ALVIN CONNOR LIMITED ™☺⊘
Natural Balance: **Natural Body Stick**
Deodorant; *Natural Balance :* **Natural**
Bodyspray Deodorant

AMAZENE ™☺❶⊘✔☼
Natural Company- Perfume Water:
Apice, Bauhnila, Lavanda Francesca,
Lima, Maca & Canela, Mandarina,
Rosa da Bulgaria

ANN ELISE SKINCARE ☺
Natural Deodorant

ANNEMARIE BORLIND ✔
Body Lind: Deodorant Spray; *Body Lind*
Sportiv: Deodorant Spray; *For Men:*
Deostick

AROMATHERAPY PRODUCTS LTD™☺
Deodorants: **Tea tree, Lemon and**
Rosemary deodorant, Wild rose &
Lemon Leaf Deodorant; *Lavender*
Products: **Lavender and Lemon**
deodorant; *Tea Tree Products:* **Tea**
Tree Lemon & Rosemary Deodorant,
Tea Tree, Lemon and Rosemary
Deodorant

AUBREY ORGANICS
Calendula Blossom Natural Deodorant
Spray; E Plus High C Roll-On Deodorant;
Mens Stock: Northwoods Herbal Pine
Deodorant

BEAUTY NATURALS ✔
Herbal; *Deodorant:* Pure

BELLECARE AG ™
Olive and Bio Melisse

BONANO GMBH ™⊘
Alviana Basic: **Deospray**

BRONNLEY & CO LTD ✔
Body Care for Men: Deodorant

BURT'S BEES ⊘✔👁
Doctor Burt's Herbal Deodorant

CAWARRA COSMETICS LTD ™
Sanctum: **Men's Deodorant**

CEBRA ETHICAL CHIC ™⊘✔
Cebra roll-ons: **Calm Me Down,
Lavender and Vanilla**

DIRK ROSSMANN GMBH ™
Alterra: **Deo-Zerstäuber Jojoba &
Salbei, Men Deo Roll-On Ginkgo &
Koffein**

DOLMA ™☺❶⊘✔👁⚖1976
Miscellaneous Products: **Roll-On
Deodorant**

DR HAUSCHKA ⊘✔
Deodorant: Floral, Fresh

DR ORGANIC
Aloe Vera: Deodorant; *Lavender:*
Deodorant; *Pomegranate:* Deodorant;
Tea Tree: Deodorant; *Vitamin E:*
Deodorant

**ECO COSMETICS GMBH
& CO. KG** ™⊘✔☼
Deodorant Stick

ESSENTIAL CARE
Bath products: Deodorant Stone

ESSENTIALLY NATURAL ™
**Fresh Man Deodorant (Organic);
Lemon and Coriander Deodorant
(Organic)**

**FAITH PRODUCTS
LIMITED** ™⊘✔👁⚖1988
Body deodorant; Spray deodorant

FLORIS ☺✔
Deodorant Stick: Cefiro

FOREVER LIVING PRODUCTS
Aloe Ever-Shield Deodorant

FREERANGERS ™☺✔
Free Spirit Organics: **Deodorant**

GREEN PEOPLE CO. ™⊘✔
Deodorant: **C024 Gentle Control
Rosemary Deodorant, C032 Gentle
Control Aloe Vera Deodorant, H009
Organic Base Deodorant, M008 Stay
Fresh Deodorant, M009 Stay Cool
Deodorant, T008 Roll-On Deodorant**

**GREEN VALLEY
TRADING CO** ™⊘❶✔
Yaoh: **All products are vegan**

GREEN WYCH LTD ™☺❶⊘✔
Natural Cream Deodorant: **Bergamot,
Fragrance free, Geranium, Lavender,
Orange Zest;** *Perfumed Body Spray:*
**Bergamot, Geranium, Lavender,
Lemongrass, Orange Zest**

I AM NATURAL ™❶⊘✔☼
Deodorant: **Organic Cypress & Tea
Tree, Organic Lavender &
Frankincense**

ICE GUARD ☺✔
Natural Crystal Deodorant Roll-on;
Natural Crystal Deodorant Spray;
Natural Crystal Deodorant Twist Up

J&D BLACK LTD ☺
Hollytrees: Deodorant

JASON NATURAL PRODUCTS
Aloe Vera Deodorant Roll, Aloe Vera
Deodorant Stick, Apricot Deodorant

Roll, Apricot Deodorant Stick, Herbs & Spice Deodorant Stick, Lavender Deodorant Roll-on, Lavender Deodorant Stick, Naturally Fresh for Men Deodorant Stick, Naturally Fresh for Women Deodorant Stick, Tea Tree Deodorant Roll-on, Tea Tree Deodorant Stick, Wild Yam Deodorant Stick

KISS MY FACE
Active Enzyme Stick: Fragrance Free, Lavender, Peaceful Patchouli, Scented, Summer; *Liquid Rock Rollon:* Fragrance Free, Lavender, Patchouli, Scented, Summer Scent

LAVERANA GMBH & CO. KG ™ ✔
Body Spa: **Fresh Deodorant Spray Organic Lavender, Fresh Deodorant Spray Organic Orange, Fresh Deodorant Spray Organic Vanilla, Fresh Deodorant Spray Organic Vervain- Organic Lime, Fresh Deodorant Spray Organic Wild Rose, Gentle Deodorant Roll-On Organic Orange, Gentle Deodorant Roll-On Organic Vervain, Gentle Deodorant Roll-On Organic Wild Rose;** *Fresh Deodorant Spray:* **Organic Apricot- Organic Citrus Fruit ;** *Lavera basis Sensitiv:* **Deo Roll-on;** *Men SPA:* **Deodorant Active Spray - Cool Lime, Deodorant Active Spray, Deodorant Active Spray - Aqua Fresh, Deodorant Active Spray - Relaxing Santal**

LIVE NATIVE ™ ☺
Citrus Fresh Deodorant; Essential Woman Deodorant

LUSH ™ ⊘ ✔
Deodorant Powders: **The Greeench;** *Solid Deodorants:* **Aromaco, Aromacreme, Aromarant;** *Solid Deodorants - Krysztals:* **T'Eo**

MAJIK BLANKIT SKIN CARE ™ ☺ ✔
Rosewood and Lemon Deodorant

MJ HEALTH(NZ) LTD ™ ☺ ❶ ⊘ ✔ 👁
Earths Gift Range: **Deodorant: lavender, cedar, citrus or rose**

NATURAL SENSE
Natural Deo Krystal; Natural Deo Krystal

NATURE'S GATE
Organics - Fruit Blend : Asian Pear & Red Tea, Grapefruit & Wild Ginger, Mandarin Orange & Patchouli, Persimmon & Rose Geranium; *Organics - Herbal Blend:* Chamomile & Lemon Verbena, Lavender & Aloe, Lemongrass & Clary Sage, Tea Tree & Blue Cypress; *Roll-on:* Autumn Breeze, Spring Fresh, Summer Spice, Winter Clean; *Stick:* Autumn Breeze, Spring Fresh, Summer Spice, Winter Clean

NEAL'S YARD REMEDIES ⊘ ✔ 👁 ⚡ 1998
Lavender & Aloe Vera Deodorant; Lemon & Coriander Deodorant

PITROK LTD ⊘ ✔
Crystal Deodorant: Original, Push-up; *Spray Deodorant:* Fragrance, Natural

PZ CUSSONS UK LTD ™ ⊘ ✔
Original Source Antiperspirant & Deodorant: **Black Walnut &**

Sandalwood, Cactus & Guarana, Olive Wood & Hemp Leaf, Rock Fennel & Icelandic Moss, Sea Kelp & White Tea, White sage & Juniper

RJ MINERAL COSMETICS INTERNATIONAL PTY LTD ™ ✔
Body: **DS Body Natural Deodorant Stick - Coriander & Lime, DS Body Natural Deodorant Stick - Lavender, DS Body Natural Deodorant Stick - Bay & Orange, DS Body Natural Deodorant Stick - Bergamot & Geranium, NDS Body Natural Deodorant Spray - Bay & Orange, NDS Body Natural Deodorant Spray - Bergamot & Geranium, NDS Body Natural Deodorant Spray - Coriander & Lime, NDS Body Natural Deodorant Spray - Lavender**

SIMPLE ✔
Deodorant: Roll On, Stick

SOLARAY NUTRITIONAL SUPPLEMENTS
Calendula Blossom Spray; E Plus High C Roll-On; Northwoods Herbal Pine Deodorant

STELLA MCCARTNEY
Stella: Soft Deodorant Roll On

TAOASIS GMBH AROMA-KOSMETIK & VERLAG ™
Zaubernuss Deo; Zitrusgarten Deo

THE DEODORANT STONE (UK) LTD ☺ ⊘ ✔
Deodorant Stone; *Roll-On Stone:* Aloe & Cucumber, Herbal Spice, Tea Tree,

Unscented; *Spray-On Stone:* Aloe & Cucumber, Herbal Spice, Tea-Tree, Unscented

TOMS OF MAINE ⊘ ✔
Natural Long-Lasting Deodorant Roll On: Lavender, Unscented; *Natural Long-Lasting Deodorant Stick:* Apricot, Lavender, Lemongrass, Unscented; *Natural Original Deodorant Stick:* Calendula, Honeysuckle Rose, Unscented, Woodspice; *Natural Sensitive Care Deodorant Stick:* Bay-Lime, Cucumber-Grapefruit, Fragrance Free

URTEKRAM
Deo Crystal: All

WELEDA ⊘ ✔ ⚚ 1985
Citrus Deodorant; Sage Deodorant; Wild Rose Deodorant

ESSENTIAL OILS & MASSAGE PRODUCTS

A. VOGEL
Po-Ho Oil; St John's Wort Oil

ABSOLUTE AROMAS ™ ⊘ ✔
Ord River: **Pure Tea Tree Oil 10ml & 25ml**

AKAMUTI
Mum's Special Oil Blend; Mum's Tummy Butter; *Body Oils:* All; *Cold Pressed Tea Tree Oils:* All; *Essential Oils:* All

TOILETRIES & COSMETICS

ANN ELISE SKINCARE ☺
Joint & Muscleez

ARBONNE 👁
SeaSource Detox Spa: 5-in-1 Essential
Massage Oil

AROMATHERAPY PRODUCTS LTD ™☺
Accessories: **Reflexology cushion
massager, Reflexology rubber tip
foot massager;** *After Treatment
Products:* **After Wax Oil, Tinted
After-Electrolysis Cream;** *Blended
Essential Oils:* **Jasmine/Jojoba, Linden
Blossom/Jojoba, Orange
Blossom/Jojoba, Rose/Jojoba;**
Blended Massage Oils: **Cellulite
Treatment Oil, Facial Treatment Oil,
Muscle Fatigue Treatment Oil,
Nourishing Facial Lotion, Refreshing
Body Lotion, Relaxing Body Lotion,
Relaxing Body Oil, Sensual Body
Oil;** *Clear Breathe:* **Clear Breathe
Concentrate, Clear Breathe Inhaler,
Clear Breathe Vapour Rub;** *Essential
Oils:* **Basil (Herb), Benzoin (resinoid
50%) Wild Crafted, Benzoin (Trees),
Bergamot, Bergamot (Rind of the
Fruit), Black Pepper, Black Pepper
(Peppercorns), Camphor White,
Cardomon (Seeds), Carrot Seed
(Seeds), Cedarwood (Virginian)
(Trees), Cedarwood Atlas (Trees),
Chamomile (Roman), Chamomile
Blue (Flowers), Chamomile Roman
(Flowers), Cinnamon, Citronella,
Citronella (Grass), Clary Sage -
ethically harvested, Clary Sage
(Herb), Clove, Coriander (Dried
Fruits), Cypress - wild crafted,
Cypress (Leaves of the Tree),
Eucalyptus, Eucalyptus (Leaves of**
the Tree), **Fennel (Herb),
Frankincense - wild crafted,
Frankincense (Tree Resin), Geranium
- ethically harvested, Geranium
(Leaves), Ginger, Ginger (Root of
the Plant), Grapefruit, Grapefruit
(Rind of the Fruit), Immortelle
(Flowers), Jasmine absolute -
ethically harvested, Jasmine
Absolute (Flowers), Juniper, Juniper
(Berries), Kanuka (Foliage),
Lavender, Lavender - ethically
harvested, Lavender (Flowers),
Lemon, Lemon (Rind of the Fruit),
Lemongrass, Lemongrass (Grass),
Lemon-Tea tree, Lime, Lime (Rind of
the Fruit), Linden Blossom Absolute
(Flowers), Mandarin, Mandarin
(Rind of the Fruit), Marjoram
(Spanish) wild crafted, Marjoram
French (Herb), Marjoram Spanish
(Herb), May Chang - ethically
harvested, May Chang (Fruit),
Melissa (Leaves & Flowers), Myrrh
(Tree Resin), Niaouli (Leaf of the
Tree), Orange, Orange (Rind of the
Fruit), Orange Blossom (Neroli)
(Flowers), Orange Blossom (Neroli)-
ethically harvested, Palmarosa
(Grass), Patchouli, Patchouli (Herb),
Peppermint, Peppermint (Herb),
Petitgrain (Orange Tree Leaf), Pine -
wild crafted, Pine (Trees), Rose
(absolute) - ethically harvested,
Rose Absolute (Flowers), Rose otto -
ethically harvested, Rose Otto
(Flowers), Rose Phytol (Flowers),
Rosemary, Rosemary (Herb),
Rosewood - tomar, Rosewood
(Tree), Sandalwood - wild crafted,
Sandalwood (Tree), Tea tree, Tea
tree (Leaves of the Tree), Thyme,**

TOILETRIES & COSMETICS

Turmeric, Vetiver (Grass), Violet Leaf Absolute (Flowers), Yarrow (Milfoil) (Flower Heads), Ylang-Ylang (Flowers); *Lavender Products:* **Lavender body Lotion, Lavender Moist Tissues, Lavender roller ball, Lavender Water;** *Massage Oil Base:* **Avocado, Evening Primrose with Vitamin E, Face & Body Massage Oil Base, Face Massage Oil Base, Grapeseed, Jojoba, Massage Lotion Base, Peach Kernel, Soya Bean, Sweet Almond, Wheatgerm;** *Masterblends:* **Energy, Euphoria, Passion, Serenity;** *Mixing bottle:* **Calibrated glass mixing bottle;** *Rescue Roller Balls:* **Concentrate Remedy Roller Ball, De-Stress Remedy Roller Ball, Goodnight Remedy Roller Ball, Tea tree roller ball, Travel Ease Remedy Roller Ball;** *Softening pre-blended body oils for massage:* **Cellulite detox body massage oil, Muscle ease body massage oil, Relaxing body massage oil, Sensuous body massage oil;** *Tea Tree Products:* **Natural Antiseptic Cream, Tea Tree & Kanuka Blemish Stick, Tea Tree & Kanuka Gel, Tea Tree & Lime Cream Body Wash, Tea Tree & Manuka Cream, Tea Tree Lotion, Tea Tree Moist Tissues, Tea Tree Roller Ball**

BAREFOOT BOTANICALS ☺️⊘⛎
Rosa Fina: **Secret Essence Face & Decolletage oil**

BRACKENCRAFT ™☺️❶⊘⛎
Rosewater

BRONNLEY & CO LTD ⛎
Royal Horticultural Society - Massage Oil: Gardener's

CAWARRA COSMETICS LTD ™
Face Massage Oil; *OrganicSpa Range:* **Rose Hip Oil;** *Sanctum:* **Massage Oil**

DARTMOOR CHILLI FARM ™❶⊘⛎
Dartmoor Chilli: **Chilli Holistic Muscle Rub**

DOLMA ™☺️❶⊘⛎👁️⚖️ 1976
Massage Oils: **Anti-Cellulite, Invigorating, Relaxing, Soothing**

ECO COSMETICS GMBH & CO. KG ™⊘⛎☼
Body Boost

ESSENTIAL CARE
Skincare: Mosimix, Muscle Ease Therapy Oil, Organic Relaxing Body Oil

ESSENTIALLY NATURAL ™
Diffusers: **Car Aromatherapy Diffuser (with Stay Awake Organic Oil), Citrus Burst, Winter Spice;** *Massage Oils:* **Relaxing, Sensual**

ESSENTIALLY YOURS LTD
Natural Elements Range: NE105 Luxury Facial Massage Oil, NE133 Elemi & Rose Body Massage Oil, NE134 Patchouli & Sandalwood Body Massage Oil, NE135 Ginger, Rosemary & Mandarin Body Massage Oil; *Professional Range:* G1 Grapeseed Oil, SA1 Sweet Almond Oil (500ml/250ml)

GREEN WYCH LTD ™☺❶⊘✔
Massage Oil: **Bath/Massage Oil**

HEALTHQUEST LIMITED ™⊘✔
Organic Blue- Massage Oils: **Muscle Rub, Relaxing, Sensual;** *Organic Blue-Mood Blends:* **Easy Breathe, Energising, Meditation, Relaxing, Restful Night, Sensual**

HERBS HANDS HEALING LTD ™⊘✔
Base Oils: **Castor, Nutmeg Kernel, St John's Wort Oil, Sweet Almond, Wheatgerm;** *Essential Oils:* **All;** *Massage Oils:* **Deep Tissue, Earth Song, Flower, Hot Zing, Intimate, Relaxing;** *Pure Essential Oils:* **All, Basil, Benzoin, Bergamot, Black Pepper, Cajaput, Camphor, Cardamom, Cedarwood, Chamomile (Roman), Cinnamon, Clary Sage, Clove, Eucalyptus, Fennel, Frankincense, Garlic, Geranium, Ginger, Juniper, Lavender, Lemon, Lime, Mandarin, Marjoram, Orange, Peppermint, Petitgrain, Rosemary, Rosewood, Sage, Spearmint, Tea Tree, Thyme, White Pine, Ylang Ylang**

HIPPY HEAVEN NATURAL BEAUTY ™☺⊘✔
Massage oil; Muscle ease balm

HOLISTIX HERBAL PRODUCTS ❶
Bath/Massage Oils: **Luscious, Recovery, Relaxing, Sensual, Skincare, Warming Circulation;** *Carrier Oils:* **All;** *Essential Oils:* **All;** *Festive:* **Festive Essential Oil;** *Tinctures:* **All**

HOWAD LTD T/A INCOGNITO ™❶⊘✔
Incognito: **Lemongrass, Citronella & Jasmine Rice Oil**

I AM NATURAL ™❶⊘✔ ✿
Organic Avocado Oil; Organic Hemp Oil; Organic Macadamia Nut Oil; Organic Sweet Almond Oil; *Essential Oils:* **Organic Ginger Essential Oil, Organic Lavender Essential Oil, Organic Peppermint Essential Oil, Organic Sweet Orange Essential Oil, Organic Tea Tree Essential Oil;** *Massage Oil:* **Organic Calming Massage Oil, Organic Sensual Massage Oil, Organic Uplifting Massage Oil, Organic Warming Massage Oil**

INNOCENT OILS ™☺⊘✔
Innocent Hemp Mint Balm; *Massage Oils:* **Innocent Baby Massage Oil - Unscented, Innocent Massage Oil**

ITS ELIXIR (UK) LIMITED ™⊘✔👁
Joint & muscle gel; Sports Oil; *Carrier Oils:* **All;** *Essential Oils:* **All;** *Floral Waters:* **All;** *Infused Oils:* **All;** *Solid Oils:* **All**

JR LIGGETT ☺
Pure Tea Tree Oil Roll On; *Moisturizing Oils Kit:* **with Nut Oil, Without Nut Oil**

JUNGLESALE LIMITED ™
Neem Massage Oil; Neem Oil

LUSH ™◎✔
Massage Bars: **Bewitched Massage Bar, Business Time, Cosmic Dreamcatcher, Each Peach (and Two's a Pear), Fever, Heavanilli, Iridescent Glitterbug, Shimmy Shimmy, Snake Oil Scalp Bar, Sore Labours, Strawberry Feels Forever, Therapy, Wiccy Magic Muscles**

MAJIK BLANKIT SKIN CARE ™☺✔
Veon Sensuous Organic Jojoba & Jasmine Massage Balm; *Pure oils:* **Sunita Olive Oil**

MJ HEALTH(NZ) LTD ™☺❶◐⊘✔👁
Body Massage oil: **Dr. Wendy's 100% Pure Botanical Body Massage Oil;** *Earths Gift Range:* **Stretch mark/scar oil;** *Salon Only Range:* **Divine Body Massage Oil, Divine Facial Massage Oil**

MY SKINCARE LTD ™☺⊘✔
Massage Oils and Lotions: **Pre Labour Massage Oil, Sleepeeze Massage Lotion, Stress Buster Massage Cream**

NATURAL BY NATURE OILS ☺
Bath Oils: Jasmine, Lavender, Meditation, Rose, Seduction, Tranquility; *Massage Blends:* Baby & Toddler, Cellulite, Hair & Scalp, Muscle & Joint, Rose, Seduction, Tranquility; *Massage Oils:* Aromatic Woods, Body Tone, Cellulite, Dry Skin, Exotic Moods, Hair Reform, Muscle Fatigue, Oriental Spice, Quiet Night, Refreshing, Relaxing, Revitalizing, Romantic Evening, Scalp Therapy, Sensual, Tired Feet; *Massage Treatment Oils:* Body Tone, Cellulite, Muscle Fatigue; *Organic Blend Massage Oils:* Baby & Toddler, Cellulite, Hair & Scalp, Muscle & Joint, Rose, Seduction, Tranquility

NATURAL SENSE
Joint Ease; Massage Oil; Muscle Rub

NATURALLY GIFTED
Bath & Massage Oil: Citrus & Lavender, Neroli & Rose

NEAL'S YARD REMEDIES ⊘✔👁✿⚖1998
Aloe Vera Cooling Spray; Aromatherapy Blend Calming; Aromatherapy Blend Cleansing; Aromatherapy Blend De-Stress; Aromatherapy Blend Focus; Aromatherapy Blend Night Time; Aromatherapy Blend Optimism; Aromatherapy Blend Vitality; Aromatherapy Blend Womens Balance; Aromatic Massage Oil; Base Massage Oil; Baseline Massage Oil; Benzoin Tincture; Calendula Macerated Oil; Calm Spritzer; Citronella Formula; Flower Essence Blends; Geranium & Orange Massage Oil; Ginger & Juniper Warming Oil; Herbal Tinctures (Blends); Herbal Tinctures (Single Tinctures); Homoeopathic Tinctures; Jojoba Oil; Mothers Massage Oil; Renew Spritzer; Soothing Massage Oil; St John's Wort Macerated Oil; Vanilla & Vetiver Massage Oil; Zest Spritzer

NOTHING NASTY ✔
Rosemary Energising Body Oil

OPTIMAH ⊘✔⚖1995
Cariad: All Essential Oils and Carrier Oils

ORGANIC BOTANICS ™⊘✪
Certified Organic French Lavender Essential Oil; Certified Organic Pure Tea-Tree Essential Oil

OSHADHI ☺✦
Essential Oils and Carrier Oils: All

POTIONS AND POSSIBILITIES ⊘✦
Carrier Oils: All; *Essential Oils:* All; *Massage:* ...And To Sleep Blend, Detox Blend, Fatigue Blend, Intimate Blend, Joint & Muscle Blend, Relaxation Blend; *Organic Range:* Detox Facial Massage, Energy Lift Body Massage, Gentle Facial Massage, Stress Ease Massage

PUKKA HERBS
All

QUINESSENCE AROMATHERAPY ☺☺✦☻
10% Dilutions: All; *5% Dilutions:* All; *Absolutes and Phytols:* All; *Essential Oil Synergies:* After Flight, Cellulite, Energising, Foot Ease, Head Ease, Immune Optimise, Problem Skin, Relaxing, Uplifting; *Hydrosols:* All; *Massage Oils:* Athletic, Cellulite, Invigorating, Joint Mobility, Muscle Ease, Relaxing, Stress, Stretch Marks; *Pure Essential Oils:* All

SCOTTISH HERBAL SUPPLIES ™❶⊘✦
Organic & Non-Organic Essential Oils; Vegetable Creams; Vegetable Oils

SIMPLY SOAPS
Faerie Therepy: 3 Colour Candle & Oil

Gift Box; *Hedgerow Herbals:* Finest Rose Body Oil; *Hedgerow Herbals- Rosa Passionata:* Rosa Body Oil; *Oils:* Aphrodisia, Invigorating, Relaxing

SOLARAY NUTRITIONAL SUPPLEMENTS
Natural Spa Sea Wonders Relaxing Massage Oil

SOPHYTO ™❶⊘✦☻
Feminine Massage Butter; Masculine Massage Butter; Meditation Massage Butter; Unfragranced Massage Butter

SUKI PURE SKIN CARE
Clean Balance Treatment Oil with Lavender & Rosemary

THE ORGANIC HERB TRADING COMPANY ⊘
Organic Macerates & Flower Waters: All

TREE-HARVEST ⊘✦
Linden Relaxation Oil; *Body Oils:* Aches and Pains, Detox, Renewed Energy, Sensuality, Soothing, Sports, Tranquility; *Essential Oils:* All; *Oils & Hydrolats:* All; *Precious Oils & Absolutes:* All; *Pulse Points:* Lavender, Linden, Rose, Willow

URTEKRAM
Body Oil: All

VERDESATIVA S.R.L. ™☺❶⊘✦✪☻
Olio Aromatico (Red Velvet Oil); Olio Balsamico (Balsamic Oil); Olio Fitness (Benessere); Olio Floreale (Flower Garden Oil); Olio Relax (Relax Oil)

TOILETRIES & COSMETICS

VISIONARY SOAP COMPANY ™☺
**Rosemary& Lavender Gardener's
Massage Oil;** *Body Oils:* **Orange
Geranium, Recuperate, Rejuvenate,
Relax, Romance**

YAOH ™☺❶⊘♂
Massage Oil

EYE PRODUCTS

**ADORN MINERAL
COSMETICS** ™☺⊘♂
Eye Liner: **Mineral Eye Liner Pencil;**
Mascara: **Mineral Mascara, Mineral
Mascara Primer**

AKAMUTI
Rose Berry Eye Reviitaliser

ALEXAMI COSMETICS ™♂
**Natural effects lashes- herbal
mineral mascara**

ANNEMARIE BORLIND ♂
Eye Make Up Remover; Pura Soft Q10
Eye Area Care

ARBONNE ◉
Wipe Out Eye Makeup Remover;
Intelligence: Daily Eye Cream; *NutriMin
C RE9:* REpair Corrective Eye Creme

AROMATHERAPY PRODUCTS LTD ™☺
Accessories: **Lilac eye mask**

AUBREY ORGANICS
Lumescence: Rejuvenating Eye Cream
with Liposomes

BAREFOOT BOTANICALS ☺⊘♂
Rosa Fina: Revelation Intensive Eye
Serum

BEAUTY NATURALS ♂
Eye Care: Contour Balm, Elderflower
Contour Gel, Gentle Cleansing Gel;
Gentle Cleansing for Eyes: Lotion

CAWARRA COSMETICS LTD ™
OrganicSpa: **Eye Balm, Eye Gel;**
OrganicSpa Range: **Eye Balm, Eye
Gel;** *Sanctum:* **Energising Eye Gel,
Firming Eye Balm**

DIRK ROSSMANN GMBH ™
Alterra: **Anti Age Augencreme
Wildrose**

DOLMA ™☺❶⊘♂◉⚼1976
Honesty Eye Gel; *Eye Care:*
**Chamomile & Aloe Vera Eye Cream,
Chamomile & Fennel Eye Make-up
Remover**

DR HAUSCHKA ⊘♂
Eye Solace

ESSENTIALLY NATURAL ™
**Anti-Wrinkle Eye Pillow; Calming
Eye Pillow; Hangover Eye Pillow;
Relaxing Eye Pillow**

ESSENTIALLY YOURS LTD
Mu Mens Range: M5 Under Eye
Firming Serum; *Natural Elements
Range:* NE021 Eye Make Up Remover,

NE022 Restoring Eye Gel, NE023 Nourishing Eye Cream, NE28 Under Eye Firming Serum

FAITH PRODUCTS LIMITED ™⊘✔👁️⤴-1988
Replenishing Aloe Vera Eye Gel 50ml

HERBS HANDS HEALING LTD ™⊘✔
Eyebright & Goldenseal Eyewash;
Allergies: **Eyebright & Goldenseal Eyewash Formula**

HIPPY HEAVEN NATURAL BEAUTY ™☺⊘✔
Cucumber and arnica eye cream for crows feet and dark circles

HONESTY COSMETICS LTD ™☺❶❶⊘✔👁️⤴-1976
Honesty Unscented Range: **Eye Gel with Eyebright**

JASON NATURAL PRODUCTS
Alpha Hydroxy Acids: 3-1/2% Plus Gentle Eye Gel New Cell Eye Area Therapy™ *Alpha Hydroxy Acids; Ester-C® Skin Care:* Ultra-C™ Eye Lift

JUICE BEAUTY
Green Apple Nutrient Eye Cream; Smoothing Eye Concentrate

KEY SUN LABORATORIES PTY LTD ™⊘
Key Sun: **Eye Balm**

KISS MY FACE
Organic Face Care: Eye Witness Eye Repair Creme; *Potent & Pure Face Care:* Eyewitness Eye Repair Creme

LAVERANA GMBH & CO. KG ™✔
Faces: **Faces Eye Gel Wild Rose;**
Lavera Faces My Age: **Cooling Eye Roll-On White Tea - Karanja Oil, Intensive Eye Cream White Tea - Karanja Oil;** *Lavere:* **Hydro Energy Cool Eye, Solution Power Eye Glow**

LIP INK ☺
Eye Restore Magic Powder Cream

LIZ EARLE ✔
Daily Eye Repair; Day & Night Eye Care Duo; Eyebright Soothing Eye Lotion; Smoothing Line Serum; *Superskin:* Eye & Lip Treatment

MAJIK BLANKIT SKIN CARE ™☺✔
Eye Shadows and Powders: **2Tone, Azul, Bronz, Choc Bronz, Dark Angel, Dotty, Dream Highlighter, Egypt, Indian Gold, Marz, Merlin, Morgana, Nubian Passion, Pan, Pewter, Rosie, Sage, Venus**

NATURE'S GATE
Ultimate Comfort Eye Cream

NEAL'S YARD REMEDIES ⊘✔👁️⤴-1998
NYR Men Rejuvenating Eye Gel; White Tea Toning Eye Gel

ORGANIC BOTANICS ™⊘✿
Pink Lotus & Aloe Vera Creamy Eye Gel

POTIONS AND POSSIBILITIES ⊘✔
Beauty: Firming Eye Gel

RARE NATURAL CARE, INC. ™☺❶◌✔☼👁
Gentle Eye Gel

RAW GAIA ™☺❶◌✔☼👁
Revitalising Eye Oil with Sea Buckthorn Fruit

REN ◌
Active 7 Radiant Eye Maintenance Gel; Conditioning Eye Make Up Remover; Lipovector Peptide Anti-Wrinkle Eye Cream

RIVER VEDA ™◌✔☼
RiverVeda: **Revival;** *The Organic Skin Company:* **Regenerate Chamomile & Primrose Eye Cream**

RJ MINERAL COSMETICS INTERNATIONAL PTY LTD ™✔
Eye: **CEMR Chamomile Eye Make Up Remover, GEC Gentle Eye Cream, VEEG Vitamin E Eye Gel**

SAUFLON PHARMACEUTICALS ◌✔
Contact Lens Care Solution: All In One Light Multipurpose Solution, Comfort Drops, ConfortVue Multipurpose Solution, CyClean® Multipurpose Solution, Multi™ Hydrogen Peroxide Solution, Preservative Free Saline, Sauflon 7 Comfort Solution, Synergi Preservative Free Multipurpose Solution; *Contact Lenses:* Bioclear™ 1Day Biomimetic Daily Disposables, Bioclear™ Biomimetic Monthly Disposables, Bioclear™ Biomimetic Toric Monthly Disposables, ClearComfort Aspheric Monthly Disposables, NewDay® Aspheric Daily Disposables, Sauflon UV55 Monthly Disposables

SIMPLE ✔
Conditioning Eye Make-Up Remover; Conditioning Eye Make-Up Remover Pads; Kind To Eyes Balm; *Eye Cream:* Age Resisting, Anti-Wrinkle, Daily Radiance

SOLARAY NUTRITIONAL SUPPLEMENTS
Lumessence Rejuvanating Eye Cream

SYNTHESIS 345 ™☺❶◌✔☼
First Love: **'Follow the Light' Eye Cream**

TREASURED EARTH SKINCARE ™☺◌
Eye Cream

TREE-HARVEST ◌✔
Elderflower Eye Gel

VEGAN STORE ™☺❶◌✔
Vizulize: **Contact Lens Cleaner, Herbal Eye Drops**

VERDESATIVA S.R.L. ™☺❶◌✔☼👁
High Performance Line: **Gel contorno occhi**

WHITE LOTUS COSMETIC ACUPUNCTURE ™❶◌✔
Herbal: **Anti-Ageing Eye Gel**

FEMININE HYGIENE

BELLECARE AG ™
Lacta Femina Wash sanmar; *Vleur:*
Femina Wash

**FAITH PRODUCTS
LIMITED** ™◎☾✦✿✦1988
Feminine Wash; Feminine Wipes

HIGHER NATURE LTD
V Gel; VagiClear

MOONCUP LTD. ™☺
Mooncup

NATRACARE
Baby Wipes; Intimate Wipes; *Organic
Applicator Tampons:* Regular, Super;
Organic Tampons: Regular, Super, Super
Plus; *Pads:* Dry & Light Incontinence,
Maternity, Night Time, Nursing, Regular,
Slender, Super; *Panty Liners:* Breathable,
Curved, Tanga, Ultra Thin; *Ultra Pads:*
Long with Wings, Regular with Wings,
Super Plus, Super w Wings

VERDESATIVA S.R.L. ™☺❶◇✦✿✦☀✿✦
Unisex Mild Intimate Cleanser

FOOT & LEG CARE

AKAMUTI
Foot Spray; Shea Cocoa Mint Foot
Butter

ALVIN CONNOR LIMITED ™☺◇
Natural Balance: **Natural Foot Powder**

ANIMAL AID ™☺❶◇✦✿✦1976
Cool Mint Foot Lotion

ARBONNE ✿
Intelligence: Cleansing Gel, Herbal Foot
Cream

AROMATHERAPY PRODUCTS LTD ™☺
Accessories: **Wooden foot file;** *Hand
& Foot Care:* **Foot Lotion, Foot Soak,
Foot Spray, Footbar;** *Restored feet:*
**White mint and Kanuka foot balm,
White mint and Kanuka foot spray**

AUBREY ORGANICS
Feet Relief: Foot Scrub, Massage Cream

BAREFOOT BOTANICALS ☺◇✦
SOS : Foot Soldier Soothing Foot Balm

BEAUTY NATURALS ✦
Moisturising Foot Balm; *Martha Hill:*
Energising Leg Gel

CAWARRA COSMETICS LTD ™
Sanctum: **Reviving Foot Balm,
Reviving Foot Soak**

CEBRA ETHICAL CHIC ™◇✦
Cebra- ethical skin care: **Soften Me
Foot and Hand Cream**

DESERT ESSENCE ◇✦✦1985
Organics: Pistachio Foot Repair

TOILETRIES & COSMETICS

DOLMA ™☺❶⊘ ✍ ☜⚒ 1976
Hand & Foot Care: **Aromatic Foot Shampoo with Lemongrass & Cypress, Aromatic Foot Shampoo with Peppermint & Tea Tree, Honesty Foot Lotion**

ESSENTIALLY NATURAL ™
Raspberry & Lemon Footpowder

ESSENTIALLY YOURS LTD
Natural Elements Range: NE044 Refreshing Foot Scrub, NE048 Luxury Foot Massage Cream, NE104 Anti-Microbial Foot Soak; *Professional Range:* NE152T Pedicure Kit (Code: NE137/138/139/140)

FREERANGERS ™☺✍
Minty foot Scrub; Zingy Lemon Foot Cream

HEALTHY HERBS ☺
Herbytoes

**HIPPY HEAVEN
NATURAL BEAUTY** ™☺⊘✍
Soothe your sole foot balm; Soothe your sole foot scrub

HOLISTIX HERBAL PRODUCTS ❶
Lavender Water Foot Spray

**HONESTY COSMETICS
LTD** ™☺❶⊘✍☜⚒1976
Honesty Essential Range: **Peppermint, Tea Tree & Lemon Foot Lotion**

I AM NATURAL ™❶⊘✍✲
Organic Peppermint Foot Cream

INNOCENT OILS ™☺⊘✍
Innocent Buff Paste; Innocent Pinkie Drops; *Innocent Angel:* **Innocent Angel Butter Mint**

ITS ELIXIR (UK) LIMITED ™⊘✍☜
Foot gel; Foot Lotion; Foot Massage Oil

KISS MY FACE
Foot Creme: Peppermint; *Foot Scrub:* Peppermint

LIVE NATIVE ™☺
Fresh Feet

LIZ EARLE ✍
Foot Repair Moisturiser; Foot Scrub; Foot Spritzer

LUSH ™⊘✍
Skin care: **Stepping Stone Foot Scrub**

MONTAGNE JEUNESSE ⊘✍
Ice Blueberry & Balm Mint Foot Cooler; Morella Cherry & Iced Mint Tired Leg Gel; Pink Grapefruit & Balm Mint Foot Soak; Spearmint & Balm Mint Foot Lotion; Watermelon & Balm Mint Foot Scrub

NATURAL SENSE
Happy Feet Butter; Hot Feet Oil

**NEAL'S YARD
REMEDIES** ⊘✍☜⚒1998
Grapefruit & Juniper Firming Hip & Thigh Gel

NOTHING NASTY ✍
Breeze Foot Spray

PURE GAISHA ™☺❶✔
Fantasy Foot Cream; Fantasy Foot Scrub; Fragrant Garden Foot Soak

QUINESSENCE AROMATHERAPY ☺⊘✔👁
Foot Balm

REN ⊘
Revivo-Tonic Cool Comfort Leg and Foot Gel

RJ MINERAL COSMETICS INTERNATIONAL PTY LTD ™✔
Foot: **PTTFL Foot Lotion - Peppermint & Tea Tree, PTTFL Foot Scrub - Peppermint & Tea Tree**

SAAF INTERNATIONAL LIMITED ™
Organic Foot Softening Balm

SOLARAY NUTRITIONAL SUPPLEMENTS
Feet Relief Massage Cream; Neat Feet Foot Scrub

THE DEODORANT STONE (UK) LTD ☺⊘✔
Peppermint Foot Spray-On Stone

GIFT BOXES & PACKS

HOLISTIX HERBAL PRODUCTS ❶
Aromatherapy 1: Bath/Massage Oil, Massager, Candles; *Aromatherapy Scent:* Oil Burner, Essential Oil, Candle; *Bathing:* Bath Oil, Soap, Flannel, Candles; *Calendula:* Cream, Soap, Bath Oil; *Facial:* Cleanser, Toner, Cream; *Feet Treat:* Pumice, Foot Balm, Soap; *Hard-Worker's Treat:* Back Rub, Bath Oil, Soap; *Pamper 1:* Spritzer, Soap, Cream, Flannel; *Pamper 2:* Cream, Bath Oil, Soap; *Pamper 3:* Bath Oil, Cream, Lip Balm; *Pamper 4:* Spritzer, Cream, Lip Balm; *Sensual:* Massage Oil, Geranium & Ylang-Ylang Cream, Lip Balm, Candles; *Winter Warmer 1:* Ointment, Bath Oil, Soap, Candles; *Winter Warmer 2:* Xmas Spray, Ointment, Wine Spice

HONESTY COSMETICS LTD ™☺❶⊘✔👁⚘1976
Honesty Essential Range: **Essential Range Gift Bag;** *Honesty Fruit Range:* **Fruit Range Gift Bag;** *Honesty Unscented Range:* **Unscented Range Gift Bag**

SHANTI PRODUCTS ⊘✔
Glycerine Soaps: Boxed Humming Bird Soap, Daisy Gift Soaps, Dragonfly boxed soaps, Large cupcake soap in Box, Mini Cupcake Soaps, Rose Shaped Soap, Soap Scroll, Vintage Collection Black & White Soaps

ULTRA GLOW COSMETICS ☺✔
Latex free accessory set; Mirror accessory

HAIR DYES

ALTERNATIVE STORES ☺
All products are vegan

AUBREY ORGANICS
Colour Me Natural: Dark Brown

DANIEL FIELD 🐰
Watercolour: All Colours

LUSH ᵀᴹ⊘🐰
Les Cacas Hair Colours: **Caca Brun, Caca Marron, Caca Noir, Caca Rouge**

MANIC PANIC
All

RENBOW 🐰
Crazy Color: All

SMART BEAUTY 🐰
Smart Blonde: Champagne, Platinum; *Smart Colour:* Hot Chocolate, Midnight Blue, Pure Purple, Real Red, Total Blonde; *Smart Highlights:* Carmine Pink, Cool Blonde, Hot Chocolate, Intense Red, Pure Purple; *Smart Multi Tonal Highlights:* Fiery Red, Hazelnut, Hot Chocolate, Mahogany

SOLARAY NUTRITIONAL SUPPLEMENTS
Colour Me Natural Hair Dye Dark Brown

SPECIAL EFFECTS HAIR DYES
All

TINTS OF NATURE ⊘🐰
Changes Semi-Permanent Hair Colour: All (8 Shades Available); *Permanent Hair Colour:* All (24 Shades Available), Highlight Kit, Lightener Kit

HAIR REMOVAL

AQUA NATURAL ᵀᴹ☺⊘🐰👁
Aqua Natural; Simply Smooth

BOOTS COMPANY PLC
Expert Sensitive Hair Removal Strips

ESSENTIALLY YOURS LTD
Professional Range: NE145T After Wax Lotion, NE146T Pre Wax Toner, NE154T Waxing Kit (NE145/NE146)

MOOM UK
M4Men Organic Refill Jar; Moom 4 Men Organic Hair Removal; Moom Organic Refill Jar; Organic Hair Removal Dry/Sensitive; Organic Hair Removal Extra Sensitive Skin; Organic Hair Removal Normal/Sensitive Skin

HAIRSPRAYS, GELS ETC

ARISE AND SHINE COSMETICS LTD ᵀᴹ☺❶
Rosemary and jojoba infusion with coconut and shea butter hair pomade

AUBREY ORGANICS
B5 Design Gel; Mandarin Magic Ginko Leaf and Ginseng Root Hair Moisturising Jelly; Natural Missst Super Hold Herbal Hairspray; White Camellia and Jasmine Shine Conditioner Spray; *Calaguala Fern:* Texturising Leave-In Treatment

AVEDA
Be Curly: Curl Control, Curl Enhancer; *Brilliant:* Anti-humectant Pomade, Damage Control, Emollient Finishing Gloss, Humectant Pomade, Medium Hold Hair Spray, Retexturing Gel, Spray-on Shine, Universal Styling Creme; *Damage Remedy:* Daily Hair Repair; *Smooth Infusion:* Glossing Straightener, Style Prep Smoother

BEAUTY NATURALS ✔
Natural Style Conditioning Hair Gel

DANIEL FIELD ✔
Anti Frizz Hairspray; Smooth & Shine Serum

ECO COSMETICS GMBH & CO. KG ™⊘✔ ✿
Hair Gel

FOREVER LIVING PRODUCTS
Aloe Pro-Set

GENTLE BEAUTY CO LTD ™☺✔
Styling Products: **Fragrance Free Hairspray, Fragrance Free Hairspray, HairSpray, HairSpray, Styling Gel, Styling Mousse, Styling Mousse**

GREEN PEOPLE CO. ™⊘✔
Cosmetic Hair Products: **C010 Aloe Vera Styling Gel, C044 Volumising Hair Mist, R026 Volume Building Hair Mist**

HOLISTIX HERBAL PRODUCTS ❶
Hair Oil

JASON NATURAL PRODUCTS
All Natural Mousse, Fresh Botanicals Hairspray Super Style Holding Mist, Hi-Shine Styling Gel, Pro-Vitamin Thin-to-Thick™ Hair Spray, Stuck-Up!™ Hair Wax; *Natural Salon Hair Care:* Aloe Vera & Bergamot Finishing Spray, Aloe Vera & Bergamot Shine Spray, Aloe Vera & Bergamot Styling Gel, Aloe Vera & Bergamot Texturizing Cream, Citrus & Mandarin Wax Pomade, Kiwi & Apricot Volumizing Mousse

KISS MY FACE
Hold Up Easy Hold Styling Mousse; Upper Management Medium Hold Styling Gel; *Organic Hair Care:* Big Body, Hold Up Easy Hold Styling Mousse, Upper Management Medium Hold Styling Gel

LAVERANA GMBH & CO. KG ™✔
Lavera Basis Sensitiv: **Special Hair Treatment;** *Lavera Hair:* **Volume and shine styling mousse**

LUSH ™⊘✔
Hair Styling: **Goth Juice Styling Gel, King Of The Mods Hair Gel, The Big Tease Styling Gel**

MONTAGNE JEUNESSE ⊘ ✓
Miracle Hair: Wild Strawberry Boost & Bounce

MORROCCO METHOD
Volumizer Mist Conditioner & Hairspray

SOLARAY NUTRITIONAL SUPPLEMENTS
B5 Design Gel; Natural Misst Super Hold Herbal Hairspray

TARA SMITH LIMITED ™☺⊘✓👁
Hard Hold Gel

HAND & NAIL PRODUCTS

ALTERNATIVE STORES ☺
All products are vegan

AMAZENE ™☺❶⊘✓☼
Avocado & Andiroba Hand Lotion;
Avocado & Andiroba Hand Wash;
Cocoa & Copaiba Hand Lotion;
Cocoa & Copaiba Hand Wash;
Coconut & Buriti Hand Lotion;
Coconut & Buriti Hand Wash;
Mango & Murumuru Hand Lotion;
Mango & Murumuru Hand Wash;
Papaya & Acerola Hand Lotion;
Papaya & Acerola Hand Wash;
Passion Fruit & Guava Hand Lotion;
Passion Fruit & Guava Hand Wash

ANIMAL AID ™☺❶⊘✓⚘1976
Marigold & Marshmallow Handcream

ANNEMARIE BORLIND ✓
Anne Lind: Lemon Grass Hand Balm;
Beauty Extras: Hand Balm

ARBONNE 👁
Intelligence: Hand Cream

AROMA COMFORTS ™☺⊘
Rich Moisture Lemon Hand Cream

AROMATHERAPY PRODUCTS LTD ™☺
**Wild rose & Lemon Leaf handwash;
Wild rose & Lemon Leaf rejuvenating
hand and nail cream;** *Accessories:* **Big
nail clippers, Cuticle nippers, Emery
board, Glass file, Manicure set, Nail
brush, Nail buffer and conditioning
set, Nail clippers, Nail scissors, Nail
stone, Nail whitening tablets,
Pointed end tweezers, Shape and
buff nail block, Slant end tweezers;**
Hand & Foot Care: **Hand & Nail
Cream;** *Hand nourishment:* **Essential
oil Rich Hand and Nail Cream;** *Hand
washes:* **Tea tree, Mandarin and
Bergamot Hand Wash;** *Lavender
Products:* **Lavender and Balm Mint
Hand Wash, Lavender Hand Cream**

ASTONISH
Liquid Hand Wash: Berry, Waterlily,
Wild Herb; *Lquid Hand Wash:* Coconut

AUSTRALIAN TEA TREE
Nail Solutions

BAREFOOT BOTANICALS ☺⊘✓
SOS: Safety Gloves Barrier Hand Cream

BARRY M COSMETICS ✓⚘1982
Nail Whitener Pencil; *3 in 1 Nail Paint:*
All; *Glitter Nail Paint:* All; *Nail Paint:* All;
Neon Nail Paint: All

BEAUTY NATURALS ✔
Gardener's Cream; Nourishing Nail Oil; Skin Smoothing Hand Scrub; *Cuticle Cream:* Gentle, Nourishing; *Martha Hill:* Nourishing Cuticle Cream, Nourishing Nail Oil

BELLECARE AG TM
Hand and Nail Creme; *Handcreme:* **Liposomes and Bio Sheabutter**

BL COSMETICS
Natural Antiseptic Hand Lotion

BONANO GMBH TM⊘
basis sensitiv: **Handcreme**

BOURGEOIS BOHEME TM☺
Beauty Without Cruelty: **High Gloss Nail Colour**

BRONNLEY & CO LTD ✔
Hand and Nail Cream: Apricot & Almond, Bird of Paradise, Gardener's, Lavender, Orchid, Passion Flower, Pink Bouquet, White Iris; *Royal Horticultural Society - Hand & Nail Cream:* Gardener's, Passion Flower; *Royal Horticultural Society - Hand Conditioner:* Passion Flower, Rose; *Royal Horticultural Society - Hand Wash:* Rose

CAWARRA COSMETICS LTD TM
Sanctum: **Hand & Nail Repair Cream**

CELLANDE MIDLANDS ⊘✔
Hand Cleaner: Coconut, Lavender & Avocado Oil, Pine

DESERT ESSENCE ⊘✔⚓1985
Organics: Pumpkin Hand Repair

DIRK ROSSMANN GMBH TM
Alterra: **Handcreme Granatapfel & Aloe Vera**

DOLMA TM☺❶⊘✔👁⚓1976
Hand & Foot Care: **Lemongrass Hand Cream, Nail & Cuticle Oil, Wild Poppy Hand Cream**

DR HAUSCHKA ⊘✔
Neem Nail Oil; Neem Nail Oil Pen

ECO COSMETICS GMBH & CO. KG TM⊘✔☼
Hand Cream

EMPATHY SKINCARE LTD (NATURAL EMPATHY) TM☺✔
Herbal Hand Wash; *Every body:* **Hand And Body Lotion**

ESSENTIALLY NATURAL TM
Lavender and Coconut Hand Balm (Organic); Lemon Cuticle Conditioner (Organic); Orange and Frankincense Hand Balm (Organic); Organic Castor Oil Nail Strengthener

ESSENTIALLY YOURS LTD
Natural Elements Range: NE103 Luxury Hand Cream, NE5236 Lavender & Patchouli Hand Wash; *Passion to Garden Range:* P2G1 Passion to Garden Hand Wash, P2G2 Passion to Garden Hand Lotion; *Professional Range:* NE153T Manicure Kit (Code: NE141/142/143/144)

FAITH PRODUCTS LIMITED ™ ⊘ ✔ ☞ ✈ 1988
Aloe Vera and Tea Tree 300ml / 5 Ltr; Lavender and Geranium 300ml / 5 Ltr; Restorative Hand Cream 50gm; Seaweed 300ml / 5 Ltr

FLORIS ☺ ✔
Natural Benefits: Gently Cleansing Hand Wash, Nourishing Hand and Nail Cream

GREEN WYCH LTD ™☺❶⊘ ✔
Hand Cream: **Bergamot, Fragrance free, Geranium, Lavender, Nourish Hand Cream - Lemongrass, Orange**

HEALTHY HERBS ☺
Lem-Nail Oil

HIPPY HEAVEN NATURAL BEAUTY ™☺⊘ ✔
Coconut & jojoba hand, nail and cuticle oil

HONESTY COSMETICS LTD ™☺❶⊘ ✔ ☞ ✈ 1976
Honesty Essential Range: **Orange Geranium & Lavender Hand Wash, Orange, Geranium & Lavender Hand Cream;** *Honesty Unscented Range:* **Hand Cream with Comfrey, Hand Wash with Chamomille**

I AM NATURAL ™❶⊘ ✔ ✧
Organic Macadamia Nut Hand Cream with Myrrh

KISS MY FACE
Hand Alert: with Rosemary and Mint; *Hand Creme:* Grapefruit and Bergamot; *Hand Lightener:* Lavender and Chamomile

LAVERANA GMBH & CO. KG ™ ✔
Hand Cream: **Orange-Sea Buckthorn, Wild Rose;** *Lavere:* **Body-Effect Protection Intensive Hand Cream, Ultra-Protection Anti-Ageing Hand Cream**

LIZ EARLE ✔
Hand Repair

LUSH ™⊘ ✔
Hand And Body Creams: **Potion**

MANAKEDI SKINCARE ™☺
Amarula Hand Lotion

MISSHU LTD T/A LANI-JO ™☺❶ ✔
Essential: **Hand Lotion, Hand Wash;** *Healing:* **Hand Balm, Handwash;** *Heaven:* **Handwash;** *Sensual:* **Hand Lotion, Handwash**

MJ HEALTH(NZ) LTD ™☺❶⊘ ✔ ☞
Ultra Treat Range: **Ultra Treat Hands Moisturiser**

NATURAL SENSE
Hand Cream; Nail Oil

NEAL'S YARD REMEDIES ⊘ ✔ ☞ ✈ 1998
Citrus Hand Lotion; Citrus Hand Wash; Garden Mint & Bergamot Hand Lotion; Garden Mint & Bergamot Hand Wash; Geranium & Orange Hand Lotion; Juniper & Black Pepper Hand Lotion; Juniper & Black Pepper Hand Wash; Nourishing Melissa Hand Polish; Nourishing Melissa Nail Balm

NEW SEASONS
Rich Moisturising Hand Cream; *Neutral & Toiletry Bases:* Hand Cream

ORGANIC BOTANICS ™⊘✿
Intensive Daily Hand Treatment

ORGANIX SOUTH INC
Thera Neem: Nail and Cuticle Scrub

POTIONS AND POSSIBILITIES ⊘✔
Hand & Nail Cream: English Garden, English Lavender, English Rose; *Hand Wash:* English Garden, English Lavender, English Rose

PURE GAISHA ™☺❶✔
Cinnamon Spice Hand Scrub; Hippy Hempy Hand Cream

QUINESSENCE AROMATHERAPY ☺⊘✔👁
Hand Cream; Hand Cream Base

RIVER VEDA ™⊘✔✿
RiverVeda: **Shea & Berry;** *The Organic Skin Company:* **Everyday Pomegranate & Shea Nut Hand Cream**

RJ MINERAL COSMETICS INTERNATIONAL PTY LTD ™✔
Hand: **CBHNC Cocoa Butter Hand & Nail Cream, HNM Hand & Nail Manicure**

SHANTI PRODUCTS ⊘✔
Almond & Sandalwood Hand Cream

SIMPLE ✔
Anti-Ageing Hand Treatment; Moisturising Hand Wash; Nourish Hand & Nail Lotion; *Hand Cream:* Intensive, Night Care; *Handwash:* Antibacterial, Deep Clean

SKIN BLOSSOM LIMITED ™☺⊘✔✿
Organic: **Organic Bloom rose geranium hand cream**

SPARITUAL ™☺
Affirming Scrub Masque; Amigo; Cuti-Clean; Cuti-Cocktail; Cuti-Quench; DBP Free Nail Lacquer; Eloquent Toner; Farewell; Fluent Conditioning Lacquer Remover; Harmonising Soak Tonic; Impeccable; Infinitely Loving Oil; Infinitely Wise Fragrant Mist; Instinctual Moisturising Lotion; Lacquer Lock; Look Inside 21 Mineral Bath Salts; Multi-Tasker; Nail Lacquer Thinner; Nail Lacquers; Nutri-Thick; Protein Boost; Resurface; Tout de Suite; Visionary Cleanser; Well-Connected Massage Creme

SUMA WHOLEFOODS
™❶⊘✔👁⚘1985
Suma - Ecoleaf range: **Anti-Bacterial Hand Wash**

THE HIGHLAND SOAP COMPANY ⊘
Hand Wash: Ginger & Lemongrass, Scottish Heather, Tea Tree & Lavender

TREASURED EARTH SKINCARE ™☺⊘
Hand Cream

TOILETRIES & COSMETICS

ULTRA GLOW COSMETICS ☺ ✔
High gloss nail colour: Birch, Candyfloss, Classic, Clear, Flame, Fushia, Pink shimmer, Praline, Raspberry, Silver lilac

VERDESATIVA S.R.L. ™☺❶⊘✔☼☻
Barrier Hand Cream

VISIONARY SOAP COMPANY ™☺
Rosemary & Lavender Gardener's Hand Salve (120ml); Rosemary & Lavender Gardener's Hand Salve 60ml

LIP PRODUCTS

ADORN MINERAL COSMETICS ™☺⊘✔
Lip Make-up: **Mineral Lip Gloss, Mineral Lip Liner Pencil, Mineral Lipsticks**

ALEXAMI COSMETICS ™✔
Natural effects lips- mineral lip gloss

AROMATHERAPY PRODUCTS LTD ™☺
Fresh face: **Tea tree and Mandarin lip butter;** *Lavender Products:* **Lavender & Raspberry Lip Balm;** *Tea Tree Products:* **Tea Tree & Mandarin Lip Balm**

BEAUTY NATURALS ✔
Aloe Vera Lip Balm

BRACKENCRAFT ™❶⊘✔
Lip Balm: **Grapefruit Lip Balm, Lemon Lip Balm;** *Lip balms:* **Unfragranced organic fairtrade shea and cocoa, Lemon and lime, Lime, Orange, Peppermint**

BURT'S BEES ⊘✔☻
Medicated Lip Balm

DOLMA ™☺❶⊘✔☻⚕1976
Honesty Lip Balm

ECO LIPS, INC ™
Lip Balms: **Bee Free Lemon & Lime**

GREEN WYCH LTD ™☺❶⊘✔
Lip Balm: **Bergamot, Fragrance free, Lip Silk with Shea Butter, Peppermint**

HEDGECRAFT ™☺⊘
Kiss This! Lip Balm Range: **Mandarin, Peppermint + vit E, Peppermint and grapefruit, Sweet Orange+vit E, Vanilla**

HOLISTIX HERBAL PRODUCTS ❶
Choc Orange Lip Balm

HONESTY COSMETICS LTD ™☺❶⊘✔☻⚕1976
Honesty Unscented Range: **Lip Balm**

I AM NATURAL ™❶⊘✔☼
Lip Balm: **Organic Chamomile & Cocoa Lipbalm, Organic Hemp Lipbalm, Organic Lime & Lavender**

JUST SOAPS ™
Chocomint Lip Balm; Just Lippy Lip Balm; Strawberry & Apricot Lip Balm

KEY SUN LABORATORIES PTY LTD TM⊘
Key Sun: **Lip Balm**

LAVERANA GMBH & CO. KG TM✓
Basis Sensitiv: **Lip Balm**; *Lavere:* **Lip Expert**

LIP INK ☺
Dermal Liquid Smoothe Scrub and Spa Treatment

LUSH TM⊘✓
Lip Balms: **Let Them eat Cake, None Of Your Beeswax, Ultra Balm Moisturiser**; *Lip Scrubs:* **Bubblegum Lip Scrub, Mint Julips Lip Scrub, Sweet Lips Lip Scrub**

MAJIK BLANKIT SKIN CARE TM☺✓
Coconut Lip Balm; Coconut Shimmer Lip Balm; Hint & Tint Lip balm; Lemon & Lime Lip Balm; Natural Lipbalm; Orange & Mandarin Lip Balm; Peppermint Lip Balm; Spearmint Hemp Lip Balm; Sweet Fennel Lip Balm; Vitamin E & Mango Butter Lip Balm SPF 5

NOTHING NASTY ✓
Rosemary & Vanilla Balm

PURE GAISHA TM☺❶✓
Lip Balm

RAW GAIA TM☺❶⊘✓✿☜
Lip Balm - Sweet Orange; Lip Balm - Sweet Peppermint

VEGAN STORE TM☺❶⊘✓
All Products Are Vegan

VISIONARY SOAP COMPANY TM☺
Lip Balms: **Grapefruit, Lemon, Orange, Peppermint**

YAOH TM☺❶⊘✓
Salve; *Lip Balm:* **Blueberry, Coconut, Mango, Spearmint, Strawberries and Cream**

PERFUMES ETC

AKAMUTI
Flower Waters: All; *Pulse Points:* All

AMAZENE TM☺❶⊘✓✿
Amazon Bath & Body - Cologne: **Canto das Aguas, Despertar, Frescor da Manha, Madeira Flor**

ARBONNE ☜
f.y.i: Personal Space Spray Fragrance

AROMATHERAPY PRODUCTS LTD TM☺
Wild rose pulse point perfume; *Pure skin perfumes- precious oils in organic jojoba:* **Jasmine absolute in Organic Jojoba, Orange blossom (neroli) in Organic Jojoba, Rose absolute in Organic Jojoba**

BRACKENCRAFT TM☺❶⊘✓
Solid perfumes: **Floral, Geranium & orange, Lavender, Lemongrass, Orange, lemongrass & cinnamon, Patchouli, Patchouli & orange, Vanilla**

TOILETRIES & COSMETICS

BRONNLEY & CO LTD ✔
Cologne: Apricot & Almond, English Fern, Lavender, Orchid, Pink Bouquet, White Iris; *Eau de Parfum:* Tulip; *Eau de Toilette:* Apricot & Almond, Lavender, Pink Bouquet, White Iris; *Eau Fraiche:* Africa, Asia, Caribbean, Europe, India, Mediterranean; *Royal Horticultural Society - Eau Fraiche:* Passion Flower, Rose

BROOKS- HILL LTD ™
Naturaleve: **Oriental Blossom Perfume**

BURT'S BEES ⊘ ✔ 👁
Bay Rum Cologne

DIRK ROSSMANN GMBH ™
Alterra: **Eau De Toilette**

DOLMA ™☺❶❶ ✔ 👁⤚ 1976
Vegan Perfumes: **Amethyst Mist, Anahita, Andromeda, Calista, Compassion, Cushie B, Keltina, Prelude, Raga, Sarabande, Sonata, Vegamusk**

ESSENTIALLY NATURAL ™
Chill Out! Lavender Roll-On (Organic); Chill Out! Sandalwood Roll-On (Organic)

FLORIS ☺✔
Eau de Parfum Atomiser: Bouquet De La Reine, Cefiro, China Rose, Edwardian Bouquet, Night Scented Jasmine, Seringa, White Rose; *Eau de Toilette Atomiser:* Cefiro, China Rose, Edwardian Bouquet, Fleur, Florissa, Lily of the Valley, Malmaison, Night Scented Jasmine, No. 127, Seringa, Stephanotis, White Rose, Zinnia

LAVERANA GMBH & CO. KG ™✔
Body Spa: **Eau de Toilette Organic Milk and Organic Honey, Eau De Toilette Organic Orange, Eau De Toilette Organic Vervain- Organic Lime, Eau De Toilette Organic Wild Rose**

LUSH ™⊘ ✔
Fragrances: **Flower Market, Ginger, Icon, Karma Atomiser, Vanilla Atomiser;** *Solid Perfumes:* **American Cream, Champagne Snowshowers, Fever, Honey I Washed The Kids, Karma, Sakura, Snow fairy, The Comforter, The Olive Branch, Vanillary solid perfume**

M.A.C. COSMETICS
Creations: MV1, MV2, MV3, Pinkaura, Turqatic

MY SKINCARE LTD ™☺✔
Herbal drops: **Sleepeeze Drops**

NATURE'S GATE
Organics: Labrinto, Presento, Sicuro

NEAL'S YARD REMEDIES
⊘ ✔ 👁⤚ 1998
Cologne; NYR Men Cologne

POTIONS AND POSSIBILITIES ⊘✔
Perfumes: Divinity Cologne, Energy Perfume, Serenity Perfume

PURE GAISHA ™☺❶✔
Solid Perfume

RAW GAIA ™☺❶⊘✔☼👁
MSM Beauty Spray - Frankincense & Argan

REN ⊘
Cologne

STELLA MCCARTNEY
Sheer Stella: Eau de Toilette; *Stella:* Eau de Parfum, Eau de Parfum Natural Spray, Parfum; *Stella in Two:* Peony Eau de Toilette Natural Spray (Not Amber); *Stella Rose Absolute:* Eau de Parfum, Eau de Parfum Natural Spray

SYNTHESIS 345 ™☺❶⊘✔☼
Organic: **Organic Perfumes**

THE PERFUMERS GUILD ☺❶⊘✔
All

TREE-HARVEST ⊘✔
Frankincense & Geranium Moisturiser; Tea Tree Cream; *Tree Colognes:* Cypress, Juniper, Moss, Rowan

VEGAN STORE ™☺❶⊘✔
All

SHAMPOOS

A. VOGEL
Neemcare: Riddance

ABSOLUTE AROMAS ™⊘✔
Ord River: **250ml.**

ALLERGENICS
Medicated Shampoo

ALOE PURA ✔
Organic Aloe Vera Herbal Shampoo Normal/Frequent Use

ALTERNATIVE STORES ☺
All products are vegan

AMAZENE ™☺❶⊘✔☼
Amazon Bath & Body: **Cupuacu;**
Amazon Bath & Body - Shampoo:
Castanha do Brasil / Brazil Nut

ANIMAL AID ™☺❶⊘✔⤚1976
Amber Shampoo; Jojoba Orange & Rosemary; Sea Spray; Tea Tree & Coconut; Woodspice Shampoo

ANN ELISE SKINCARE ☺
Nourishing & Conditioning Shampoo with Organic Lavender, Chamomile and Rosemary

ARBONNE 👁
Intelligence: Daily Self-Adjusting Shampoo, Daily Self-Adjusting Shampoo with Tea Tree Oil

AROMATHERAPY PRODUCTS LTD™☺
Hair Care: **Three in One;** *Lavender Products:* **Lavender & Mint Conditioning;** *Tea Tree Products:* **Tea Tree Lemon & Rosemary, Tea Tree, Lemon and Rosemary Balancing Shampoo**

AUBREY ORGANICS
Blue Camomile: Hydrating Shampoo;
Calaguala Fern: Treatment Shampoo;

Camomile Luxurious: Volumising Shampoo; *Green Tea:* Shampoo; *Honeysuckle Rose:* Moisturising Shampoo; *J.A.Y Desert Herb:* Revitilising Shampoo for Dry Damaged Hair; *Mens Stock:* Ginseng Biotin Shampoo; *Primrose and Lavender:* Scalp-Soothing Shampoo; *Rosa Mosqueta Rose Hip:* Herbal Shampoo; *Swimmers:* Shampoo

AUSTRALIAN TEA TREE
Anti-Dandruff; Deep Cleansing

AVEDA
Be Curly; Brilliant; Color Conserve; Dry Remedy; Smooth Infusion; *Damage Remedy:* Restructuring Shampoo

BAREFOOT BOTANICALS ☺◌✔
SOS: Intensive Care Dry Scalp Shampoo

BEAUTY NATURALS ✔
Deep Moisturising; Gentle Balancing; Protein Enriched; *Martha Hill Purely Natural Haircare:* Enhancing, Mild & Gentle, Moisturising, Treatment, Volumising

BELLECARE AG ™
Repair Shampoo; *Hair and Body:* **Ylang Ylang;** *Repair Shampoo:* **Lemongrass**

BONANO GMBH™◌
Alviana Basic: **Shampoo Feuchtigkeit, Shampoo Sensitiv**

BRACKENCRAFT ™☺❶◌✔
Soaps: **Chamomile Shampoo, Doggy**

Shampoo, Grapefruit Shampoo, Rosemary Shampoo, Tea Tree & Neem Shampoo

BURT'S BEES ◌✔👁
Rosemary Mint Shampoo Bar

CAURNIE SOAPERIE ☺◌✔⚘1976
Nettle; Pure

CAWARRA COSMETICS LTD ™
OrganicSpa: **Shampoo For Dry Hair, Shampoo For Normal Hair, Shampoo For Treated Hair;** *Sanctum:* **Men's Shampoo / Body Wash, Shampoo - Dry, Shampoo - Normal, Shampoo - Treated**

DESERT ESSENCE ◌✔⚘1985
Organics: Green Apple & Ginger, Italian Red Grape, Lemon Tea Tree, Red Raspberry

DIRK ROSSMANN GMBH ™
Alterra: **Dusch Shampoo Parfümfrei, Men Dusch Shampoo Ginkgo & Koffein**

DOLMA ™☺❶◌✔👁⚘1976
Hair Preparations: **Jojoba & Sandalwood;** *Nettle & Pectin Hair Shampoos:* **Bitter Orange & Tangerine, Cedarwood & Cypress, Lavender & Sage, Rosemary, Tea Tree & Thyme**

DR ORGANIC
Aloe Vera: Shampoo; *Lavender:* Shampoo; *Pomegranate:* Shampoo; *Tea Tree:* Shampoo; *Vitamin E:* Shampoo

EARTHPURE ☺🐇
Luxury Shampoo Bar: Geranium and Lavender (Normal Hair), May Chang (Normal to Oily Hair)

ECO COSMETICS GMBH
& CO. KG ™🚫🐇☼
Moisturising Shampoo; Repair Shampoo Tube; Volumising Shampoo

ESSENTIAL CARE
Haircare: Gentle Herb Shampoo, Tea Tree & Herb Shampoo

ESSENTIALLY NATURAL ™
Chamomile Soother Shampoo Bar (Organic); Nettle, Marshmallow and Rosemary Shampoo Bar (Organic)

ESSENTIALLY YOURS LTD
Therapeutics Range: NE033 Therapeutic Shampoo; *Wish Range:* W1 Wild Peppermint & Rosemary Shampoo, W2 Passion Flower & Chamomile Shampoo, W3 Mandarin & Cucumber Shampoo, W4 Lemongrass & Alphine Moss Shampoo

FAITH PRODUCTS
LIMITED ™🚫🐇👁🔬1988
Aloe Vera 400ml / 5 Ltr; Chocolate 400ml / 5 Ltr; Ginkgo Biloba 400ml / 5 Ltr; Hemp and Meadowfoam 400ml / 5 Ltr; Jojoba 400ml / 5 Ltr; Lavender and Geranium 400ml / 5 Ltr; Rosemary 400ml / 5 Ltr; Seaweed 400ml / 5 Ltr; Tea Tree 400ml/ 5 Ltr

FLORIS ☺🐇
Conditioning Shampoo; *Natural Benefits:* Shine Boosting Conditioning Shampoo

FOREVER LIVING PRODUCTS
Aloe Jojoba Shampoo

FREERANGERS ™☺🐇
Mane Taming Conditioning Shampoo

FUNK BUBBLE ™☺
Organic: **Aloe Vera, Chocolate;** *Shampoo:* **Jojoba, Lavender/Geranium, Tea Tree**

GREEN PEOPLE CO. ™🚫🐇
Shampoo: **C001 Aloe Vera Shampoo, C004 Rosemary Shampoo, C014 Vitamin Shampoo, C030 Intensive Repair Shampoo, C033 Moisturising Shampoo, F016 Kids Shampoo Lavender, F020 Kids Shampoo Citrus & Aloe Vera, H004 Organic Base Shampoo, M010 Itch Away Shampoo, R022 Nourishing Spa Shampoo, R024 Volume Building Spa Shampoo, T027 Shampoo & Shower**

GREEN VALLEY
TRADING CO ™☺❶🐇
Yaoh: **All products are vegan**

GREEN WYCH LTD ™☺❶🐇
Shampoo: **Bayleaf and Sweet Orange, Liquid Soap Handwash with Chamomile, Luxury Conditioning Shampoo with Herbal Extracts, Nettle and Lavender, Rosemary and Geranium**

HEALTHQUEST LIMITED ™🚫🐇
Organic Blue- Body Care: **Normal/Dry, Normal/Greasy;** *Pure Adore:*

Chamomile Shampoo & Bodywash,
Lavender Shampoo & Bodywash,
Mandarin Shampoo & Bodywash

HEMP GARDEN ™
Shampoo: **Carrot & Nettle for dry/damaged hair, Kelp & Cucumber for all hair types, Sage and Echinacea for lacklustre/greasy hair**

HERBS HANDS HEALING LTD ™ ⊘ ✔
Head & Hair

HERBSGO LIMITED T/A CLIVE FOOT ☺
Clive Foot: Kelp and Olive Oil, Orange and Cider, Patchouli and Tea Tree, Soya and Kelp

HOLISTIX HERBAL PRODUCTS ❶
Neem Shampoo Bar

HONESTY COSMETICS LTD ™☺❶⊘ ✔ ☜ ✄ 1976
Chamomile & Orange; Hair & Body; Lemon & Vanilla; Nettle & Lavender; Peach & Coconut; *Honesty Essential Range:* **Nettle & Lavender Shampoo;** *Honesty Fruit Range:* **Apple & Rosemary Conditioning Shampoo, Lemon & Vanilla Shampoo, Orange & Chamomille Shampoo, Peach & Coconut Shampoo;** *Honesty Unscented Range:* **Hair & Body Shampoo**

HOWAD LTD T/A INCOGNITO ™❶⊘✔
Incognito: **Java Citronella 2 in 1 Shampoo+Conditioner**

I AM NATURAL ™❶⊘ ✔ ☼
Shampoo: **Organic Lavender & Geranium Shampoo for Dry Hair, Organic Lime and Rosemary For Oily Hair, Organic Tea Tree - Anti Dandruff**

INNGINNI LIMITED (OHSOBO) ™☺
Ohsobo: **Anti-Dandruff Shampoo with Bergamot, Shampoo - Original Formula**

ITS ELIXIR (UK) LIMITED ™⊘ ✔ ☜
Normal Hair Shampoo

JASON NATURAL PRODUCTS
84% Pure Aloe Vera Shampoo, Damage Control, Dandruff Relief™, Hemp Super Moisturizing, Henna Hi-Lights, Lavender Shampoo Hair Strengthening, Natural Apricot, Natural Biotin Shampoo, Natural Jojoba Shampoo, Natural Sea Kelp, Pro-Vitamin Thin-to-Thick™, Rosewater Shampoo – 70% Organic, Swimmers & Sports™, Tall Grass™, Tea Tree Scalp Normalizing, Vitamin E with A & C Shampoo; *All Natural Color Enhancing Temporary Shampoos:* Black Hair, Blonde Hair, Brown Hair, Red Hair; *Natural Salon Hair Care:* Kiwi & Apricot Volumizing, Plumeria & Sea Kelp Moisturizing, Rosewater & Chamomile Normalizing

JR LIGGETT ☺
Shampoo Bars: Damaged Hair Formula, Herbal Formula, Jojoba & Peppermint, Original Formula

JUNGLESALE LIMITED ™
Neem Herbal Shampoo; Neem
Herbal Shampoo

KEY SUN LABORATORIES
PTY LTD ™⊘
Key Sun: **Shampoo**

KISS MY FACE
Big Body; Miss Treated; Whenever;
Organic Hair Care: Big Body, Miss
Treated, Whenever

LAVERANA GMBH & CO. KG ™✓
Lavera Basis Sensitiv: **Balm Shampoo,**
Regenerative Shampoo, Shower
Shampoo, Vital Shampoo; *Lavera*
HAIR: **Almond Milk Shampoo, Apple**
Milk Shampoo, Cornflower
Shampoo, Lemon Milk Shampoo,
Mango Milk Shampoo, Orange Milk
Shampoo, Rose Milk Shampoo;
Lavera Neutral: **Shower shampoo**

LUSH ™⊘✓
Hair Care: **Antiphilitron Shampoo,**
Gentle Lentil Solid Shampoo, Ibiza
Party, Ice Blue Shampoo, Washday
Greens Shampoo; *Liquid Shampoos:*
Big, Cynthia Sylvia Stout, Daddyo, I
Love Juicy, Rehab; *Shampoo Bars:*
New, Soak and Float, Squeaky
Green; *Solid Shampoo Bar:* **Godiva;**
Solid Shampoo Bars: **Jumping Juniper,**
Karma Comba, Seanik, Soft, The
Blonde, Trichomania, Ultimate Shine

MJ HEALTH(NZ) LTD ™☺❶⊘✓👁
Earths Gift Range: **Solid shampoo bar**

MORROCCO METHOD
Apple Cider Vinegar Natural Holistic;
Holistic Organic: Earth Essence, Pine
Shale, Sea Essence

MY HANDMADE SOAPS ™☺⊘✓
Men's collection: **Cool for men**
shampoo bar, Sea Breeze shampoo
bar; *Shampoo bars:* **Almond Milk**
Shampoo bar, Aloe Vera Shampoo
bar, Coconut shampoo bar,
Lavender Shampoo bar, Lemongrass
& Lime Shampoo bar, Soft Oatmeal
shampoo bar

NATURA ORGANICS ⊘✓☼
Fortifying with Vitamin E, Nettle and
Lemon; Nourishing with Jojoba, Vitamin
E and Aloe Vera

NATURAL SENSE
Shampoo

NATURE'S GATE
Aloe Vera Moisturizing Shampoo;
Awapuhi Volumizing Shampoo; Biotin
Strengthening Shampoo; Chamomile
Replenishing Shampoo; Hemp
Nourishing Shampoo; Henna Shine
Enhancing Shampoo; Herbal Daily
Shampoo; Jojoba Revitalizing Shampoo;
Pomegranate Sunflower Shampoo;
Rainwater Clarifying Shampoo; Tea Tree
Calming Shampoo; *Organics - Fruit*
Blend: Asian Pear & Red Tea, Grapefruit
& Wild Ginger, Mandarin Orange &
Patchouli, Persimmon & Rose
Geranium; *Organics - Herbal Blend:*
Chamomile & Lemon Verbena,
Lavender & Aloe, Lemongrass & Clary
Sage, Tea Tree & Blue Cypress

TOILETRIES & COSMETICS

NEAL'S YARD REMEDIES
🚫 🐇 👁 ⚘ 1998
Baseline Hair Shampoo; Calendula
Shampoo; Chamomile & Orange Flower
Shampoo; Coconut & Jojoba Shampoo;
Geranium (Rejuvenating) Shampoo;
Nettle & Sage Shampoo; Rosemary &
Thyme Shampoo; Seaweed (Invigorating)
Shampoo; Seaweed Shampoo

OPTIMAH 🚫 🐇 ⚘ 1995
Raw Aloe: Shampoo with Tea Tree,
Vitamin B5 & Citrus Oils

ORGANIC SOAP COMPANY ™🚫✿
Organic Shampoo Bars: **Anti dandruff
shampoo- Seaweed and Sage, Anti
headlice shampoo- Neem and Tea
Tree, Chamomile and Orange,
Mandarin and Orange Blossom,
Nettle and Horsetail, Organic
Shampoo For Dogs, Tea Tree, Tea
Tree and Peppermint;**
Shampoo/Conditioner Bars: **Anti
Headlice, Chamomile & Orange
Blossom, Nettle & Horsetail,
Seaweed & Sage, Specially for
Mums - Orange Blossom**

ORGANIX SOUTH INC
Thera Neem: Shampoo

POTIONS AND POSSIBILITIES 🚫 🐇
Hair Shampoo: Essential Moisture
Repair, Tea Tree Shampoo

PZ CUSSONS UK LTD ™🚫 🐇
Original Source Shampoos: **Almond &
Coconut, Lime and Guarana, Rose &
Aloe, Tangerine & Bergamot, Tea**

Tree & Mint, White Pear and
Avocado

QUINESSENCE
AROMATHERAPY ☺🚫 🐇 👁
Frequent Shampoo; Mild Shampoo
Base; Tea Tree

REN 🚫
Moringa Seed Micro-Protein Universal
Shampoo

RJ MINERAL COSMETICS
INTERNATIONAL PTY LTD ™🐇
Hair: **HS Hair Shampoo -
Sandalwood & Ylang Ylang, HS Hair
Shampoo - Unscented**

SAHFEE HALAL CARE ™☺🚫 🐇
Halal products - Shampoos: **Gents'
shampoo - Herenshampoo, Ladies'
shampoo - Damesshampoo,
Shampoo for veiled hair - Bedekt
haar shampoo**

SHANTI PRODUCTS 🚫 🐇
Herbal Shampoo

SIMPLE 🐇
Shampoo: Colour Protect, Frequent

SIMPLY SOAPS
Cleansing Body Shampoo; Invigorating
Shower Shampoo; Liquid; *Shampoo
Bars:* Chamomile, Rosemary & Lavender

SKIN BLOSSOM
LIMITED ™☺🚫 🐇 ✿
Organic: **Complete Care Shampoo**

214

**SOLARAY NUTRITIONAL
SUPPLEMENTS**
Blue Camomile Hydrating; Calaguala
Fern Treatment; Chamomile Luxurious
Volumising; Ginseng Biotin; Green Tea;
Honeysuckle Rose Moisturising; J.A.Y.
Revitalising; Primrose & Lavender Scalp-
Soothing; Rosa Mesqueta Rose Hip
Nourishing; Selenium Natural
Treatment; Swimmers

SUKI PURE SKIN CARE
Clean Balance with Yerba Protein &
Sugar Extracts

SUMA WHOLEFOODS
™❶⊘✔👁🏃‍1985
**Clear & Simple; Cucumber;
Grapefruit & Aloe Vera; Mandarin;
Rose Petal & Geranium; White
Lavender**

TARA SMITH LIMITED ™☺⊘✔👁
Tara Smith: **Big Baby Shampoo, C
Curl Shampoo, Feed The Root
Shampoo, Shampoo for Straight Hair**

THE HIGHLAND SOAP COMPANY ⊘
Rosemary & Wild Nettle; Shampoo Bar;
Wild Nettle & Heather Shampoo

TINTS OF NATURE ⊘✔
Shampoo (Not sulphate Free)

TREE-HARVEST ⊘✔
Organic shampoo bars: Neem, Tropical
Coconut

**TRUTHFUL CO. LTD
(PURELY SKINCARE)** ™☺⊘
Purely Skincare: **Shampoo-
normal/oily variant, Shampoo-
sensitive variant, Shampoo-
Volumising Variant, Shampoo-
Smooth and Sleek variant**

URTEKRAM
Shampoo: All

VERDESATIVA S.R.L. ™☺❶⊘✔☼🌐
**Purifying Cream Shampoo - Hemp
and White Mud; Restoring Shampoo
- Shine and Volume; Shampoo
Antiforfora Canapa e Betulla (Anti-
dandruff Shampoo Hemp and Birch);
Shampoo Delicato Canapa e Proteine
Del Grano (Mild Shampoo Hemp and
Wheat Proteins); Shampoo Doccia
Fitness & Sport - 200ml (Fitness &
Sport Shampoo and Bath/Shower
Gel); Shampoo Energizzante Canapa
e Ginseng (Energising Shampoo for
Prevention of Hairloss); Shampoo
Fitness and Sport - 1 litre; Shampoo
per Capelli Grassi Canapa e Tea Tree
(Equilibratine Shampoo for Greasy Hair)**

YAOH ™☺❶⊘✔
Shampoo

SHAVING PRODUCTS

ANNEMARIE BORLIND ✔
For Men: Aftershave Balm, Aftershave
Gel, Caring Shaving Cream

ARBONNE 👁
NutriMenC RE: REveal Shave Gel

AUBREY ORGANICS
Mens Stock: Northwoods Shaving
Cream; *Womens Shaving:* Creme de la
Shave Toasted Almond

BAREFOOT BOTANICALS ☺🚫🐰
SOS: Calm Down Post-Shave Face Balm,
Close Shave Hydrating Shaving Cream

BEAUTY NATURALS 🐰
David Hill: Cleansing & Shaving Gel,
Skin Calming Aftershave Balm, Skin
Calming Shaving Oil, Skin Refreshing
Aftershave Gel, Skin Soothing Cream
Shave

BRONNLEY & CO LTD 🐰
Body Care for Men: After Shave, After
Shave Balm, Shaving Cream

BURT'S BEES 🚫🐰👁
Bay Rum: Aftershave Balm

CAWARRA COSMETICS LTD ™
Organic Soap Shave; *Sanctum:* **Men's
Shaving Gel**

DOLMA ™☺❶🚫🐰👁⚒1976
Especially For Men: De-luxe
Aftershave Balm, Wet Shaving Fluid

DROYT PRODUCTS 🚫🐰⚒1984
Shaving Soap

EARTHPURE ☺🐰
Soap Bars: Shaving Bar

ESSENTIALLY NATURAL ™
**Lime and Lavender Shaving Soap
(Organic)**

ESSENTIALLY YOURS LTD
Mu Mens Range: M7 Orange &
Grapefruit Preshave Toner, M9
Cedarwood & Tea Tree Shave Oil

FLORIS ☺🐰
Aftershave Balm: Elite, JF, No 89,
Santal; *Conditioning Shaving Cream:*
Elite, JF, No 89, Santal; *Eau de Toilette
Atomiser:* Elite, JF, Limes, No 89, Santal,
Vetiver; *Shaving Soap and Bowl:* Elite,
JF, No 89; *Shaving Soap Refill:* Elite, JF,
No 89

HERBS HANDS HEALING LTD ™🚫🐰
**Splash on Toner; Sunrise After
Shave Water**

**HIPPY HEAVEN
NATURAL BEAUTY** ™☺🚫🐰
**Foaming shave gel for men;
Soothing shave oil for men**

INNOCENT OILS ™☺🚫🐰
Shaving Oil: **Innocent Shave Oil**

ITS ELIXIR (UK) LIMITED ™🚫🐰👁
**Aloe Vera After Shave Gel; Shaving
oil - women; Shaving oil Men;
Shaving oil men sensitive**

JASON NATURAL PRODUCTS
All Natural After Shave Tonic, All
Natural Shaving Lotion

JR LIGGETT ☺
Shaving Foam

JUST SOAPS ™
Shaving Soap

KISS MY FACE
Moisture Shave: Cool Mint, Fragrance Free, Key Lime, Lavender and Shea, Peaceful Patchouli, Peaches & Creme, Vanilla Earth

LAVERANA GMBH & CO. KG ™ 🐰
Men SPA: **Aftershave Balm, Aftershave Lotion**

LIZ EARLE 🐰
Skincare for Men: After-Shaving Moisturiser, Sensitive Shave Cream

LUSH ™ ⊘ 🐰
Shaving Creams: **Shave the Planet Shaving Cream**

MAJIK BLANKIT SKIN CARE ™☺ 🐰
Jojoba & Cocoa Butter Shave Lotion; Organic Calendula and Rosewood shave oil

MY HANDMADE SOAPS ™☺⊘ 🐰
Men's collection: **Cool for men shaving bar, Sea Breeze shaving bar**

NATURAL BY NATURE OILS ☺
Easy Shave Oil

NATURAL SENSE
Shaving Oil

NATURE'S GATE
Organics - Herbal Blend Shave Tubes: Cucumber & Mint, Lavender & Aloe, Lemongrass & Clary Sage

NEAL'S YARD REMEDIES
⊘ 🐰 👁 ⅄ 1998
After Shave Balm; NYR Men Calming After Shave Balm; NYR Men Close Shave Cream; NYR Men Close Shave Oil; NYR Men Close Shave Soap; Red Clay Shaving Cream; Shaving Oil

NEW SEASONS
After Shave Gel

NOTHING NASTY 🐰
Smoothly Does it Shave Oil

ORGANIC SOAP COMPANY ™⊘ ✿
Organic Shaving Bars: **Buccaneer Shave, Old Original Shave, Patchouli Shave, Tea Tree Shave, Zanzybar shaving bar;** *Shaving Soaps:* **Old Original, Patchouli Peculier Shave, Tea Tree**

ORGANIX SOUTH INC
Thera Neem: Men's Shaving Bar

PURE GAISHA ™☺❶ 🐰
Soothing Shaving Balm - For Men

PZ CUSSONS UK LTD ™⊘ 🐰
Original Source Shaving Balm: **Whole Leaf Aloe Ginseng After-Shave Balm;** *Original Source Shaving Gel:* **Avocado & Aloe Vera, Kelp Oil & Zinc Ore, Mint & Tea Tree, Pure Lime shave gel**

TOILETRIES & COSMETICS

QUINESSENCE
AROMATHERAPY ☺⊘✓👁
Aftershave Balm

REN ⊘
Multi-Tasking After Shave Balm;
Tamanu High Glide Shaving Oil

RIVER VEDA ™⊘✓✿
RiverVeda: **Best Day;** *The Organic Skin
Company:* **Aloe & Lemon Balm
Shaving Soap**

SIMPLE ✓
Daily Face Wash; *Balm:* Cooling,
Soothing; *Shave:* Foam, Gel, Silicon Gel

SIMPLY SOAPS
Shaving Bars: Eucalyptus & Lavender

SOLARAY NUTRITIONAL
SUPPLEMENTS
Northwoods Shaving Cream

THE HIGHLAND SOAP COMPANY ⊘
Soaps: Shaving soap

TREE-HARVEST ⊘✓
Shaving Soap Bowl: Bay, Juniper,
Patchouli & Sandlewood

VERDESATIVA S.R.L. ™☺❶⊘✓✿👁
**Anti Age Face Cream and
Aftershave; Anti-Age Face Cream &
Aftershave; Emulsione Post
Depilazione
(Post-Depilation Lotion)**

WELEDA ⊘✓⚘1985
Smooth Shave Toner

SKIN CARE
- MASKS, WRAPS, ETC

AKAMUTI
Clay Mask Pack

AMAZENE ™☺❶⊘✓✿
**Avocado & Andiroba Body Scrub;
Cocoa & Copaiba Body Scrub;
Coconut & Buriti Body Scrub;
Mango & Murumuru Body Scrub;
Papaya & Acerola Body Scrub;
Passion Fruit & Guava Body Scrub**

ANNEMARIE BORLIND ✓
Beauty Extras: Anti-Stress Mask,
Exfoliating Peel; *LL Regeneration Series:*
Moisturising Cream Mask, Vital Cream
Mask; *Purifying Care Series:* Cleansing
Mask

ARBONNE 👁
f.y.i: Sugar Slush Body Scrub;
Intelligence: Exfoliating Masque with
Thermal Fusion; *NutriMin C RE9:* REgain
Illuminating Enzyme Peel, RElease Deep
Pore Cleansing Masque, REtaliate
Wrinkle Filler, REveal Facial Scrub,
REversing Gellee Transforming Lift;
SeaSource Detox Spa: Foaming Sea Salt
Scrub, Sea Mud Face and Body Mask

ARISE AND SHINE
COSMETICS LTD ™☺❶
**Dead sea mud & green clay face &
body mask with goldenseal**

AROMATHERAPY PRODUCTS LTD ™☺
Accessories: **White exfoliating gloves;**
Lavender Products: **Lavender exfoliating body scrub;** *Skin treatments and solutions:* **Tea tree and Kanuka gel**

AUBREY ORGANICS
Blue Green Algae : Soothing Mask;
Green Tea and Ginkgo: Clay Rejuvenating Mask; *Natural Herbal:* Sea Clay with Goa Herb Oil Balancing Mask; *Rosa Mosqueta:* Jojoba and Oatmeal Mask and Scrub, Rose Hip Seed Oil Moisturising Nutrient; *Sea Buckthorn:* Moisturising Mask; *Vegecell:* Nightime Hydrator with Green Tea; *Vegecol with Organic Aloe:* Oatmeal Soothing Mask

AUSTRALIAN TEA TREE
Blemish Gel; Blemish Stick

BAREFOOT BOTANICALS ☺☺⊘✒
Rosa Fina: Masquerade Rejuvenating Masque

BEAUTY NATURALS ✒
Facial Care - Treatments: Seaweed Peeling Mask; *Skin Revivals - Refining:* Hydrating Gel Mask

BELLECARE AG ™
2 Phases Mask; Bodypeeling; Kaolina; Terra Vita Pure; *Vleur:* **Kaolin Maske, Peeling 2 in 1, Terra Vital Maske**

BIO-OIL
Specialist Skincare Oil: For the Treatment of Scars and Stretch Marks

BL COSMETICS
Million Year Old Mud Body Pack;
Tomato & Red Pepper Food Mask; *Face Packs:* Mango & Honeydew Melon, Orange Sage & Fennel, Pulp Friction, Tea Tree, Watercress

BONANO GMBH ™⊘
Alviana Feuchtigkeit: **Feuchtigkeitsmaske;** *Alviana Rose:* **Pflegemaske**

BURT'S BEES ⊘✒👁
Healthy Treatment: Pore-Refining Mask

CAWARRA COSMETICS LTD ™
OrganicSpa: **Body Mask, Clay Mask, Face Exfoliant, Gel Mask, Treatment C, Treatment Clay Mixed;** *OrganicSpa Range:* **Clay Mask, Gel Mask;** *Sanctum:* **Hydrating Gel Mask, Purifying Clay Mask**

CEBRA ETHICAL CHIC ™⊘✒
Cebra- ethical skin care: **Chocolate Orange Body scrub, Glacial Mud Masque, Shea Butter Coffee Body Scrub**

DOLMA ™☺❶⊘✒👁✂1976
Skin Care: **Honesty Facial Mask**

DR HAUSCHKA ⊘✒
Facial Steam Bath

DR ORGANIC
Tea Tree: Blemish Stick

ESSENTIALLY YOURS LTD
Fragrance Free Range: FF7 Fragrance Free Face Mask; *Mu Mens Range:* M3

Patchouli & Lavender Face Mask;
Natural Elements Range: NE007
Lemongrass & Rosemary Face Mask,
NE014 Patchouli & Lavender Face
Mask, NE020 Lavender & Geranium
Face Mask; *Professional Range:* AV2T
Seaweed Wrap Concentrate, NE098T
Seaweed Body Wrap Gel

FAITH PRODUCTS LTD
TM⊘ ✔ ☞ ✈−1988
Purifying Facial Wash 150ml

FOREVER LIVING PRODUCTS
Aloe Scrub

GREEN PEOPLE CO. TM⊘ ✔
Face Masks: **R006 Purifying Mineral
Mask, T003 Peel Off Face Mask Kit**

GREEN WYCH LTD TM☺❶⊘ ✔
Face Mask: **ChocMouse Face Mask**

**HIPPY HEAVEN
NATURAL BEAUTY** TM☺ ✔
**Mens energy face and body scrub;
Natural purity face mask- all skin
types**

HOLISTIX HERBAL PRODUCTS ❶
Face Pack - 200ml Kilner Jar; Face Pack
Kit

HONESTY COSMETICS LTD
TM☺❶⊘ ✔ ☞ ✈−1976
Face Mask w Tea Tree & Lavender

**HOWAD LTD
T/A INCOGNITO** TM❶⊘ ✔
Incognito: **Exfoliating scrub**

I AM NATURAL TM❶⊘ ✔ ✿
**Organic Ylang Ylang & Tea Tree
Face Mask**

INNOCENT OILS TM☺⊘ ✔
Face Mask: **Innocent Rhassoothe
Mask;** *Innocent Angel:* **Innocent
Angel Face Scrub**

ITS ELIXIR (UK) LIMITED TM⊘ ✔ ☞
**Face scrubbing gel; Peeling cream-
dry skin; Peeling cream- oily skin;
Peeling cream- sensitive skin**

JASON NATURAL PRODUCTS
Ester-C® Skin Care: C-Lite™ Skin Tone
Balancer, Ester-C® Hydrating Masque,
Hyper-C Serum™ Anti-Aging Therapy,
Vita-C Max™ One Minute Facial

**KEY SUN LABORATORIES
PTY LTD** TM⊘
Key Sun: **Face Mask, Hydrating Mask**

KISS MY FACE
Organic Face Care: Pore Shrink Deep
Pore Mask Cleansing Masque; *Potent &
Pure Face Care:* Pore Shrink Deep Pore
Cleansing Mask, So Refined Jojoba &
Mint Facial Scrub, Start Up Exfoliating
Face Wash

LAVERANA GMBH & CO. KG TM✔
Special Effect; *Lavere:* **Body-Effect
Active Body Scrub, Hydro Energy
Effect Gel Facial Mask, Hydro
Energy Peel**

LIZ EARL ✔
Brightening Treatment Mask; Energising
Body Scrub; Energising Hip and Thigh

Gel; Intensive Nourishing Treatment
Mask; Spot-On

LUSH ™🚫🐇
Bio Fresh: **Catastrophe Cosmetic,
Cupcake, Santa's Rice Porridge**

MAJIK BLANKIT SKIN CARE ™☺🐇
Mandarin & Apricot Body Scrub

MANAKEDI SKINCARE ™☺
Active Face and Body Mask

MJ HEALTH(NZ) LTD ™☺❶🚫🐇👁
Earths Gift Range: **Normal/dry skin
face mask, Oily skin face mask,
Softly softly facial exfoliant;** *Salon
Only Range:* **Divine Facial Scrub**

MONTAGNE JEUNESSE 🚫🐇
Green Tea Chin & Forehead Strips;
Orange Nose Strips; Tea Tree Blemish
Dots; *Face Masque:* Collagen,
Cucumber Peel-Off, Dead Sea Mud
Tired Skin Reviving, Microderma
Abrasion, Peach Kernel & Walnut
Exfoliating, Peel Off Deep Pore
Cleaning, Pore Refining, Red Hot Earth
Sauna; *Masque:* Algae & Dead Sea Salt
Cellulite Body Mud, Anti Cellulite Body
Mud; *Night Face Masque:* Marine Algae
& Shea Butter Ultra Firming,
Pomegranate & Nori Juice Ultra
Moisturising

MY SKINCARE LTD ™☺🚫🐇
Cleansing: **Cellular Renewal Facial
Peel, Cellular Renewal Masque,
Hydrating Masque**

NATURA ORGANICS 🚫🐇☼
Hydrating Mask; Purifying Mask

NATURAL SENSE
Chocolate Dreams Face Mask

NATURE'S GATE
Organics - Advanced Care:
Microdermabrasion System, Natural
Results Acne Extra Strength Spot
Corrector, Natural Results Acne
Treatment Kit

NEAL'S YARD REMEDIES
🚫🐇👁🔬1998
Kaolin

NEW SEASONS
Gentle Face Mask

OPTIMAH 🚫🐇🔬1995
Raw Aloe: Cellulite Massage Gel

ORGANIC BOTANICS ™🚫☼
**Refining French Clay & Seaweed
Creamy Face Mask**

ORGANIX SOUTH INC
Thera Neem: Mud Masque

PURE GAISHA ™☺❶🐇
**Clay Face Mask - Mature Skin; Clay
Face Mask - Normal Skin; Wake Up
and Smell The Coffee Scrub**

QUINESSENCE
AROMATHERAPY ☺🚫🐇👁
Marine Clay Mask

RARE NATURAL CARE, INC. ™☺❶◐✎ ✿👁

Rare2B Vegan Skincare: **Detox facial Mask**

RAW GAIA ™☺❶◐✎✿👁

Raw Chocolate Face Pack; Sun-Dried Green Clay Face Pack

REN ◐

Body Scrubs: Ginger, Revivo-Tonic Two Sugar Body Scrub, Guerande Salt Exfoliating Body Balm, Monoi and Shea Butter Body Balm; *Face Masks:* F10 Enzymatic Smooth Radiance Facial Mask, Glycolactic Skin Renewal Peel Mask, Jiaogulan Revitalising Facial Mask, Multi-Mineral Detoxifying Facial Mask, Phyto-Dynamic Instant Lifting Gel

SIMPLE ✎

Deep Cleansing Face Mask; Nourishing Moisture Mask

SIMPLY SOAPS

Hedgerow Herbals: Purifying Green French Clay

SKINCARE CAFE LTD ☺

Organic grapeseed & aloe vera exfoliator; Organic rose petals body scrub

SKINVAC ™☺◐✎

Exfoliation Cloth

SOLARAY NUTRITIONAL SUPPLEMENTS

Mask: Blue Green Algae, Green Tea & Green Clay, Natural Herbal Sea Clay with Goa Herb Oil, Rosa Mosqueta

Jojoba & Oatmeal, Sea Buckthorn, Vegecol with Organic Aloe & Oatmeal

SOPHYTO ™❶◐✎👁

Anti-aging antioxidant serum; Dual Action Exfoliating Treatment; Marine Peptide Brightening Treatment

SUKI PURE SKIN CARE

Transformative Facial Clay with Green Tea Roses & White Willow

SUPERDRUG

Amie: New Leaf Skin Exfoliating Polish; *Naturals:* Mango & Papaya Body Polish

TREASURED EARTH SKINCARE ™☺◐

Face Scrub

VANILLA TREE NATURAL SKIN CARE ™☺✎

Exfoliating Face Mask - Normal/Dry; Exfoliating Face Mask - Oily/Combination; Hydrating Face Mist; Moisture Balance Face Cream; Moisture Replenish Face Cream

WELEDA ◐✎🐾1985

Almond Facial Masque; Iris Facial Masque; Iris Intensive Treatment Masque; Wild Rose Intensive Facial Masque

SKIN CARE - MOISTURISERS & BODY LOTIONS

ABSOLUTE AROMAS ™⊘ 🖌
Ord River: **Hand & Body Lotion 250ml**

ABSOLUTELY PURE
Shea Butter

AINSWORTHS
Recovery Cream

AKAMUTI
Repleneshing Rose Facial Oil; Shea Soothing Salve; *Body Butter:* Cocoa & Almond, Shea & Olive, Shea Mandarin; *Butter:* Mango, Murumuru, Neem, Organic Cocoa Butter, Red Palm, Shea, Sweet Almond Tree

AKOMA INTERNATIONAL (UK) LTD ™⊘ 🖌
Raw Shea Butter

ALOE PURA 🖌
Organic Aloe Vera Gel; Organic Aloe Vera Gel with Tea Tree; Organic Aloe Vera Gel with Vitamins A, C & E

ALTERNATIVE STORES ☺
All products are vegan

ALVIN CONNOR LIMITED ™☺⊘
Natural Balance: **Natural Body Polish, Lavender Body Polish, Rose Body Polish**

223

AMAZENE ™☺❶⓪☀✦☼
Avocado & Andiroba Body Butter;
Avocado & Andiroba Body Lotion;
Cocoa & Copaiba Body Butter;
Cocoa & Copaiba Body Lotion;
Coconut & Buriti Body Butter;
Coconut & Buriti Body Lotion;
Mango & Murumuru Body Butter;
Mango & Murumuru Body Lotion;
Papaya & Acerola Body Butter;
Papaya & Acerola Body Lotion;
Passion Fruit & Guava Body Butter;
Passion Fruit & Guava Body Lotion;
amaZene/Phytophilo : **Body Lotion
Desodorante Calendula, Primola e
Lavanda, Body Lotion Desodorante
Cha Verde, Aloe Vera e Erva Doce,
Creamy Oil Desodorante Chocolate
& Cupuacu, Creamy Oil Desodorante
Morango com Chantilly, Creamy Oil
Desodorante Papaia, Maracuja e
Acerola;** *Amazon Bath & Body:* **Brazil
Nut Oil;** *Amazon Bath & Body- Body
Lotion:* **Frutas Tropicais, Maracuja,
Murumuru;** *Natural Company-
Moisturising Cream:* **Baunilha, Lima,
Maca & Canela, Mandarina, Pessego
com Chantilly;** *Natural Company-
Moisturising Cream:* **Mousse de
Maracuja;** *Phytophilo Aromatherapy
Range- Body Cremes* **Cocoa &
Cupuacu, Papaya, Passion Fruit &
Acerola, Strawberry n Cream;**
*Phytophilo Aromatherapy Range- Body
Lotions:* **Green Tea, Aloe Vera & Anise,
Lavender, Calendula & Primrose**

ANIMAL AID ™☺❶⓪☀⚖-1976
**Apricot & Jojoba Moisturising
Cream; Olive Body Cream; Vanilla &
Macadamia Nourishing Cream;** *Body
Lotion:* **Calendula and Vanilla
Moisturising Lotion, Exotic Body
Lotion, Unscented Vitamin E Cream,
Unscented Vitamin E Lotion**

ANN ELISE SKINCARE ☺
Pure Magic Moisture

ANNEMARIE BORLIND ☀
Aqua Bleu Vitality Gel; *Anne Lind:* Body
Lotions (All); *Beauty Extras:* Ceramide
Vital Fluid, Facial Firming Gel,
Natursome, Skin Whitening Fluid; *Body
Effect:* Anti Cellulite Gel, Energising
Scrub, Firming Cream; *For Men:* Anti-
Ageing Revitalizing Cream, Revitalizing
Body Lotion; *LL Regeneration Series:*
Concentrate Ampoules, Decollete
Cream, Moisturising Ampoules;
Purifying Care Series: Facial Cream For
Day and Night, Ultra Stick; *Young
Beauty - Peach Series:* Facial Cream

ARBONNE ☞
f.y.i: Body Better Body Cream;
Intelligence: Body Lotion, Personalizer,
Rejuvenating Cream, Skin Conditioning
Oil; *NutriMenC RE:* REality Moisturiser
with Suncreen; *NutriMin C RE9:*
REactivating Body Serum, REactivating
Facial Serum Day & Night, REality SPF8
Day Creme, REcover Night Creme,
REfinish Hydrating Body Lotion;
SeaSource Detox Spa: Re-Mineralizing
Body Lotion 24H, Renewing Body Gelee

ARISE AND SHINE
COSMETICS LTD ™☺❶
**Coconut and lavender moisturiser;
Rosemary and Jojoba Infusion with
Peppermint; Shea butter**

AROMA COMFORTS ™☺⊘
Ma Ma's Belly Butter; Organic Almond & Cocoa Butter Body Lotion; Skin Comforting Creamy Body Butter

AROMATHERAPY PRODUCTS LTD™☺
Essential Oil Rich Hydrating Body Lotion; Lavender, Sweet orange and Bergamot body butter; Lavender, Ylang Ylang and bergamot body lotion; Orange and Jasmine Body Lotion; Wild rose & Lemon Leaf Body Lotion; *Accessories:* White cotton moisturising gloves; *Body moisturisers:* Bitter orange hand and body lotion; *Lavender Products:* Lavender gel, Lavender hand and body lotion; *Skin nourishing pure blending oils:* Face and body base, Grapeseed, Jojoba, Peach kernel, Sweet almond, Wheatgerm; *Skin treatments and solutions:* Essential rich antiseptic cream, Tea tree and Manuka cream, Tea tree skin balm; *Tea Tree Products:* Tea Tree & Grapefruit Skinwash, Tea Tree, Rosemary and Shea Skin Care

AUBREY ORGANICS
Pure Aloe Vera; *Blue Green Algae :* SPF15 Moisturiser; *Green Tea and Ginkgo:* SPF15 Moisturiser; *Hand and Body Lotion:* Rosa Mosqueta, Ultimate Moist Passionflower, Ultimate Moist Unscented; *Lumessence:* Lift Firming Renewal Cream with CoQ10 Liposomes; *Mens Stock:* Mens Daily Moisturiser; *Natural Herbal:* Maintenance Oil Balancing Moisturiser; *Rosa Mosqueta:* (With Rose Hip)

Moisturising Cream; *Rosa Mosqueta:* Night Creme; *Vegecol with Organic Aloe:* Moisturising Cream

AUSTRALIAN TEA TREE
Hand & Body Lotion

BAREFOOT BOTANICALS ☺⊘♦
Rosa Fina: Hourglass Lifting & Firming Body Lotion, Radiance Anti-ageing Day Cream, Supernatural Instant Youth Serum; *SOS:* Protect Me Daily Body Lotion, Rescue Me Face & Body Cream

BEAUTY NATURALS ♦
Body Oil: Evening Primrose & Lavender, Orange; *Camomile Skin Care:* Moisture Milk; *David Hill:* Extra Rich Treatment Cream, Skin Soothing Daytime Moisturiser; *Evening Primrose:* Moisturiser; *Herbal Skin Care:* No 3 Day Cream; *Martha Hill:* Enriched Body Moisturiser; *Martha Hill Evening Primrose:* Body Lotion; *Moisturiser:* Enriched Body; *Seaweed:* Body Toning Gel, Enriched Body Treatment Cream; *Skin Revivals - Moisturising:* Pure Skin Treatment, Revitalising Cream

BELLECARE AG™
24H Cream; Bodylotion sanmar; Crème Purifiante; Crème Teintée; Hautgel braun; Hautgel weiss / Daily Protective Moisturiser; Nightcream; Terra Vita 2 in 1; *Vleur:* 24H Pflege, Creme Balance, Getönte Pflege, Nachtpflege, Tinktur Bei Hautrötungen, Tinktur Bei Pigmentierter Haut, Tinktur Bei Sensibler Haut, Tinktur Bei Unreiner Haut, Tinktur Für Straffere Haut

TOILETRIES & COSMETICS

BIO-HEALTH LTD ⊘ ✍
Vitamin E Cream; Vitamin E Lotion

BL COSMETICS
Aloe Vera Lotion; Fresh as a Daisy Body
Lotion; Heel Appeal Foot Lotion; Rich
Moisturiser; Rosewater Cream;
Strawberry Ginger & Lime Moisturiser;
Super Pure Cream; Tea Tree Treatment
Cream; White Grape & Pumpkin Body
Souffle; *Body Butter:* Coconut,
Marigold, Olive Oil, Satsuma,
Strawberry

BONANO GMBH ™⊘
Alviana Basic: **Pflegecreme (Tiegel);**
Alviana Feuchtigkeit: **Gesichstcreme,
Koerperlotion;** *Alviana Rose:*
**Koerperlotion, Nachtcreme,
Tagescreme;** *Alviana Sensitiv:*
**Gesichstcreme (reichhaltig),
Gesichscreme (feuchtigkeit),
Koerperlotion**

BRACKENCRAFT ™☺❶❶⊘ ✍
moisturiser: **Floral, Gardeners Salve,
Grapefruit moisturiser, Mature Skin
Cream, Moisturiser/Hand Cream,
Unfragranced;** *Shea body butters:*
**Grapefruit and lime, Lavender,
Orange and geranium, Vanilla**

BRONNLEY & CO LTD ✍
Body Balm: Africa, Asia, Bird of
Paradise, Caribbean, Europe, India,
Lavender, Medterranean, Passion
Flower, Rose, Tulip; *Body Lotion:*
Apricot & Almond, English Fern,
Lavender, Orchid, Pink Bouquet, White
Iris; *Royal Horticultural Society - Body
Balm:* Passion Flower, Rose

BROOKS- HILL LTD ™
Naturaleve: **Nourishing Therapy Oil**

BURT'S BEES ⊘ ✍ ◉
Miracle Salve; Peppermint Foot Lotion;
Radiance Body Lotion; Repair Serum;
Body Butter: Richly Repairing,
Therapeutic

CAWARRA COSMETICS LTD ™
OrganicSpa: **Body Butter, Body Oil,
Day Moisture, Face Oil, Intense
Moisture, OS Age Vita Renewal
Treatment (Mixed), OS Clay
Renewal Body Cocoon, OS Hydra
Herbal Body Indulgence, Rose Hip
Oil, Skin Whitening Cream, Vitamin
C Serum, Wrinkle Defence, Wrinkle
Defense Cream;** *OrganicSpa Range:*
**Day Moisture, Intense Moisture,
Vitamin C Serum;** *Sanctum:* **Body
Detox, Body Polish, Body Soothe,
Hy C Intensive Repair Cream, Hy C
Recovery Serum, Men's Moisture
Balance, Moisture Balance Gel,
Moisture Concentrate, Moisture
Replenish, Night Conditioning
Cream, Pure Brightening Serum**

CEBRA ETHICAL CHIC ™⊘ ✍
Cebra- ethical skin care:
**Pina Colada Body Soufflé, Balance
Me Moisturising Butter Bars, Calm
Me Down - Skin Soothing Mango
Shea Butter, Chocolate Orange Body
Soufflé, Perk Me Up Body Oil,
Summer Fruit Body Soufflé,
Whipped Perk Me Up Body Soufflé,
Whipped Shea Butter Cream**

DESERT ESSENCE ⊘ ✔ ⚡1985
Organics Hand and Body Lotion :
Almond, Bulgarian Lavender, Coconut,
Spicy Citrus, Vanilla Chai

DIRK ROSSMANN GMBH ™
Alterra: **Anti Age Nachtcreme
Wildrose, Anti Age Tagescreme
Wildrose, Bodylotion Granatapfel
Aloe Vera, Cellulite Hautöl Birke
Orange, Körperlotion Aprikose
Zitronengras, Körpermilch Pfirsich
Litschi, Körperöl Aloe Vera Limette,
Massageöl Mandel Papaya,
Nachtcreme Pfirsich Wassermelone,
Peelingcreme Pfirsich Wassermelone,
Pflegeöl Granatapfel Avocado,
Reichhaltige Pflegecreme
Granatapfel, Sensitivcreme
Parfümfrei**

DOLMA ™☺🌑⊘ ✔ ☁⚡1976
Miscellaneous Body Preparations: **Aloe
Vera Hand & Body Lotion, Ho-Leaf
& Orange Moisturising Body Wash,
Niamh De-luxe Body Lotion;** *Skin
Care:* **Avocado & Ylang Ylang
Moisture Cream, Carotene Enriched
Fragrance Free Moisture Cream,
Carotene Ho-Leaf & Orange
Moisture Cream, Chamomile
Moisture Lotion, De-luxe Facial Oil,
Facial Oil for Dehydrated Skin,
Facial Oil for Dry Skin, Facial Oil for
Mature Skin, Facial Oil for Sensitive
Skin, Facial Oil for Thread Veins,
Fragrance Free Moisture Lotion,
Geranium & Evening Primrose Night
Cream, Wheatgerm & Lavender
Moisture Cream**

DR HAUSCHKA ⊘ ✔
Moisturising Day Cream; Normalising
Day Oil; Quince Body Moisturiser; *Body
Oil:* Birch Arnica, Blackthorn, Lavender,
Lemon, Moor Lavender, Rose,
Rosemary, St. John's Wort

DR ORGANIC
Aloe Vera: Aloe Gel, Body Butter,
Concentrated Cream, Lotion; *Lavender:*
Lotion; *Pomegranate:* Anti-aging
Cream, Body Butter, Eye Cream, Lotion;
Tea Tree: Lotion; *Vitamin E:* Bioactive
Oil, Body Butter, Lotion, Super
Hydrating Cream

EARTHPURE ☺ ✔
Moisturiser: Eastern Rose, Luxurious
Rose, Orange and Frankincense, Pure
and Rich

ECO COSMETICS GMBH
& CO. KG ™⊘ ✔ ☼
**Body Lotion; Face Treatment Lotion;
Facial cream; Moisturising Cream;
Moisturising Lotion**

EMPATHY SKINCARE LTD
(NATURAL EMPATHY) ™☺ ✔
Luxury Body Butter; *Care and repair:*
**Signature Light Moisturiser No1,
Signature Moisturiser For Men,
Signature Moisturiser No3,
Signature Rich Moisturiser No2**

ESSENTIAL CARE
Skincare: Organic Avocado Replenishing
Cream, Organic Hand & Body Lotion,
Organic Repair Lotion, Organic Rose
Moisturiser

ESSENTIALLY YOURS LTD

Fragrance Free Range: FF3 Fragrance Free Moisturiser, FF9 Fragrance Free Body Lotion; *LYB Range:* LYB001 Neroli & Sandalwood Body Cream, LYB007 Body Firming Gel, LYB024 Orange & Cinnamon Body Lotion, LYB107 Rose & Lavender Body Lotion; *Mu Mens Range:* M2 Lemon & Orange Daytime Moisturiser, M4 Multi-Vitamin Anti-Ageing Moisturiser, M6 Luxury Facial Oil for fine lines; *Natural Elements Range:* NE004 Cucumber & Lime Moisturiser, NE012 Lemon, Orange & Kiwi Moisturiser, NE018 Geranium & Lavender Moisturiser, NE019 Multi-Vitamin Night Cream, NE025 Intensive Body Lotion, NE026 Replenishing Neck Serum, NE027 Face Contouring Serum, NE029 Rejuvenating Day Serum, NE030 Hydrating Night Serum, NE130 Rehydrating Facial Oil, NE131 Regenerating Facial Oil, NE132 Holistic Facial Oil; *Therapeutics Range:* NE031 Therapeutic Moisturising Cream, NE032 Therapeutic Body Lotion, NE035 Therapeutic Moisturising Oil

FAITH PRODUCTS LIMITED

TM ◎ ✔ ☜ ⚕ 1988

Deep Moisturising Night Cream 50g; Pre natal leg lotion; Preventive stretch mark lotion; Replenishing Moisturising Body Lotion 150ml; Replenishing Moisturising Cream 50ml; Stretch mark lotion

FLORIS ◎ ✔

Enriched Body Moisturiser: Cefiro, China Rose, Edwardian Bouquet, Fleur, Florissa, Lily of the Valley, Night Scented Jasmine, Seringa Enriched, Stephanotis, White Rose; *Natural Benefits:* Soothing Skin Balm

FOREVER LIVING PRODUCTS

Aloe Activator; Aloe Vera Gelly; Alpha - E Factor

FREERANGERS TM ◎ ✔

Arnica Gel; Funky Finger Hand Cream; Self tan cream

FUNK BUBBLE TM ◎

Body Cream: **Aloe Vera/Lemon, Chocolate/Orange, Jojoba/Ylang Ylang;** *Moisturiser:* **Jasmin/Lemon Cream**

GENTLE BEAUTY CO LTD TM ◎ ✔

Oil: **Golden Silk Oil, Golden Silk Oil**

GREEN PEOPLE CO. TM ◯ ✔

Moisturiser: **B013 Eye Cream, B014 Body Comfort, B022 Day Solution SPF15, B031 Hand/Body Lotion, B034 Anti-Ageing Facial Oil, C013 Soft Lips 'No Scent', C034 Moisturising Shower Bath, F013 Mum & Baby Moisturiser, F015 Lavender Top to Toe Lotion, F030 Baby Lotion No Scent, H002 Organic Base 24-Hour Cream, H003 Organic Base Hand & Body Lotion, L001 & L002 Rejuvenating Body Lotion, L006 Day/Night Cream, L009 & L010 Moisturise & Go, M003 Cool Down - After Shave Moisturiser, M004 Skin Guard - Face Lotion with SPF15, M007 Active Fix - Repair Serum, R008 Rejuvenating Facial Oil, R014 Hydrating Body Lotion, R019 Sheer**

Pamper Body Oil; *Moisturiser & Cleanser:* **R003 Hydrating Cleanser, T001 Cleanse & Moisturise**

GREEN VALLEY TRADING CO ™☺❶✓
Yaoh: **All products are vegan**

GREEN WYCH LTD ™☺❶⊘✓
Body Butter: **Bergamot, Cocoa & Almond Body Butter, Geranium, Cocoa & Almond Body Butter, Lavender, Cocoa & Almond, Lemongrass, Cocoa & Almond Body Butter, Orange, Cocoa & Almond Body Butter;** *Cocoa & Almond Body Butter:* **Fragrance free;** *Face Cream:* **Bergamot, Fragrance Free, Geranium, Lavender, Lemongrass face day cream, SheerSilk Day Cream - Geranium, Sweet Orange;** *Face Mask:* **SkinBoost - Anti-aging**

HALO SKINCARE LTD ™☺⊘✓
Halo Light Moisturising Cream

HEALTHQUEST LIMITED ™⊘✓
Earth Friendly Baby: **Chamomile Body Lotion, Lavender Body Lotion, Mandarin Body Lotion;** *Organic Blue- Body Care:* **Body Lotion;** *Organic Blues - Mens:* **Body Lotion;** *Pure Adore:* **Baby Oil, Chamomile Body Lotion, Lavender Body Lotion, Mandarin Body Lotion**

HEMP GARDEN ™
Refining Face Cream; Revitalising Body Lotion; *Body Oil:* **Sensual, Soothing, Stimulating**

HERBS HANDS HEALING LTD ™⊘✓
Organic Rose Geranium Body Moisturiser

HIGHER NATURE LTD
Ultimate Aloe Vera Skin Gel; Aloe Vein Gel; Energys Energy Gel; Energys Youthful Skin Elixir; MSM Cream Light; MSM Cream Rose; MSM Lotion Rose

HIPPY HEAVEN NATURAL BEAUTY ™☺⊘✓
Frankincense and lavender moisturiser- normal and combination skin; Intensive moisture night serum; Men moisturise; Patchouli and grapefruit daily facial moisturiser for mature, dry and sun damaged skin; Save sensitive skin cream; Silk skin contour cream; Soothing facial lotion- for rosacea and other red, inflamed skin conditions; Stretchmark and scar cream; Velvet glow natural facial serum

HOLISTIX HERBAL PRODUCTS ❶
Face and Hand Cream: Base Cream; *Moisturising Skincare Cream:* Calendula, Chickweed, Geranium, Lavender & Mandarin, Orange, Geranium & Palmarosa, Rose & Frankincense, Ylang-Ylang & Geranium

HONESTY COSMETICS LTD ™☺❶⊘✓☖1976
Honesty Essential Range: **Geranium & Ylang Ylang Moisturising Lotion, Lavender & Geranium Moisturising Cream, Olive Body Cream, Rose**

&Shea Butter Body Cream, Rose Body Lotion; *Honesty Unscented Range:* Cocoa Butter Moisturising Lotion, Grapeseed Oil, Moisturising Cream with Vitamin E, Rich Moisture Cream with Carrot & Jojoba, Sweet Almond Oil; *Unscented Moisturiser:* Cream with Vitamin E, Lotion with Cocoa Butter, Rich Cream with Carrot & Jojoba

HOWAD LTD
T/A INCOGNITO ™❶⊘✔
Incognito: Calendula, ginseng and aloe vera body moisturising lotion

I AM NATURAL ™❶❶✔ ✿
Organic Calendula Healing Cream; Organic Cocoa Butter; Organic Cocoa Butter with Ginger; Organic Cocoa Butter with Orange; Organic Frankincense Face Cream; Organic Hemp Protection Balm; Organic Shea Butter; Organic Sweet Orange Body Cream; Organic Tea Tree Gel

INNOCENT OILS ™☺⊘✔
100% Innocent Hemp Seed Oil; *Balms:* Innocent Hemp Seed Oil Balm, Innocent Lavender and Geranium Balm, Patchouli & Geranium Balm; *Innocent Angel:* Innocent Angel Butter, Innocent Angel Face Drops, Innocent Angel Silk Cream, Innocent Angel Silk Lotion; *Soaps:* Luna Drops

ITS ELIXIR (UK) LIMITED ™⊘✔👁
Aloe Vera and Collagen Lotion; Aloe vera cream; Aloe Vera Gel; Cellulite Gel; Dry skin cream; Evening primrose cream; Night cream; Problem skin cream; Pseudo collagen cream; Rose & lavender; Rosehip cream; Rosehip & vitamin cream; Shea butter moisturiser F; Shea butter moisturiser G; Shea butter moisturiser L; Shea butter moisturiser P; Silk cream; Simple moisturiser; Vitamin C cream; Vitamin cream

JASON NATURAL PRODUCTS
25,000 IU Vitamin E Age Renewal Moisturizing Crème 70% Organic, Aloe Vera 70% Comforting Moisturizing Crème 70% Organic, Aqua Moist™ Balancing Moisture Lotion, Cocoa Butter,Intensive Moisturizing Crème 70% Organic, Hemp Ultra-Rich Moisturizing Crème 70% Organic, Mango Butter, Pro-Vita Moisture Plus, Quick Recovery™ Re-Hydrating Lotion, Tea Time Anti-Aging Moisturizing Crème 70% Organic, Wild Yam Balancing Moisturizing Crème 70% Organic; *Alpha Hydroxy Acids:* 10% Plus Nighttime Creme New Cell Therapy™ Alpha Hydroxy Acids Night Time Creme, 12-1/2% Plus Oil-Free Gel New Cell Therapy™ Alpha Hydroxy Acids, 12-1/2% Plus with SPF 12-1/2 Protective Moisturizer New Cell Therapy™ Alpha Hydroxy Acids; *Ester-C® Skin Care:* Ester-C® Crème, Ester-C® Lotion; *Hand & Body Therapy:* Chamomile 70% Organic Hand & Body Therapy, Hemp 70% Organic Hand & Body, Lavender 70% Organic Hand & Body, Vanilla 70% Organic Hand & Body Therapy, Wild Yam 70% Organic

Hand & Body Therapy; *Jason:* 5,000 I.U.
Vitamin E Revitalizing Moisturizing
Crème 70% Organic, Aloe Vera 84%
Ultra-Comforting Moisturizing Crème
70% Organic; *Organic Hand & Body
Lotion:* 84% Pure Aloe Vera 70%
Organic Hand & Body Lotion, Cocoa
Butter 70% Organic Hand & Body
Lotion, Glycerine & Rosewater 70%
Organic Hand & Body Lotion, Natural
Apricot 70% Organic Hand & Body
Lotion, Natural EFA 70% Organic Hand
and Body Lotion, Vitamin E 70%
Organic Hand and Body Lotion; *Organic
Pure Beauty Oils:* All; *Red Elements™
Antioxidant Skin Care:* Daily
Moisturizing Lotion with SPF 15,
Exfoliating Scrub, Hydrating Night
Crème, Lifting Eye Crème, Red Clay
Masque

JR LIGGETT ☺
Body Oil Spray: Lavender, Lemon Lime,
White Sage

JUICE BEAUTY
Antioxidant Serum; Blemish Clearing
Serum; Soothing Serum

JUNGLESALE LIMITED ™
Neem Herbal Oil

JUST SOAPS ™
**Moisturising Rejuvenating Face
Cream**

KATHARINE
BOTANICALS LTD ⊘ ⫘ ◉
Anti-Stretch Mark Lotion; Baby Cream;
Nipple Cream; Pure Indulgence

KEY SUN LABORATORIES
PTY LTD ™⊘
Key Sun: **Body Balm, Body Polish,
Body Spa, Moisture Replenish,
Night Cream**

KISS MY FACE
All Day Creme; *Body Balm:* Olive my
Body; *Organic Face Care:* C the Change
Ester C Serum, Cell Mate 15 Facial
Moisturiser SPF15, So Refined Jojoba &
Mint Facial Scrub, Under Age Ultra
Moisturizer; *Organic Moisturisers:*
Almost Butter Rosemary Melon, Cs the
Day, Filthy Rich Citrus Lavender, Tighten
Up; *Potent & Pure Face Care:* Breakout
Botanical Acne Gel, Brightening Day
Creme, C the Change Ester C Serum,
Cell Mate Facial Creme & SPF 15
Suncreen, Intensive Repair Night
Creme, Under Age Ultra Moisturizer;
Tinted Moisturizers: All; *Ultra
Moisturisers:* Chinese Botanical,
Everyday SPF15, Lavender & Shea
Butter, Olive & Aloe, Olive and Aloe
Fragrance Free, Peaceful Patchouli,
Peaches & Creme, Vitamin A & E

LAVERANA GMBH & CO. KG ™⫘
Faces: **Moisturizing Fluid Aloe Vera,
Summer Glow Facial Moisturiser;**
Lavera Basis Sensitiv: **Basis Sensitiv
Carrot Cream, Basis Sensitiv
Moisturizing Body Lotion, Basis
Sensitiv Moisturizing Cream, Basis
Sensitiv Protection Body Lotion,
Handcreme;** *Lavera Body Spa:* **Body
Lotion (Citrus), Body Lotion
(Lavender/Aloe Vera), Body Lotion
(Orange/Sea Buckthorn), Body
Lotion (Vanilla/Coconut), Body
Lotion (Vervain/Lemon), Body**

BOTANICALS

Katharine Botanicals brings you a range of superior products containing active essential oils, plant-oils, waxes and juices. You can rest assured that we provide only the best products for you and your baby.

Baby's Bottom Cream - for the prevention and treatment of nappy rash.

Nipple Cream - a special natural cream to help sooth your nipples after each feed.

Stretch Mark Lotion - retains moisture and conditions the skin during and after pregnancy.

Pure Indulgence - the finest beauty cream designed to target wrinkles and moisturise effectively. It contains exceptional ingredients of vitamins and collagen to feed the skin making it smooth and soft with a lovely aroma.

Lotion (Wild Rose); *Lavera BodySPA Body Oil:* **Exclusive pampering Wild Rose, Fruity revival Orange-Sea Buckthorn, Refreshment Vervain-Lime, Relaxation Lavender-Aloe Vera, Warmth Vanilla-Coconut;** *Lavera Faces- dry and mature skin:* **Moisturizing Cream Wild Rose;** *Lavera Faces My Age:* **Concentrated Lifting Serum White Tea - Karanja, Regenerating Night Cream White Tea - Karanja Oil, Restoring Day Cream White Tea - Karanja Oil;** *Lavera Neutral:* **Body Lotion, Cleansing Gel, Facial Fluid;** *Lavere:* **Body-Effect Active Care Body Lotion, Body-Effect Active Control, Body-Effect Active Silhouette Spray, Hydro Energy Lift, Hydro Energy Sensation Cream, Lifting Serum, Repair Relax Absolute Day, Repair Relax Absolute Night, Repair Relax Impression, Repair Relax Meeting, Solution Power Glamour, Solution Power Performance, Solution Power Promise, Solution Power Royal Day;** *Men SPA:* **All-Round Moisturizing Cream;** *Young Faces:* **Moisturizing Fluid Mint**

LIVE NATIVE ™☺
Essential Woman; Every Body Every day; Head To Toe For Men; Pure Natal

LIZ EARLE ✍
Botanical Essence Eau De Parfum No1; Nourishing Botanical Body Cream; Sheer Gold Shimmer; Vital Oils Body Sprays; *Skin Repair:* Light - Combination/Oily, Moisturiser - Dry/Sensitve, Moisturiser - Normal/Combination; *Superskin:* Body Cream, Bust Treatment, Concentrate, Moisturiser

LUSH ™⊘✍
Bio Fresh: **Coco lotion hand and body lotion;** *Body Butters:* **Aqua Mirabilis, Buffy, Ego Massage Bar, Into Thin Air Massage Bar, King of Skin, Running To The Embassy, Schnuggle, You Snap The Whip;** *Hand and Body Creams:* **Charity Pot, Crème Anglaise, Dream Cream, Handy Gurugu Hand Cream, Pied de Pepper, Steam, Sympathy for the Skin, Vanilla Dee Lite;** *Karma Products:* **Karma Kream;** *Moisturisers:* **Celestial, Enzymion, Imperialis, Paradise Regained Moisturiser, Skin Drink, Ultralight;** *Tinted Moisturiser:* **Charlotte Island**

MAJIK BLANKIT SKIN CARE ™☺✍
Acmella and Almond Face Moisturiser; Hand & Body Cocoa Butter Cream; Hand & Body Shea Butter Cream; Veon Organic Shea & Pumpkin Body Quench

MANAKEDI SKINCARE ™☺
Active E1 Cream; Biolift Daily Nourishing Moisturiser; Biolift Night Oil

MISSHU LTD T/A LANI-JO ™☺❶✍
Essential: **Body Cream;** *Healing:* **Body Cream, Day Cream, Hand Lotion, Night Cream;** *Heaven:* **Body Cream;** *Sensual:* **Body Cream**

TOILETRIES & COSMETICS

MJ HEALTH(NZ) LTD ™☺❶❶ 🖊 👁
Balance Range: **Balance Moisturizer;**
Earths Gift Range: **Citrus Body
Moisturiser, Facial serum, Lavender
Body Moisturiser, Neutral base
cream, Normal skin face moisturiser,
Oily skin face moisturiser, Rich base
cream;** *Gentle Range:* **Gentle
Moisturizer;** *Replenish Range:*
Replenish Moisturizer; *Ultra Light
Range:* **Ultra Light Moisturiser;** *Ultra
Treat Range:* **Ultra Treat Face
Moisturiser, Ultra Treat Body
Moisturiser, Ultra Treat White Tea
Serum**

MONTAGNE JEUNESSE 🚫 🖊
Face Tonic: Dead Sea Fabric, Spearmint
& Tea Tree Fabric

MULONDON ™☺❶🚫 🖊 ☼ 👁
**Organic Hemp Moisturiser; Organic
Lavender Moisturiser; Organic
Marigold Frankincense & Myrrh
Moisturiser; Organic rose
moisturiser; Organic White
Chocolate Truffle Moisturiser**

MY SKINCARE LTD ™☺🚫 🖊
Moisturising: **Alpine Rose Stem Cell
Day Cream SPF15, Anti-Cellulite
Cream, Brazilian Body Butter,
Brazilian Body Polish, Brazilian Body
Wash, Deeply Relaxing Cream,
Malus Stem Cell Day Cream SPF15,
Malus Stem Cell Night Cream,
Nutrient Rich Night Cream, Olive
Body Butter, Olive Body Polish,
Pregnancy Skin Supple Body Cream,
Stretch Mark Oil**

NATURA ORGANICS 🚫 🖊 ☼
Body Lotion: Nourishing with Aloe
Vera, Vitamin E and Grapefruit,
Revitalising with Shea Butter, Vitamin E
and Mandarin, Soothing with Shea
Butter, Vitamin E and Rosemary; *Face
Cream:* Hydrating Cream, Purifying
Cream

NATURAL SENSE
Body Butter; Face and Body Cream;
Fade Away Balm

NATURE'S GATE
Colloidal Oatmeal For Itchy Dry
Sensitive Skin; Daily SPF 15 Moisture
Cream; Fragrance Free Moisturizing
Sensitive; Hemp Moisturizing; Herbal
Moisturizing Lotion All Types; Papaya
Moisturizing All Skin Types;
Pomegranate Sunflower Lotion; Skin
Therapy Moisturizing; Tea Tree Calming
Lotion; Vitamin E Oil; Vitamin E Roll-
on; *Organics - Advanced Care:* C For
Yourself Serum, Forget Your Lines
Serum, Have A Vine Day Cream, Light
Switch Serum, Oh What A Night
Cream; *Organics - Fruit Blend:* Asian
Pear & Red Tea, Grapefruit & Wild
Ginger, Mandarin Orange & Patchouli,
Persimmon & Rose Geranium; *Organics
- Herbal Blend:* Chamomile, Lavender &
Aloe, Lemongrass & Clary Sage, Neroli
Orange & Chocolate Mint Lotion

NEAL'S YARD REMEDIES
🚫 🖊 👁 ⚷ 1998
Chamomile & Aloe Vera Lotion; English
Lavender Body Lotion; Frankincense &
Mandarin Body Lotion; Frankincense &

234

Mandarin Body Polish; Frankincense
Hydrating Cream; Frankincense
Hydrating Facial Mist; Frankincense
Nourishing Cream; Frankincense Toning
Body Cream; Glycerine (Vegetable);
Jasmine Enriching Cream; Jasmine Skin
Nourishing Oil; Nourishing Orange
Flower Daily Moisture; Nourishing
Orange Flower Facial Mask; Nourishing
Orange Flower Night Cream; NYR Men
Rejuvenating Moisturiser; Orange
Flower Facial Oil; Orange Flower
Nourishing Decollete Gel; Power Berry
Daily Moisture; Power Berry Facial
mask; Purifying Palmarosa Daily
Moisture; Purifying Palmarosa Facial
Serum; Purifying Palmarosa Night
Cream; Rehydrating Rose Daily
Moisture; Rejuvenating Frankincense
Facial Serum; Rose & Geranium Body
Polish; Rose Facial Oil; Rosehip Seed
Oil; Vitamin E & Avocado Night Cream;
White Tea Facial Mist

NEW SEASONS
Men's Moisturiser; Relaxing
Moisturising Lotion; Rich Rose
Moisturising Cream; Travel Moisturiser;
Neutral & Toiletry Bases: Aloe Vera Gel
Base, Moisturising Cream, Moisturising
Lotion

NOTHING NASTY ✔
Big Belly Pregnancy Moisturiser; *Facial
Moisturiser:* Flawless for Problem Skin,
Ideal for Normal Skin, Prime for Mature
& Sensitve Skin; *Moisturiser:* Bliss
Sensual, Chill Relaxing, Zest Uplifting

OLEADOR UG
(HAFTUNGSBESCHRÄNKT) ™
Argan Oil Pure

ORGANATURAL ™☺❶◐✔👁
Forest Secrets Skincare: **Rejuvenate
Step 1 Lifting Pro-Youth Face Oil,
Rejuvenate Step 2 Regenerating
Skin Serum**

ORGANIC BOTANICS ™◐✿
**Damask Rose & Orange Flower Daily
Elixir; Moisturising Nutritive (Extra
Rich); Moisturising Nutritive
(Medium/Light); Organic Damask
Rose and Orange Flower Daily
Moisturising Elixir; Organic Fragrance
Free Hand + Body Lotion; Organic
Satin Hand & Body Lotion; Pink Lotus
& Jasmine Facial Elixir; Simpler Daily
Moisturiser (Essential oil free)**

ORGANIX SOUTH INC
Thera Neem: Neem Leaf & Aloe Vera
Gel, Neem Leaf & Oil Cream, Neem
Leaf & Oil Lotion, Neem Oil Botanical
Fading Cream

POTIONS AND POSSIBILITIES ◐✔
Beauty: English Garden Hand & Body
Lotion, English Lavender Hand & Body
Lotion, English Rose Hand & Body
Lotion, Essential Night Repair Formula,
Evening Primrose Moisture Relief For
The Complexion, Hand & Body Lotion,
Luxury Body Souffle, Moisture Repair
For Complexion Of Men; *Essentials:*
Heavy Duty Relief Gel; *Hand & Foot
Care:* Foot Relief Cream, Luxury Hand
Cream w Lavender; *Organic Range:* Day
Cream, Hand & Body Lotion, Night Cream

TOILETRIES & COSMETICS

POTTER'S HERBAL MEDICINE ✎
Skin Clear Ointment

PURATY LTD ☺✎
Balancing Body Moisturizer; Balancing Facial Moisturizer; Refreshing Body Moisturizer

PURE GAISHA ™☺❶✎
Creamy Body Whip; Decadent Body Lotion; Facial Moisturiser - Dry/Mature Skin; Facial Moisturiser - Normal Skin; Facial Moisturiser - Oily Skin; Facial Toner - Dry/Mature Skin; Mens Hydrating Face Cream; Rich Body Butter

PURE HEALTH LIMITED ™☺✎
100% Shea Butter; 100% Shea Oil

QUINESSENCE AROMATHERAPY ☺⊘✎👁
Age Defying Cream; Aloe Vera & Lavender Gel; Aloe Vera & Seaweed Gel; Anti Wrinkle Cream; Anti Wrinkle Cream Base; Hydrating Cream Base; Hydrating Day Cream; Hydrating Night Cream; Moisture Lotion Base; Night Repair Cream Base; Reflex Cream Base; Shea Butter Cream Base; Vitamin E Cream; Vitamin E Cream Base; *Lotion:* After Sun, Antiseptic, Base Carrier, Hand and Body, Insect Repellent, Moisture, Problem Skin

RARE NATURAL CARE, INC. ™☺❶⊘✎✿👁
Conditioning Body Lotion; *Rare2B Vegan Skincare:* **Body Lotion, Hydrating Day Cream, Restorative Night Cream**

RAW GAIA ™☺❶⊘✎✿👁
Body Bar - Detox; Body Bar - Lavender; Coconut Body Butter; Living Hemp Moisturizer; Living Moisturiser - for her daughters; Living Moisturiser - for her sons; Living Moisturiser For Her Babies; Living MSM Beauty Cream; Red Palm Kernel Body Butter; Shea Body Butter

REN ⊘
Body Products: Damask Rose Ramnose Biosaccharide Body Cream, Grapeseed, Jojoba and Shea Butter Body Cream, Laminaria Firming Body Gel, Monoi Moisturising Body Rinse, Monoi Nourishing Body Oil, Moroccan Rose Otto Ultra Nourishing Body Oil, Wild Yam Omega 7 Firming Body Repair Cream; *Face Care:* Calendula Omega 3/7 Hydra-Calm Moisturiser, Frankincense and Boswellia Serrata Revitalising Repair Cream, Mayblossom and Konjac Balancing Moisturiser, Omega 3 Overnight Lipid Renewal Serum - All skin types, Phyto-Dynamic Instant Lifting Gel, Phytostimuline Instant Replenishment Moisturiser, Revivo-Lift H11 Intensive Night Serum, Revivo-Lift Radiant Day Serum, Rose Complex Moisturiser - Normal skin

RIMON WINERY ™☺
Pomegranate seed oil

RIVER VEDA ™⊘✎✿
RiverVeda: **Evening Primrose, Heavenly Rose, Moisture Me, Morning Star, Organic Calendula, Rose Attar Elixir, Vital;** *The Organic*

Skin Company: **Ageless Amaranth & Vanilla Night Moisturizer, Luminous Rosehip & Orange Day Moisturizer**

RJ MINERAL COSMETICS INTERNATIONAL PTY LTD ™ ✔
Body: **ALGEL Body - Aloe Vera Gel, ALOEJ Body - Aloe Vera Juice, BBG Body Butter, BL Body Lotion - Lavender, BL Body Lotion - Rose, BL Body Lotion - Unscented, CBS Body Cocoa Butter Stick, DMB Body Deep Muscle Balm, ISR Body - Itchy Soothe Rub;** *Face:* **INT Face Intensive Night Treatment, M Face Moisturiser - Calendula, M Face Moisturiser - Calendula + AHA, M Face Moisturiser - Deep Sea, M Face Moisturiser - Deluxe, M Face Moisturiser - Rosewood, TTLM Face Moisturiser - Lemon & Juniper Berry**

SAAF INTERNATIONAL LIMITED ™
Organic Complexion Boosting Serum; Organic Eraser Body Oil; Organic Hydrating Face and Lip Balm; Organic Super Hydrating Body Balm; Organic Ultimate Moisturising Serum

SHANTI PRODUCTS ◌ ✔
Face Care: Apricot Kernal Facial Scrub, Frankincense & Rose Face Cream, Rich Borage Night Cream

SHEA BY NATURE ☺
Body Oil; Shea Body Butter; Shea Body Butter with Green Tea

SHEACARE ☺
Shea Butter

SIMPLE ✔
Age Resisting Night Renewal; Hydrate Body Moisturiser; Intensive Line Reducing Serum; Moisture Rich Anti-Wrinkle Cream; Nourish Body Cream; Protecting Moisture Cream; Summer Look Body Lotion; *Day Cream:* Age Resisting, Anti-Wrinkle; *Men:* Advanced Moisturiser, Daily Moisturiser; *Moisturiser:* Daily Radiance spf 10, Hydrating Light, Oil Balancing, Replenishing Rich; *Night Cream:* Anti-Wrinkle, Restoring

SIMPLY SOAPS
Hydrating Face Oil; *Hedgerow Herbals-Black Palm Natural Range:* Wild Shea Butter; *Hedgerow Herbals- Rosa Passionata:* Rose Night Butter

SKIN BLOSSOM LIMITED ™☺◌ ✔ ☼
Body Lotion: **Body Lotion;** *Moisturisers:* **Nourishing Face Moisturiser**

SKINCARE CAFE LTD ☺
Organic Almond & Patchouli Anti-ageing Night Oil; Organic Anti-cellulite Body Firming Gel; Organic Chinese Geranium Anti-Ageing Night Oil; Organic Grapeseed & Aloe Vera Cleanser; Organic Lavender & Rose Geranium Moisturiser; Organic Lemongrass & Rosemary Face Mask; Organic Lemongrass Purifying Face Mask; Organic Mandarin & Chamomille Body Conditioning Lotion; Organic Orange & Chamomile Body Wash; Organic Orange & Vanilla Body Lotion; Organic Rose Geranium Moisturiser w 5 vitamins; Organic Vitamin Enriched Anti-ageing Day Serum

SOLARAY NUTRITIONAL SUPPLEMENTS

Men's Daily Moisturiser; Organic 100% Aloe Vera Gel; Rosa Mosquesta Hand & Body Lotion; Rosa Mosquesta Rose Hip Moisturiser; Rose Mosqueta Night Creme; Sparkling Mineral Water Complexion Mist; Vegecell Nighttime Hydrator w Green Tea; *Moisturising Cream:* Blue Green Algae SPF15, Green Tea & Gingko SPF15, Natural Herbal Maintenance Oil, Rosa Mosqueta w Rose Hip, Sea Buckthorn, Vegecol w Organic Aloe; *Ultimate Moist Hand & Body Lotion:* Passionflower, Unscented

SOPHYTO ™❶⊘✔👁

Multivitamin Skin Drops

STELLA MCCARTNEY

Care: 5 Benefits Moisturising Cream, 5 Benefits Moisturising Fluid, Calming and Soothing Elixir, Nourishing Elixir, Radiance and Youth Elixir; *Stella:* Soft Body Milk; *Stella in Two:* Moisturising Body Milk

SUKI PURE SKIN CARE

Delicate Moisture Body Oil w Cedar Rose & Bergamot; Velvet Hand & Body Creme; *Facial Moisture Serum:* Blue Chamomile & Echinacea, Carrot, Myrrh & Sandalwood

SUPERDRUG

Amie: Morning Dew Matte Finish Moisturiser; *Naturals:* Bergamont Body Milk, Mango & Papaya Body Butter, Olive & Bergamont Body Lotion; *Optimum:* Line Decrease Radiance Balm

SYNTHESIS 345 ™☺❶⊘✔✲

Earth Rising: **Body Lotion;** *First Love:* **Day Cream with Sunscreen, Night Cream, Regenerative Elixir;** *Light Haven:* **Body Oil**

TAOASIS GMBH AROMA-KOSMETIK & VERLAG ™

Lavendel Nachtcreme; Mandel Sensitiv Creme; Neroli Intensiv Creme; Teebaum Intensiv Creme; Wildrose Tagescreme

TREASURED EARTH SKINCARE ™☺⊘

Body Custard; Moisturiser; Night Cream

TREE-HARVEST ⊘✔

Avocado & Geranium Night Cram; Frankincense Rejuvenating Cream; Holy Thorn Healing Cream; Horsechestnut & Rowan Gel; Pau d'Arco; *Tropical Skin Butters:* All

TRUTHFUL CO. LTD (PURELY SKINCARE) ™☺⊘

Purely Skincare: **Intense Moisturiser (female variant), Light Moisturiser (male variant), Light Moisturiser (refreshing variant), Moisturiser-sensitive variant**

URTEKRAM

Body Lotion: All

VANILLA TREE NATURAL SKIN CARE ™☺✔

Refreshing Body cream

VERDESATIVA S.R.L. ™☺❶⊘ɩ☼☻
Bioactive Day and Night Face
Cream; Crema Idratante Bioattiva
(BioActive Moisturising Face
Cream); Crema Lifting Bioattiva
(BioActive Eye Contour Cream);
Crema Piedi & Gambe (Leg & Foot
Cream); Crema Viso Antirughe
(Anti-age Face Cream); Latte Corpo
Canapa e aloe (Body Lotion Hemp
and Aloe); Latte Corpo Canapa e
Calendula (Body Lotion Hemp and
Marigold); Piedi E Gambe for Sport;
High Performance Line: Anti age bio
complex, Latte corpo

VISIONARY SOAP COMPANY ™☺
Body Butters: **Geranium, Lavender,
Lemongrass, Orange Geranium,
Patchouli, Unscented**

WELEDA ⊘ɩ⚗-1985
Almond Facial Oil; Birch Cellulite Oil;
Lavender Body Lotion; Mallow Body
Lotion; Sea Buckthorn Body Oil; Sea
Buckthorn Lotion

YAOH ™☺❶⊘ɩ
Body Lotion; Coco Bean Moisturiser;
Moisturiser; Papaya Moisturiser

SKIN MAKE-UP

**ADORN MINERAL
COSMETICS** ™☺⊘ɩ
Foundation: **Mineral Foundation
Cream Compact, Mineral
Foundation Liquid SPF, Mineral
Loose Foundation SPE 20+;** *Make-up:*
**Mineral Bronzers, Mineral Brow
Dust, Mineral Cream Corrector,
Mineral Loose Blush, Mineral
Mattifying Primer, Mineral Setting
Powder;** *Shadows:* **Mineral Cream
Shadow Trios & Cream Blush,
Mineral Shadows - Matte, Mineral
Shadows - Metallics**

ALEXAMI COSMETICS ™ɩ
Dramatic effect eyes mineral
eyeshadow; Lasting effect powder
mineral setting powder; Matifying
effect primer; Matte effect eyes-
mineral matte eye shadows trio;
Sparkle effects- mineral illuminating
powder; Sunkissed effects- mineral
bronzer; *Mineral Foundation Powders
SPF 20+:* **Glowing effects**

ALTERNATIVE STORES ☺
All products are vegan

ANNEMARIE BORLIND ɩ
Eyebrow Crayons; Kohl Crayons; Lip
Liner; Powder Eye Shadow; Powder
Make-Up; Powder Rouge; *Beauty
Extras:* Cosmetic Sponges; *Compact
Powder:* All; *Fluid Make Up:* All; *Natural
Velvet Cream:* All

ARBONNE ☻
Virtual Illusion Makeup Primer; *BefoRE
Sun:* No Sun Intended Bronzing
Powder; *Blusher:* All; *Brow Wax:* All;
Cream Concealer: All; *Eye Shadow:* All;
f.y.i: EyeQ Cream Eye Shadows, Get
Even SPF 15 Tinted Moisturiser; *Lash
Colour:* All; *Line Defiance Liquid
Foundation SPF15:* All; *Lipstick:* All;
Mineral Powder Foundation SPF 15: All;

Prep & Plump: All; *Sheer Shine For Lips:* All; *Translucent Loose Powder:* All; *Translucent Pressed Powder:* All; *Virtual Illusion Duel Volume Mascara:* All; *Virtual Illusion Eye Definer:* All; *Virtual Illusion Lash Enhancer:* All; *Virtual Illusion Lip Definer:* All

BARRY M COSMETICS ✔ ☂ 1982

Dazzle Dust; Face and Body Shimmer Powder; Fine Glitter Dust; Natural Dazzle Powder Loose (Not Compact); Translucent Powder Loose (Not Compact); *Glitter Eye Crayon:* All; *Glitter Liquid Eyeliner:* All; *Kohl Pencils:* All; *Lip Glosses:* Glossy Tubes; *Lip Liners:* All; *Liquid Eyeliner:* All; *Neon Kohl Pencils:* All

BEAUTY NATURALS ✔

Dual Concealer & Eye Stick; Dual Wet & Dry Foundation; Herbal Enriched Lip Twist; Herbal Lip Primer; Ultra Sheer Liquid Foundation; Vitamin E Lip Treatment; *Eye Colours:* Eye Crayon, Eye Liner Pencil, Herbal Silky 'Diamonds' Shadow, Powder Eye Shadow Duos

BEAUTY WITHOUT CRUELTY ™☺◎ ✔ ☁ ☂ 1996

Cream Concealer Pencil: **Cream Concealer Pencil Light, Cream Concealer Pencil Medium;** *Foundation:* **Ultimate Foundation;** *Mascara:* **Black Ultimate Natural Mascara, Walnut Ultimate Natural Mascara;** *Mineral Powder:* **Mineral Loose Powder;** *Ultimate Natural Soft Kohl Pencil:* **Ultimate Natural Soft Kohl Pencil Carbon Black, Ultimate Natural Soft Kohl Pencil Cedar**

Green, Ultimate Natural Soft Kohl Pencil Charcoal Grey, Ultimate Natural Soft Kohl Pencil Delft Blue

BOURGEOIS BOHEME ™☺

Beauty Without Cruelty: **Cream Concealer, Eye Defining Pencil, Lip Defining Pencil, Lip Gloss, Liquid Eyeliner, Moisturising Lipstick, Natural Look Tinted Moisturiser, Satin Finish Blusher, Superfine Pressed Powder, Ultrafine Loose Powder;** *Beauty Without Cruelty Eyeliner:* **Soft Kohl Pencil;** *Beauty Without Cruelty Eyeshadow:* **Satin Finish Duos;** *Beauty Without Cruelty Mascara:* **Full Volume, Waterproof;** *Beauty Without Cruelty Moisturising Makeup:* **Matte, Satin**

BURT'S BEES ◎ ✔ ☁

Healthy Treatment: Parsley Blemish Stick; *Natural Remedies:* Doctor Burt's Herbal Blemish Stick

CAWARRA COSMETICS LTD ™

OrganicSpa Range: **Skin Whitening Cream**

COSMETIC INNOVATIONS AUSTRALIA PTY LTD ™☺◎ ✔

Lip and Cheek Stain; Mineral Body Shimmers; Mineral Bronzers; Mineral Gloss; Mineral Liquid Lipsticks; Mineral Mascara Blend; Mineral Powder Blush; Mineral Powder Foundation; Mineral Setting / Veil; Mineral Shadows - EM Range; Mineral Shadows - ES Range; Mineral Shadows - ESSE Range; Volume Natural Mascara

DR HAUSCHKA ⊘ ⬩
Concealer: 01, 02, 03; *Kajal Eyeliner:* 02, 03, 04, 05

EARTH'S BEAUTY
Blush: All; *Eye Shadow:* All; *Foundation Powders:* All; *Loose Eye Liner:* All

ECCO BELLA
FlowerColor Blush: All Except Burgundy Rose Wild Rose Orchid Rose and Coral Rose; *FlowerColor Face Powder Compact:* All; *FlowerColor Natural Liquid Foundation:* All; *FlowerColor Natural Mascara:* All; *FlowerColor Powder Eye Liner:* All; *FlowerColour Bronzing Powder:* All; *FlowerColour Eye Shadow:* All; *Good for you Gloss:* Colours Peace and Pleasure (Not the Colours Passion and Power); *Paperback Duo Compact:* All; *Shimmer Dust:* All; *Soft Eyeliner Pencils:* All; *Vitamin E Lip Smoother:* All

ETERNITY DESIGNS INTERNATIONAL PTY LTD ™☺☺ ⬩
Claytime Australia: **Vegan Friendly Mineral Applicator Brush;** *Mineral based makeup:* **Botanical Eyeliner, Mineral Mascara, Mineral Shadows, Pure Mineral Blush, Pure Mineral Bronzer, Pure Mineral Cover SPF24, Shimmer Shadow Primer Stick**

FOREVER LIVING PRODUCTS
Lip/Eye Pencil; Mascara/Eyebrow Fix; Sonya Eye Makeup Remover

GENTLE BEAUTY CO LTD ™⊘ ⬩
Liquid Eyeliner: **Black, Blue, Bronzer,** Brown, Classic Tan, Green, Ivory, Purple, Smokey Grey, Transparent; *Liquid Foundation:* **Transparent;** *Mascara:* **Brown, Navy Blue;** *Nail Polish:* **Pearl White, Almond Nude, Beige, Berry, Chic Black, Cinnamon, Desert Sunset, Gold, Purple Haze, , Remover, Sienna, Silver, Tangerine, Top Coat**

GREEN PEOPLE CO. ™⊘ ⬩
Self Tan: **G009 Self Tan Lotion, T009 'Soft Glow' Gradual Tan**

INIKA ™ ⬩
Blusher and Illuminisor; Body Bronze/Mousse; Eye Shadow; Eye& Lip Liner; Lip Gloss; Mascara; Mineral Bronzer; Mineral Foundation; Mineral Lipsticks - All; Pure Primer; Setting Powder

KISS MY FACE
Tinted Moisturisers: Beach, Branch, Clay, Manila, Rattan, Sisal

KITTEN VIXEN COSMETICS ™
Put Your Lips Together lip gloss

LIP INK ☺
3D LipMax Lip Volumiser; *Blush and Bronzing Gels:* All; *Eye Liners:* All; *Lash Tints:* All; *Lip Gel Lipstick:* All; *Lip Inks Semi Permanent Lip Colours:* All; *Lip Liners:* All; *Lip Shines and Moisturisers:* All; *Magic Powders:* All; *Miracle Brow Liner:* All; *Miracle Brow Tint:* All; *Off Solutions :* All; *ShadowGels:* All

TOILETRIES & COSMETICS

LUSH ™ ⊘ ⛊
Colour Supplement: **Dark Pink Colour Supplement, Dark Yellow Colour Supplement, Light Pink Colour Supplement, Light Yellow Colour Supplement;** *Dusting Powder:* **Vanilla puff**

MAJIK BLANKIT SKIN CARE ™ ☺ ⛊
Gentle Self-Tanner; Peppermint Pout Lip Ploss; Strawberry Glimmer Lip Gloss

NOHARM ™ ☺ ❶ ⊘ ⛊ ☼
TanOrganic

PURE GAISHA ™ ☺ ❶ ⛊
All Nautral Lipstick; Eye Pencils; Mineral Body Shimmer; Mineral Bronzer; Mineral Brow Dust; Mineral Corrector; Mineral Foundation compact; Mineral Foundation Powder; Mineral Lip Pencils; Mineral Lipgloss; Mineral Powder Blusher; Mineral Powder Eyeshadow; Mineral Setting Powder; Natural Mascara

RJ MINERAL COSMETICS INTERNATIONAL PTY LTD ™ ⛊
Body: **BBGT Body Butter - Tinted, BLBR Body Bronzer Lotion**

ULTRA GLOW COSMETICS ☺ ⛊
Eye defining pencil: Black, Soft brown; *Full volume mascara:* Black, Brown; *High gloss nail colour:* Coral mist, Pink whisper; *Jojoba Lip gloss:* Apricot Shimmer, Coral mist, Deeply berry, Gold sunset, Pink crush, Rosewood, Silver lilac; *Lip defining pencil:* Morello, Pinky brown; *Lip gloss:* Clear; *Liqiud concealer:* Fair, Medium; *Liqiud eyeliner:* Black; *Moisturing lipstick:* Spiced grape; *Moisturing makeup satin:* Beige Matte, Bronze Satin, Gold satin, Light matte, Natural matte, Warm satin; *Moisturising lipstick:* Rosewood, Barely Pink, Birch, Butterscotch, Cappuccino, Caramel Cream, Chilli red, Clover pearl, Coppernob, Coral, Mulberry, Peach dream, Perfect plum, Rebel rose, Red red, Silver rose, Soft pink, Sugar plum, Sweet apricot, Tangerine, Tansy tease, Terracotta, Toffee apple; *Moisurising makeup satin:* Light satin; *Natural look tinted moisturiser:* Light, Medium; *Satin finish blusher:* Cranberry, Hot chestnut, Rosetta, Sun gold, Tawny whisper; *Satin Finish Eye Shadow Duo:* Aquamarine, Graphite, Lilac, Oakmoss, Tamarind; *Soft kohl pencil:* Black, Walnut; *Ultrafine loose powder:* Fair translucent, Medium; *Ultrafine loose power:* Light; *Ultrafine pressed powder:* Fair translucent, Light, Medium, Sheer translucent, Warm; *Waterproof mascara:* Black, Brownish black

URBAN DECAY
24/7 Concealer; Baked Body Glow; Big Fatty Lip Plumper; Blow Lip Plumper; De-Slick Mattifying Powder; Eyeshadow Transforming Potion; Flavoured Body Powder; Lip Pencil; Lip Stain; Santa Tanita Body Bronzer; Surreal Skin Universal Mineral Powder; *24/7 Glide-On Eye Pencil:* Baked,

Covet, Deviant, Dime, Electric, Flipside, Graffiti, Gunmetal, Honey, Lucky, Stash, Underground, Yeyo, Zero; *24/7 Glide-On Lip Pencil* : All; *Afterglow Blush:* Exhale, Fetish; *Baked Bronzer:* All; *Brow Beater:* All; *Cream Eyeshadow:* Asphalt, Grass, Midnight Rodeo, Moonshine, Mushroom, Radium, Rehab, Suburbia, Weeds; *Deluxe Eyeshadow:* Graffiti, Honey, Peace, Shag, Underground, Zero; *Eyeshadow :* Acid Rain, Baked, Chains, Chopper, Eldorado, Flipside, Goddess, Green Goddess, Gunmetal, Half Baked, Kiddie Pool, Lounge, Maui Wowie, Midnight Cowboy Rides Again, Mildew, Oil Slick, Roach, S&M, Shattered, Smog, Speed, Stray Dog, Strip, Twice Baked, URB, Vapor, Vert; *Flavoured Powder Body Brush:* Mia Tai, Pina Colada; *Heavy Metal Glitter Eyeliner:* All; *Lip Envy:* All; *Lipsticks:* All; *Loose Pigment:* Baked, Goddess, Graffiti, Gunmetal, Protest, Rockstar, Shag, Shattered, Smog, Yeyo; *Matte Eyeshadow:* ABC Gum, Chronic, Electric, Foxy, Naked, Narcotic, Perversion, Revolver, Secret Service, Shakedown, Yeyo; *Shot-O-Gloss:* All; *Smoke Out Eye Pencil:* All; *Sparkler Pen for Lips:* All; *Surreal Skin Creamy Concealer:* All; *Surreal Skin Liquid Foundation:* All; *Surreal Skin Mineral Makeup:* All; *Ultraglide Lip Gloss:* Deep, Gash, Heat, O; *XXX Shine Lip Gloss:* Baked, Guys Love Betsay, Heatherette, JoyRide, Kinky, Love Junkie, Ozone, Quickie

VEGAN STORE ™☺❶◌ⓥ
All

VICTORIA MANOR SPA RETREAT T/A LIVINIA NATURAL SKINCARE ™◌ⓥ
Mineral Blush; Mineral Bronzer; Mineral Cream Foundation; Mineral Eyeshadow; Mineral Liners; Mineral Lipgloss; Mineral lipsticks; Mineral Mascara; Mineral Powder Foundation

SKINCARE - CLEANSERS & TONERS

AKAMUTI
Toners: All

ALEXAMI COSMETICS ™ⓥ
Alexami clean effect facial cloth

ALTERNATIVE STORES ☺
All products are vegan

ANIMAL AID ™☺❶◌ⓥ ⚘1976
Aloe & Papaya Cleansing Lotion; Aloe & Papaya Toner; Fruit & Nut Scrub; *Facial Wash:* **Kiwi & Grapefruit Facial Wash**

ANN ELISE SKINCARE ☺
Deep Cleansing Oil; Revitalising Toner

ANNEMARIE BORLIND ⓥ
Aqua Rose Vitality Essence; *Combination Series:* Cleansing Gel, Day Essence, Facial Toner; *LL Regeneration Series:* Blossom Dew Gel, Cleansing Milk; *Purifying Care Series:* Cleansing Gel, Facial Toner; *Rosedew Series:*

Cleansing Milk, Facial Toner; *System Absolute Series:* Beauty Fluid, Cleanser; *Young Beauty – Peach Series:* Cleanser; *ZZ Sensitive Series:* Cleansing, Facial Toner

AQUA NATURAL ™☺🚫 ✸ ◉
Toner spray

ARBONNE ◉
Intelligence: Daily Balancer, Daily Cleanser, Daily Moisturising Cream Day & Night; *NutriMenC RE:* REstoring Toner, REveal Exfoliating Wash; *NutriMin C RE9:* REnewing Gelee Creme Hydrating Wash, REstoring Mist Balancing Toner; *SeaSource Detox Spa:* Detoxifying Rescue Wash

AROMA CRYSTAL THERAPY 🚫 ✸
Acne Face Wash

AROMATHERAPY PRODUCTS LTD ™☺
Lavender Products: **Lavender facial cleansing foam, Lavender Foaming Face Wash;** *Skin treatments and solutions:* **Tea tree and Kanuka blemish stick;** *Tea Tree Products:* **Tea Tree and Manuka Anti Blemish Roller ball**

AUBREY ORGANICS
Sparkling Mineral Water Complexion Mist; *Blue Green Algae:* Cleansing Lotion, Facial Toner; *Green Tea and Ginkgo:* Facial Cleansing Lotion, Facial Cleansing Toner; *Harbessence:* Make Up Remover; *Natural Herbal:* Facial Astringent, Facial Cleanser; *Rosa Mosqueta and English Lavender:* Facial Toner; *Sea Buckthorn:* Facial Cleansing

Cream, Facial Toner, Moisturising Cream; *Seaware with Rosa Mosqueta:* Facial Cleansing Cream; *Vegecol with Organic Aloe:* Alcohol Free Facial Toner, Facial Cleansing Lotion

BAREFOOT BOTANICALS ☺🚫 ✸
Rosa Fina: Innocence Creamy Face Wash, Naked Beauty Nourishing Cleansing Milk; *SOS:* Lifeguard Soothing Face Wash

BEAUTY NATURALS ✸
Camomile Skin Care: Cleansing Gel; *David Hill:* Deep Cleansing Lotion; *Evening Primrose:* Cleansing Lotion, Toning Gel; *Herbal Skin Care:* No 1 Cleansing & Conditioning Milk, No 2 Toning Gel; *Herbal Skin Tonic:* Cucumber, Rosewater; *Skin Revivals:* Harmonising Cream Cleanser; *Skin Revivals - Reviving:* Harmonising Tonic

BELLECARE AG ™
24hr Liposomecreme; Anti-aging Nightcreme; Fitness Gel; *Body Lotion:* Liposomes with Bio Jojoba and Bio Sheabutter; *Vleur:* Lifting Serum, Lifting Serum Plus, Tiefenreinegung / Make Up Remover; *White Skin Gel:* Liposomes and Bio Jojoba

BL COSMETICS
Carrot Cleansing & Nourishing Milk; Cucumber Cleansing Milk; Lemon & Oatmeal Facial Lather

BONANO GMBH ™🚫
Alviana Feuchtigkeit: **Gesichtswasser, Reinigungsschaum;** *Alviana Rose:* **Gesichtswasser, Reinigungsmilch;** *Alviana Sensitiv:* **Reinigungsmilch**

BURT'S BEES ⊘ 🖋 👁
Deep Clean Cleanser; Deep Pore Scrub; *Complexion Mist:* Carrot Seed Oil, Cucumber Chamomile, Grapefruit, Lavender; *Face & Body:* Citrus Facial Scrub, Garden Tomato Toner; *Healthy Treatment:* Rosewater & Glycerin Toner

CAWARRA COSMETICS LTD ™
OrganicSpa: **Cream Cleanser, Foam Cleanser, Toner;** *OrganicSpa Range:* **Cream Cleanser, Foaming Cleanser, Toner;** *Sanctum:* **Body Buff, Body Spa, Gentle Face Exfoliant, Men's Face Exfoliant, Men's Purifying Face Cleanser, On The Spot, Purifying Foam Cleanser, Skin Renewal Treatment, Skin Whitening Lotion, Soothing Cream Cleanser, Tone & Refresh Mist**

CEBRA ETHICAL CHIC ™⊘ 🖋
Cebra- ethical skin care: **Uncover Me Facial Cleanser**

DESERT ESSENCE ⊘ 🖋 ⚘ 1985
Organics : Age Reversal Pomegranate Facial Cleansing Gel

DIRK ROSSMANN GMBH ™
Alterra: **Ampullenkur Orchidee, Anti Age Gesichtswasser Wildrose, Anti Age Waschcreme Wildrose, Intensiv Körpermilch Parfümfrei, Reinigungsmilch Parfümfrei, Serum Orchidee, Tagescreme Pfirsich - Wassermelone**

DOLMA ™☺❶⊘ 🖋 👁⚘ 1976
Skin Care: **Aromatic Face Shampoo, Astringent Toner, Evening Primrose**

& Marigold Moisture Cream, Fragrance Free Cleansing Lotion, Freshening Toner, Gentle Toner, Honesty Spicy Orange Scrub, Lavender & Chamomile Cleansing Lotion, Oil Free Cleanser, Purifying Toner

DR HAUSCHKA ⊘ 🖋
Cleansing Clay Mask; Cleansing Cream; Cleansing Milk; *Toner:* Clarifying, Facial, Rosemary Leg & Arm

DR ORGANIC
Aloe Vera: Wet Wipes; *Tea Tree:* Wet Wipes

EARTHPURE ☺ 🖋
Cleanser: Pure and Rich Cleansing Cream; *Toner:* Luxurious Rose Cleanser and Toner

ECO COSMETICS GMBH & CO. KG ™⊘ 🖋 ✺
Cleansing Milk 3-in-1; Facial Wash; Freshener

EMPATHY SKINCARE LTD (NATURAL EMPATHY) ™☺ 🖋
Clean and green: **Fresh And Floral Cleanser**

ESSENTIAL CARE
Skincare: Creamy Coconut Cleanser, Lemon & Tea Tree Facial Wash, Organic Citrus Fruit Tonic, Organic Rose Petal Tonic

ESSENTIALLY NATURAL ™
Elderflower and Glycerine Toner (Organic); Fennel Soother Rinse

(Organic); **Luxury Rose and Glycerine Cleanser (Organic); Orange Flower and Rose Toner (Organic); Tangerine Toner (Organic)**

ESSENTIALLY YOURS LTD

Fragrance Free Range: FF1 Fragrance Free Cleanser, FF2 Fragrance Free Toner, FF4 Fragrance Free Face Wash, FF8 Fragrance Free Exfoliating Lotion; *Mu Mens Range:* M8 Grapefruit & Orange Scrub; *Natural Elements Range:* NE001 Lemongrass Face Wash, NE002 Cucumber & Lime Cleanser, NE003 Lemon Grass & Witchhazel Toner, NE006 Spot Serum, NE008 Spearmint Exfoliating Lotion, NE009 Orange, Lemon & kiwi Face Wash, NE010 Orange & Kiwi Cleanser, NE011 Lemon, Kiwi & Witch Hazel Toner, NE015 Aloe Vera & Lavender Face Wash, NE016 Lavender & Aloe Vera Cleanser, NE017 Aloe Vera & Coconut Toner, NE101 Orange & Grapefruit Exfoliating Lotion, NE102 Aloe Vera & Lavender Exfoliating Lotion; *Professional Range:* NE147T Exfoliating Body Polish

FAITH PRODUCTS LIMITED
TM⊘✔☜♨–1988
3-In-1 Facial Wipes; Purifying Cleansing Lotion 150ml; Refining Toning Lotion 150ml

FOREVER LIVING PRODUCTS
Exfoliating Cleanser

GREEN PEOPLE CO. TM⊘✔
Cleanser: **B002 Gentle Cleanse, B004 Fruit Scrub, B005 Vita Min Mask, B006 Day Splution, B010 Vita Min**

Fix, B012 Eye Gel, B032 Foaming Face Wash, B11 Fruitful Nights, F012 Baby Wash Lavender, F018 Baby Wash Chamomile, F032 Baby Wash No Scent, F33 Baby Foaming Cleanser, H001 Organic Base Cleanser, L003 & L004 Exfoliating Shower Wash, L007 & L008 Wash & Shave, M001 Scrub It - Facial Exfoliator, M002 Shave Now - Face Wash & Shave, R009 Revitalising Face & Neck Serum, R020 Sensuous Sugar Scrub, T002 'Face It' Foaming Anti-Bac Facewash, T026 Wash & Shave; *Toner:* **B030 Gentle Tone, R007 Firming Facial Gel**

GREEN WYCH LTD TM☺❶⊘✔
Facial Toner: **Lavender, Rose**

HEALTHQUEST LIMITED TM⊘✔
Pure Adore: **Baby Wipes**

HEDGECRAFT TM☺⊘
Main Soap Range: **Kitchen Garden Coffee Scrub**

HEMP GARDEN TM
Face Oil: Sensual for all skin types; Face Oil: Soothing for dry, mature and weathered skin; Face Oil: Stimulating for greasy skin; Renewing Cleanser

HERBS HANDS HEALING LTD TM⊘✔
Herbs & Flowers Skin Toner; Lavender Skin Water; Rose Water Facial Tonic; Skin Guard Water

HIPPY HEAVEN
NATURAL BEAUTY ™☺⊘✔
Save sensitive skin foaming cleanser and toner in one; Soothing cream cleanser; Tea tree and peppermint blemish treatment lotion-oily and blemish prone skin; Tea tree and peppermint foaming facial cleanser and toner in one-oily and blemish prone skin

HOLISTIX HERBAL PRODUCTS ❶
Rosewater Spritzer; Rosewater Toner; Teatree & Orange Cleanser 60ml

HONESTY COSMETICS LTD
™☺❶⊘✔☜⚘1976
Spicy Orange Scrub; *Cleansers:* **Lavender & Geranium, Unscented w Chamomile;** *Facial Toners:* **Lavender & Geranium, Unscented w Chamomile;** *Honesty Essential Range:* **Face Mask with Tea Tree & Lavender, Lavender & Geranium Cleanser, Lavender & Geranium Toner, Spicy Orange Scrub;** *Honesty Fruit Range:* **Papaya Facial Wash;** *Honesty Unscented Range:* **Cleansing Lotion with Chamomille, Toner with Chamomille**

I AM NATURAL ™❶⊘✔✧
Organic Avocado Face Cream; Organic Balancing Toner; Organic Coconut Cleanser; Organic Fruit Facial Scrub; Organic Healing Toner; Organic Hemp Cleanser; Organic Macadamia Cleanser; Organic Nourishing Toner

INNOCENT OILS ™☺⊘✔
Cleanser: **Himalayan Crystal Body Spray**

ITS ELIXIR (UK) LIMITED ™⊘✔☜
Acne oil; Aloe & avocado lotion; Avocado Spray; Cleansing Acne Cream; Cleansing cream- dry skins; Cleansing cream- oily skins; Cleansing cream- sensitive skins; Cleansing Gel; Cleansing oil dry skin; Cleansing oil sensitive skin; Oily Skin Toner; Rosehip Spray; Sensitive Skin Toner; Tea tree gel; Vitamin lotion

JASON NATURAL PRODUCTS
Apricot Scrubble Wash and Scrub, Beta-Gold™Re-Hydrating Freshener, Citrus 6-in-1 Wash and Scrub with Ester-C®, Clean Start™Refreshing Cleanser, D-Clog Naturally™Balancing Cleanser, Fruit Cooler™Refreshing Toner, Vegee Tonic™Balancing Astringent; *Ester-C® Skin Care:* Super-C Toner, Super-C™ Cleanser Gentle Facial Wash; *Red Elements™ Antioxidant Skin Care:* Calming Toner, Gentle Gel Cleanser, Hydrating Lotion Cleanser

JUICE BEAUTY
Cleansing Gel; Cleansing Milk; Hydrating Mist

KEY SUN LABORATORIES PTY LTD ™⊘
Key Sun: **Face Exfoliant, Purifying Foaming Cleanser**

KISS MY FACE
Cleansing Cream; Cleansing Creme; *Organic Face Care:* Aloe and Bergamot Facial Toner, Break Out Botanical Acne Gel, Clean for a Day Facial Cleanser, Facial Treats (8 Piece Sample Pack),

TOILETRIES & COSMETICS

Startup Exfoliant Facewash; *Potent & Pure Face Care:* Balancing Antioxidant Toner, Clean for a Day Creamy Face Cleanser, Shea Soy Facial Cleansing Bar

LAVERANA GMBH & CO. KG ™ 🖋

Faces: **Cleansing Gel Mint, Faces Balancing Cream Calendula, Faces Cleansing Gel Calendula, Faces Cleansing Milk Aloe Vera, Faces Cleansing Milk Wild Rose, Faces Exfoliant Mask Mint & Rosemary, Faces Exfoliant Wash Calendula, Faces Exfoliant Wild Rose, Faces Toner Aloe Vera, Faces Toner Wild Rose;** *Lavera Basis Sensitiv:* **Cleansing Gel, Cleansing Milk 2 in 1;** *Lavera Faces My Age:* **Gentle Foaming Cleanser White Tea - Karanja Oil;** *Lavera Young Faces:* **Cleansing gel Mint, Toner Mint;** *Lavere:* **Body-Effect Active Shower, Hydro Energy Cleanser 2-Phase Cleansing Mousse, Hydro Energy Splash, Repair Relax Cleanser, Repair Relax Splash, Solution Power Cleansing, Solution Power Splash**

LIVE NATIVE ™☺

Essential Earth exfoliating cleanser; Essential mist toner

LIZ EARLE 🖋

Instant Boost Skin Tonic; *Skincare for Men:* Face and Body Wash

LUSH ™◌🖋

Cleansers: **Angels on Bare Skin, Aqua Marina, Baby Face, Buche De Noel Facial Cleanser, Coalface, Dark Angels, Fresh Farmacy, Herbalism,**

Oatifix, Volcano Foot Mask; *Facial Cleanser:* **Babe Facial Cleanser;** *Solid Facial Serum:* **Oily Skin Facial Serum, Sensitive Skin Facial Serum;** *Spot gel:* **Grease lightning;** *Toner:* **Breath of Fresh Air, Eau Roma Water, Q10 Tab, Tea Tree Toner Tab, Tea Tree Water, Vitamin C Toner Tab, Vitamin E Toner Tab**

MAJIK BLANKIT SKIN CARE ™☺🖋

Jojoba and vitamin E Sensitive cleanser; Organic Jojoba & Apricot Face Cleanser

MANAKEDI SKINCARE ™☺

Active E1 Cream Cleanser; Biolift Cleanser Lotion

MJ HEALTH(NZ) LTD ™☺❶◌🖋👁

Balance Range: **Balance Cleanser, Balance Toner;** *Earths Gift Range:* **Everyday toner, Normal skin cleanser, Oily skin cleanser;** *Gentle Range:* **Gentle Cleanser, Gentle Toner;** *Replenish Range:* **Replenish Cleanser, Replenish Toner;** *Ultra Light Range:* **Ultra Light Cleanser, Ultra Light Toner**

MY SKINCARE LTD ™☺◌🖋

Cleansing: **Bio-Active Serum, Cellular Renewal Day Cream SPF15, Deep Cleansing Lotion, Firming Brightening Serum, Multi Mineral Day Cream SPF15, Nourishing Cleansing Lotion, Pro Active Moisturising Day Cream, Pro Active Moisturising Day Cream SPF15**

NATURA ORGANICS ⊘ ✐ ✿
Hydrating Cleansing Milk; Hydrating Toner Spray; Purifying Cleansing Gel; Purifying Toner Spray

NATURAL SENSE
Face Mister; Marigold Cleanser; Marigold Cleanser; Orange Flower Toner; Rose Flower Toner

NATURE'S GATE
Deep Cleansing Face Wash; Gentle Moisturizing Facial Toner; Revitalizing Facial Scrub; *Organics - Advanced Care:* In The Beginning Cleanser, Tone Back the Clock Toner

NEAL'S YARD REMEDIES
⊘ ✐ ☙ ⚷ 1998
Calendula Cleanser; Detox Toning Oil; Frankincense Facial Wash; Mahonia Clear Skin Gel; NYR Men Face Lotion; NYR Men Purifying Face Wash; Orange Flower Facial Wash; Orange Flower Water; Power Berry Facial Wash; Purifying Palmarosa Pore Minimiser; Rejuvenating Frankincense Facial Wash; Rose Facial Wash; Rose Water; Witch Hazel

NEW SEASONS
Creamy Body Scrub; Rose Cleanser; *Neutral & Toiletry Bases:* Cleanser, Facial & Body Scrub

NOTHING NASTY ✐
Facial Toner: Flawless for Problem Skin, Ideal for Normal Skin, Prime for Mature & Sensitve Skin

ORGANIC BOTANICS ™⊘ ✿
Fragrance Free Organic Deep Cleansing Milk; Organic Tea Tree & Lavender Face & Body Wash; *Cleanser:* **Organic Gentle Deep Cleansing Milk;** *Toner:* **Organic Floral Toning Lotion, Organic Gentle Deep Cleansing Milk**

POTIONS AND POSSIBILITIES ⊘ ✐
Beauty: Essential Cleanser, Essential Toner, Invigorating Salt Scrub For Men, Tea Tree & Lavender Facial Cleanser; *Organic Range:* Facial Cleanser, Facial Scrub, Facial Toner, Gentle Facial Wash

PURATY LTD ☺ ✐
Balancing Facial Wash

PURE GAISHA ™☺ ❶ ✐
Aloha Sugar & Salt Scrub; Creamy Cleanser - Dry/Mature Skin; Creamy Cleanser - Sensitive Skin; Facial Toner - Normal Skin; Facial Toner - Oily Skin; Facial Toner - Sensitive Skin; Floral Waters; Foamy Cleanser - Normal Skin; Foamy Cleanser - Oily Skin; Luxury Facial Scrub and Polish; Mens Reviving Face & Body Polish

QUINESSENCE AROMATHERAPY ☺☺ ✐ ☙
Damask Rose Toner; Facial Exfoliator; Rose Facial; *Lotion:* Cleansing

RARE NATURAL CARE, INC. ™☺ ❶ ⊘ ✐ ✿ ☙
Rare2B Vegan Skincare: **Toning Cleanser**

RAW GAIA ™☺❶◐⊘◍☼◉
Facial Cleanser; Floral Face Toner; MSM Beauty Spray

REN ⊘
Calendula and Arctic Blackcurrant Seed Cleansing Milk Wash; Jojoba Micro Bead Purifying Facial Scrub; Mayblossom and Blue Cypress Facial Wash; Phyto-Dynamic Instant Lifting Facial Spray; Rosa Centifolia Facial Wash; Zostera Marina Cleansing Milk Wash

RIVER VEDA ™⊘◍☼
RiverVeda: **Carefree, Fresh Face, Freshly Free, Luminous Day, Newly You, Spot Eraser, Wonder Lift;** *The Organic Skin Company:* **Brightening Almond Seed Face Exfoliant, Freshness Juniper Berry Face Wash, Joy Sweet Orange Cleansing Milk, Spot Free Nutmeg & Neem Blemish Treatment, Timeless Seabuckthorn Facial Serum**

RJ MINERAL COSMETICS INTERNATIONAL PTY LTD ™◍
Face: **CCL Face Cream Cleanser - Chamomile, CCL Face Cream Cleanser - Neroli, CCL Face Cream Cleanser - Rose, CCL Face Cream Cleanser - Sandalwood & Ylang Ylang, CCL Face Cream Cleanser - Unscented, FCL Face Cleanser Foaming - Chamomile, FCL Face Cleanser Foaming - Lemon & Juniper Berry, FCL Face Cleanser Foaming - Rose, FCL Face Cleanser Foaming - Unscented, FCRC Face Scrub - Neroli, FCRC Face Scrub - Rose, FCRC Face Scrub - Unscented,**

LF Face Freshner - Chamomile, LF Face Freshner - Lavender, LF Face Freshner - Rosewater, LF Face Freshner - Witchazel, TTC Face - Tea Tree Clearer

SAAF INTERNATIONAL LIMITED ™
Organic Pure Face Cleanser; Skincare kit/travel set

SIMPLE ◍
Age Resisting Facial Wash; Cleansing Glycerine Bar; Daily Radiance Foaming Cream Cleanser; Energise Body Bar; Men's Face Scrub; Moisturising Foaming Facial Wash; Oil Balancing Exfoliating Wash; Purifying Cleansing Lotion; Refreshing Facial Wash Gel; Smoothing Cleansing Scrub; Softening Facial Cleansing Mousse; Soothing Facial Toner; *Cleansing Wipes:* Oil Balancing, Original, Regeneration, Revitalising Exfoliating, Smoothing Facial

SIMPLY SOAPS
Exfoliating Facial Scrub; Lavender Toner; *Hedgerow Herbals:* Gentle Rose Wash Grains; *Hedgerow Herbals- Rosa Passionata:* Rosa Facial Steam Bags, Rosa Organic Hydrosol, Rose Facial Serum

SKIN BLOSSOM LIMITED ™☺⊘◍☼
Cleansers: **Gentle Cleansing Milk**

SKINCARE CAFE LTD ☺
Organic aloe vera toner

SKINVAC ™☺⊘◍
Deep Daily Cleansing Cloth; Pore Gripper Acne Control Cloth

SOLARAY NUTRITIONAL SUPPLEMENTS

Herbessence Make Up Remover; Natural Herbal Facial Astringent; *Facial Cleansing Cream:* Sea Buckthorn, Seaware w Rosa Mosqueta; *Facial Cleansing Lotion:* Blue Green Algae, Green Tea & Gingko, Natural Herbal, Vegecol w Organic Aloe; *Facial Toner:* Blue Green Algae, Green Tea & Gingko, Rosa Mosqueta & English Lavender, Sea Buckthorn, Vegecol w Organic Aloe Alcohol Free

SOPHYTO ™❶⊘✔👁

Deep Pore Foaming Cleanser; Ph optimising restorative toner; Purify & Energise Super Bioactives; Ultra Mild Silken Cleanser

STELLA MCCARTNEY

Care: Gentle Cleansing Milk, Purifying Foaming Cleanser, Toning Floral Water; *Stella:* Gentle Body Cleanser, Precious Body Cream

SUKI PURE SKIN CARE

Exfoliating Lemongrass Cleanser w Chamomile & Vitamin C; *Concentrated Toner:* Shitake, Burdock & Olive Leaf, White Willow, Aloe, Chamomile & Tea Tree

SUPERDRUG

Amie: Petal Perfect Refreshing Cleansing Lotion

SYNTHESIS 345 ™☺⊘✔✿

First Love: **Cleanser, Skin Hydrating Tonic**

THE HIMALAYA DRUG COMPANY ™

Cleansing Bar: **Purifying Neem & Turmeric Handcrafted Cleansing Bar**

TREASURED EARTH SKINCARE ™☺⊘

Body Scrub; Cleanser; Toner

TRUTHFUL CO. LTD (PURELY SKINCARE) ™☺⊘

Purely Skincare: **Face wash - refreshing variant, Face wash (female variant), Face wash (male variant), Face wash- sensitive variant**

URTEKRAM

Body Scrub: All

VANILLA TREE NATURAL SKIN CARE ™☺✔

Clarify Cleansing Gel; Invigorate Bodywash

VERDESATIVA S.R.L. ™☺❶⊘✔✿❀

Cleansing Lotion - Hemp and Red Grape; Latte Detergente Canapa e Malva (Cleansing Lotion Hemp and Mallow); *High Performance Line:* **Latte detergente**

WELEDA ⊘✔⚘1985

Almond Cleansing Lotion; Iris Facial Toner; Wild Rose Cleansing Lotion

WHITE LOTUS COSMETIC ACUPUNCTURE ™❶⊘✔

Herbal: **Facial Toner**

SOAPS

ABSOLUTE AROMAS ™⊘ ✔
Ord River: **Ord River Handwash 250ml, Tea Tree & Lavender 125g**

ADVANCED FORMULATIONS (EUROPE LTD) ™⊘
NOE: **NOE Hand Wash;** *No-Germs:* **No-Germs Hand Sanitizer, No-Germs Hand Wash**

AKAMUTI
African Black Soap Bars; *Liquid African Black Soap:* Scented, Unscented; *Soap:* Red Palm, Shea Butter & Baobab, Shea Butter & Neem

AKOMA INTERNATIONAL (UK) LTD ™⊘ ✔
Akoma original saop: **Black Soap**

AMAZENE ™☺❶⊘ ✔ ✿
Natural Company- Moisturising Toilet Soap: **Lavanda Francesca, Rosa da Bulgaria;** *Phytophilo Aromatherapy Range- Glycerine Body Bar:* **Andiroba, Buriti & Aroeira, Anise, Calendula, Carobinha & Cupuacu, Cocoa & Vanilla, Guarana, Jua & Jaborandi, Kiwi;** *Phytophilo Aromatherapy Range- Liquid Soaps:* **Cocoa & Cupuacu, Green Tea, Aloe Vera & Anise, Lavender, Calendula & Primrose, Strawberry n Cream;** *Phytophilo Aromatherapy Range- Vegetable Bar Soaps:* **Acerola, Passion Fruit & Avocado, Andiroba, Buriti, & Aroeira, Calendula, Carombinha &** Cupuacu, Cocoa, Coconut, Buriti & Brazil Nut, Lavender, Passion Fruit, Strawberry n Cream; *Phytophilo Aromatherapy Range-Liquid Soaps:* **Papaya, Passion Fruit & Acerola**

ANIMAL AID ™☺❶⊘ ✔ ⅍1976
Calendula & Vanilla Liquid Soap; Lavender & Aloe Vera Liquid Soap

AROMATHERAPY PRODUCTS LTD™☺
Lavender Products: **Lavender & Evening Primrose, Lavender and Evening Primrose;** *Skin softening soaps:* **Bitter Orange and Jasmine, Tea Tree and Avocado;** *Tea Tree Products:* **Tea Tree, Tea Tree & Avocado**

AUBREY ORGANICS
Rosa Mosqueta Moisturising Cleansing Bar; *Bar Soaps:* Men's Cleansing Bar Soap, Sea Buckthorn with Sandalwood Bar, White Camellia and Jasmine Bar; *Liquid Soaps:* Herbal Liquid Every Day Body Soap, Rosa Mosqueta Luxurious Body Wash Soap, Rosa Mosqueta Mositurising Bath and Shower Gel

AUSTRALIAN TEA TREE
Skin Care Soap

BABY'S BUM PREMIUM NATURAL SOAPS ☺⊘ ✔ ◉⅍1980
Liquid Soaps: Lavender, Tea Tree; *Little Squirt Natural Liquid Soaps for Kids 50ml:* Lavender; *Natural Liquid Soaps:* Fragrance Free; *Natural Liquid Soaps 250ml:* Lemon & Lime, Peppermint

BIO-D ™☺⊘ ✔ ◉⅍1988
Hemp Bran; Hemp Oil

BONANO GMBH ™⊘
Alviana Basic: **Flussigseife**

BRACKENCRAFT ™☺❶⊘ ⚅
English Lavender Soap; *Bsoaps:*
**Calendula & Orange, Chamomile &
Lemon Soap, Cinnamon Swirl Soap,
Citrus soap, Ginger and lime,
Gourmet Bar, Lavender & Coconut
Soap, Orange & Geranium Soap,
Orange, lemongrass and cinnamon,
Patchouli & Orange Soap, Peppermint
& Green Tea with Nettles Soap, Rose
& Geranium Soap, Unfragranced
with Cranberries Soap, White
Cinammon Soap; Carrot Soap;
Cedarwood Pine & Rosemary Soap;
Christmas Spice Soap; Coconut Milk
Soap; Frankinsence & Myhrr Soap;
Gardeners Soap**

BRONNLEY & CO LTD ⚅
Body Care for Men: Soap; *Face Wash:*
Bird of Paradise, Tulip; *Royal
Horticultural Society - Hand Wash:*
Gardener's, Passion Flower; *Royal
Horticultural Society - Soap:* Passion
Flower, Rose; *Royal Horticultural
Society- Soap:* Gardener's; *Soap Body
Bar:* Bird of Paradise, Tulip; Africa;
Apricot & Almond; Asia; Caribbean;
English Fern; Gardener's; India;
Lavender; Lemon; Orchid; Passion
Flower; Pink Bouquet; White Iris

BURT'S BEES ⊘⚅👁
Face & Body: Garden Carrot
Complexion Soap, Wild Lettuce
Complexion Soap; *Natural Remedies:*
Poison Ivy; *Shower Soap:* Citrus Spice
Exfoliating, Peppermint

**CALDER VALLEY SOAP
CO. LTD** ™☺⊘ ⚅ 👁
**Almond Blossom; Aloe Vera; Apple
& Elderflower; Camomile Flowers;
Coconut Palm and Oats;
Frankincense & Lemongrass;
Lavender flowers; Lemongrass and
Hemp Bran; Lime and Mint Leaf;
Oatmeal Scrub; Orange & Clove;
Peppermint & Poppyseed; Rose
Petals; Rosemary Leaf; Sandalwood;
Tea Tree; Vanilla; Wild Raspberry
and Wild Raspberry Leaf; Ylang
Ylang**

CAURNIE SOAPERIE ☺⊘ ⚅ ⚘1976
Bog Myrtle; Loofah Imbedded; Nettle;
Pure; Rosemary

CAWARRA COSMETICS LTD ™
**Organic Soap Cedarwood & Olive
Leaf; Organic Soap Lavender &
Chamomille; Organic Soap
Lemongrass & Witch Hazel; Organic
Soap Rose Geranium & Calendula;
Organic Soap Sanctum;** *OrganicSpa:*
Face Exfoliant

CEBRA ETHICAL CHIC ™⊘ ⚅
Cebra- ethical skin care: **Pure Me
Liquid African Black Soap,
unscented, Replenish me African
black soap body wash**

CELLANDE MIDLANDS ⊘ ⚅
Liquid Soap: Almond, Mint Bactericidal

CHIKPE ⊘ ⚅
Banana; Blue Heart; Bluebell Wood
Soap; Chocolate; Coconut; Cool
Cucumber; Elderflower & Oatmeal;

Freshly Cut Grass; Gardener's Soap; Honeysuckle & Heather; Lavender; Lemon Zest; Morrello Cherry; Orange; Pastel Heart; Pink Heart; Purple Heart; Rose; Sea Breeze; St Clements; Strawberry; Vanilla Ice-Cream; Yellow Jasmine; *Mini Bath Bombs:* Rose & Lavender, Sea Breeze, Strawberry & Banana; *Soap Cake Slices:* Birthday Cake, Chocolate Gateau, Lemon Meringe Pie, Numbered Celebration Cake, Occassion Celebration Cake, Strawberry Cheesecake, Victoria Sponge

DIRK ROSSMANN GMBH ™
Alterra: **Cremseife Mandarine Jojoba**

DOLMA ™☺❶⊘◌◔⊶1976
Glycerine Soap: **'Niamh' De-luxe, Carrot Ho-Leaf & Orange, Hemp Seed Fragrance Free, Lavender & Jojoba, Tea-Tree & Calendula**

DR ORGANIC
Aloe Vera: Bar Soap, Handwash; *Lavender:* Bar Soap, Handwash; *Pomegranate:* Bar Soap; *Tea Tree:* Bar Soap, Handwash; *Vitamin E:* Bar Soap

DROYT PRODUCTS ⊘◌⊶1984
Bath Bar: Fresh Green, Lavender, Lemon, Mint, Pine & Juniper; *Craft Collection:* Eau de Cologne, Fresh Green, Red Rose, Unperfumed; *Glycerose:* Avocado, Mandarin, Rose Scented, Yellow Rose; *Liquid Soap:* Glycerine Soap, Glycerine Soap Refill; *Organic Range:* Liquid Soap with Glycerine, Soap Bar with Glycerine; *Original:* Glycerine Soap, Unperfumed

Glycerine Soap; *Soap Bars:* Lavender Soap, Vegetas; *Soap Square:* Apple, Avocado, Chamomile, Coconut, Fresh Green, Lavender, Lemon, Mandarin, Mint, Pine; *Stripe Soaps:* Coconut & Vanilla, Mint

EARTHPURE ☺◌
Soap Bars: Eastern Rose, Geranium and Lavender, Lavender, Neem +, Peppermint, Eucalyptus & Clove, Pure Soap, Spiced Orange, Vetivert and Lavender

ECOSOAPIA ☺
Liquid Soap: Almond, Eucalyptus, Lavender, Peppermint, Rose Geranium, Tee Tree, Unscented

ESSENTIALLY NATURAL ™
Cucumber and Almond Scrub (Organic); Cucumber and Elderflower Soap (Organic); Feet Treat Soap; Gardener's Delight Soap with Pumice (Organic); Gardener's Delight Soap without Pumice (Organic); Hemp and Patchouli Soap (Organic); Hemp Soap (Organic); Insect Repellent Soap (Organic); Luxury Rose and Cocoa Butter Soap (Organic); Oranges & Lemons Soap

FAITH PRODUCTS LIMITED ™⊘◌◔⊶1988
Aloe Vera 100g / unwrapped; Chocolate 100g / unwrapped; Gingko Biloba 100g / unwrapped; Hemp with Lemongrass & Green Tea 100g / unwrapped; Lavender 100g / unwrapped; Orange 100g / unwrapped; Pine (Loose and

unwrapped only); Rosemary 100g / unwrapped; Seaweed 100g / unwrapped; Tea Tree 100g / unwrapped

FLORIS ☺ ✔
Luxury Soap: Cefiro Luxury, China Rose, Edwardian Bouquet, Elite, Fleur, Florissa, Guest Soap, JF, Lily of the Valley Luxury Soap, Luxury Soap Collection, Night Scented Jasmine, No 89, Rose Geranium, Santal, Seringa, Stephanotis, White Rose

FOREVER LIVING PRODUCTS
Aloe Liquid Soap

FREERANGERS ™☺✔
Lavender Lullaby Soap; Lemon Zing Soap; Summer Garden Soap; *Pamper Products:* **Single Soap**

FUNK BUBBLE ™☺
Chocolate/Orange; Cinnamon/Oatmeal; Orange/Lemon; Rose; Tea Tree; Ylang Ylang/Neroli

GREEN PEOPLE CO. ™⊘✔
Antibacterial Soap: **C037 Organic Antibacterial Soap, C038 Foaming Hand Sanitizer; C035 Organic Aloe Vera Soap; H008 Organic Base Liquid Soap**

GREEN WYCH LTD ™☺❶⊘✔
Soap: **Bergamot Soap, Geranium Soap, Lavender Soap, Lemongrass Soap, Orange Zest Soap**

GREENCITY WHOLEFOODS ❶⊘
Organic Soaps: Geranium & Rose Petal, Grapefruit & Aloe Vera, Hemp Oil Fragrance Free, Lime & Lemongrass, Mandarin & Ginger, Sandalwood & Cedar, White Lavender

HEDGECRAFT ™☺⊘
Castille Soap Range: **Lavender, Lavender and Oat;** *Main Soap Range:* **Grapefruit, Lavender, Lavender and Oat, Orange and Patchouli, Ylang Yland and Orange**

HIGHER NATURE LTD
Omega Nutrition Handmade Soaps: Flax Orange, Rainforest

HOLISTIX HERBAL PRODUCTS ❶
Handmade Soap: Calendula, Hardworking Hands, Hemp, White Lavender

HONESTY COSMETICS LTD
™☺❶⊘✔ ⚖1976
Apple & Sandalwood; Carrot & Jojoba; Geranium & Lavender; Orange; Strawberry & Papaya

HOWAD LTD T/A INCOGNITO ™❶⊘✔
Incognito: **Ginger & Citronella Soap, Lemongrass & Citronella Soap**

I AM NATURAL ™❶⊘✔ ✿
Organic Tea Tree Hand Soap

INNOCENT OILS ™☺⊘✔
Innocent Baby Soap; Innocent Hemp Soap; Love One Soap

JASON NATURAL PRODUCTS
All-Natural Liquid Satin Soaps: Aloe

Vera, Apricot, Chamomile, Glycerine &
Rosewater, Herbal Extracts, Lavender,
Mango & Papaya, Tea Tree Oil

JUST SOAPS ™

**Citrus Zing Liquid Soap; Fresh &
Minty Liquid Soap; Gardeners Soap
Block; Geranium & Lavender Loofah
Soap; Grapefruit & Lime Loofah
Soap; Grapefruit & Lime Soap Block;
Just Liquid Soap; Just Soap Block;
Kitchen Soap Block; Lavender Bud
Soap Block; Lavender Liquid Soap;
Lemongrass & Lime Loofah Soap;
Lemongrass & Lime Soap Block;
Orange & Cinnamon Soap Cake;
Patchouli Liquid Soap; Patchouli
Soap Block; Rose Geranium Soap
Block; Rose Geranium Soap Cake;
Rosemary & Pine Soap Block;
Rosemary Liquid Soap; Soap on a
Rope; Wild Lavender Soap Cake**

KISS MY FACE

Bar Soap: Olive & Aloe, Olive &
Chamomile, Olive & Green Tea, Olive &
Lavender, Olive & Verbena, Pure Olive
Oil; *Liquid Moisture:* Almond, Fragrance
Free, Germaside with Tea Tree, Melon,
Olive and Aloe, Orange Blossom,
Peaceful Patchouli, Peach, Pear; *Organic
Face Care:* Shea Soy Facial Cleansing
Bar; *Organic Foaming Soap:* Close
Encounter, In the Pink, Sports Complex;
Self Foaming: Grapefruit & Bergamot,
Lavender & Chamomile, Lemon and
Ginger, Rosemary and Melon; *Sudz
Organic Bar Soap:* C-Weed, In the Pink,
Rough Seas, Sports Complex

LAVERANA GMBH & CO. KG ™ ⚘

Basis Sensitiv: **Liquid Soap - Almond
Milk & Shea Butter, Liquid Soap -
Calendula & Sea Buckthorn;** *Men
SPA:* **Face Wash with Scrub Effect**

LIZ EARLE ⚘

Orange Flower Hand Wash

LUSH ™ ⊘ ⚘

Karma Products: **Karma Soap; 17
Cherry Tree Lane; A Ring of Roses;
Angels delights; Bamboo Soap;
Beautiful Pea Green Soap;
Bohemian; Cocktail Guest Soap;
Demon In The Dark; Father frost;
Figs and Leaves; Garvanie;
Gingerman Soap; Godmother;
Happy Soap; I Should Coco; Ice
Blue; Icon; Lemslip; Miranda; Mud
Flats; No.1 Seed; Palm oil free sexy
naked Noubar; Pineapple Grunt;
Porridge; Prince Soap; Pumkin seed;
Queen of Hearts Complexion Soap;
Quinquereme of Nineveh; Red
Rooster; Rock Star; Sandstone; Sea
Vegetable; Sexy Peel; Snowcake;
Soap Sod; Sultana of Soap; Sunny
Citrus; Temptation; Tiptoe Through
the Tulips; Vanilla in the mist;
Waylander Rhassoul**

MAXIM MARKETING COMPANY ™

Amber : **Sandalwood Beauty Soap**

MISSHU LTD T/A LANI-JO ™☺❶⚘

Essential: **Soap Bar;** *Healing:* **Soap Bar
Aloe Vera;** *Heaven:* **Soap Bar;**
Sensual: **Soap Bar;** *Soap Bar:* **Aloe
Vera, Citrus and Nutmeg, Lavender**

N Rosemary, Melon N Cucumber, Mimosa Osmanthus Ylang Ylang, Olive Oil N Glycerine, Orange N Geranium, Peach, Rosewater, Tea Tree

MY HANDMADE SOAPS ™☺⊘ⓘ
Bath Novelty Soaps: **All fragrances- fun shapes;** *Crystal Natural Soaps:* **Lemon Grass Soap, Patchouli Soap, Tea Tree and Lavender Soap;** *Handmade soap bars:* **Almond milk soap bar, Aloe vera soap bar, Cherry soap bar, Coconut soap bar, English rose soap bar, Fresh cotton soap bar, Gardeners Essential soap bar, Grapefruit soap bar, Green Apple soap bar, Lavender soap bar, Lemon soap bar, Mango soap bar, Oatmeal Essential soap bar, Olive oil soap bar, Orange and cinammon soap bar, Sandalwood soap bar, Simply soap bar, Soft Oatmeal soap bar, Strawberry soap bar;** *Men's collection:* **Cool for men soap bar, Sea Breeze soap bar;** *Mini Soaps:* **All fragrances- bar shape, All fragrances- round shape;** *Soap Slices:* **Almond Soap Slice, Cherry Soap Slice, Chocolate Indulgence Soap Slice, Lemon surprise Soap Slice, Strawberry Cream Soap Slice, Strawberry Soap Slice**

NATURAL SENSE
Aleppo Cubes; Aleppo Soap with Damascus Rose Oil; Aleppo Soap with Oil of Jasmine; Aleppo Soap with Oil of Nigella; Liquid Soap; Liquid Soap

NATURALLY GIFTED
Bed of Roses; Citrus Grove Bar; Hemp & Walnut; Herbal Mint; Oatmeal & Spice Scrub; Olive Oil; Seaweed Bar; Summer Solstice; T Tree

NATURE'S GATE
Liquid Soaps: Deep Cleansing, Moisturizing, Purifying, Soothing; *Organics - Fruit Blend Liquid Soaps:* Asian Pear & Red Tea, Grapefruit & Wild Ginger, Mandarin Orange & Patchouli, Persimmon & Rose Geranium; *Organics - Herbal Blend Liquid Soaps:* Lavender & Aloe, Lemongrass & Clary Sage, Neroli Orange & Chocolate Mint, Tea Tree & Blue Cypress

NEAL'S YARD REMEDIES
⊘ⓘ👁⚹1998
Calendula Soap; French Almond Soap; French Lavender Soap (Hand Made); Geranium & Orange Soap; Lavender & Olive Oil Soap; Lavender & Tea Tree Soap; Lavender & Vitamin E Shaving Soap; Marseille Soap Block; Neem Soap

NEW SEASONS
Liquid Soap; *Neutral & Toiletry Bases:* Liquid Soap

NOTHING NASTY ⓘ
Liquid Castille Soaps: Lavender, Mandarin, Rosemary, Tea Tree

OPTIMAH ⊘ⓘ⚹1995
Olivera: Olive Oil & Aloe Vera Soap, Olive Oil & Aloe Vera Soap with Lavender Essential Oil, Olive Oil & Aloe

Vera Soap with Tea Tree Antiseptic, Olive Oil & Aloe Vera Soap with Vitamin E Moisturiser

ORGANIC BOTANICS ™ ⊘ ✿
Organic Bar Soap With Flower Oils

ORGANIC SOAP COMPANY ™ ⊘ ✿
Adam the Gardener's Tea Tree Scrub; Aloe Vera & Lavender; Bergamot; Cheer Up; Frankincense & Myrrh; Geranium; Geranium & Orange Blossom; Lavender; Lavender & Chamomile; Lavender Scrub; Lemongrass & Rosemary; Patchouli; Patchouli Soap; Relax & Chill Out; Rose & Jasmine; Rose & Vanilla; Rose Garden; Sandalwood; Soothing Smoothing; Tea Tree & Lavender; Vanilla Marble; *New :***No Worries, Rosemary, Soothing Smoothing 1, Soothing Smoothing 2;** *Soap:* **Adam the Gardener's Hand Scrup, Avocado Soap / Baby Soap, Buzz Off / Midge Repellent Soap, Cheer Up Soap, Cinnamon and Oatmeal Scrub, Frankincense and Myrrh, Lavender and Aloe Vera, Lavender and Chamomile, Lavender Flowers Scrub, Lemon Sorbet, No Worries, Olive Oil, Patchouli, Patchouli, Bergamot, Geranium, Rose and Jasmine, Rose Garden, Sandalwood, Soothing Smoothing, Spice Island, Tea Tree, Tea Tree and Lavender, Venus Aphrodite**

ORGANIX SOUTH INC
Thera Neem: Facial Complexion Bar,

Lemongrass Patchouli & Neem Oil Bar, Max Strength Neem Oil Bar, Max Strength Sweet Orange Bar, Neem Leaf Oil & Bark Soap Bar, Oatmeal Lavender & Neem Oil Bar

POTIONS AND POSSIBILITIES ⊘ ⬤
Double Luxury Soaps: Bergamot, English Garden, English Jasmine, English Lavender, English Rose, Frankincense, French Lavender & Evening Primrose, Orange & Calendula, Rose & Cinnamon, Rosemary & Wild Mint, Violet; *Luxury Soap Stack:* Contemporary Soap Collection, Traditional Soap Collection; *Organic Range:* Luxury Double Soap

PZ CUSSONS UK LTD ™ ⊘ ⬤
Original Source Liquid Soap: **Mint & Tea Tree, White Pear & Avocado**

QUINTESSENTIAL SOAPS ☺
Calendula Comfort; Terra Rosa; Essential Spice, Sublime; Cobblestone, Pure and Natural; Citrus Swirl, Rosemary and Time

RAW GAIA ™ ☺ ❶ ⊘ ⬤ ✿ ◉
Organic Raw - clear and refreshing; Organic Raw - Lavender; Organic Raw - Rose Geranium

REDBUSH TEA CO
Redbush Exfoliating Soap; Redbush Soap

SHANTI PRODUCTS ⊘ ⬤
Christmas Range: Christmas Cake Soap Slice, Christmas Cupcake, Cinnamon Christmas Cake Slice; *Cold Process Bars:*

Cinnamon & Nutmeg, Coconut Soap, English Rose Soap, Eucalyptus & Tea Tree Soap, Garden Mint, Gardener, Lavender Soap, Lemon Zest Soap, Lime & Patchouli Soap, Ocean Fresh, Pure & Simple, Rosemary Soap, Sandalwood Soap, Sweet Orange & Patchouli, Vanilla Soap

SHEA BY NATURE ☺
Liquid Soaps: African Black Soap - Cocovanille, African Black Soap - Coffee Fragrance, African Black Soap - Exotica with Lemongrass, Lemon and Orange, African Black Soap - Jungle Spice, African Black Soap - Strawberry and Vanilla, African Black Soap - Sweet Romance (Geranium, Lavender and Ylang, African Black Soap - Tea Tree and Peppermint, African Black Soap - Unscented; *Soap Bars:* African Black Soap - Unscented, African Black Soap - with Lemongrass,Lavender and YlangYlang

SIMPLY SOAPS
Banana & Citron; Calendula & Lavender; Cedarwood; Geranium & Rose; Guys Bar Natural and Organic; Hemp; Liquid Soap; Mandarin Liquid Soap; Orange, Neroli & Sandalwood; Poppy Bar; Rosemary & Lavender; Seaweed; Tea Tree; *Gift Sets:* 3-Soap Gift Box, 5-Soap Gift Box; *Hedgerow Herbals:* Comfrey & Calendula, Rose & Oatmeal; *Hedgerow Herbals-Black Palm Natural Range:* Natural Soft Soap

SODASAN ™ ⬤
Liquid Soap: **Sodasan Liquid Rose;** *Soap Bar:* **Bar Soap, Body Care Soaps, Cream Vanilla, Olive Soaps, Pure Berries, Pure Flower, Pure Lemon, Pure Ocean**

SOLANO TRADING ™ ⊘ ⬤
Organic Soaps: **Lavender, Mint, Sage Bergamot;** *Rampal Patou:* **Almond Soap, Lavender Soap, Olive Oil Soap, Scented Soap;** *Savon Liquide:* **Lavande, The Vert**

SOLARAY NUTRITIONAL SUPPLEMENTS
Herbal Liquid Every Day Body Soap; Men's Cleansing Bar; Rosa Mosqueta Cleansing Bar; Rosa Mosqueta Luxurious Bodywash; Sea Buckthorn w Sandalwood; White Camelia w Jasmine

SONETT OHG ™
Citrus Handsoap; Curd Soap; Épure; Handsoap Rosemary; Lavender Handsoap; Liquid Soap; Neutral Handsoap; Neutral Plant Soap Bar; Rose Handsoap

SUMA WHOLEFOODS
™ ❶ ⊘ ⬤ ⬤ ✂ 1985
Country Garden: **Chamomile, Mixed Pack, Rosemary, Violet;** *Exotic:* **Cinnamon & Sandalwood, Mixed Pack, Nutmeg & Vanilla, Tea Tree;** *Extra Gentle:* **Avocado & Cucumber, Desert Aloe Vera, Fragrant Coco Palm, Mixed Pack;** *Glycerine Soaps:* **Grapefruit & Aloe Vera, Hemp & Vitamin E, Rose & Geranium, White Lavender;** *Handmade Gifts:* **Box of Soaps - Gift Box;** *Handmade Soaps:* **Almond Soap, Wild Raspberry Soap;** *Old English:* **Elderflower & Apple, English Lavender Blossom, Mixed Pack, Rose of York;** *'Winter Collection giftbox handmade soaps':* **Frankincense and**

Lemongrass/Orange and Clove/
Ylang Ylang/Cinnamon and
Sandalwood

TANJERO ™☺◌✍

Aloeswood; Apple & Orchid;
Aquarius; Aries; Cancer; Capricorn;
Carrot & Hempseed; Chamomile;
Coconut & Kelp; Cucumber & Mint;
Gardenia; Gemini; Geranium;
Geranium & Lime; Grapefruit &
Orange; Jasmine; Just Carrot;
Kitchen Coffee Bar; Lavender;
Lavender & Aloe Vera; Lavender &
Chamomile; Lavender & Oatmeal;
Lavender with Flowers; Leo; Libra;
Litsea Cubeba; Musk; Patchouli;
Pisces; Pure Aloe Vera; Rose;
Sagittarius; Scorpio; Sea Breeze;
Strawberry; Sultan; Tanjero No. 1;
Tanjero No. 2; Tanjero No. 3; Taurus;
Tea Tree & Aloe Vera; Tea Tree &
Lavender; Tea Tree & Lavender with
Oatmeal; Tea Tree & Mint; Tea Tree
& Oatmeal; Violet; Virgo; Ylang
Ylang

THE HIGHLAND SOAP COMPANY ◌

Aloe & White tea; Chamomille;
Cinnamon & Orange; Gardeners Soap;
Highland Lavender; Lavender Luxury
Soap; Lemongrass; Lemongrass & Ginger
Soap; Mango Butter; Passion Fruit; Red
Clay & Ylang Ylang; Rose Geranium &
Lavender Soap; Rose & Patchouli; Rose
& Ylang Ylang; Rosehip & Patchouli
Soap; Rosemary & Wild Nettle;
Sandalwood; Scottish Heather; Tea Tree
& Peppermint; White Jasmine; Wild Nettle
& Heather; Wild Scottish Strawberry

TOMS OF MAINE ◌✍

Natural Clear Body Bar: Lavender,
Unscented; *Natural Deodorant Body
Bar:* Lemongrass, Unscented; *Natural
Moisturising Body Bar:* Calendula,
Lavender, Unscented

TREASURED EARTH SKINCARE ™☺◌

Soaps

TREE-HARVEST ◌✍

Artisan Handmade Soap: Bay,
Calendula, Cedar & Lemon, Forest
Spice, Frankincense & Myrrh,
Gardener's, Geranium Lavender &
Chamomile, Hemp, Orange Cardamon
& Clove, Patchouli & Sandalwood, St
Clement's, Tea Tree

TROPICAL WHOLEFOODS

Clean: Aloe Vera and Baobab Purity,
Neem, Seaweed & Lemongrass Scrub

URTEKRAM

Handsoap: All

VERDESATIVA S.R.L. ™☺❶◌✍✿👁

Liquid Soap - Hemp and Citrus Fruit;
Sapone Canap e Papavero (Hemp
and Poppy Soap); Sapone Canapa e
Aloe (Hemp and Aloe Soap); Sapone
Canapa e Argilla (Hemp and Clay
Soap); Sapone Canapa e Arumi (Hemp
and Citrus Fruits Soap); Sapone
Canapa e Calendula (Hemp and
Marigold Soap); Sapone Canapa e
Camomilla (Hemp and Chamomile);
Sapone Canapa e Crusca (Hemp and
Bran); Sapone Canapa e Fior di Loto
(Hemp and Lotus Flower); Sapone
Canapa e Lavanda (Hemp and

Lavender Soap); Sapone Canapa e Mango (Hemp and Mango); Sapone Canapa e Menta (Hemp and Mint); Sapone Canapa e Neem (Hemp and Neem Soap); Sapone Canapa e Papaia (Hemp and Papaya); Sapone Canapa e Pezzetti di Canapa (Hemp and Hemp Pieces Soap); Sapone Canapa e Rosa (Hemp and Rose); Sapone Canapa e Sandalo (Hemp and Sandalwood Soap); Sapone Canapa e Spirulina (Hemp and Spirulina); Sapone Canapa e Tea Tree (Hemp and Tea Tree); Sapone Canapa e Uva Rossa (Hemp and Grapeseed Oil); Sapone Canapa e Vetiver Java (Hemp and Vetiver Java Soap); Sapone Variegato Canapa e Argilla (Marble Soap Hemp and Clay); Sapone Variegato Canapa e Menta (Marbled Hemp and Mint); Sapone Variegato Canapa e Pezzetti di Canapa (Marble Soap Hemp and Hemp Pieces); Sapone Vegetale Canapa e Olio di Oliva Delicato (Pure Vegetable Soap Hemp and Olive Oil); Sapone Vegetale Canapa e Spirulina Levigante (Pure Vegetable Soap Hemp and Spirulina); Spone Canapa e Malva (Hemp and Mallow); Sapone Canapa ed Olio di Oliva Levigante (Hemp and Olive Oil)

VISIONARY SOAP COMPANY ™☺
Anise Poppy Seed; Cinnamon Orange Clove; Eucalyptus; Geranium Rose; Lavender; Lemon Lavender; Lemongrass; Melon & Ginger; Patchouli and Ylang Ylang; Peppermint Orange; Rooibos & Shea Butter; Rosemary & Lavender Gardener's; Rosemary Spearmint;

Shea Butter and Oatmeal; Tea Tree; Unscented

WELEDA ◌ ✔ ⚘ 1985
Iris Soap; Rosemary Soap; Wild Rose Soap

YAOH ™☺❶◌✔
Liquid Soap

SUN CARE

ALTERNATIVE STORES ☺
All products are vegan

ANNEMARIE BORLIND ✔
After-Sun Gel; Sun Lotion Factor 15; Sun Milk Factor 10; Sun Milk Factor 15; Sunless Bronze

ARBONNE ☞
BefoRE Sun: Damage Control SPF 30 Water Resistant, Glow With It After Sun Lotion, Lip Saver SPF 30, Liquid Sunshine Tan Enhancer SPF15, Made in the Shade Seld Tanner SPF 15, Save Face & Body SPF 15, To the Rescue Hair Protectant

AUBREY ORGANICS
Natural Sun: SPF 12 Protective Tanning Butter, SPF 25 Protective Sunscreen

BEAUTY NATURALS ✔
Hair Protection Mist; *After Sun:* Skin Calming Gel, Skin Repair Lotion; *Martha Hill:* After-Sun Skin Calming Gel, After-Sun Skin Repair Lotion; *Sun Protection Lotion:* SPF 15, SPF 25; *Sun Protection Oil:* SPF 10

TOILETRIES & COSMETICS

**ECO COSMETICS GMBH
& CO. KG** ™⊘◑✿
**After Sun; Sun Cream SPF 30; Sun
Cream SPF 13; Sun Cream SPF 24**

ESSENTIALLY YOURS LTD
LYB Range: LYB013

FOREVER LIVING PRODUCTS
Aloe Sunless Tanning Lotion; Aloe
Sunscreen SPF30

GREEN PEOPLE CO. ™⊘◑
Sunscreen: **G001 Sun Lotion SPF15,
G006 After Sun Lotion, T010 'Face
The Sun' SPF15**

**HOWAD LTD
T/A INCOGNITO** ™❶⊘◑
Incognito: **100% Natural After Sun**

ITS ELIXIR (UK) LIMITED ™⊘◑👁
After Sun Gel

JASON NATURAL PRODUCTS
Active Block SPF40; Complete Block
SPF26; Daily Block SPF30; Family Block
SPF 36; Kid's Block SPF46; Natural Lip
Care SPF 20; Sunbrellas® Chemical Free
Sun Block SPF30+; Sunbrellas® Complete
Block Spray SPF 26; Sunbrellas® Facial
Block SPF20; *After Sun:* Aloe Vera 98%
Moisturizing Gel, Tea Tree Soothing Gel

**KEY SUN LABORATORIES
PTY LTD** ™⊘
Key Sun: **After Sun**

KISS MY FACE
Sun Screen SPF 18 with Oat Protein
Complex; Sunspray with SPF 30;

Aftersun: Aloe Soother; *Instant Sunless
Tanner:* SPF8; *Oat Protein Sunblock:*
SPF18; *Sunswat + Insect Repellant:* SPF15

LAVERANA GMBH & CO. KG ™◑
Lavera Sun Sensitiv: **After Sun Lotion,
Anti-Age Sun Milk SPF 15, Baby &
Children Neutral Sun-Spray SPF 20,
Family Sun-Spray LSF 15, Kids Sun-
Spray LSF 20, Lip Balm SPF 10,
Neutral Sun Milk SPF 20, Self
Tanning, Self-tanning Shimmer Spray**

LIZ EARLE ◑
Mineral Sun Cream SPF20; Sun Shade
Botanical Aftersun Gel

MALIBU ⊘◑
Moisturising Self-Tanning Lotion;
Moisturising Self-Tanning Mousse;
Smoothing Self-Tanning Gel; *After Sun:*
Aloe Vera Moisturising Gel, Glitter Gel,
Ice Blue Cooling Gel, Moisturising
Spray, Moisturising w Tan Extender,
Soothing, Soothing w Insect Repellent;
Dry Oil: SPF12 Spray For Men, SPF15 Gel,
SPF15 Spray, SPF8 Gel, SPF8 Spray;
High Protection Lotion: SPF15, SPF15
Facial Fluid, SPF20, SPF30, Spray SPF15,
Spray SPF30; *Protective Mousse:* SPF12
Sun Protection, SPF20 High Protection;
Protective Sun Lotion: SPF12, Spray SPF8

NATURE'S GATE
Aqua Block SPF 50; Kids Block
Giggleberry SPF30; Kids SPF 30; Lotion
SPF 30; Mineral Kidsblock SPF20;
Mineral Sportblock SPF20; Mineral
Sunblock SPF20; Sport SPF 30; *Organics
- Advanced Care:* Be Selective SPF30 for
face, Happy Glow Lucky Citrus Bronzer,

Happy Glow Lucky Floral Bronzer, Sundercover SPF30 for body, Tanagement Self Tanner

NEW SEASONS
After Sun Gel

**RJ MINERAL COSMETICS
INTERNATIONAL PTY LTD** ™ ✔
Body: **SUNS Body Zinc Screen Base, SUNST Body Zinc Screen Base - Tinted**

SIMPLE ✔
Face Protector Hydrolotion SPF 30; Face Self Tan Hydrolotion; Lip Protector; Lotion SPF 30; Tender Places SPF 50; *Aftersun:* Balm, Hydrating Lotion, Insect Repellant Lotion; *Babies:* Baby Cream SPF 50, Baby Lotion SPF 50; *Body Self Tan:* Lotion, Mousse, Spray; *Children:* Kid's Lotion SPF 30, Kid's Lotion SPF 50, Kid's Spray SPF 30

SOLARAY NUTRITIONAL SUPPLEMENTS
Green Tea Sunblock for Children SPF25; Rosa Mosqueta Sun Protection Herbal Butter SPF12

SUN ZAPPER ☺
Lip Balm; *Sun Block:* Blue Zinc Stick, Pink Zinc Stick, Skin Tone Colour Zinc Stick, White Zinc Stick

WHITE LOTUS COSMETIC ACUPUNCTURE ™ ❶ ⊘ ✔
Herbal: **Pigmentation Serum**

YAOH ™ ☺ ❶ ⊘ ✔
AfterSun; Sun Cream; Sunblock 15; Sunblock 30

TALCUM POWDERS

BEAUTY NATURALS ✔
Body Talc; Lavender

BRONNLEY & CO LTD ✔
Body Care for Men: Talc; *Dusting Powder:* Apricot & Almond, English Fern, Lavender, Orchid, Passion Flower, Pink Bouquet, Rose, White Iris; *Royal Horticultural Society - Dusting Powder:* Passion Flower, Rose; *Talcum Powder:* Apricot & Almond, English Fern, Lavender, Orchid, Pink Bouquet, White Iris

ESSENTIALLY NATURAL ™
Lavender Body Powder; Sandalwood Body Powder

GREEN WYCH LTD ™ ☺ ❶ ⊘ ✔
Dusting Powder: **Bergamot, Geranium, Lavender, Orange Zest**

JASON NATURAL PRODUCTS
Aloe Vera Body Powder Talc Free, Tea Tree Body Powder Talc Free

LUSH ™ ⊘ ✔
Dusting Powders: **Bare Naked Lady, Candy Fluff, Silky Underwear, T for Toes;** *Karma Products:* **Karma Dusting Powder**

SIMPLE ✔
Pure Fine Talc

TOOTHPASTES & ORAL HYGIENE

A. VOGEL
Echinacea Toothpaste; *Dentaforce:* Mouthspray and Wash, Toothpaste

ABSOLUTE AROMAS ™◌✦
Ord River: **Tea Tree Toothpaste 75 g**

ABSOLUTELY PURE
Peppermint Dental Soap

ALOE DENT
Aloe Vera Mouthwash with Vitamin K & Tea Tree; Childrens Toothpaste - Strawberry Flavour; Night Time Aloe Vera Toothpaste with Chamomile - Mint Flavour; Sensitive Aloe Vera Toothpaste with Silica - Mint Flavour; Wake Up Aloe Vera Toothpaste with Ginseng - Mint Flavour; Wake Up Toothpaste with Ginseng; Whitening Aloe Vera Toothpaste with Echinacea - Mint Flavour

ALTERNATIVE STORES ☺
All products are vegan

AUSTRALIAN TEA TREE
Toothpaste

BELLECARE AG ™
Zahngel

BURT'S BEES ◌✦☻
Peppermint Breath Drops; *Doctor Burt's Toothpaste:* Cinna-Mint, Lavender Mint

CLEARSPRING ™☺❶◌✦☻
Dentie toothpaste; Dentie toothpowder

DR HAUSCHKA ◌✦
Wala Vita Lemon & Salt Toothpaste

DR ORGANIC
Aloe Vera: Mouthwash, Toothpaste; *Pomegranate:* Toothpaste; *Tea Tree:* Mouthwash, Toothpaste

FLORIS ☺✦
Concentrated Mouthwash: Rose

GREEN PEOPLE CO. ™◌✦
Toothpaste: **D003 Citrus & Aloe Vera Toothpaste, D004 Peppermint Toothpaste, D008 Minty Cool Toothpaste, F001 Mandarin Toothpaste, F007 Spearmint & Aloe Vera Toothpaste**

GREEN WYCH LTD ™☺❶◌✦
Toothpaste: **Lemon, Peppermint**

HERBS HANDS HEALING LTD ™◌✦
Ears, Eyes & Mouth: **Mouthwash Water;** *Herbal Formula:* **Mouthwash**

J&D BLACK LTD ☺
Hollytrees: Citrus Toothpaste, Fennel Mouthwash, Fennel Toothpaste, Garden Mint Mouthwash, Garden Mint Toothpaste, Sage and Calendula Mouthwash

JASON NATURAL PRODUCTS
Healthy Mouth Toothpaste and Mouthwash, NutriSmile Toothpaste and

Mouthwash, PowerSmile Toothpaste
and Mouthwash, PowerSmile®
Cinnamon Mint Mouthwash,
PowerSmile® Cinnamon Mint Toothpaste,
PowerSmile® Vanilla Mint Toothpaste,
Sea Fresh Toothpaste and Mouthwash

JUNGLESALE LIMITED TM
**Neem Mouthwash; Neem
Mouthwash**

**KINGFISHER NATURAL
TOOTHPASTE** ☺
Fluoride-Free Toothpaste: Aloe Vera Tea
Tree Fennel, Aloe Vera Tea Tree Mint,
Baking Soda Mint, Fennel, Mint;
Toothpaste with Fluoride: Fennel, Mint

KISS MY FACE
Mouthwash: Fresh Breath; *Toothpaste:*
Anticavity Aloe Vera, Sensitive Aloe
Vera, Tartar Control Aloe Vera, Triple

Action Aloe Vera, Tripple Action Aloe
Vera, Whitening Aloe Vera

LAVERANA GMBH & CO. KG TM *i*
Lavera Basis Sensitiv: **Kid's Tooth Gel
Strawberry-Rasperry, Toothpaste Mint**

MAXIM MARKETING COMPANY TM
Amber : **Toothpaste (Sugar Free)**

NATURAL SENSE
Natural Toothpastes (all flavours)

NATURE'S GATE
Cherry Gel; Cool Mint Gel; Crème de
Anise; Crème de Mint; Crème de
Peppermint; Whitening Gel; Wintergreen
Gel; *Organics - Advanced
Care:*Peppermint Mouthwash,
Peppermint Whitening Toothpaste,
Raspberry Mint Mouthwash, Raspberry
Mint Whitening Toothpaste

NEAL'S YARD REMEDIES

⊘ 🥄 👁 ⚓ 1998

Fennel Toothpaste; Gardenmint Toothpaste; Lemon & Mint Mouth Freshener

ORGANIX SOUTH INC

Thera Neem: Herbal Mouthwash, Herbal Neem Toothpaste Cinnamon, Herbal Neem Toothpaste Mint

TOMS OF MAINE ⊘ 🥄

Natural Anticavity Fluoride Mouthwash: Spearmint; *Natural Anticavity Fluoride Mouthwash for a Dry Mouth:* Lemon Lime; *Natural Anticavity Fluoride Toothpaste:* Peppermint Baking Soda, Spearmint; *Natural Antiplaque Plus Tatar Control and Whitening Toothpaste:* Fennel, Peppermint, Spearmint; *Natural Antiplaque Plus Whitening Gel Toothpaste:* Peppermint; *Natural Clean and Gentle Care Fluoride Free Toothpaste:* Cinnamon-Clove, Spearmint; *Natural Clean and Gentle Care SLS-Free:* Apricot, Lemon-Lime; *Natural Clean and Gentle Care SLS-Free Plus Dry Mouth Soother:* Apricot, Lemon-Lime; *Natural Clean and Gentle Care SLS-Free Plus Whitening:* Fennel, Peppermint; *Natural Cleansing Mouthwash:* Cinnamint, Peppermint Baking Soda, Spearmint; *Natural Sensitive Care:* Black Currant, Wintermint; *Natural Tartar Control Mouthwash:* Peppermint; *Natural Whole Care Toothpaste:* Cinnamon-Clove, Peppermint, Spearmint, Wintermint; *Natural Whole Care Toothpaste Gel:* Cinnamon-Clove, Orange-Mango, Peppermint, Spearmint

TRINITY LIFECARE (HOLDINGS) LIMITED ™⊘

Peri-Gum

URTEKRAM

Aloe Vera Toothpaste

VICCO

Vicco Vajradanti

WELEDA ⊘ 🥄 ⚓ 1985

Calendula Toothpaste; Children's Tooth Gel; Plant Gel Toothpaste; Ratanhia Toothpaste; Salt Toothpaste

NOTES

■ **Contact lenses** are classed as a
medicine under the Medicines Act,
all contact lens solutions and
associated products have been
safety-tested (which invariably entails
animal testing at some point). Such
products are listed in the Animal Free
Shopper *only* if the company under
whose name they are sold meet our
animal testing criteria (see **ANIMAL-
FREE CRITERIA**, page 9).

■ **Dental floss** may contain beeswax
or propolis.

■ **Disposable razors** may include a
moisturising strip that could contain
animal-tested or animal-derived
ingredients.

■ **Mascara** may contain silk, as can
other types of make-up products.
Other animal ingredients in make up
include beeswax (E901 or Cera Alba)
and carnine/cochineal E120
(CI75470)

■ **Toothpastes and mouthwashes**
may contain glycerine, which can be
animal-derived.

VEG 1

VEGAN MULTIVITAMIN
90 chewable tablets

Suitable for everyone
Perfect for vegans

HEALTHCARE

CONTRACEPTIVES

BODYLOVE
Orgasm Gel

DUREX
Condoms: Avanti Ultima

GLYDE HEALTH PTY LTD ™
Latex Condoms; Sheer Glyde Dams

NVS LTD ™☺
Fusion Condoms: **Dotted banana flavour condom, Dotted chocolate flavour condom, Dotted strawberry flavour condom, Plain banana flavour condom, Plain chocolate flavour condom, Plain strawberry flavour condom, Unflavoured plain condom**

PASANTE HEALTH CARE
Condoms: Delay, Extra, Large, Mixed Flavours, Naturelle, Ribbed, Trim, Xtra Sensitive

SIR RICHARD'S CONDOM COMPANY ☺
Classic Ribbed; Extra Large; Pleasure Dots; Ultra Thin

INSECT REPELLENTS

A. VOGEL
Neemcare : Shampoo

BURT'S BEES ⊘ 🐇 👁
Bug Bite Relief; *Natural Remedies:* Herbal Insect Repellent

KISS MY FACE
Sunswat with Lemon Eucalyptus and SPF 15; Swyflotter with Lemon Eucalyptus

ORGANIX SOUTH INC
Thera Neem: Herbal Outdoor Spray

LUBRICANTS

ASTROGLIDE ☺
Gel; Glycerin & Paraben Free; Liquid; Natural; Silken Secret; Warming; X

BODYLOVE
Anal Joy Intimate Lubricant; Ultra Gel Lubricant

GLYDE HEALTH PTY LTD ™
Lubricant

JASON NATURAL PRODUCTS
Women Wise Intimate Lubricant

LIVE NATIVE ™☺
Love Lube

REMEDIES

A. VOGEL
Aesculus Gel; Aesculus Tablets; Atro Bath Oil; Atrogel; Comfrey Cream;

Echinacea Cream; Hypericum Tablets; Luffa Nasal Spray; Silecea Gel; Silicea Cold Sore Lip Gel; *Animal Essence Range:* All; *Jan de Vries Essences:* All; *Jan de Vries Range Tincture Range:* All; *Neemcare :* Oil; *Tinctures:* All

ABSOLUTE AROMAS ™⊘✓
Ord River: **Tea Tree Antiseptic Cream 50ml**

AINSWORTHS
Recovery Plus Emergency Formula; Recovery Remedy; *Bach Flower Remedies:* All; *Homeopathic Remedies:* All (Pills & Coarse Granules)

ANN ELISE SKINCARE ☺
Relief from Eczema

AROMA CRYSTAL THERAPY ⊘✓
Natures First Defence

AUSTRALIAN TEA TREE
Antiseptic Cream; Antiseptic Spray

BERWITZ HOMEOPATHY ☺
Homeopathic Remedy Creams: Anal Itching, Arnica, Athletes Foot, Burn, Cuts & Sores, Dry Skin Cream, Echinacea, First Aid, Healing, Itching Eczema, Psoriasis, Rheumatism, Tea Tree, Tennis Elbow, Varicose Vein, Wart

BIO-HEALTH LTD ⊘✓
Licensed Herbal Medicinal Products: Blue Fag Rood Compound, Boldo Aid to Slimming, Damiana, Digestive, Echinacea, Garlic, Lobelia Compound, Motherworth Compound, Natural Herb Laxative; *Ointments:* Arnica, Chamomile,

Chickweed, Comfrey, Echinacea, Garlic, Marigold, Tea Tree, Witch Hazel; *The Star Range:* Goodnight, Lowater, Neurotone, Runo, Strength

CEDAR HEALTH LTD
Ortis: Devils Claw Gel

DENDRON LTD ✓
Adios: A Natural aid for Slimming; *Stressless:* A Natural Remedy For Stress; *Yariba:* A Natural Way to Revive Your Day

DIOMED DEVELOPMENTS LTD ⊘
Headache Relief Stick

DOLMA ™☺❶⊘✓☀⚒1976
Miscellaneous Products: **Avasafab Antiseptic Cream**

DR ORGANIC
Tea Tree: Antiseptic Cream

ESSENTIALLY NATURAL ™
Organic Acne Astringent

HALLS
Cough Sweets: Blackcurrant, Cherry Sugar Free, Original, Original Mentho-Lyptus Medicated; *Soothers:* Blackcurrant, Cherry, Peach and Raspberry, Strawberry

HEALTHY HERBS ☺
Aloe Vera Gel; Balancing-The-Change Oil; Burdock&Chickweed Oil; Calendula Oil; Chamomile Oll; Comfrey; Evening Primrose Oil; Herb Oil; Manuka Stick; Musc-Ease Gel; Nit-Away Oil; Pilewort Oil; Soothing Botanical Oil; Sportshyp Oil

HERBS HANDS HEALING LTD ™⊘ⓘ

Adrenal; Bringing on a period; Cystitis; Endometriosis; Fibroid; Galactogogue (for bringing on breast milk postnatal); Libido & Fertility; Ovulation Pain; PCO (polycystic Ovary); Strong Fibroid/Heavy Bleeding; Underactive Thyroid; Womb Lining and Thickening; *Bowel Cleanse:* **Olive & Artemisia Formula, Organic Cloves (Whole), Walnut & Wormwood Formula;** *Capsules/Powders/Culinary & Medicinal Herbs:* **Cayenne Powder, Chickweed Powder, Clay & Linseed, Comfrey Root Powder, Deep Repair Powder, Marigold Powder, Marshmallow Powder, Mediterranean Medley Culinary Herbs, Milk Thistle Seeds, Organic Pot Barley Seeds, Poultice Powder, Slippery Elm Powder, Tumeric Powder;** *Colds & Chest Support:* **Cherry Bark & Elderberry Syrup, Onion & Horseradish Elixir;** *Digestive Assistance:* **Cleanse & Balance Heb Tea, Digestion Heal Pack, Meadowsweet Herb Tea, Meadowsweet Tincture;** *Ears, Eyes & Mouth:* **Dr. Christopher's B & B Ear Formula;** *For all Menopausal Stages:* **Chamomile & Vervain Formula, Siberian Ginseng Tincture, Valerian & Passionflower Formula, Vitex & Black Cohosh Formula (Menopause);** *Fungal Overload:* **Pau d'Arco & Chamomile Formula, Pau d'Arco Bark Tea;** *Heart & Circulatory Health:* **Ginger & Hawthorn Formula, Ginkgo & Rosemary Formula, Hawthorn Tincture;** *Heart & Circulatory Heath:* **Prickly Ash & Rosemary Formula;** *Herbal Formula:*

Burdock & Silver Birch, Sarsaparilla & Tumeric; *Hormone Assistance for Men:* **Saw Palmetto & Damiana Formula;** *Immune Stimulation:* **Echinacea & Thyme Formula, Echinacea Tincture, Immuno Herbal Tea;** *Immune Tonics:* **American Ginseng & Astragalus Formula, Gentian & Liquorice, Siberian Ginseng & Liquorice, Siberian Ginseng Tincture;** *Immune Travel Support:* **Olive & Artemisia Formula;** *Immunity & Allergies:* **Immune Heal Pack, Juniper & Eyebright Formula;** *Kidney & Bladder Health:* **Dandelion & Marshmallow Formula, Nettle Leaf Tea;** *Kidney Cleanses:* **28 Day Kidney Cleanse, One Day Kidney Cleanse;** *Lazy Bowel:* **Barberry Capsules, Chamomile & Cascara Capsules, Organic Linseed Seeds, Organic Psyllium Husks;** *Liver Cleanses:* **28 Day Liver Cleanse, One Day Liver Cleanse;** *Lungs & Breathing:* **Breathe & Clear Herbal Tea, Mullein & Eucalyptus Formula;** *Menstrual Help:* **Agnus Castus & Raspberry Formula (Premenstrual), Agnus Castus Tincture, Crampbark Tincture, Menstruation Heal Pack, Parsley & Cornsilk Herb Tea, Squaw Vine & Fennel Formula (Monthly Cycle);** *Muscles, Joints & Tendons:* **Angelica & Meadowsweet Formula, Body Ease Herbal Tea, Castor Oil Pack Kit, Deep Tissue Oil;** *Nervous System Health & Support:* **Nerve Heal Pack;** *Night Support:* **Evening Peace Herbal Tea;** *Prostate Support:* **Saw Palmetto & Damiana Formula;** *Single Tinctures:* **Artichoke, Black Cohosh, Black Walnut, Burdock, Cayenne,**

Chamomile, Cleavers, Dandelion, Fennel, Fenugreek, Gingko, Gotu Kola, Lemon Balm, Lobelia, Milk Thistle, Nettle, Olive, Pau d'arco, Saw Palmetto, Schisandra, Skullcap, St. John's Wort, Valerian, Wild Yam, Yellow Dock; *Skin Support:* Cleavers & Burdock Formula, Skin Guard Water; *Soothing & Nurturing the Bowel:* Chamomile Flowers Tea, Gentian & Liquorice Formula, Marigold & Crampbark Formula, Slippery Elm & Marshmallow Powder; *Useful Tonics for both Sexes:* American Ginseng & Astragalus Formula, Milk Thistle & Dandelion Formula; *Uterine Cleansing:* Marshmallow & Squaw Vine Pessaries

HOLISTIX HERBAL PRODUCTS ❶
Anti-Fungal Foot Cream

HOLLAND AND BARRETT RETAIL LTD ✓
Cough Syrup: Chesty

INWINEX PHARMACEUTICALS ™☺
Sri Sri Ayurveda (Churna): Amla Churna, Amruth Churna, Arjuna Churna, Ashwagandha Churna, Atasi Churna, Bael Churna, Brahmi Churna, Bringaraj Churna, Ginger Churna, Harithaki Churna, Kalamegh Churna, Kali musali Churna, Kanchanara Churna, Neem Churna, Nisaamlaki Churna, Punarnava Churna, Satavari Churna, Shanka pushpi Churna, Sigru Churna, Triphala Churna, Tulasi Churna, Tumeric Churna, Yashtimadhu Churna; *Sri Sri Ayurveda (Tablets):* Amla Tablets, Amruth Tablets,

Arjuna Tablets, Ashwagandha Tablets, Atasi Tablets, Bael Tablets, Brahmi Tablets, Bringaraj Tablets, Ginger Tablets, Harithaki Tablets, Kalamegh Tablets, Kali musali Tablets, Kanchanara Tablets, Neem Tablets, Nisaamlaki Tablets, Punarnava Tablets, Satavari Tablets, Shanka pushpi Tablets, Sigru Tablets, Triphala Tablets, Tulasi Tablets, Tumeric Tablets, Yashtimadhu Tablets

ITS ELIXIR (UK) LIMITED ™⊘ ✓ ◉
Bump oil; Post bump oil; Scar oil

J.L. BRAGG ☺⊘ ✓
Bragg's Medicinal Charcoal Biscuits & Tablets

JUNGLESALE LIMITED ™
Neem bark powder; Neem leaves powder; Neem leaves whole (dried)

KOBASHI ☺
Roller Balls: Relax & Sleep, Stress Buster, Study, Travel

LANES HEALTH
Aqua Ban: Tablets; *Duel Lax:* Extra Strong Tablets; *Olbas:* Olbas Inhaler Stick, Olbas Oil, Olbas Oil for Children, Olbas Original Pastilles

MASTERFOODS ⊘
Aquadrops: Lemon

MY SKINCARE LTD ™☺⊘ ✓
Topical Relief: Haemorrhoid Control Bath Oil, Haemorrhoid Control Cream, Headache & Migraine

Cream, Hormonal Balance Creams, Joint Problems Bath Oil, Joint Problems Creams, Muscle Aches & Pains Bath Oil, Muscle Aches & Pains Cream, Psoriasease Bath Oil, Psoriasease Massage Cream, Xma Bath Oil, Xma Massage Cream, Yeast Infections (Thrush) Bath Oil, Yeast Infections (Thrush) Cream

NATURES AID - DUPLICATE - ⊘ ✓
5HTP Complex 100mg; Almond Oil; Aloe Vera Juice Double Strength; Alpha Lipoic Acid & Acetyl-L-Carnitine 250mg; Black Cohosh Complex w Sage; Boldo Complex w Dandelion; Celery Seed Complex w Devils Claw; Coconut Oil; Comfrey Oil; Echinacea Complex w Elderberry; Ginger, Turmeric & Boswellia; Gingko Biloba 3000mg; Glucosamine Hydrochloride 750mg; Green Food Complex & Wheat Grass; Green Tea 1000mg; Hair, Skin & Nails Formula; Passiflora, Lemon Balm & Avena Sativa; Pomegranate Juice (double strength) 500ml; Raspberry Leaf 750mg; Rosehip 750mg; Sage Leaf 500mg; Sasparilla Complex w Burdock; Saw Palmetto Complex For Men; Senna Complex w Liquorice; Senna Extract 875mg; Slippery Elm Complex w Peppermint; Spirulina Blue/Green Algae 500mg; St. Johns Wort 333mg; Valerian Complex w Passiflora; Zinc Lozenge (peppermint)

NEAL'S YARD REMEDIES
⊘ ✓ ✆ ⚱ 1998
Australian Bush Flower Remedies; Bach Flower Remedies; Chinese Herbal Tinctures; Homoeopathic Kits (Pillules)

but not Apis, Cantharis or Sepia remedies; Inhalation Oil; Remedies to Roll for Energy; Remedies to Roll for Night Time; Remedies to Roll for Relaxation; Remedies to Roll for Study; Remedies to Roll for Travel

OBBEKJAERS ⊘ ✓
Peppermint oil tablets; Peppermint powder; Pure peppermint oil

OPTIMAH ⊘ ✓ ⚱ 1995
Echinacea Throat Spray Mint Flavour; Maxicol; Maxicol Capsules; XS Acid Aloe Vera Digestive Aid Tablets

ORCHID HEALTHCARE LIMITED
Isovon

POTTER'S HERBAL MEDICINE ✓
Cleansing tablets; Elixir of Echinacea; Indian Brandee; Nodoff; Out of Sorts; Skin Clear Tablets; Slippery Elm; Tabritis Tablets; Vegetable Cough Remover

QUINESSENCE AROMATHERAPY ☺⊘✓👁
Essential Oil Synergies: Anti-Pollen, Antiseptic, Anti-Virus, Breathe Ease, Joint Mobility, Menopause, Muscle Ease, Pre-Menstrual, Restful Sleep, Sinus, Stress

SCOTTISH HERBAL SUPPLIES™❶⊘✓
Clays; Herbal Alcoholic Tinctures; Vegetable/Herbal Ointments

SHANTI PRODUCTS ⊘✓
Hair Lice Lotion

**TAYLOR JACKSON
HEALTH PRODUCTS** ☺❶⊘✔
M-folia for Psoriasis & Eczema: Bath Oil, Body Lotion, Body Wash, Conditioner, Cream, Herbal Extract, Mild Tablets, Ointment, Scalp Oil, Shampoo, Super Tablets

THE HEMP COMPANY LTD
BPA Safe Solutions Body Piercing Aftercare

**THE ORGANIC HERB
TRADING COMPANY** ⊘
Organic Medicinal Tinctures: All except Propolis

TREE-HARVEST ⊘✔
Gemmotherapy Remedies: All; *Spagyric Remedies:* All

WELLFOODS LTD ⊘✔
Linda Kearns Cake - The wholly natural approach to relieveing the symptoms of the menopause: Cherry, Cranberry, Date & Walnut, Original, Tropical

**WHITE LOTUS
COSMETIC ACUPUNCTURE** ™❶⊘✔
Herbal: **Scar Serum, White Lotus Anti-Aging Serum;** *Herbal Medicine:* **Ants formula, Bai Zhi Yi Mu Wan, Ban Tu Ca Ji, Bo He Wan, Breast Serum, Bu Zhong Yi Qi Tang, Cancer Formula, Chronic Sinus, Da Cheng Qi Tang, Dang Gui Bu Xue Tang, Dang Gui Bu Xue Tang Powder, Du Huo Ji Sheng Tang, Formula 4, Gui Pi Tang, Hou Xiang Zheng Qi Tang, Hua Shen He Ji, Immunity, Jiao Wei Xiao Yao San, Ling Zhi 60g**, Ganoderma Lucidum, Long Dan Xie Gan Tang, Lung Function, Powder 1, Powder 2, Powder 3, Qi Bao Mei Ran Dan, Qi Ju Di Huang Wan, Run Chang Wan, San Ren Tang, Tian Ma Gou Teng Yin, Wen Dan Tang, Wu Ling San, Wu Wei Xiao Du Yin, Xiang Sha Liu Jun Zi Tang, Xiao Feng San, Xiao Qing Long Tang, Xue Fu Zhu Yu Tang, Yin Qiao San, You Gui Wan, Zhi Bai Di Huang Wan, Zi Shen Zan Yu Dan**

WHOLISTIC RESEARCH COMPANY
Colon Cleanse Herbal Programme; Liver, Kidney, Colon Detox Herbal Programme

SUPPLEMENTS

A. VOGEL
Aesculus Forte Tablets; Anti Ageing Complex; Detox Box; Helix Slim Tablets; Kelp Tablets; Linoforce; Menosan Tablets; Milk Thistle Tablets; Nature-C; Pomegranate Spirulina Complex; Silecea Capsules; Silecea Liquid

AGE VERT LYNX INDUSTRIES
Guarana

ALL SEASONS HEALTH ™
Chlorella Powder; Chlorella Tablets; Spirulina Powder; Spirulina Tablets

ALOE PURA ✔
Aloe Liquid Fibre Juice; Aloe Vera Colon Cleanse; Aloe Vera Digestive Aid; Aloe

HEALTHCARE

Vera Juice Maximum Strength;
Cranberry Flavoured Aloe Vera Juice;
Organic Aloe Vera Juice; Pineapple and
Papaya Flavoured Aloe Vera Juice;
Wildberry Flavoured Aloe Vera Juice

AQUASOURCE ™⊘✔

**Acidophilus & Aquasource Algae 50
Capsules; Aquasource Algae 60 &
120 Capsules; Aquasource Algae
Liquid with Bilberry & Cranberry
60ml; Aquasource Algae Powder 50g;
Bifidus Complex & Aquasource Algae
50 Capsules; Cell Power – Instant
Nutrition 25g; CoQ10 Complex w
Chromium & AquaSource Algae 30
Capsules; Digestive Enzymes &
Aquasource Algae 60 Capsules;
Green Energy 120 Vegetable Capsules
(Aquasource Algae & Hawaiian
Spirulina & Organic Alfalfa);
Lighten-Up! Nutritional Protein
Drink Mix with Aquasource Algae
200g; Sea Power Algae 120 capsules;
Start Easy Programme (Aquasource
Algae 50 Capsules, Digestive
Enzymes & Aquasource Algae 60
Capsules, Acidophilus & Aquasource
Algae 50 Capsules, Bifidus Complex
& Aquasource Algae 50 Capsules);
Sun Power – Instant Nutrition 25g;
Super Antioxidant with Pycnogenol
60 Capsules**

BEAUTY NATURALS ✔
Eye Bright Vision Support Formula;
Nails & Skin Nutrient Formula

BELLECARE AG ™
**Aloe anmaris Kapseln; Organic Aloe
Ferox Juice**

BENECOL
Strawberry & Berries Dairy free Drink;
Tropical Dairy free Drink

BIO-HEALTH LTD ⊘✔
Pure-fil: Kelp + Vitamins; *Pure-fil:*
Agnus Castus, Anti-Oxidant Herbs, B
Complex (High Potency & Yeast-free),
Bio-Caps Multivitamin & Mineral, Bio-E,
Black Cohosh, Buchu Leaf, Buffered C
Crystals, Capiscum Fruit, Celery Seed,
Chamomile Flowers, Cinnamon Bark,
Co-Enzyme Q10, Cramp Bark,
Cranesbill Root, Damiana Herb,
Dandelion Leaf, Devil's Claw, Echinacea
Root, Extra Calcium with Magnesium
Zinc and Vitamin D, Extra Iron, Extra
Magnesium, Extra Mineral Complex,
Extra Selenium, Extra Zinc, Fenugreek
Seed, Feverfew Leaf, Ginger Root,
Gingko Leaf, Glucosamine HCL, Golden
Seal, Hawthorn Berry, Hop Strobile,
Iceland Moss, Korean Ginseng,
Liquorice Root, Melilot Herb, Melissa
Leaf, Milk Thistle, Misteltoe Herb,
Nettle Root, Passiflora Herb, Prickly Ash
Bark, Primula Root, Psyllium Husk,
Raspberry Leaf, Red Clover Flowers,
Rutin + Buckwheat, Sage Leaf, Senna
Leaf, Skullcap Herb, Slippery Elm, St
John's Wort, Turmeric Rhizome, Valerian
Root, Vitamin B&C, Vitamin C – 500mg
(Buffered), Vitamin C – 500mg with
Bioflavonoids, Whole Garlic, Wild Yam
Root, Willow Bark, Wormwood Herb

BIONA
Pressed Multi-Vital Juice

BIOSYM A/S ™☺✔
Vegan Multivitamin: **OmniVegan**

BRUNEL HEALTHCARE ⊘ ♨ ⚒-1992
Vertese Capsules: Evening Primrose Oil, Flaxseed, Glucosamine & Flaxseed, High Strength Coenzyme Q10, Natural Vitamin E, Omega Oils 3, 6 & 9, Omega Oils 3, 6 & 9 Plus CoQ10 & Ginseng, Omega Oils 3, 6 & 9 Plus Pomegranate

CEDAR HEALTH LTD
Bio-Strath Elixir Tablets; *Innovia:* Lestrin; *Ortis:* Ginseng, Ortisan Tablets, Vital Iron Plus; *Ortis Pure Plan:* Apple, Prune, Tablets; *Padma 28:* Padma; *Serra Pamies:* Keravit, Pil-Food

COUNTRY LIFE
2 Methyl 13-C™ "Fruit Punch"; 4 Thought® The Ultimate Brain Formula; 5-HTP Trytophan; 7-KetoTrim™; Acerola C with Bioflavonoids; Acetyl L-Carnitine 500 mg with B-6 (Veg. Caps); Action B-100; Action B-50; Action Max® XXXTREME™; Active B-12 (Dibencozide 3,000 mcg); Active Lipoic Acid; Basic-B; Beyond Food®; Biotin; Brewer's Yeast; Buffer-C; Buffered Vitamin C with RH; Burn N Trim™; Calcium Ascorbate Crystals; Calcium Citrate; Calcium with Boron; Calcium-Magnesium with Vitamin D Complex; Cal-Mag; Cal-Mag (Mini Tabs); Cal-Mag Complex; Cal-Mag Potassium; Cal-Mag-Zinc; Cal-Snack (Calcium with Magnesium Wafer); Cap C-500; Caralluma Extract; Carb Phaser; Chewable Adult Multi with Antioxidants; Chewable Vitamin E Wafer; Choline; Chromium; Chromium Picolinate; Circulation Factors®; Circu-Pressure®; Citrus Bioflavonoid Complex; Citrus Bioflavonoid/Rutin Complex; Coenzyme Active B-6 50 mg; Coenzyme B-Complex; Daily Fiberx; Daily Total One™ Iron-Free; Dairy-Zyme; DHEA; DHEA 25 mg Complex For Women; DHEA 50 mg Complex For Men; Diet Power®; DMAE; E Vitamin + Selenium; Enhances QM-1™ Iron-Free; Essential Amino Stack; Essential Creatine Monohydrate; Essential Glutamine; Essential Life; Essential Liquid Carnitine; Ester-C® w/Bioflavonoids; Flush-Free Niacin; Folic Acid; GABA Relaxer; Genaslim™; Ginseng Supreme Complex; GlucoLean™ (Ephedra Free); Glycemic Factors™; Glycine 500 mg with B-6; Go Less™; Grape Seed Extract; Green Edge II™ Powder Vegan Formula; Green Tea Extract; GTF Chromium; Herbal Mood Boost; Hi-B-100; Homocysteine Shield®; Inositol Powder; Iron 25 mg; Iron Aid™; Iron-Free Multi-Mineral Complex; L-Arginine 500mg with B-6 (Veg. Caps); L-Carnitine 500 mg with B-6 (Veg. Caps); Lean Results™ "Ephedra Free Weight Loss"; Lecithin Granules; L-Glutamine 1,000 mg with B-6; L-Glutamine 500 mg with B-6 (Veg. Caps); Lipoic Acid; Liquid Goji & Acai; Liver Support Factors®; L-Lysine 1000 mg with B-6; L-Lysine 500 mg with B-6; L-Lysine 500 mg with B-6 (Veg Caps); L-Methionine 500 mg with B-6; L-Phenylalanine 500 mg with B-6 (Veg Caps); L-Theanine (Veg Caps); L-Tyrosine 500 mg with B-6 (Veg Caps); Lumatol AC™; Mag/Potassium/Aspartate; Magnesium; Magnesium 300 mg with Silica; Malic Relief Formula; Max For Men®; Max-Growth P. M.™; Maxi Baby-C® (Liquid); Maxi B-Caps w/Taurine; Maxi C-Complex; Maxi Pre-Natal®; Maxine® For Women; Maxine® For Women Iron-

Free; Maxine's Intima Roses & Chocolate; Maxine's Menopause Formula; Maxi-Zinc; Maxi-Zyme® Extra Strength; Melatonin; Memory Formula; Menopause Support; Metabolizer (Lipotropic); Milk Thistle Extract; MSM; Multi-Mineral Complex; N, N-Dimethylglycine 125 mg (Sublingual); Nerve & Osteo Support; Niacin; Niacinamide; Norwegian Kelp; Nutri Chol-less®; Olive Leaf Extract; Omega Fiber™ Powder; Omega Vegetarian™ 3-6-9 (Liquid); PABA; Pantothenic Acid; Papaya 22 mg Chewable; Potassium; Pregnenolone; Prosta-Max For Men; Pro-Vaso NO2™; Psyllium Seed Husk; Pycnogenol®; Resveratrol Plus; R-Lipoic Acid; Rutin; Saw Palmetto & Pygeum Extract; Selenium; Seniority; Sleep Tight Factors®; Sour Gummy Dolphin Pals; Stress "M"®; Super 10 Antioxidant; Superior B-12 Sublingual Berry Flavored Lozenges; Superior Multiple™; Superior Vitamin C; Tall Tree Children's Chewable; Tall Tree Children's Chewable Wafer; Taurine 500 mg with B-6; Taurine 500 mg with B-6 (Veg Caps); The Maximized® Masculine Formulation; Thyro-Max; Triple Strength Bromelain; Ultimate Fat Metabolizer®; Vanadyl Sulfate; Vegetarian Support™; Vitamin B-1 100 mg; Vitamin A 10,000 units Dry; Vitamin B-12 1,000 mcg; Vitamin B-12 with Folic Acid; Vitamin C Complex; Vitamin C Crystals; Vitamin C Wafer; Vitamin C with RH; Vitamin E; Vitamin E Complex (Liquid); Vitamin K; Water Factors™; Yohimbe Extract; Yohimbe Power; Zinc; Zinc Lozenges; *Herbal Extracts Liquid Pharmacy™* : Black Walnut/Wormwood, Children's Echinacea Complex,

Echinacea Superior, Echinacea/Goldenseal, Milk Thistle Extract, Yohimbe Extract, Yohimbe Wild African Bark

CUBANA PRODUCE LTD ™
Spirel C (180 tablets); Spirel G (180 tablets); *100% Cuban Spirulina Platensis:* **Spirel Powder 100g and 500g, Spirel Spirulina (100 Vege capsules), Spirel Spirulina (180 tablets)**

DEVA NUTRITION LLC ™☺✓
Deva Nutrition supplements: **Calcium Plus, CLA, Coenzyme Q10, Deva Digestive Support, Flax Seed Oil Capsules, Iron Free Vegan Multivitamin One Daily, Omega-3 DHA, Sublingual B-12, Vegan Borage Oil, Vegan Chia Seed Oil, Vegan Evening Primrose Oil capsules, Vegan Glucosamine HCL, Vegan Glucosamine MSM/CMO, Vegan Hair Nails and Skin, Vegan Multivitamin, Vegan Prenatal Multivitamin, Vegan Vitamin D, Vitamin E 400 IU with mixed tocopherols;** *Vegan Herbal Line:* **Brain Support, Colon Cleanse, Gingko Biloba, Kava Kava, Liver Support, Saw Palmetto, St John's Wort, Valerian**

EMERGEN-C
Electro Mix Lemon Lime; Essentially All Advanced Multi-Vitamin; Sleep Health Night-Time Vitamin C; Super Gram 2 Vitamin C; Super Gram 3 Enhanced Vitamin C; Tangerine Ora-Pops Vitamin C; *Multi-Vitamin:* Kids Multi-Vitamin Strawberry, Multi-Vitamin Strawberry; *Speciality Health:* Bone Health Mixed

Berry, Heart Health Black Cherry, MSM Lite 5 Calories; *Super Energy Booster: 1,000mg Vitamin C:* Acai Berry, Cranberry, Lemon Lime, Lite 5 Calories, Pink Lemonade, Raspberry, Super Orange, Tangerine, Tropical

ESB DEVELOPMENTS LTD ™☺❶◯ℓ👁
Omega 3 supplement: **Omega 3 Capsules, Opti3 Complete Omega-3**

FOREVER LIVING PRODUCTS
Aloe Berry Nectar; Aloe Bits 'n Peaches; Aloe Blossom Tea; Aloe Vera Gel; B12 Plus; Gingko Plus; Lycium Plus

FOREVER YOUNG INTERNATIONAL LIMITED
Friendly Bacteria: Prebio 7V

G & G VITAMINS
Acidophilus; Aloe Vera; Atriplex; B Complex; B Complex with Vitamin C; Betacarotene; Betaine; Bifido; Biotin; C plus Minerals; C with Bioflavonoids; Cal Mag Kit; Calcium Ascorbate; Calcium Citrate; Calcium Gluconate; Cal-M; Cal-M Capsules; Cat's Claw; Chewable C (Raspberry & Cherry Flavour); Choline & Inositol; Choline Bitartrate; Chromium; Chromium GTF; Co Q10; Cranberry Extract; Craze-Away; Dolomite; Echinacea; Energy Plus Protein; EssentialFood; Eyebright & L-Lutein; Fibre Detox; Fibre Flora; Fizz C (Orange Flavour); Folic Acid; Fruit Fortress; Garlic; GC70; Ginkgo Biloba; Good Morning Protein Plus; GUK; Herbal energy Formula; Inositol; Iron Amino Acid Chelated; L-Arginine; Lecithin Granules; Lemon Balm & Ginkgo Biloba; Lipoic Acid & Acetyle Carnitine;

Magnesium Ascorbate; Magnesium Carbonate; Magnesium Citrate; Magnolia; Manganese Amino Acid Chelated; MSM; MSM Pure Powder; MSM with Vitamin C; Multiminerals with Amino Acid Chelated; Multiminerals with Chelate Factors; Natural E 400 (Capsules not Softgels); Organic Devil's Claw; Organic Goldenseal; Organic Guarana; Organic Milk Thistle; Organic Peppermint; Organic Saw Palmetto; Organic Siberian Ginseng; Organic St John's Wort; Organic Valerian; PABA (Para Amino Benzoic Acid); Papain; Potassium; Practitioner's Acidophilus; Practitioner's Bifidus; Pro-Bifidus; Pro-Dophilus; Psyllium Husks; Pure C Powder (Ascorbic Acid); Pycnogenol; Rutin; Salt Capsules; Saw Palmetto with Zinc; Seagreens Food; Selenium; Selenium + A, C, E and EPO; Siberian Ginseng; SlimaSleep; SlimaWake; Spirulina; St Johns Wort; Sublingual B Complex; Sublingual B12 (Cyanocobalamin); Sublingual CoQ10; Sublingual Vitamin C & Bioflavonoids; Tropical C; Vitamin B1 (Thiamin); Vitamin B12 (Cyanocobalamin); Vitamin B15 Pangamic Acid; Vitamin B2 (Riboflavin); Vitamin B3 (Nicotinamide); Vitamin B3 Niacin (Nicotinic Acid); Vitamin B5 (Pantothenic Acid); Vitamin B6 (Pyridoxine); Vitamin C (with Rosehips, Acerola & Dolomite); Wormwood; Zinc Amino Acid Chelated; Zinc Citrate

GLASGOW HEALTH SOLUTIONS™
Essential Woman; Forti Flax; Omega Man; Omega Twin

GREEN VALLEY TRADING CO ™☺❶✔
Deva Nutrition: **All products are vegan;** *Health plus- Veganicity range:* **All products are vegan**

GUARANA COMPANY LTD ™
Cacao butter, organic; Açaí, organic; Agave syrup, organic; Apricot kernels; Barleygrass, organic; Brazilian Ginseng (Pfaffia paniculata), organic; Cacao beans; Cacao nibs, organic; Cacao powder, organic; Camu-camu powder; Catuaba; Cola nut powder; Dehulled Hemp seeds, organic; Guarana extract powder; Guarana Powder, organic; Guarana tincture; Korean ginseng root; Lacuma powder; Maca, organic; Milk thistle tincture; Muira Puama; Purple corn powder; Siberian ginseng powder; Spirulina Powder, organic; Wheatgrass, organic; *Drink Powders:* Jungle Detox Plus, Jungle Energy Boost, Jungle Gym, Jungle Love, Jungle protein mix, Jungle Super Energy Boost

HEALTH + PLUS LTD ™⊘✔
Health + Plus Ltd: **Devil's Claw, 5-HTP Complex, Acai Berry Extract, Acidophilus, Agnus Castus, Agnus Castus 500mg, Aloe Vera Juice, Amino L-Arginine, Amino L-Glutamine, Amino L-Lysine, Amino L-Methionine, Amino L-Tyrosine, Artichoke, Ascorbic Acid Powder 250g, B12 1000mcg, B25 Complex, Beta Carotene 15mg, Bilberry, Bilberry with Eyebright, Black** Cohosh, Brewer's Yeast, Calcium Ascorbate + Ascorbic Acid Powder 250g, Calcium Ascorbate Powder 250g, Cats Claw, Chamomile, Chelated Iron, Chewable Vit C 500mg, Chromium Picolinate, Cinnamon 500mg, Citri-Trim Plus, Co Enzyme Q10 30mg, Co Enzyme Q10 60mg, Dandelion, Digest Plus, Dolomite + D, Dong Quai, E400, Echinacea, Elderberry, EPO Liquid, Ester C 1000, Feverfew, Fibre Gum, First Probiotic, Folic Acid, FOS, Ginger, Ginger Root, Ginkgo Biloba, Glucosamine + MSM, Glucosamine HCL 1500, Glucosamine HCL 750mg, Goldenseal, Gotu Kola, Gotu Kola, Guarana 750mg, Hawthorn, Horsechestnut, Horsetail, Junior B Complex, Junior Multivitamin and Mineral, Kelp 300mg, Konjac Fibre, Konjac Fibre Powder, Korean Ginseng, Lecithin 550mg, Lecithin Granules, Lycopene Plus, Magnesium L-Aspartate, Marigold, Megadophilus, Milk Thistle, Milk Thistle, MSM, Multi Probiotic, Mushroom Extract Complex, Nettle, Octocosanol, Optim-Eyes, Organic Selenium, Phase 2 500mg, Potassium 100mg, Premier Garlic, Psyllium Seed Husk Fibre, Red Clover, Red Clover, Sage, Sage, Saw Palmetto, Saw Palmetto + Zinc, Selenium 200mcg, Selenium 50mcg, Serrapeptase, Slippery Elm Formula, Sodium Ascorbate Powder, Spirulina, St. John's Wort, St. John's Wort, TMG Complex, Tribula Plus, Tyro Tan, Uva Ursi, Valerian, Whole Grape Complex, Wild Yam, Zinc, Zinc Citrate; *Liquiforce Traditional*

Plant Tinctures: **Agnus Castus, Bilberry, Black Cohosh, Cat's Claw, Chamomile, Dandelion, Devil's Claw, Echinacea, Elderberry, Feverfew, Ginger, Ginkgo Biloba, Goldenseal, Gotu Kola, Hawthorn, Horsechestnut, Horsetail, Marigold, Milk Thistle, Nettle, Red Clover, Red Clover, Sage, Saw Palmetto, Slippery Elm Formula, St. John's Wort, Uva Ursi, Valerian, Wild Yam;** *Veganicity:* **Glucosamine 1500, 5-HTP Complex, Acai Berry Extract, Agnus Castus 500mg, Agnus Castus Tincture, Artichoke, B12 1000mcg, B25 Complex, Beta Carotene, Bilberry Tincture, Bilberry with Eyebright, Black Cohosh, Black Cohosh Tincture, Brewer's Yeast 300mg, Calcium Extra, Cats Claw Tincture, Chamomille Tincture, Chelated Iron 24mg, Chromium 200µg, Cinnamon 500mg, Co Enzyme Q10 30mg, Co Enzyme Q10 60mg, Dandelion Tincture, Devil's claw Tincture, Digest-Ase, E400, Echinacea Tincture, Elderberry Tincture, Ester-C 1000, Feverfew Tincture, Folic Acid 400µg, Ginger Tincture, Ginkgo Biloba Tincture, Glucosamine + MSM, Glucosamine 1500, Glucosamine 750mg, Goldenseal, Goldenseal Tincture, Gotu Kola Tincture, Guarana 750mg, Hawthorn Tincture, Horsechestnut Tincture, Horsetail Tincture, Junior B Complex, Junior Multivitamin and Mineral, Kelp 300mg, Konjac Fibre 500mg, Korean Ginseng, Lecithin 550mg, Lycopene Extra 10mg, Marigold Tincture, Megadophilus, Milk Thistle, Milk Thistle Tincture,** MSM 1000mg, Multi Probiotic, Multivitamin+Mineral, Mushroom Complex, Nettle Tincture, Optim-Eyes, Palmetto Extra, Phase 2 500mg, Premier Garlic 500mg, Red Clover, Red Clover Tincture, Sage, Sage Tincture, Saw Palmetto Tincture, Selenium 200µg, Serrapeptase, Slippery Elm Tincture, Spirulina 500mg, St John's Wort, St. John's Wort, St.John's Wort Tincture, Tasty C 500mg, TMG Extra, Tribula Extra, Uva Ursi Tincture, Valerian Tincture, Vitamin B12 100mcg, Whole Grape Complex, Wild Yam Tincture, Zinc 10mg**

HEALTH PERCEPTION *🖊*
Seredrin; Super Antioxidant; Vegetarian Glucosamine 750mg

HEALTHQUEST LIMITED ™ ⊘ *🖊*
Body Shield; Chill Out; Lift; Man; Nutri-Aid; Woman

HEALTHSPAN LTD
Multivitamins for Vegetarians

HERBS HANDS HEALING LTD ™ ⊘ *🖊*
Empty Vegetable Cellulose Capsules; Superfood; *Single Herbs:* **Agnus Castus Berry, Agrimony Herb, American Ginseng root, Angelica Root, Artemisia Herb, Artichoke Leaves, Astragalus Root, Balm of Gilead Buds Glyc, Barberry Root Bark, Bayberry Herb, Bitter Orange Peel, Black Cohosh Root, Black Walnut Hulls, Bladderwrack Seaweed, Blessed Thistle Seed, Blue**

Cohosh Root, Boneset Herb, Borage Leaves, Boswellia Resin, Buchu Leaves, Bupleurum Root, Burdock Root, Burdock Seed, Californian Poppy Leaves & Flowers, Cascara Sagrada Bark, Catmint Herb, Cayenne Pods, Celery Seed, Chamomile Flowers, Chickweed Herb, Chicory Root, Chinese Liquorice Root, Cinnamon Bark Squills, Cleavers Herb, Cornsilk, Corydalis Tuber, Cramp Bark, Damiana Leaves, Dandelion Root, Devils Claw Root, Dong Quai Root, Echinacea Root, Elderberry Glycerate, Elecampane Root, Eucalyptus Leaves, Eyebright Herb, False Unicorn Root, Fennel Seed, Fenugreek Seed, Figwort Herb, Gentian Root, Geranium Herb, Ginger Root, Gingko Leaf, Goats Rue Herb, Golden Seal Root, Gotu Cola Herb, Gravel Root, Hawthorn Berries, Hawthorn Flower Tops, Hops Strobiles, Horehound (White) flw, lfe, Horse Chestnut Fruit, Bark, Hyssop Herb, Juniper Berries, Lady's Mantle Herb, Lavender Flowers, Limeflowers, Liquorice Root, Lobelia Herb, Marigold Flowers, Marshmallow Root, Meadowsweet Herb, Milk Thistle Seed, Motherwort Herb, Mugwort Leaves, Mullein flw/lfe, Myrrh Gum Resin, Nettle Root, Nettles Leaves, Oak Bark, Olive Leaves, Oregano Leaves, Oregon Grape Root, Osha Root, Parsley Root, Pasque Flower Herb, Passion Flower Herb, Pau d'Arco Bark, Pennyroyal Herb, Peppermint Leaves, Plantain Leaves, Poke Root, Prickly Ash Bark, Red Clover Flowers, Red Raspberry Leaves, Rehmannia, Rhen Shen Ginseng Root, Rhubarb Root, Rosemary Leaves, Sage Leaves, Sarsaparilla Root, Saw Palmetto Berries, Schisandra Berries, Shativari, Siberian Ginseng Root, Silver Birch Leaves, Skullcap Herb, Solomons Seal, Squaw Vine Tuber, St Johns Wort Herb, Thuja Leaves, Thyme Herb, Triphala Fruits, Tumeric (Yu Jin) Root, Usnea Herb, Uva Ursi Leaves, Valerian Root, Vegetable Glycerine, Vervain Herb, White Willow Bark, Wild Cherry Bark, Wild Lettuce Herb, Wild Oats/ Herb/ Seed, Wild Yam Root, Withania (Ashwaganda) Root, Wood Betony Herb, Yarrow Herb, Yellow Dock Root

HIGH BARN OILS™
Linseed Oil 500ml; Linseed oil for Horses; Linseed Oil in capsules; Linseeds; Milled Linseed

HIGHER NATURE LTD
Advanced Brain Nutrients; Advanced Nutrition Complex; AEterna Gold Hyaluronic Acid; Alka-Clear (Powder & Capsules); Aloe Gold (Cherry/Cranberry); Aloe Gold (Natural); Alpha; Arginine; Astaxanthin and Blackcurrant; Awake™ Food Formula; Balance For Nerves; Betaine HCL; Bio Minerals; Boswellia & Devil's Claw; Bromelain; Butterbur; B-Vital; Calcium Ascorbate; Calma-C; Candiclear; Cardio Heart Nutrients; Cat's Claw Concentrate; Cat's Claw Tea Bags; Chlorella; Chromium Polynicotinate 200mcg; Citricidal Liquid; Citrisafe®;

Co-Enzyme Q10; ColoClear Extra; DLPA Complex; Dong Quai & Agnus Castus; Easy 3(powder); Echinacea & Black Elderberry; Energy Breakfast Shake; Fizzy C Effervescent Vitamin C; Folic Acid 400mcg; FOS; FreeCarb; Glutamine Capsules; Glutamine Powder; H Factors; HCA; Herbal SpringClean; High Fibre Vitality Shake; High PC Lecithin Granules; High Stability Colloidal Silver; High Strength Mexican Yam; Immune +; Imunoglukan®; IntestAid IB; Lactogest; Lysine 500mg; Lysine-C; Maxi Multi (Iron Free); Mega Potency Ginkgo 6000; Menophase; Milk Thistle & Artichoke; Mood™ Food Formula; Muira Puama & Damiana Aphrodisiaca; Mum-2-Be; Neversnore; Nucell® Support; Nutrition For Healthy Veins; Ocean Kelp; Olive Leaf Extract; Osteofood; Paraclens; Periwinkle extract; Phosphatidyl Serine; PreMenstrual Complex; Probio- Daily; Probio- Easy; Probiogest; Probio-Mints; Red Sterol Complex; Rhodiola & Ashwagandha; Rosehips C 1000; Saw Palmetto & Pygeum Bark; Sea Calcium; Selenium 200mcg; Serotone 5HTP; Sheep's Sorrel Complex; Sher Skin Support Formula; St John's Wort; Sublingual High Potency Vitamin B12 200mcg; Sublingual Vitamin B12 200mcg; Sublingual Zinc; Super Osteofood; Super Strength Cranberry; Super Strength Supergar 8000; Supergest; Superphyte; Sx; Theanine 100mg; TMG; Ultra C Plus; UltraTrace® Trace Mineral Drops; VagiClear; Vegetarian Glucosamine Hydrochloride; Visualeyes; X Factors; Zinc; *ColoClear Extra:* Capsules, Powder; *MSM:* Capsules, Crystals, Joint & Muscle Body

Balm, Tablets; *Natural Medicine Company:* Children's chewable, Daily Probiotic Formula, Healthy Eyes, Liquid Silver, Multivitamin & Mineral Complex For Men, Multivitamin & Mineral Complex For Women, Optimum Pregnancy Nutrients, Skin, Hair and Nails, Snore-free, The Sweet Alternative; *Omega Excellence:* Apple Cider Vinegar, Hi-Lignan Nutri-Flax; *Omega Nutrition:* Pumpkin Seed Butter; *Sambucol®:* All Season Supplement for Adults (with Glucose), Lozenge; *True Food®:* All Man, B Complex, B6, Beta Carotene, C, Calcium & Magnesium, Easy Iron, GTF Chromium, Magnesium, Maxi Q10, Natural Vitamin E, Selenium, Soyagen®, Super Potency Soyagen®, Supernutrition Plus, Wise Woman, Zinc

HOLISTIX HERBAL PRODUCTS ❶

Spirulina: Powder 150g, Powder 250g, Powder 50g, Powder 50g Refills, Tablets 150g, Tablets 250g, Tablets 50g, Tablets 50g Refills

HOLLAND AND BARRETT RETAIL LTD ⬈

Aloe Vera Juice Drink; Damiana Leaves Liquid; DGL Chewable Liquorice; Oats Avena; *Tablets:* Magnesium Tablets; *Chewable Tablets:* Acerola C with Bioflavonoids, All Natural Pineapple Bromelain, Papaya Enzyme Chewable; *Childrens Supplements:* Echinacea for Juniors Liquid Extract; *Liquid Extract:* Cranberry, Ginkgo-Bilboa, Guarana, Japanese Oil of Peppermint, Milk Thistle, Mullein Leaf, Peppermint, Saw Palmetto, Siberian Ginseng, St. Johns Wort, Valerian Root; *Powder:* Brewers Yeast, Creatine, Oil of Peppermint, Pure Vitamin C; *Protein Powders:* Pure Soya

Protein Powder; *Slimming:* Diet Aid; *Tablets:* Absorbable Magnesium, Alfalfa, Amino Acid Chelated Manganese, B - 100 (Vitamin B Complex), B - 100 (Vitamin B Complex) Timed Release, B - 50 (Vitamin B Complex), B-1 100mg, B-12, Biotin, Brewers Yeast, C with Rose Hips, C-500mg Buffered, Caprylic Acid, C-Complex with Bioflavonoids, Chelated Boron, Chelated Copper, Chelated Zinc Tablets, Chewable Calcium, Chinese Chlorella, Choline, Chromium Picolinate, Cider Vinegar, Citrus Bioflavonoids, Complete B, DLPA 500mg, Dolomite, Folic Acid, Gotu Kola, Green Barley Grass 500mg, GTF Chromium, Guarana, High Strength Zinc 15mg, Horse Chestnut, Iron + Vitamin C, Iron Tablets with Vitamins & Minerals, L-Glutamine 500mg, Magnesium 250mg, Natural Amino 1000mg, Niacin B-3, Pantothenic Acid, Potassium Chelated 99mg, Rutin, Selenium, Selenium Seven Day Souper Cabbage Diet, Siberian Ginseng, Silica Complex, Spirulina, Taurine, Timed Release Pantothenic Acid Tablets, Vitamins for the Hair, Zinc Picolinate

JUNGLESALE LIMITED ™
Just virgin coconut oil

KORDEL'S
Enzogenol VegCaps; Lysine VegCaps; OptiMSM® 1000mg Tablets; *Advanced Herbals:* Black Cohosh & Isoflavone Veg Caps, Celery Plus Tablets, Cranberry with Uva Ursi & Buchu VegCaps, Dong Quai Plus VegCaps, Ginkgo Plus VegCaps, Milk Thistle Plus VegCaps, St John's Wort with Ginkgo & Ginseng

VegCaps; *Advanced Lifestyle:* Advanced Pro-biotic Complex VegCaps, B' at Eze Tablets, Bilberry 5000 & Eyebright Tablets, Horse Chestnut & Butchers Broom Complex Tablets, Junior Time Multivitamins Plus Tablets, Perilla with Coleus VegCaps, Red Clover Plus Isoflavone Complex Tablets, Saw Palmetto Plus Tablets, Silica 2500 Plus Tablets, Super Calcium Magnesium Bone Formula Tablets, Teenage Multi Tablets, Tribulus Plus Herbal Complex Tablets, Valerian Plus Herbal Complex Tablets, Women's Multi Tablets; *Herbs:* Agnus Castus Tablets, Boswellia VegCaps, Dong Quai Standardised Extract 1000mg Tablets, Griffonia Seed VegCaps, Guarana Ginseng Complex VegCaps, Milk Thistle Standardised Extract 1000mg Tablets, Rhodiola Root Extract VegCaps, Sea Kelp Tablets, Siberian Ginseng 600mg Tablets, St John's Wort Standardised Extract 1000mg Tablets; *Minerals:* Chromium 200ug (from Picolinate) VegCaps, Magnesium Chelate Tablets, Silica Tablets, Zinc (from Amino Acid Chelate) VegCaps; *Multivitamins:* Nutri Time Tablets, Super 75 One a Day Multivitamin & Mineral Formula Tablets, Women's Iron Complete VegCaps; *Vitamins:* Balanced B50 Capsules, Ester C Tablets

KUDOS VITAMINS AND HERBALS ⊘ ⫶
Acidophilus plus Bifidus; AllerPlex; Calcium Magnesium and Zinc; Cats Claw 900mg; Chromium GTF; Circuplex Formula; ClensoPlex; Co Enzyme Q 10 40mg; Cranberry Complex; Devil's Claw 900mg; Digestive Enzymes; Dong Quai 900mg; Echinacea 900mg; Eye Bright

Chlorella and **Spirulina** are both forms of algae, nature's most potent superfood.

Chlorella is particularly highly valued in Japan as a natural food that not only detoxifies the body, but also strengthens the immune system. It's also nature's richest plant source of chlorophyll. **Chlorella** contains unique Chlorella Growth Factor (CGF), which is believed to help repair damaged tissue.

'You are not what you eat, you are what you can digest.' says Patrick Holford, one of the UK's best-known nutrition experts. **Spirulina** is 60-70% pure protein that is 95% digestible. It is nature's most potent gamma linolenic acid (GLA) and beta-carotene - these are widely used to help your brain, blood and eyes and skin healthy. **Spirulina** is Australia's favourite energy boosting supplement, consumed by family members of all ages.

Nature Complete Chlorella and **Spirulina** is the UK's only certified organic product of its kind. This is available in both powder and tablets. Suitable for everyone, including children, vegans, pregnant and nursing mothers. For more information visit www.naturecomplete.com

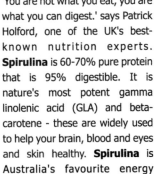

Vision Support Formula; Feverfew 900mg; Ginkgo Biloba 900mg; Hair Nutrient Formula; Korean Ginseng 900mg; LivoPlex; Maca (Lepedium meyenii) 900mg; MenoPlex; Milk Thistle; Prenatal; Rhodiola Rosea 900mg; Saw Palmetto 900mg plus Zinc; Siberian Ginseng 900mg; Soya Isoflavones 30mg; St John's Wort 900mg; Valerian 900mg; *Free Form:* Amino Acid Complex, L-Carnitine, L-Glutamine, L-Lysine

LIFEPLAN PRODUCTS LTD ™⊘✦👁
Culture Care - 28g; 5-HTP; Acetyl L Carnitine & Alpha Lipoic Acid; ACTIValoe; Agnus Castus; Biotin 2.5mg; Boron Triple Source Trace Mineral; Brewer's Yeast; Buffered Vitamin C with Rosehip & Acerola & Citrus Bioflavonoids - 500mg; Calcium & Magnesium - 500mg Powdered Dolomite; Calcium & Magnesium - 800mg Powdered Dolomite; Calcium Pantothenate - 250mg; Caprylic Acid; Chamomile Blend; Chelated Multiminerals; Chewable Vitamin C - 100mg; Chewable Vitamin C High Strength with Acerola & Bioflavonoids - 500mg; COQ10 30mg; Cranberry Extract - 200mg; Damiana Leaf Capsules; Dandelion Root; Devils Claw - 500mg; Digestive Enzymes; Echinacea - 1000mg Time Release; Echinacea - 360mg; EPO 1000mg; Evening Primrose Oil Capsules; Eyebright; Feverfew; Fibre - 440mg; Flaxseed Oil Capsules; Folic Acid; Golden Seal - 420mg; Guarana Powder; Hair Care Nutrients;

Hawthorn; **High Strength Vitamin B6 - 100mg; Horny Goat Weed Formula; Horse Chestnut Formula; L-arginine; Lecithin Granules; L-glutamine; Lutein; Nettle Leaf & Eyebright & Echinacea; Nettle Powder; Omega Blend Oil; Parsley Piert Powder - 125mg; Prune and Senna; Pycnogenol - Maritime Pine Bark Extract - 30mg; Raspberry Leaf; Red Clover; Rhodiola Rosea; Rutin; Sage; Saw Palmetto; Sea Kelp with Added Calcium - 400mg; Siberian Ginseng High Strength - 600mg; Slippery Elm; Soyplus - Soya Isoflavones with Folic Acid; St. John's Wort Extract - 333mg; Standardised Extract of Ginger - 50mg; Standardised Extract of Milk Thistle - 175mg; Super Multinutrient; Swiss Hayflower; Thiamine 100mg; Triple Source Magnesium; Valerian; Valerian Formula; Valerian Passiflora & Hops; Vegetarian Glucosamine; Vitamin B12 - 25mcg; Vitamin B12 1000mcg; Vitamin B12 -1000mcg; Vitamin B6 - 50mg; Vitamin C & Zinc; White Willow Bark; Women's Multinutrient; Zinc - 10mg; Zinc Amino Acid Chelate; Zinc and Lysine Tablets; Zinc Citrate 15mg**

MCKEITH ☺
24 Hour Detox; Fast Formula Slim; Living Food Energy Powder; Living Food Immune Defence Capsules; Organic Turbo Greens

MELBROSIN UK LIMITED
Acidophilus plus Bifidus; AllerPlex; Amino Acid complex; Black cohosh

900mg- high potency; Calcium, Magnesium & Zinc; Cats claw 900mg high potency; Chromium GTF; Circuplex Formula; ClensoPlex; Co-enzyme Q10 40mg; Cranberry complex; Devil's claw; Digestive enzymes; Dong Quai 900mg; Echinacea 900mg; Eye bright (vision support formula); Feverfew 900mg; Gingko Biloba 900mg; Hair Nutrient formula; Korean Ginseng 900mg; L-Carnitine; L-Glutamine; LivoPlex; L-Lysine; Maca 900mg; MenoPlex; Milk Thistle; Pre-natal; Rhodiola Rosea 900mg; Saw Palmeto 900mg plus Zinc; Siberian Ginseng 900mg; Soya Isoflavones 30mg; St John's Wort 900mg; Valerian 900mg; Zinc citrate 20mg; Zinc gluconate 50mg

NATROL ✓

Acai; Activin Grape Seed Extract; Calcium D-Glucarate; Calcium with Magnesium; China Chlorella; Cholesterol Balance Beta Sitosterol; Cinnamon Extract; CitriMax Balance; DHEA 10 mg; DHEA 25 mg; DHEA 50 mg; GarliPure Maximum Allicin caplets; GarliPure Once Daily tablet; Ginkgo Biloba 120 mg tablet; Hot Flashex tablet; Iron Liquid; Lycopene 15 mg tablet; Melatonin 1 mg tablet; Melatonin 1 mg time release tablet; Melatonin 3 mg tablet; Melatonin 3 mg time release tablet; Melatonin 5 mg tablet; Melatonin 5 mg time release tablet; Melatonin Liquid; NADH - 5, 10 & 20 mg; Niacin 500 mg time release tablet; Oat Bran tablet; ProstatExcell tablet; SelenoExcell; Sleep n Restore tablet; Slenderite; St. John's Wort tablet; Stress Complex tablet; Theanine tablet; Vegetarian Hyaluronic Acid MSM & Glucosamine capsule; Water Pill tablet

NATURE COMPLETE LTD ™☺
Chlorella capsules; Organic Chlorella; Organic Chlorella tablets; Organic Spirulina; Organic Spirulina tablets; Spirulina capsules

NATURES AID ⊘ ✓

Acetyl-L-Carnitine 250mg; Agnus Castus 1000mg; Aloe Vera 10000mg; Alpha Lipoic Acid 200mg; Bilberry 5000mg; Black Cohosh 500mg; Boldo 200mg; Boswellia 400mg; Brewer's Yeast 300mg; Calcium, Magnesium & Zinc; Chromium Picolinate 200ug; Conc. Garlic Allicin 2000ug; Cranberry 5000mg; Devil's Claw 1000mg; Dong Quai 500mg; Echinacea 500mg; Feverfew 200mg; Folic Acid 400ug; Ginger 500mg; Ginkgo Biloba 6000mg; Korean Ginseng 600mg; Magnesium 150mg Amino Acid Chelate (w Vit B6); Mega Potency Vit B Complex 100 Time Release; Milk Thistle 150mg; Passiflora 300mg; Pycnogenol 30mg; Red Clover 500mg; Rhodiola 500mg; Saw Palmetto 500mg; Sea Kelp 187mg; Siberian Ginseng 600mg; Soya Isoflavones 50mg; St Johns Wort 500mg; Super Vit B6 (high potency) 100mg; Traditional Herbal Bronchial Balsam (cough mixture); Valerian 500mg; Vit B Complex; Vit B Complex & C High Potency; Vit B6 50mg; Wild Yam 500mg; Zinc Gluconate 4mg elemental; Zinc Picolinate 15mg elemental; *Vit C:* 1000mg Time Release (w citrus bioflavonoids), 200mg Chewable (with rosehips & citrus bioflavonoids), 500mg Chewable (with rosehips & citrus bioflavonoids), Low Acid (w rosehips & bioflavonoids) 1000mg, Sugar Free Chewable (w citrus bioflavonoids) 500mg

NATURES AID LIMITED ™❶⊘✓
5 - HTP Complex 100mg Tablets;
Acetyl - L - Carnitine 250mg Tablets;
Acidophilus Complex Capsules;
Agnus Castus 100mg Tablets; Aloe
Vera 50mg Tablets; Aloe Vera Juice;
Alpha Lipoic Acid 200mg Tablets; B
Complex + C Tablets; Bilberry 50mg
Tablets; Black Cohosh 200mg
Tablets; Boldo 50mg Tablets;
Boswellia 400mg Capsules; Brewers
Yeast 300mg Tablets; Calcium,
Magnesium and Boron Tablets;
Calcium, Magnesium and Zinc
Tablets; Chromium Picolinate 200mg
Tablets; Complete Multivitamin and
Minerals; Concentrated Garlic
Tablets; Cranberry 200mg Tablets;
Devils Claw 1000mg Tablets;
Digestive Enzyme Complex (with
Betaine HCl); Dong Quai 500mg
Tablets; Echinacea 70mg Tablets;
Echinacea Complex Tablets; Ester-C
1300mg 30 + 90 tablets; Ester-C
650mg 90 VCaps; Feverfew 200mg
Tablets; Flaxseed Oil 1000mg 90 +
180 VCaps; Folic Acid 400mg Tablet;
Ginger Root 500mg Tablets; Ginger,
Turmeric and Boswellia Tablets;
Ginkgo Biloba Tablets; Glucosamine
Hcl 750mg Tablets; Green Food
Complex with Wheat Grass; Green
Tea 1000mg Tablets; Hair, Skin and
Nail Tablets; Hyaluronic Acid 50mg
30 + 90 VCaps; Korean Ginseng
600mg Tablets; Magnesium 150mg
Tablets; Milk Thistle 150 mg Tablets;
MSM 1000mg 90 Tablets; Passiflora
300mg Capsules; Passiflora, Lemon
Balm and Avena Sativa Tablets;
Pomegranate Juice; Pycnogenol
30mg Tablets; Quercetin 30 + 90

VCaps; Raspberry Leaf 375mg
Tablets; Red Clover 500mg Tablets;
Rhodiola Root 500mg Tablets;
Rosehip 750mg Tablets; Sage Leaf
50mg Tablets; Saw Palmetto 500mg
Tablets; Sea Kelp Tablets; Senna
125mg Tablets; Siberian Ginseng
600mg Tablets; Soya Isoflavones
Tablets; Spirulina 500mg Tablets; St
Johns Wort; Super Vitamin B6
Tablets; Valerian Root 500mg
Tablets; Vitamin B Complex Tablets;
Vitamin C Chewable 200mg Tablets;
Vitamin C Chewable 500mg Tablets;
Vitamin C Low Acid 1000mg Tablets;
Vitamin C Time Release 1000mg
Tablets; Wild Yam 500mg Tablets;
Zinc Gluconate Tablets; Zinc
Lozenges; Zinc Picolinate Tablets

NATURES REMEDIES ⊘✓
Zotrim

NATURKRAFTWERKE™
Black Cumin Oil Capsules

**NEAL'S YARD
REMEDIES** ⊘✓✿🧬1998
Organic Beauty Oil; Viridian Products
(except Glucosamine Chondroitin
Complex)

NEWAYS INTERNATIONAL UK LTD
Green Qi; Orachel

NUTRILABS
Supasulf Powder; Supasulf Tablets; Zest

**OLEADOR UG
(HAFTUNGSBESCHRÄNKT)** ™
Black Seed Oil; Prickly pear seed oil

OPTIMAH ⊘ ✓ ⚡ 1995

Aloe Vera 20,000mg Lemon & Lime Flavour Tablets; Bamboo Silica VegCaps; Boldo Herbal Complex Tablets; Calcium Plus Magnesium & Boron Tablets; Cat's Claw Standardised Extract 1000mg Tablets; Creatine Powder; Dolomite Tablets; Dong Quai Standardised Extract 1000mg Tablets; Echinacea 512mg Tablets; Echinacea Alcohol-Free Liquid Extract Fresh Fruit Flavour; Echinacea High Potency Liquid Extract; Echinacea High Potency VegCaps; Echinacea Standardised Extract 750mg Tablets; Folic Acid Complex Tablets; Gentle C Tablets; Ginkgo Biloba Standardised Extract 2000mg Tablets; High Potency Multivitamin & Mineral Tablets; Kelp Tablets; Korean Ginseng 600mg Orange Flavour Tablets; Liquid Evening Primrose Oil Lemon; Liquid Evening Primrose Oil Natural; Milk Thistle Standardised Extract 1000mg Tablets; MSM 1000mg Tablets; Multi B & C Complex Tablets; Multivitamin & Mineral One A Day Tablets; Organic Noni Juice; Original Herbal Complex for Women VegCaps; Peppermint Tablets; Selenium + Vitamins A, C & E Tablets; Siberian Ginseng Tablets; St John's Wort Standardised Extract 2000mg Tablets; Super Strength Aloe Vera Tablets; Vitamin B Complex Tablets; Vitamin B1 100mg Tablets; Vitamin B12 Tablets; Vitamin B5 Tablets; Vitamin B6 100mg Tablets; Vitamin C & Bioflavonoids Tablets; Vitamin C Chewable Tablets; Zinc Gluconate Tablets; *Childrens Chewable Multivitamins & Minerals:* Kordel's Junior Time; *Manuka Gold:* Lecithin Granules; *Thursday Plantation Tea Tree:* Echinafizz Fresh Fruit Flavour

ORGANIX SOUTH INC

Thera Neem: Neem Leaf Alcohol Extract, Neem Leaf Capsules; *Thera Veda:* Aller Support, Anti-Oxidant Cellular Support, Day Stress, Headache Support, Heart & Cholesterol Support, Hormonal Balance Women 14-40s, Joint Support, Liver Support, Male Vitality Formula, Menopause Support, Night Stress, Respiratory Support

POTTER'S HERBAL MEDICINE ✓

Life Drops; New Relax; Potters Cleansing Herbs; *Red Kooga:* Energise Sachets, Energise Tablets, Ginseng and Ginkgo Biloba Tablets, Ginseng Capsules, Ginseng Tablets

POWER HEALTH PRODUCTS ⊘ ✓

Alfalfa 500mg; Aloe Vera 10,000 Double Strength; Aloe Vera Juice Drink 99.7%; Alpha Lipoic Acid 200mg; Alpha Lipoic Acid 200mg & L-Carnitine 500mg; B Complex 100% RDA; B12 500ug; B6 100mg; Bilberry 2500mg; Black Cohosh 350mg; Blue Green Algae 200mg; Borage Oil (Starflower Oil) Liquid Cold Pressed; Bromelain 10mg & Papain 100mg; Butterbur Root Powder 100mg; Calcium 400mg; Calcium 400mg, Magnesium 150mg & Vitamin D 2.5µg; Calcium Pangamate (B15) 50mg; Calcium Pantothenate (B5) 500mg; Cat's Claw 34mg; Chromium Picolinate 200ug; Citrin 500 500mg (250mg HCA); Co Enzyme Q10 30mg; Cranberry Juice 1675mg with Vitamin C 100mg Sugar Free; Cranberry Juice Concentrate Drink Mix; Cranberry Juice Double Strength 4500mg; Echinacea 300 Standardised 4% Extract; Ester C 500mg; Folic Acid 400ug; Goji Berry;

Green Tea 1000mg; Hi Zinc 2mg
Elemental; Iron - Amino Acid Chelate
14mg; Kelp 500mg; Magnesium
300mg; Mega H40; Mega H40
Vegetarian Hard Shell Capsule; Mexican
Wild Yam 500mg; Multi Fibre Plus;
Multimineral & Zinc; Oral Zinc 25mg
(3.5mg Elemental); Phytosterols 400mg;
Pomegranate Extract 500mg; Potassium
200mg + Vitamin C 50mg; Power ACE
Super Antioxidant; Pregnancy
Multivitamin; Rhodiola 500mg; Rutivite;
S.O.D. 5000 (Super Oxide Dismutase);
Saw Palmetto (4:1 extract) 1000mg &
Uva Ursi 100mg; Selenium 100ug &
Zinc 2mg; Senna 37.5mg (7.5mg
Sennosides); Soya Isoflavones, Kudzu
Root & Red Clover; Spirulina 500mg;
Super Ginkgo Plus (with Green
Buckwheat & Vit E); Vit C 1000mg with
Citrus Bioflavonoids; Vit C Powder
(drink mix); Vitamin C 500mg Orange
with Betacarotene Chewable; Xtra Zinc
15mg Elemental; : Olive Leaf 450mg

PRINCIPLE HEALTHCARE
Active Defence Vit C + Zinc; Brain
Smart; Echinacea; Energise Tablets;
Evening Primrose oil; Garlic 2mg;
Gingko Bilboa; Iron 14mg; Korean
Ginseng; Leg Vein Health; Magnesium;
Peppermint capsules; Pomegranate;
Selenium ACE; Skin, Hair & Nails; St
Johns Wort; Vitamin B6; Zinc 15mg

QUEST VITAMINS ⊘ ✔
Acidophillus Plus 2 billion lactic
bacteria; Agnus Castus 71mg Extract;
Bilberry 60mg Extract; Bio C Complex
500mg vitamin C with bioflavonoids;
Black Cohosh 40mg Extract; Boron
3mg; Buffered C 700mg with

Bioflavonoids; Cal-Mag Plus
multiminerals; Coenzyme Q10 30mg;
Cranberry 200mg Extract; Devils Claw
17mg Extract; DL-Phenylalanine 500mg;
Echinacea 294mg Extract; Energy
Nutrient Complex; Enzyme Digest with
Betaine HCl; Folic Acid 400ug; Ginger
250mg Extract; Ginkgo Biloba 150mg
Extract; Ginkgo Biloba 40mg Extract;
Green Coffee Extract – 200mg Extract;
Green Tea 100mg Extract; Heart
Nutrient Complex magnesium & Co
Q10 with vitamins; Horse Chestnut
250mg Extract; Iron 15mg with
vitamins & Minerals; Isoflavones 40mg
Extract; Kyolic Garlic 100mg – Aged
Garlic Extract; Kyolic Garlic 600mg
Extract; Kyolic Garlic Extract 1000mg
Extract; Kyolic Liquid – Aged Garlic
Extract; Lactase 200mg; L-Arginine
500mg; L-Cysteine 500mg; L-Glutamine
500mg; L-Lysine 500mg; L-Orthithine
500mg; Lp299v 1 billion Lactobacillus
Bacteria; L-Phenylalanine 500mg; L-
Tyrosine 500mg; Magnesium 150 mg
with vitamin B6; Mega B 100 timed
release; Mega B50; Milk Thistle 150mg
Extract; Multi B Complex plus 500mg
vitamin C; Piperine 10mg Extract
providing 10mg piperine; Red Clover
500mg Extract; Rhodiola 250mg
Extract; Saw Palmetto 36mg Extract;
Selenium 200ug with vitamins C & E;
Senna 16.7mg Extract; Siberian
Ginseng 35mg Extract ; St. Johns Wort
333mg Extract; Super Mega B&C plus
1000mg vitamin C & Herbs; Super
Once A Day vegan timed release
multivitamins & minerals; Turmeric Plus
263mg Extract; Uva-Ursi 90mg Extract;
Valerian 83mg Extract; Vitamin B12
500ug plus uva ursi extract; Vitamin B6

50mg plus parsley leaf extract; Vitamin C 1000mg Timed Release with bioflavonoids; Vitamin C 500mg with bioflavonoids; Zinc 15mg with copper

RAW LIVING ™☺❶❹ ✔
Acai Powder; Ashwaganda powder; Barleygrass powder; Cacao Beans; Cacao Butter; Cacao Nibs; Camu Camu powder; Carob Pods; Carob Powder; Coconut butter; Gingko biloba powder; Goji Berries; Greener Grass powder; He Shou Wu; Hemp seeds; Klamath Lake Algae powder; Maca Bar; Maca Powder; MSM crystals; Muira puama powder; Purple Corn extract powder; Schizanda powder; Spirulina Powder; Suma powder; Sunseeds; Vanilla Pods; *Hi:* **Hi-Bar**

RAWCREATION LTD ™☺❶❹ ✔
Brazilian Ginseng; Goji Berries; Guarana Powder

RELIV UK ™⊘ ✔
Reliv Classic 504g

SALUS ⊘ ✔
Calcium; Floravital Liquid Iron; Gallexier; IntestCare; Protecor; Siberian Ginseng

SAVANT DISTRIBUTION LTD ™❶❹ ✔
Health Elements Spirulina; Health Elements Wheatgrass Powder; Udo's Choice Ultimate Oil Blend; Udo's Choice Ultimate Milled Seed Blend - Organic Omega 3-6-9

SEAGREENS LTD ™☺⊘
Seagreens- Ascophyllum Fine Granules:

Iodine Plus Capsules; *Seagreens- Mixed Wrack:* **Food Capsules;** *Seagreens- Mixed Wrack:* **Food Granules**

SEVEN SEAS ™⊘ ✔
One-a-Day Multivitamins plus Minerals for Vegetarians & Vegans

SHIFA LIFEHERBS INTERNATIONAL (UK) ™
Shifa Blackseed Oil; Shifa Blackseed Oil Vega Capsules

SOLGAR VITAMINS ⊘ ✔
Acetyl-L-Carnitine Vegicaps; Amino 75 Capsules; Arginine-Ornithine Vegicaps; BCAA Plus Capsules; L-Arginine Vegicaps; Maxi L-Carnitine

SUPERNUTRIENTS LTD ™☺⊘ ✔
Organic: **Organic Acai Powder Freeze Dried, Organic barleygrass powder, Organic chlorella powder, Organic Chlorella Tablets, Organic Hemp Protein Powder, Organic Lucuma Powder, Organic maca powder, Organic Mesquite Powder, Organic wheatgrass**

SWISS HERBAL CONFECTIONERY
Organic Echinacea Cherry Flavoured Lozenges; Organic Echinacea Strawberry Flavoured Lozenges

TALOOZA INC ™☺❶❹ ✔ ✿ ☙
Pre-natal Multi-vitamin: **Bebe-O pre-natal supplement**

THE GREEN SUPERFOOD COMPANY LLP ™☺ ✔
Plant Supplement Capsules: **Chlorella**

powder capsules, Spirulina powder capsules, Wheatgrass powder capsules; *Plant Supplements:* Chlorella powder, Spirulina powder, Wheatgrass powder

THE VEGAN SOCIETY ™☺❶♪
Chewable Supplement: **Veg1**

TORQ UK
Vegan Recovery; *Bar:* 1 Apricot, 2 Sundried Banana, 3 Raspberry & Apple, 4 Pineapple & Ginger, Mixed Box, Sample Pack; *Energy:* Natural, Natural Lemon, Natural Lime & Lemon, Natural Orange, Natural Pink Grapefruit; *Energy Gel:* All Mixed Boxes, Black Cherry Yoghurt Flavour, Forest Fruits w Guarana, Orange & Banana, Sample Pack, Strawberry Yoghurt Flavour; *Raw:* Carnitine, Glutamine, HMB, Ribose

VEGA NUTRITIONALS ™☒♪
Active Mature Plus Multivitamin & Mineral; Active Mens Multivitamin & Mineral; Active Womens Multivitamin & Mineral; Black Cohosh Complex; Calcium + Vitamin D Tablets; Iron Citrate (15mg); Vega Calcium Chewable; Zinc Citrate (15mg); *Vega antioxidants:* **Dunaliella salina (natural betacarotene) 100mg, Multi Antioxidant complex, Pine Bark Complex 30mg;** *Vega minerals:* **Calcium (Citrate) 100mg, Calcium + vitamin D high strength, Calcium, Magnesium & Zinc, Chelated Calcium 500mg, Chromium 200mcg + vitamin B3, Colloidal Minerals+ Kelp Formula, Iron (Bisglycinate)**

50mg non Constipating, Iron (citrate)14mg +vitamin C, Kelp & Greens Formula, Magnesium (Citrate) 100mg, Selenium (methionine) 200mcg Yeast Free, Zinc (citrate) 15 mg +vitamin C, Zinc Citrate 50mg, ZMM High Potency Multi Mineral formula; *Vega multivitamins and minerals:* **Active Mature 50+ Multivitamins and minerals, Active women's multivitamin and minerals, Anti-Oxidant selenium- ACE formula, Spectrum Multi Vitamin and minerals, ZM3 Multivitamin & Minerals formula;** *Vega omega 6 essential fatty acids:* **Evening primrose oil formula, Soya Lecithin plus Starflower Oil (Omega 3+6);** *Vega probiotics and digestive aids:* **Digestive Enzymes formula, Gastrocalm Formula, Non Dairy Acidophilus plus Bifidus Complex, Psyllium Husk Fibre 450mg;** *Vega special care formulas:* **Cardiohealth Formula, Energizer Formula, Hair-Skin-Nails formula, Menopause Formula, Opti-care 20:20 Formula, PMS Formula, Pre-Natal Formula, Prostate Formula, Slimaide Formula;** *Vega specialised nutritional supplements:* **Allermex Formula, Alpha lipoic acid+ Acetyl L-carnitine 500 -Complex, Champignon Detox Formula, Co-enzyme Q10 30 mg- phyto- antioxidants, Co-enzyme Q10 30mg Extra High Potency, Cranberry Plus Formula, Garlic (Deodorised) 400mg High Potency, Hematinic Blood co-factors, Maxijoint Formula, Multi Detox Complex, Multigluco Tolerance Factors with Karella, Smokers**

bebe-O

Vegan Prenatal Vitamins

Over 40 All-Natural plant based ingredients packed into one ground breaking supplement!

✓ Vitamins
✓ Minerals
✓ Antioxidants
✓ Enzyme Blend
✓ Phytonutrients
✓ and more!

100% Natural Plant Based Prenatal Vitamins

Buy online and save 25%

www.bebe-O.com

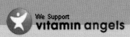

formula, Vitalize-Regenerative
Formula; *Vega Standardised herbs - V
caps:* **Agnus Castus 300mg High
Potency, Aloe Vera 500mg High
Potency, Dong Quai 750mg High
Potency, Echinacea 750mg High
Potency;** *Vega Standardised herbs - V
caps:* **Devil's Claw 300mg High
Potency;** *Vega standardised herbs- V
caps:* **Black cohosh herbal extract,
Echinacea + ginseng and astragalus
herbal complex, Feverfew 750mg
High Potency, Ginkgo Biloba 750mg
High Potency, Ginseng (Siberian)
1700 Complex, Milk Thistle 200-
Complex, Neem Leaf herbal
complex, Panax Ginseng (Korean)
800 Complex, Rhodiola herbal
extract, St John's Wort 333-
Complex, Valerian 900-Complex;**
Vega Standardised herbs -V caps: **Cat's
Claw 1000mg High Potency;** *Vega
vitamin B supplements:* **Biotin (vitamin
H) 900mcg, Choline plus Inositol
250mg/250mg, Folic Acid(vitamin B9)
400mcg, P.A.B.A Para Aminobenzoic
Acid 300mg, Vitamin B Complex
formula, Vitamin B1 100mg
(Thiamine), Vitamin B12 1000mcg,
Vitamin B2 40mg (Riboflavin),
Vitamin B3 No Flush (Nicotinamide),
Vitamin B5 200mg (Calcium
Pantothenate), Vitamin B6 plus p-5-
p 100mg, Vitamin B6 plus p-5-p
50mg;** *Vega vitamin C supplements:*
**Vitamin C 1000mg (Calcium
Ascorbate)- non acidic, Ester-C
Formula, Vitamin B & C Complex,
Vitamin C 1000mg - high strength,
Vitamin C 1000mg Slow Release,
Vitamin C 1500mg- super strength,
Vitamin C(calcium ascorbate)**

500mg - non acidic, Zinc C Formula;
Vega vitamin E supplements: **Natural
Vitamin E(D-Alpha tocopherol)
400iu 335mg dry, Vitamin E 200iu
134mg dry plus Selenium Yeast Free**

WASSEN INTERNATIONAL ◯ ⚫
Coenzyme Q10 + Magnesium;
Coenzyme Q10 + Vitamin E; Confiance;
Magnesium-B; Selene-Activ; *Efamol:*
Pure Evening Primrose Liquid

WHOLISTIC RESEARCH COMPANY
Cascara Compound; Colon Detox Herbs
and Herbal Drops; Organic Wheatgrass
Powder; Spirulina Tablets

YAOH™☺❶◯⚫
Hemp Protein Powder 454g

NOTES

■ **Complementary/Alternative healthcare** includes herbalists, homoeopaths acupuncturists etc and the use of herbal remedies available from health/wholefood shops and chemists. Herbal and homeopathic formulas may contain animal ingredients

■ **Beta-carotene and vitamin D2**: see FOOD NOTES, page 136.

■ **Capsules** may be made from gelatine but animal-free alternatives are increasingly being used.

■ **Contraceptives** may have been tested on animals or contain animal-derived ingredients:
Condoms are usually made from latex, in which case casein (a milk protein) will usually have been used as a processing aid.
Oral contraceptives may contain lactose (milk sugar) and / or magnesium stearate (possibly animal-derived).

■ **Medications** may or may not contain animal-derived ingredients, but will have been tested on animals at some stage in production. The website www.medicines.org.uk lists the ingredients of all UK medicines.

■ **Prescriptions:** In order for a medicinal product to be allowed onto the UK market, it must have marketing authorisation, also known as a product licence. However, doctors can lawfully prescribe unlicensed drugs. Theoretically, this means that, providing an animal-free product is available, a GP can prescribe it. However, doing so increases the doctor's personal liability, should anything go wrong; many doctors are, therefore, reluctant to prescribe unlicensed alternatives. Pharmacists are useful sources of information, having a greater knowledge of ingredients and formulations compared to GPs. A pharmacist may be able to determine an animal free version of a medication, it may then be possible to return to your GP and ask for the animal free version to be prescribed

■ **Vitamin K** is routinely injected into newborn babies to protect against rare but serious haemorrhage (including brain haemorrhage). In the past, the injection was vegan but now includes a carrier made from cow bile, making it unsuitable for vegans. The Vegan Society has made representations on the issue of no vegan suitable alternative currently being available. Contact the Vegan Society office for the most up to date information.

Holistic Health

Heal your mind, heal your body, heal your life

At Maison de Aurore, Pays de la Loire, France

Which one are you?
1 New to veggie nutrition and food prep?
2 In a food rut?
3 Exploring a higher raw diet?
4 Want to benefit from a veggie retreat?
5 Looking for veggie B&B?
6 Struggling with an eating disorder (ED)?
7 Enduring niggling health problems?

I've been in all those situations. As a life long vegetarian, I became vegan in my twenties and transitioned to a high raw diet in my thirties (all with the hope of finally overcoming my ED). The combination of raw living foods, life coaching and training as a holistic health practitioner helped me reclaim great health. Now in my forties I'm genuinely slimmer, healthier, fitter and happier than ever! Whatever your reasons, as a fellow health seeker I will support you to genuinely feel good about yourself, consequently, you'll truly look good too

Steps to feeling good and looking good
1 Increase your knowledge at my nutritional workshops.
2 Be inspired at my multicultural cooking classes.
3 Discover self sufficiency skills at my Living Foods workshops.
4 Feed your mind, body and spirit during our tailored holistic health retreats.
5 Eat and sleep naturally at our B&B.
6 Feel safe and supported throughout your ED recovery.
7 Benefit from our tailored health programmes and regain your zest for life.

To book B&B accommodation; Workshops, Tailored Retreats or Coaching, contact Dawn Campbell, Holistic Health Coach & Living Foods Practitioner on e-mail: dawn@holistichealthcoach.eu or visit

http://www.dawncampbellholistichealth.eu

BABY, INFANT & CHILDCARE

BABY, INFANT & CHILDCARE

FOOD & DRINK

BABYNAT
Apple & Banana Muesli; Apple & Raspberry Cereal; Baby Rice; Banana Porridge; *Fruit Compotes:* Apple & Apricot Stage II, Apple & Banana Stage II, Apple & Blueberry, Apple & Vanilla/Banana & Plum Dual, Apple Peach/Apple Strawberry Doubles, Banana, Apple & Apricot, Pear and Raspberry, Summer Pudding; *Goodies Fruit Competes:* Apple & Berries Puree, Banana & Mango Puree

BICKIEPEGS ☺⊘✦
Teething Biscuits for Babies

COW & GATE
Baby Balance Desserts Jars, Stages 1, 2 and 3: Baby Fruit Cocktail, Exotic Fruit Combo, Fruity Muesli, Juicy Fruit Crumble, Juicy Pear & Banana, Mango Surprise, Plum and Apricot Compote, Summer Fruit Salad; *Baby Balance Savoury Jars, Stage 1 (+4 months):* A Taste of Apple, A Taste of Carrot, A Taste of Pear, A Taste of Pumpkin, Sweet Potato Bake, Yummy Baby Veg Risotto; *Baby Balance Savoury Jars, Stage 2 (+ 7 months):* Baby Bean Feast; *Baby Balance Savoury Jars, Stage 3 (+ 10 months):* Mild Mexican Bean Pot, Simply Scrummy Lentil Bake; *Cereals, Stage 1:* Apple & Banana Burst, Pure Baby Rice, Totally Oaty Porridge; *Cereals, Stage 2:* Apple & Blueberry Sunburst, Multigrain Porridge, Tropical Sunrise; *Cereals, Stage 3:* Fruity Crunch;

Cereals, Stage 4: Fruity, Sun, Moon & Stars, Hoop-a-Loops, My First Muesli; *Frutapura Pots:* Apple & Apricot, Apple & Banana, Apple & Pear, Apple, Apricot & Strawberry, Apple, Orange & Banana, Banana, Peach & Strawberry, Fruit Cocktail, Pear, Pear & Pineapple, Plum & Apple; *Frutapura Pouches:* Apple & Banana, Exotic Fruit, Fruit Cocktail

HIPP ORGANIC BABY FOODS ⊘✦☼
Dried Stage 1: Apple, Orange & Banana, Baby Rice, Banana Porridge, Hipp-a-bisc, Mashed Potato with Rosemary; *Stage 1 - Baby Menu:* Mixed Vegetable Medley, Tender Carrots & Potatoes; *Stage 1 - Desserts:* Apple & Blueberry Dessert, Apple & Pear Pudding, Apple & Plum Pudding, Banana & Peach Dessert, Banana & Rice Pudding, Fruit Pots Apple & Pear, Fruit Pots Apple and Strawberry, Mango & Banana Melba, Red Fruit & Apple Compote, William Christ Pears; *Stage 1- Desserts:* Fruit Pots Apple with Banana & Peach, Purley Fruits Apple & Banana, Purley Fruits Apple Strawberry & Blueberry; *Stage 1- First Tastes:* Apple & Banana, Apple Puree, Carrots & Sweetcorn, Pumpkin and Rice; *Stage 2- Desserts:* Tropical Fruit Salad

ORGANIX BRANDS PLC ⊘☼
Baby Sweetcorn Rings; Jumbo Carrot Sticks; *Biscuits:* ABC's, Animal Biscuits, Gingerbread Men

PETER RABBIT ORGANICS ⊘☼
Apple Jelly; Orange Jelly; *Organic Puree:* Apple, Peach & Apricot

300

BABY, INFANT & CHILDCARE

FOOTWEAR & CLOTHING

GREEN SHOES ™⊘✔
Boys Vegan Range: **Sweet Pea Baby Boots;** *Girls Vegan Range:* **Sweet Pea Baby Boots**

HEALTH CARE

A. VOGEL
Echinacea Junior

BEAMING BABY ™
Organic Facial Cleansing Wipes; Organic Lavender Nappy Cream; Organic Lavender Baby Lotion; Organic Lavender Baby Oil; Organic Lavender Bubble Bath

BIO-HEALTH LTD ⊘✔
Pure-fil: Junior Bio-Caps Multivitamin & Mineral

DEVA NUTRITION LLC ™☺✔
Deva Nutrition supplements: **Tiny Tablets Multivitamin and Mineral**

FAITH PRODUCTS LIMITED
™⊘✔👁⚘1988
Baby Shampoo & Body Wash

HERBS HANDS HEALING LTD ™⊘✔
Herbal Formula: **Little One's Cough Syrup**

HIGHER NATURE LTD
Dinochews; Herbal Aloe Gold Ear Drops; *Omega Excellence:* Essential Balance Junior

TOMS OF MAINE ⊘✔
Natural Moisturising Body Wash: Lavender

NAPPIES

BEAMING BABY ™
Bio Degradable Nappies in 5 sizes

BIO-D ™☺✔👁⚘1988
Nappy Fresh

TOILETRIES ETC

AKAMUTI
Baby Bottom Butter; Bedtime Baby Bath Milk; Organic Baby Flower Wash; Organic Baby Soap; *Baby Oil:* Peach & Chamomile, Sunshine

ARBONNE 👁
ABC Baby Care: Body Lotion, Body Oil, Hair and Body Wash, Herbal Diaper Rash Cream, Sunscreen SPF 30+

AROMA COMFORTS ™☺⊘
Baby's Bottom Butter

BABY, INFANT & CHILDCARE

AROMATHERAPY PRODUCTS LTD ™☺
Baby Bliss: **Gentle Cleansing Bar, Gently Foaming Bath Wash, Nursery Oil For Vaporisation, Soft Soothing Lotion, Soft Touch Massage Oil**

AUBREY ORGANICS
Natural Baby Bath Soap; Natural Baby Body Lotion; Natural Baby Shampoo

BABYBOO ORGANICS LTD
™☺◐�𝓲 ✿
Babyboo products: **Baby Massage Oil, Citrus bodywash, Detox foaming bath, Lavender Body Lotion, Lavender foaming cleanser, Lavender lotion, Lavender shampoo, Mum's Relaxing Massage Blend, Muscle foaming bath, Strawberry bodywash, Stretch Mark Oil**

BEAMING BABY ™
Organic Baby Wipes; Organic Bathtime Bubble Bath; Organic Bathtime Shampoo & Bodywash; Organic Nappy Cream; Organic Skincare Baby Lotion

BURT'S BEES ◐𝓲👁
Baby Bee: Apricot Baby Oil, Dusting Powder, Shampoo & Wash

CAWARRA COSMETICS LTD ™
Sanctum: **Baby Bath Wash, Baby Conditioner, Baby Moisturiser, Baby Powder, Baby Shampoo**

ECO COSMETICS GMBH & CO. KG ™◐𝓲✿
Baby Body Lotion; Baby Body Oil; Baby Bubble Bath; Baby Face Cream; Baby Nappy Cream; Baby Shampoo/Shower

ENERGIZER PERSONAL CARE ™
Wet Ones: Little Bottoms- toilet training wipes, Sticky Fingers- hand wipes

ESSENTIAL CARE
Gentle Wash & Shampoo for Baby; Organic Baby Massage Oil; Organic Baby Repair Lotion; Organic Calming Spritz; Organic Labour Oil; Organic Soothing Salve

ESSENTIALLY YOURS LTD
My Baby Range: MB3 Mandarin & Camomile Baby Lotion, MB4 Lavender, Rose & Tea Tree Nappy Cream, MB5 Mandarin & Lavender Massage Oil

FAITH PRODUCTS LIMITED
™◐𝓲👁⅄1988
Baby bath; Baby Body Lotion; Baby Shampoo; Baby Soap; Baby tushie cleanse; Nappy cream

HEALTHQUEST LIMITED ™◐𝓲
Earth Friendly Baby: **Eco Baby Wipes, Natural Lavender Cleansing Bar, Natural Unscented Massage Oil (100ml), Organic Chamomile Bubble Bath (370ml), Organic Chamomile Shampoo & Bodywash, Organic Lavender Bubble Bath (370 ml), Organic Lavender Shampoo & Bodywash, Organic Mandarin Bubble Bath (370ml), Organic Mandarin Shampoo & Bodywash, Organic Massage Oil;** *Earth Friendly Kids:* **Gentle Kids Wipes, Minty**

Lavender Body Lotion, Minty
Lavender Bubblebath, Minty
Lavender Handwash, Minty Lavender
Shampoo & Bodywash, Zingy Citrus
Body Lotion, Zingy Citrus Bubblebath,
Zingy Citrus Handwash, Zingy Citrus
Shampoo & Bodywash

**HIPPY HEAVEN
NATURAL BEAUTY** TM☺◌⃠🖌
Baby soothe cream- nappy rash,
colic, calming

JASON NATURAL PRODUCTS
Kids Only!™ Extra Gentle Conditioner,
Kids Only™ Extra Gentle Shampoo;
Earth's Best®: 2-in-1 Shampoo & Body
Wash, Baby Oil, Diaper Relief Ointment,
Everyday Lotion, Extra Rich Therapy
Crème, Hair Detangler, Mineral Based
Sunblock SPF30+, Toddler Toothpaste

LAVERANA GMBH & CO. KG TM🖌
Lavera Baby & Kinder Neutral: **Baby &
Kinder Lotion, Baby & Kinder
Shower Shampoo, Hair & Body
Shampoo, Lotion, Oil Bath, Skin Oil;**
Lavera Basis Sensitiv: **Kid's Tooth Gel
Strawberry-Raspberry;** *Serie Baby &
Kinder:* **Baby & Kinder Bath Oil, Baby
& Kinder Skin Oil, Shampoo**

MALIBU ◌⃠🖌
High Protection Sun Lotion: SPF30
Disappearing Coloured Spray for Kids,
SPF30 Spray for Kids

NATURALLY GIFTED
Lavender Baby Soap

NATURE'S GATE
Baby Soothing Shampoo; *Organics:* Baby
Oil, Gentle Baby Wash, Naturally Soft
Baby Lotion, Soothing Diaper Rash Cream

NEAL'S YARD REMEDIES
◌⃠🖌👁✈1998
Baby Massage Oil; Baby Soap; Baby
Wash; Pure Baby Oil

NOTHING NASTY 🖌
Bonbon Baby Oil

ORGANIC BOTANICS TM◌⃠✿
Oils: **Organic Baby Mild Baby Oil;**
Wash: **Organic Baby Mild Baby Wash**

ORGANIC SOAP COMPANY TM◌⃠✿
Baby

PURE GAISHA TM☺❶🖌
**Kids Only Lip Balm; Kids Only
Shower Gel**

RAW GAIA TM☺❶◌⃠🖌✿👁
**Floral Water Spray For Her Babies;
Massage Oil For Her Babies**

**RJ MINERAL COSMETICS
INTERNATIONAL PTY LTD** TM🖌
Baby: **BBB Baby Bottom Butter, BBG
Baby Bath Gel - Lavender and
Chamomile, BCL Baby Cleansing
Lotion - Lavender and Chamomile,
BEBB Baby Breath Ezy Baby Balm,
BMO Baby Massage Oil - Lavender
and Chamomile, BMO Baby Massage
Oil - Unscented, BP Baby Powder -
Lavender and Chamomile, BP Baby
Powder - Unscented, MBBB Mummy
& Baby Body Butter**

SIMPLE ✔
Baby: Body Wash, Extra Soft Wipes, Moisturising All-In-One Wash, Moisturising Bath, Moisturising Oil Gel, Moisturising Shampoo, Pure Talc, Soothing Lotion, Zinc & Castor Oil Barrier Cream

SOLARAY NUTRITIONAL SUPPLEMENTS
Baby Bath Shampoo; Baby Bath Soap; Baby Body Lotion

THE HIGHLAND SOAP COMPANY ⊘
Body Wash: Mandarin Baby Body Wash

TOMS OF MAINE ⊘ ✔
Natural Anticavity Fluoride Toothpaste for Children: Silly Strawberry; *Natural Anticavity Fluoride Toothpaste For Children:* Silly Strawberry; *Natural Fluoride-Free Toothpaste for Children:* Silly Strawberry; *Natural Moisturising Body Wash:* Unscented

VERDESATIVA S.R.L. ™☺❶⊘ ✔ ✿ ☻
Shampoo Bimbi; *Barriera Verdesativa:* **Crema Pasta Pannolind**

WELEDA ⊘ ✔ ⚘ 1985
Baby Calendula

NOTES

- **Baby wipes** may contain lanolin, which is derived from wool.

- **Infant Formula**, despite the best efforts of dietician Sandra Hood and The Vegan Society who have been talking to Cow & Gate, SMA and The Department of Health, there currently is no vegan infant formula on sale since Heinz discontinued their Nurture Soya. Other soya formulas such as Cow & Gate's Infasoy and SMA's Wysoy contain vitamin D taken from sheep's wool (lanolin). To find out more, or ask these companies to produce a formula suitable for vegan babies' please phone:
Heinz Baby Careline 0800 212991
Cow & Gate Careline 08457 623 623
SMA Careline 0800 0818 180 or contact each company through their online contact form on their websites.

- The first food for a vegan baby should ideally be breast milk. It is important that ordinary soya milk should not substituted for soya infant formula as it does not contain the proper ratio of protein, fat, carbohydrate, nor the vitamins and minerals required to be used as a sole food. *Fortified* soya milk can be included in the diet from 6 months of age but be aware that it is lower in calories than formula therefore the extra calories would need to be ensured elsewhere in the diet.

■ **Vegan pregnancy and parenting advice;** the Vegan Society produces a range of information on raising vegan children, including the book *Raising your Vegan Infant - With Confidence* by State Registered Dietitian, Sandra Hood – visit http://shop.vegansociety.com or call 0121 523 1731 for details. See 'SUGGESTED READING' (page 49) for further resources.

■ **Vegan families list;** the Vegan Society holds a list of vegan families in the UK. This is a network of families who have vegan children and are happy to be contacted for advice and support. Please contact the Vegan Society Office for more details.

FOOTWEAR & CLOTHING

FOOTWEAR & CLOTHING

BELTS, WALLETS, BAGS ETC

ACORN PRODUCTS CO, LLC ™ 🛈
15" leg warmer, Fleece wrap, Leg Warmer, Neck Gaitor, Scarf;

BOURGEOIS BOHEME ™☺
Mobile/Mini Ipod Muffs; Mens Wallets (various); Womens Bags (various); Womens Purses (various); *Belts:* Men & women- various styles; Hultquist: **Jewellery (various)**

ETHICAL WARES ☺🛈🛈
Accessories: Hemp Shopping Bag, Key Fob Black, Key Fob Brown; *Belts:* Style A, Style B, Style C, Style D, Style E, Webbed Belt

FEEL GOOD HANDBAGS ☺
Handbags : All Products are Vegan

FREERANGERS ™☺🛈
Acorn rucksack; Celtic Bag; Star bag; *Accessories:* Alex Belt, Aragon Belt, Coin Purse, Conker II Rucksack, Credit Card Holder, Full Wallet, Half Wallet, Lucy Bag, Molly Bag, Palm Pilot Case, Prairie Belt, Purse, Sporran, Strider Belt, Watch Strap, Wave Bag, Zoe Bag

GREEN SHOES ™🛇🛈
Men's Vegan Range: **Men's Jeans Belt, Traditional Satchel - Large, Traditional Satchel - Standard;**
Women's Vegan Range: **2-Leaf Purse,**

Corset Belt, Cuff Bracelet, Curvy Belt, Curvy Belt with Leaves, Edith Bag, Evening Bag, Half Moon Purse, Hazelnut Purse, Narrow Belt, Plaited Belt, Traditional Satchel - Large, Traditional Satchel - Standard, Tribal Necklace, Women's Jeans Belt

MATT & NAT ☺
Bags: All

MISS BELLASIS ☺
Knickers: Carmen, Celestine, Vivian; *Ribbon Collection:* Annie, Hesther, Laurel, Marguerite, Peggy, Velvet; *Satin Collection:* Anis, Catherine, Celestine, Judy, Kitty, Lily, Lina, Lise, Mary, Mary - Collar, Mary - Cuffs, Mima, Rosalie, Roslyn, Tae, Tansy, Violette; *Sequin Collection:* Dorita, Florrie, Margo; *Vintage Trims, Limited Editions:* Bella, Charlotte, Emily, Eve, Irma

URBAN JUNGLE SARL ™🛈🛇🛈
Women's bags: **Kindy, Sambra, Shaila**

VEGAN CHIC ™☺
Bags - All designs; Belts and accessories - All designs

VEGAN STORE ™☺🛈🛇🛈
Business Belt; Faux Leather Wallet; Lorica Watch Strap

VEGANLINE ™☺🛈
Microfibre belts made to order in the UK; PVC Wallets made in the UK

VEGETARIAN SHOES ☺🛈
Belts: All; *Insoles:* All; *Shoe Laces:* All; *Wallets:* All

308

CLOTHING

ADEENA ☺ ⊘
Non Silk Vegan Satin Ties- various colours

BOURGEOIS BOHEME ™☺
Scarves (various)

URBAN JUNGLE SARL ™ ❶ ⊘ ✔
Adho Mukha Svanasana T-shirt; Bakasana T-shirt; Garudasana T-shirt; Izza Cami Top; Leela Long Pants; Nejma Tee Top; Noor Long Sleeve Top; Rim Tank Top; Rio Short Pants; Roxana Harem Pants; Simhasana T-shirt; Ustrasana T-shirt

VEGAN STORE ™☺ ❶ ⊘ ✔
Fleece Gloves

VEGETARIAN SHOES ☺ ❶
Gloves: All; *Jackets:* All; *Leather Look Jeans:* All

WELL CULTIVATED LTD ™ ⊘
Bamboo Clothing; Bamboo Robes; Bamboo Towels; Hemp Clothing; Organic Cotton Clothing

FOOTWEAR - FORMAL

BEYOND SKIN ☺
All

NOHARM ™☺ ❶ ⊘ ✔ ✿
Mens: Hidden-lace Shoe, Lace-up Ankle Boot, Lace-up Shoe, Slip-on Shoe

VEGAN CHIC ™☺
Shoes - All designs

309

FOOTWEAR - GENERAL

ACORN PRODUCTS CO, LLC ™ 🦶
Accessories/clothing: Adult Sox:
**Double Duty Knee High, Double
Duty Sox, High versa 2-Way Tread,
OTC slipper sock, PTEC 16" sock,
PTEC 200 14" sock, PTEC 300 14"
sock, Reg Ptec Sandal Sock, Reg
sandal sock, Rei 2-Way Fleece Sock,
Ultra therm (sock) w/cuff, Versa 2-
way 2 packs, Versa 2-Way Mid,
Versa 2-way Mid Mn, Versa 2-way
Mid Wm, Versa 2-Way Sox, Versa 2-
Way Tread, Versa 2-Way W/Cuff,
Versa Fit;** *Classic:* **Baxter Moc, Berber
Cozy Bootie Womens, Berber**
highlander for men, Berber
highlander for women, Berber tex
mule for women, Chinchilla Bootie,
Chinchilla bootie II for women,
Chinchilla Collar, Chinchilla Mule,
Cozy Bootie, Cozy bootie for
women, New tech travel moc for
men, Nex Tex Clog, Nex Tex clog for
women, Nex Tex Moc, Nex Tex Moc
Mn, Ocelot Thong, Plush Scuff MN,
Plush Scuff WM, Plush Tex Moc for
Men & Women, Tech Travel II, Tech
Travel maryjane for women, Tech
Travel Moc Mens, Tech Travel Moc
WM, Tex Bootie WM II (Brown Plush
+ Pink Ocelot), TLC Ballet for
women, TLC Mary Jane for women,
TLC Moc for men, TLC moc for
women, TLC Shaggy moc for
women, TLC shaggy mule for

women; *Kids Slippers:* **Cozy Slipper II, Easy Bootie, Fat Cat Moc, Gavin Gore Moc, Gidget Gore Moc - Blueberry Duo & Additional Colours, Go Fish - Charcoal Multi, Kids Mule, Kids Spa Bootie, Kids Spa Mule, Lounger Bootie, Love Child Moc, Quilted Terry Mule K, Spa Ballet for Kids, Spa Bella, Spa Hugger Kid - Melon, French Blue & Scarlet, Spa Terry Bootie, Tex Easy Bootie, Top Dog Moc - Malt Multi;** *Kids Sox:* **Double Duty Sox Kids, Rei Kids Sock W/Tread, Rei Versa Kid Sock, Versa Fit Kid, Versa Kid Sox;** *Shoes:* **Ergo Bootie WM, Espie Moc, Espie Thong, Strata Moc MN, Via Moc WM;** *Spa:* **Adjustable Spa Hugger, Brit Spa Thong, Eco Mule Womens, New Spa Slide, New Spa Thong, Piped Spa Bella- Women's, Quilted Eco Scuff - Ivory Colour Only, Quilted Terry Scuff - Ivory Colour Only, Sensoria Ballet- Women's, Sensoria Collar- Women's, Sensoria Scuff, Sensoria Slide, Sensoria Thong, Shaggy spa scuff for women, Shaggy spa thong for women, Spa ballet for women, Spa Bella- Women's, Spa Fit Scuff, Spa Fit Z Strap, Spa Hugger WM, Spa Mary Jane- Women's, Spa Mule for Women, Spa Quilt Scuff- Women's, Spa Slide Mens, Spa Slide- Women's, Spa Slip-On WM, Spa Thong- Women's, Spa wrap for women, Sporty Spa Moc- Women's, Sporty Spa Slide- Women's, Sporty Spa Thong, Wide Spa Slip-On;** *Studio:* **Cabana spa thong for women, Caftan Mule, Caftan Thong, Dahlia Mule- Women's, Dahlia Thong- Women's, Serendipity, Shimmer Ballet, Shimmer Thong, Sophie-women's, Tribal ballet for women, Wildflower Ballet WM, Wildflower Thong WM**

ALTERNATIVE STORES ☺
All products are vegan

AROMATHERAPY PRODUCTS LTD™☺
Accessories: **Foot socks**

BEYOND SKIN ☺
All

BOURGEOIS BOHEME ™☺
Men & women- various styles

EARTH FOOTWEAR ™
Men's Vegan Line: **Acadia-K, Aquatix-K, Cabo San Lucas-K, Glide-K, Kinetic-K, Lazer-K, Oak, Rebound-K, Retrain-K, Vapor-K;** *Women's Vegan Line:* **Acadia 2, Aquatix, Cabo San Lucas 2, Elite, Glide, Kinetic, Lazer - Microfiber, Lazer-twistech, Pride, Rebound, Retrain, Solar - Solestream, Solar-twistech, Vapor**

ETHICAL WARES ☺❶✔
Dance shoes: Ladies Dance Sandal, Ladies Practice Dance Shoe, Men's Dance Shoe, Oxford, Men's Dance Shoe, Patent; *Men's/Unisex boots:* (Positively) No Comment, Beatnick Boot, Buckle Book, Captain Swing, Chandler Boot, Chelsea Boot, Dealer Boot, Derby Boot, Liberator, Scandinavian, Sloane Boot, Tregaron Boot; *Men's/Unisex shoes:* 'Suede' Creeper, 'Suede' Gibson, Brogue Shoe, Creeper, Gibson, Hans Blix, Monk, Oxford, Respect, Tie Shoe;

NEUAURA
ANIMAL FRIENDLY FOOTWEAR

Safety: Out of Step Safety Shoes, Safety Boots; *Vegan clogs:* Buckle Sandal Clog, Original Clog, T-Bar Sandal Clog, Two Bar Sandal Clog, Webbed Sandal Clog; *Walkers:* Ranger Walking Boots, Tibet Walking Boots, Weald Walking Boots; *Women's boots:* 'new' Holly Boot, 'Viva' Cuba, All That Jazz, Berry Boot, Daise Roots, Dept X, Laced Ankle Boot, Misty Boot; *Women's shoes:* Madrid, Megan Too Shoe, Nice, Pump Bow, Venice

FREERANGERS ™☺🐾
Babs bar shoe; Connie shoe; Denim Kalahari sandals; Ladies Autumn Boot; Ladies Bramble boot; Mens ty loafer; Pippa bag; Rosie shoe; Sparkle sandal; Star shoe; Toe loop mule; *Ladies:* Alder Shoe, Ash Sandal, Beech Shoe, Birch Shoe, Brook Sandal, Clover Shoe, Criss Cross Sandal, Drifter Shoe, Fern Shoe, Fig Sandal, Gemini Sandal, Heather Clog, Jess Boot, Kate Shoes, Laurel Shoe, Lucy Shoe, Mary Jane Shoe, Meg Mule, Posy Sandal, Shamrock Shoe, Snowflake Mule; *Mens:* Ben Boot, Bracken Shoe, Crag Shoe, Dale Mule, Dene Mule, Drifter Shoe, Elm Sandal, Glen Boot, Heather Clog; *Mens :* Maple Shoe; *Mens:* Pine Shoe

GREEN SHOES ™⊘🐾
Boys Vegan Range: Badger Boot, Buzzard Boot, Kestrel Lace-Up, Kingfisher Sandal, Otter Shoe, Robin Boot, Swallow T-Bar; *Girls Vegan Range:* Buttercup T-bar, Celandine Lace-Up, Cornflower Boot, Dandelion Sandal, Honeysuckle Boot, Primrose Sandal, Snapdragon Boot; *Men's Vegan Range:* Ashburton Shoe, Belstone Boot, Branscombe Sandal, Chagford

House Shoe, Dartmoor Boot, Dartmoor Shoe, Exeter Shoe, Field Boot, Prawle Mule, Salcombe Sandal, Staverton Mule, Tavistock Boot; *Women's Vegan Range:* **Bracken Boot, Bryony Boot, Chamomile Boot, Chamomile Shoe, Champion T-Bar Sandal, Cowslip Sandal, Foxglove Pump, Geranium Shoe, Heather Shoe, Holly Boot, Hollyhock Pump, Iris Boot, Iris Calf Boot, Ivy Sandal, Larkspur Sandal, Laurel Shoe, Lily Boot, Lovage Sandal, Meadowsweet Sandal, Oxeye Sandal, Poppy Boot, Rowan Boot, Samphire T-Bar Sandal, Tansy Pump, Teasel Shoe, Violet Mule, Willow Boot, Willow Shoe**

NAE, LDA ™☺❶◐✔
Boots; Casual; Dress; Shoes

NATURAL SHOE STORE
Clog: Boston; *Sandal:* Arizona, Gizeh, Madrid, Milano, Ramses

NEUAURA ™☺❶◐✔
Boots; Flats; Pumps; Sandals; Wedges

ONITSUKA TIGER
All footwear that has an N as the second letter of the product code

RAGAZZI VEGAN ☺◐
Vegan shoes- all products are vegan

VEGAN CHIC ™☺
Shoes - All designs

VEGAN STORE ™☺❶◐✔
Mens Footwear: **Atlanta Shoe, Bean Shoe, Eagle Pass Boot, Fitter Flop, President Slipper, Savage Boot Black, Sonic Sneaker, Trekker Sandal, Washington Gibson, Yukon Boot, Yukon High Leg Boot, Yukon Zip Up Boot;** *Womens Boots:* **Berlin, Berlin Zip, Buckle, Lace, Milano Boot Black, Polar, Polar Ankle, Polar Star, Polar Stitch, Savage Boot Black, Slouch, Tula, Tula Ankle, Tula Faux Fur, Twister, Yukon, Zip Up;** *Womens Footwear:* **Baci Sandal, Ballerina Pump, Ballerina Strap Pump, Bella Loafer, Betty Shoe, Buckle Pump, Cetim Sandal, Charm Toe Post, Chunky Mule, Coite Loafer, Coite Mule, Comfort Sandal, Debra Sandal, Fitter Flop, Flower Toe Post, Hamptons Sandal, Honey Sandal, Jupiter Sandal, Kate Shoe, Love 100 Sandal, Miami Sandal, Nancy Sandal, Olivia Cross Strap Sandal, Olivia Sandal, Oxygen Sandal, Palma Pump, Paula Shoe Black, Romiclog, Sahana Sandal, Sally Pump, Santa Monica Sandal, Savana Toe Post, Skinny Trekker, Sonic Sneaker, Sophisto Sandal, Sorrento Sandal, Star Sandal, Strappy Mule, Susy Sandal, Sweetie Sandal, Tallulah Mule, Trip Sandal, Twist Sandal, Venice Sandal, Wheat Sandal, Zizi Mule, Zizi Shoe**

VEGANLINE ™☺❶
Sandals: Various women's sandals including Denim & Strappy Sandals; Canvas Fairtrade Camouflage Boots & shoes UK made; Canvas: Various, including Unswoosher Hemp & Fairtrade; Microfibre boots and shoes including Bouncing Boots;

Sandals: Various women's sandals including denim & strappy sandals; Women's including Sanitex waterproof breathable; Women's Synthetics: Various Winter boots including Sanitex waterproof breathable

VEGETARIAN SHOES ☺❶
Boots and Shoes: All - Over 150 Styles;

WELL CULTIVATED LTD ™⊘
Hemp Shoes

FOOTWEAR - SPORTS

ASICS
All footwear that has an N as the second letter of the product code

GREENVEE ☺
Dalesway Walking Boot

NEW BALANCE
All synthetic styles are suitable

VEGAN CHIC ™☺
Shoes - All designs

WATERPROOFERS, POLISHES & CLEANERS

SUPERDRUG
Cushion insoles

VEGETARIAN SHOES ☺❶
Shoe Care: Black Polish, Clear Dubbin

NOTES

■ **Footwear:** Shops selling entirely vegan footwear are rare; Vegetarian Shoes has a shop in Brighton and Bourgeois Boheme and the Secret Society of Vegans each have a shop in London. Cheap non-leather styles are stocked by many high-street shops, the use of synthetic adhesives is commonplace but it may difficult to obtain guarantees.

Be wary of "synthetic" or "artificial" leather; which *may* describe a leather product that has been treated differently to 'normal' leather e.g. 'Nubuck' is leather. Non-leather, animal free materials include Lorica, Pleather, Chlorenol, Hydrolite, Durabuck, Vegetan, PVC, Birkibuc and Cork Leather.

■ **Running and training shoes:** Many sports footwear companies stock models made entirely of non-animal materials but may be unable or unwilling to guarantee that the adhesives used are non-animal, though the trend is towards using synthetic based adhesives.

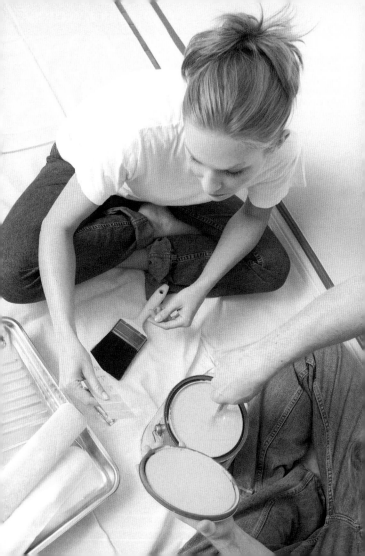

HOME & OFFICE

AIR FRESHENERS

AMAZENE TM☺❶◌◍✿
Natural Company- Thematic Home Spray: **Acordes Citricos, Brisa que vem do Mar, Ervas Finas, Frutas Vermelhas, Meta Selvagem, Terra Molhada de Chuva;** *Natural Company-Thematic Home Spray:* **Jardim Oriental**

AROMATHERAPY PRODUCTS LTD TM☺
At home: **Bitter orange and Jasmine fresh linen mist;** *Lavender Products:* **Lavender bed linen mist;** *Pre-mix 100% pure essential oil blends exclusively for vaporisation:* **Energy, Menthol clear, Sleep tight;** *Vaporising units:* **Aroma-stream, Aroma-stream replacement cartridge, Car clear kit, Personal vaporiser**

BRACKENCRAFT TM☺❶◌◍
Cedarwood, Pine & Rosemary Room Spray; CITRUS Room Spray with Orange and Lemon Essential Oils; FESTIVAL Room Spray with Clove, Frankincense and Mandarin Essential Oils; Floral Room Spray with Geranium & Lavender Essential Oils; Geranium & Orange Room Spray; Lavender Room Spray with Lavender Essential Oil; Lemongrass Room Spray; Spice Room Spray with Cinnamon, Patchouli, Orange and Lemon Essential Oils

EARTH FRIENDLY PRODUCTS UK TM☺◍👁
Earth Friendly Products: **Uni-Fresh (Cinnamon), Uni-Fresh (Citrus), Uni-Fresh (Lavender), Uni-Fresh (Parsley), Uni-Fresh (Vanilla)**

ESSENTIALLY NATURAL TM
Lavender Pillows; Sliding Door Oil Burner

HOLISTIX HERBAL PRODUCTS ❶
Festive: Festive Spray

NATURAL BY NATURE OILS ☺
Vaporizing Oils: Aromatic Woods, Breathe Ease, Bug-a-Way, Calming Moods, Christmas Spice, Citrus Fresh, Exotic Moods, Fresh Fields, Hay-a-Way, Meditation, Mountain Breeze, Oriental Spice, Quiet Night, Refreshing, Revitalizing, Romantic Evening, Summer Bouquet

NATURAL SENSE
Room Fragrance

NOTHING NASTY ◍
Room Spray: Relaxing, Sensual, Uplifting

POTIONS AND POSSIBILITIES ◌◍
Room Spray: Atmosphere Spray For Computer Room, English Garden, English Lavender, English Rose

QUINESSENCE AROMATHERAPY ☺◌◍👁
Mood Enhancers: Arabian Nights, Autumn Meadows, Celestial Dream, Elemental Forest, Fantasia, Forbidden Fruit, Illuminessence, Moonflower, Secret Garden, Tranquilla, Wild Passion

BLEACHES

ASTONISH
Bathroom Range: Cream Cleaner

SONETT OHG ™
Bleaching Complex

BRUSHES

ASTONISH
Multi-Surface Cleaner

CANDLES AND INCENSE

ABSOLUTELY PURE
Travel Candle

ANIMAL AID ™☺❶⊘ ⚡ ⚓-1976
Eco Soya Candles

**AROMATHERAPY
PRODUCTS LTD** ™☺
Candles: **Citrus, Exotic Spice, In
Perpetuum, In Toto**

BRACKENCRAFT ™☺❶⊘ ⚡
**Hand made ECO-SOYA CITRONELLA
CANDLE with Essential Oil; Hand
made ECO-SOYA CITRUS CANDLE
with Essential Oils; Hand made
ECO-SOYA FESTIVAL CANDLE with**
**Essential Oils; Hand made ECO-
SOYA FLORAL CANDLE with
Essential Oils; Hand made ECO-
SOYA LAVENDER CANDLE with
Essential Oil; Hand made ECO-SOYA
LEMONGRASS CANDLE with
Essential Oils; Hand made ECO-
SOYA PATCHOULI & ORANGE
CANDLE with Essential Oil; Hand
made ECO-SOYA SPICE CANDLE
with Essential Oils**

**CALDER VALLEY
SOAP CO. LTD** ™☺⊘ ⚡ 👁
Candles: **Soy wax Candles, Coconut
Scented**

ESSENTIALLY NATURAL ™
Sisal Insense Sticks; *Eco Soy Wax
candles:* **Frankincense Essential Oil,
Geranium & Ylang Ylang, Lavender,
Lavender & Bergamot, Lavender &
Chamomille, Lavender & Citronella,
Lavender & Eucalyptus, Lavender &
Geranium, Lavender & Ylang Ylang,
Lover's Lavender, Orange &
Lemongrass, Patchouli & Geranium,
Peppermint & Cinnamon, Stay
Awake !**

**HOWAD LTD
T/A INCOGNITO** ™❶⊘ ⚡
Incognito: **Incense Sticks**

LIZ EARLE ⚡
Vital Oils Candles

NO COWS ☺
Soya Wax Candles: Tea Lights (set of 6),
Votive Candles

319

POTIONS AND POSSIBILITIES ⊘ ✔
Scented Candles: English Garden, English Lavender, English Rose

SHEARER CANDLES ⊘ ✔
Candles: All except church candles marked as containing 10% beeswax.

SIMPLY SOAPS
India; Love; Mesopotamia; Om

SKINCARE CAFE LTD ☺
Lemongrass candle; Ylang ylang candle

TREE-HARVEST ⊘ ✔
Incense: All; *Pure Plant Wax Candles:* Pillar Candles, Scented Dinner Candles, Scented Glass Pot Candles, Taper Candles, Tea Lights, Unscented Dinner Candles, with Essential Oils

CARPET PRODUCTS

ASTONISH
Floor & Carpet Range: Carpet Shampoo for Electric Machines, Shampoo for Carpets & Upholstery

CLEANERS - GENERAL

ASTONISH
Orange Multi-Purpose Cleaning Paste; Window Cleaner; *Bathroom Range:* Bathroom Cleaner, Glass & Tile Cleaner, Shower Self Clean, Toilet Bowl Cleaner; *Germ Killers:* 4 in 1 Germ Killer Disinfectant, Mould & Mildew Remover; *Glass, Ceramic, Tile & Household Range:* Household Antibacterial Paste Cleaner, Orange Household Paste Cleaner, Window Cleaner; *Kitchen & Cookware:* Grease Buster; *Kitchen & Cookware:* Grease Off; *Kitchen & Cookware:* Grime Blast, Kitchen Cleaner, Marble & Granite Clean & Polish, Oven Cleaner; *Kitchen & Cookware:* Oxy-Plus Multi-Purpose Surface Cleaner; *Kitchen & Cookware :* Stainless Steel Cleaner; *Special Cleaners:* Orange Power Multi-Surface, Silver Cleaner

AUBREY ORGANICS
Earth Aware: All-purpose Household Cleanser, Liquid Sparkle Natrural Spray Cleaner

AURO
Plant Soap Concentrate

BIO-D ™☺⊘ ✔ ☜✂1988
Glass & Mirror Cleaner; Multi-Surface Cleaner; Ready- to- use Multi Purpose Cleaner; Ready-to-use Bathroom Cleaner

CELLANDE MIDLANDS ⊘ ✔
Glass & Plastic Cleaner for Computers Spectacles etc

DRI-PAK LTD ☺
Liquid Soda Crystal Spray; *Clean and Natural Cleaning Products:* Bicarbonate of Soda, Citric Acid, Household Borax, Limescale Remover Spray, White Vinegar

**EARTH FRIENDLY
PRODUCTS UK** TM☺◢👁
Earth Friendly Products: **Creamy
Cleanser, Earth Enzymes, Everyday
Stain & Odor Remover, Floor
Kleener, Fruit & Vegetable Wash,
Furniture Polish, Orange Mate
Concentrate, Orange Mate RTU,
Parsley Plus RTU, Shower Kleener,
Toilet Bowl Cleaner, Window
Kleener, Window Kleener (Lavender)**

FOOD SAFE
Veggie-Wash Concentrate; Veggie-Wipes

FOREVER LIVING PRODUCTS
Aloe MPD Detergent

**HERBS HANDS
HEALING LTD** TM◌◢
Home & Kitchen Cleaner

JUNGLESALE LIMITED TM
**Neem Bathroom Cleaner; Neem
Household Cleaner**

OSMO UK ◌◢
Gard Clean Green Growth Remover;
Liquid Wax Cleaner

SODASAN TM◢
**All Purpose Cleaner; Bath and
Shower Cleaner; Glass Cleaner; Lime
Remover; Orange Universal Cleaner;
Scouring Cream; Scouring Powder;
Toilet Bowl Cleaner; Vinegar
Cleaner;** *Detergent:* **Cool Detergent,
Heavy Duty Detergent;** *Stain
Remover:* **liquid Spot Remover Soap,
Spot Remover Soap, Stain Remover**

SOLARAY NUTRITIONAL SUPPLEMENTS
Earthaware All-Purpose Household
Cleanser; Liquid Sparkle Spray Cleaner

SONETT OHG TM
**All Purpose Cleanser; Bathroom
Cleaner; Grease Dissolver; Orange
Power Cleaner; Scouring Liquid;
Scouring Powder; Window Cleaner**

SUMA WHOLEFOODS
TM❶◌◢👁⚒1985
Suma - Ecoleaf range: **All purpose
anti bacterial cleaner**

CLEANERS - INDUSTRIAL

**GREEN PLANET
SOLUTIONS LTD** TM◌
Cleaner: **Glass and Stainless Steel
Cleaner, Masonry and Stone
Cleaner, Multi-Purpose Cleaner,
Washroom Cleaner;** *Degreaser
cleaner:* **Heavy Duty Degreaser**

DISHWASHER PRODUCTS

AQUADOS LTD TM☺
Dishwasher Powder: **Aquados
Dishwash Phosphate free, Aquados
Pro Dishwash, Simply Dishwash
Active, Simply Dishwash Active
Phosphate free, Simply Dishwash
Citrus, Simply Dishwash Citrus
phosphate free**

ASTONISH
Dishwashing Range: 5 in 1 Dishwasher
Tablets, Limescale Remover, Oxy-Plus
Tea & Coffee Stain Remover

BIO-D ™☺⊘✔👁⅄1988
Dishwasher Rinse Aid

**FAITH PRODUCTS
LIMITED** ™⊘✔👁⅄1988
**Dishwasher Gel 1 Ltr / 5 Ltr; Rinse
Aid 500ml / 5 Ltr**

GREEN PLANET SOLUTIONS LTD ™⊘
Cleaner: **Dishwasher Liquid
Concentrate, Dishwasher Rinse Aid**

SODASAN ™✔
**Auto Dish Tabs; Automatic
Dishwashing Powder**

SONETT OHG ™
**Dishwasher Detergent; Tablets For
Dishwashers**

DISINFECTANTS

ASTONISH
Germ Killers: Anti-Bacterial Cleanser,
Germ Clear Disinfectant

BIO-D ™☺⊘✔👁⅄1988
Eucalyptus Disinfectant

GAMA HEALTHCARE LIMITED ☺
Clinell: Disinfectant Spray, Instant Hand
Sanitiser, Universal Sanitising Wipes

**GREEN PLANET
SOLUTIONS LTD** ™⊘
Sanitiser: **Antibacterial Sanitiser,
Handwash**

SONETT OHG ™
Surface Disinfectant

FABRIC CONDITIONERS

AQUADOS LTD ™☺
Fabric Softeners: **Aquados Softpro +,
Aquados Softpro 0, Aquados
Softpro+, Simply Softer perfume
free, Simply Softer with perfume**

BIO-D ™☺⊘✔👁⅄1988
Fabric Conditioner

SONETT OHG ™
Fabric Softener

SUMA WHOLEFOODS
™❶⊘✔👁⅄1985
Suma - Ecoleaf range: **Fabric
Conditionner Liquid**

FLOOR PRODUCTS

ASTONISH
Floor & Carpet Range: No Rinse Floor
Cleaner, No Rinse Wood Floor Cleaner

AURO
Floorcare

**GREEN PLANET
SOLUTIONS LTD** ™⊘
Maintainer: **Floor Maintainer**

OSMO UK ⊘🐾
Wash & Care Floor Cleaner

FURNITURE
& OTHER POLISHES

ASTONISH
Special Cleaners: Brass & Copper
Cleaner

BIO-D ™☺⊘🐾👁✂1988
General Purpose Polish

GENERAL

AROMATHERAPY PRODUCTS LTD™☺
**Aroma Bowl and Warming Dish;
Aroma Stream; Aroma Stream
Replacement Cartridge; Personal
Vaporiser;** *Lavender Products:*
**Lavender Head Cooling Cushion,
Organic Lavender Wheat Cushion**

HOME FURNISHINGS

AROMATHERAPY PRODUCTS LTD™☺
Lavender Products: **Lavender Head
Cooling Cushion, Lavender Wheat
Cushion**

ESSENTIALLY NATURAL ™
**Lavender Neck Rescue; Luxury
Comfort Cushion; Luxury Comfort
Tube; Luxury Lavender Keyboard
Rest; Wooden Soap Dish**

NATURAL INSULATION
Roof Insulation: Isonat, Isovlas, Non-
Itch, Warmcel

NO COWS ☺
Organic Cotton Bath Sheet; Organic
Cotton Bath Towel; Organic Cotton
Bathrobe; Organic Cotton Flannel;
Organic Cotton Hand Towel; Organic
Cotton Towel Bale

INSECT REPELLENTS

**HOWAD LTD
T/A INCOGNITO** ™❶⊘🐾
Incognito: **Anti-Mosquito Camouflage**

PAINT BRUSHES - DIY

OSMO UK ⊘◇◢
Quality Brushes & Polishing Pad

PAINT, VARNISHES, WOODSTAINS,ETC

AURO
Thinner and Brush Cleaner; : Wallpaper Adhesive; *Airfresh Paint:* White; *Chalk Paint:* White; *Coloured Natural Resin Wall Paint:* Matt - See Colour Chart; *Fillers:* Multi Filler, Wood Filler; *Gloss:* Coloured - See Colour Chart; *Lacquer:* Clear Gloss, Clear Matt; *Matt Silk:* Coloured - See Colour Chart; *Natural Resin Oil Professional Wall Paint:* Semi Matt - See Colour Chart, Semi Matt - White; *Natural Resin Wall Paint:* Matt - White; *Primers:* Wood Primer; *Primers:* Hard Primer, Natural Metal Primer, Priming Oil, Special Primer; *Radiator Paint:* White - Matt Finish; *Topcoats:* White Topcoat - Gloss, White Topcoat - Matt Silk, Woodstain Topcoat; *Undercoats:* White Undercoat

B&Q
Colours Range - Emulsions for Walls: All; *Colours Range - Trim Paints for Wood and Metal:* All Gloss and Satin

EARTHBORN NATURAL PAINTS
Silicate Primer; Wall Glaze; Wallpaper Paste; *Claypaint:* All; *Eco Chic:* All; *Emulsion:* All; *Pigments:* All; *proAqua Eggshell:* All; *proAqua Satin Varnish:* All

ECOS PAINTS ☺☺⊘◢
Ecos Garden Spectrum Shed & Fence Treatment: All; *Exterior Woodstains:* All; *Interior Woodstain Varnishes:* All; *Odourless Solvent-Free Organic Paints:* All

NUTSHELL NATURAL PAINTS
Wallpaper Paste; *Emulsion:* Super 2.5 litres, Super 5 litres

OSMO UK ⊘◇◢
Brush Cleaner & Thinner; Door Oil; Paint-Remover; Top Oil; Wood Filler; Wood Protector; Wood Reviver; *Exterior Country Colour:* All; *Exterior One Coat Only:* All; *Exterior Wood:* Clear Oil Wood Finish, Fence & Garden Stain, Wood Oils, Wood Stain & Preservation, WR Base Coat; *Interior Hardwax Oil:* For Floors, Special Floor Finish, White Foundation; *Interior Wood Wax Finish:* Clear Extra Thin, Opaque, Transparent; *Opaque Gloss Exterior Wood Stain:* All

PHOTOGRAPHIC PAPERS

EPSON
Digital Photo Papers: All

HP
Digital Photograph Paper: Everyday Photo Paper Semi Gloss, Tri-fold Brochure Paper Matte

TOILET PRODUCTS

BIO-D ™☺⊘ ✔ ☞♒ 1988
Toilet Cleaner

GREEN PLANET SOLUTIONS LTD ™⊘
Cleaner: **Daily Toilet Cleaner**

HERBS HANDS HEALING LTD ™⊘ ✔
Bathroom Deep Cleaner

SONETT OHG ™
Toilet Cleaner

SUMA WHOLEFOODS
™❶⊘ ✔ ☞♒ 1985
Suma - Ecoleaf range: **Toilet Cleaner**

TYRES

MICHELIN ☺
All Tyres

WASHING POWDERS, STARCH ETC

AKAMUTI
Soapnuts

AQUADOS LTD ™☺
Washing Powder: **Aquados Pro Bio, Aquados Pro Bio Phosphate free, Aquados Pro Non Bio, Aquados Pro Non Bio Phosphate free, Simply Active - Biological, Simply Active Biological Phosphate free, Simply Pure, Simply Pure Phosphate free, Simply Sensitive - Non Biological, Simply Sensitive Biological Phosphate free**

ASTONISH
Fabric & Laundry Range: 4 in 1 Non Bio Laundry Liquid, Fabric Freshener & Deodoriser, Oxy-Plus Stain Remover, Stain Remover, Stain Remover Bar, Starch, Whites Booster

BIO-D ™☺⊘ ✔ ☞♒ 1988
Dishwasher Powder; Laundry Liquid; Washing Powder

CYBERDYNE TECHNOLOGIES LTD, T/A MAMA SHAMBA ™☺
Soap nuts: **Naked pods**

DRI-PAK LTD ☺
Soda Crystals; *Aqua Softna:* Washing Machine Descaler; *Clean and Natural Cleaning Products:* Pure Liquid Soap (for laundry)

EARTH FRIENDLY PRODUCTS UK ™☺ ✔ ☞
Earth Friendly Products: **Baby Laundry Soap, Delicate Wash, ECOS Free & Clear, Ecos Laundry Powder, ECOS Lavender, ECOS Lemongrass, ECOS Magnolia & Lilies, Oxo Brite, Spray Starch, Zainz Laundry Pre-Wash**

FAITH PRODUCTS LIMITED
™⊘ ✔ ☞♒ 1988
Laundry Liquid 1 Ltr / 5 Ltr

IN A SOAPNUT SHELL ☺
Soapnut Pieces; Soapnut Shells

KITCHEN GARDEN
Detergent Free Laundry Disks

SODASAN ™ ✔
Bleaching Additive; Clear Rinse;
Compact Laundry Detergent;
Regenerating Salt; Soap Flakes; Soft
Soap; Water Softener; *Detergent:*
Comfort-Sensitiv Laundry Detergent,
Liquid Laundry Detergent, Wool
Detergent

SONETT OHG ™
Cleanser for Autoscrubbing Washing
Machines; Industrial Washing
Booster; Industrial Washing Powder;
Laundry Rinse/Decalcifier; Olive
Washing Liquid; Starch Spray and
Ironing Aid; Washing Liquid; Washing
Liquid - Colour; Washing Powder

SUMA WHOLEFOODS
™❶🚫✔👁⚒1985
Suma - Ecoleaf range: **Laundry Liquid**

WASHING-UP PRODUCTS

ASTONISH
Washing Up Liquid; *Kitchen &
Cookware :* Multi Spray with Bleach
Power; *Kitchen & Cookware:* Oven &
Cookware Cleaner

BIO-D ™☺🚫✔👁⚒1988
Washing Up Liquid

**EARTH FRIENDLY
PRODUCTS UK** ™☺✔👁
Earth Friendly Products: **Dishmate
Almond, Dishmate Apricot,
Dishmate Grapefruit, Dishmate
Lavender, Dishmate Pear, Dishmate
Washing Up Liquid Free & Clear,
Wave, Wave Powder - Sachets,
Wavejet**

FAITH PRODUCTS LIMITED
™🚫✔👁⚒1988
Washing Up Liquid 1 Ltr / 5 Ltr

GREEN PLANET SOLUTIONS LTD ™🚫
Cleaner: **Washing Up Liquid**

SODASAN ™ ✔
Washing Up Liquid

SONETT OHG ™
Washing Up Liquid

SUMA WHOLEFOODS
™❶🚫✔👁⚒1985
Suma - Ecoleaf range: **Washing Up
Liquid**

NOTES

- **Adhesives** may be processed from hide, bones, fish or dairy products such as casein. Non-animal adhesives are based on starch, cellulose, natural rubbers, or inorganic substances based on silicone. The trend is towards using cheaper, synthetic materials.

- **Banknotes** are produced from cotton fibre and linen rag, without the use of gelatine.

- **Beds and mattresses** generally contain synthetic materials, such as acrylic, viscose, polyester, polypropylene, nylon or acetate. However, wool or other types of animal hair may be used in some mattresses.

- **Pillows and duvets** are increasingly being made from cotton and polyester but some may be stuffed with feathers, often termed 'down'. Covers may be silk.

- **Ceramics, glass, pottery:** Bone china goods contain around 50% bone ash. Porcelain, *plain* sanitary items (toilets, cisterns, sinks, etc) and *plain* earthenware glazed mugs (the glazes used are inorganic pigments made from minerals) appear to be animal-free. However, if a motif is added, it may be fixed with animal-derived glues. Glass consists of silica (in the form of sand), sodium oxide, calcium oxide, magnesium oxide and aluminium oxide, and appears to be animal-free.

- **Envelope adhesives** are usually animal-free.

- **Fabric dyes** for home use are usually synthetic but have often been tested on animals at some stage. 'Natural' dyes may contain animal substances, such as cochineal / carmine.

- **Floor coverings** made from PVC may be manufactured using possibly animal-derived stearates as stabilisers and stearic acid as a lubricant during certain production processes.

- **Furniture** may contain synthetic or plant-based fibres (e.g. nylon, acrylic, polyester, cotton, hemp) or animal-derived materials, including leather, suede, wool, animal hair (especially horse) or feathers.

- **Incense sticks** may contain gelatine or other animal substance as a binder.

- **Match heads** may contain gelatine, which is used as a binder.

- **Paint** may contain casein or shellac and the ingredients may have been animal-tested.

- **Paper** is usually sized (enhances the resistance of paper to liquid penetration and provides surface strength, stiffness and a glaze to the finished sheet) with starch derived from maize, wheat, potatoes or rice, but gelatine is still used for some high-grade paper products. Casein is sometimes used as a binder in high quality food board and art papers. Some very specialist grades may contain chitin / chitosan.

- **Postage stamps:** the gum on British stamps is animal-free, consisting of polyvinyl alcohol (petroleum based) and dextrin (from starch).

- **Rubber:** Natural rubber is made from latex (sap obtained from rubber trees) combined with other materials, including the following which could be animal-derived: carbon black (E153), glycerol (E422), salts of fatty acids (E470), stearic acid (E570), calcium stearate (E572). Synthetic rubbers are made from oil and a combination of chemicals.

- **Rubber gloves** may involve the use of milk casein as a processing aid in the latex.

- **Water filters** contain charcoal, usually vegetable-based

ANIMAL CARE

FOOD & FOOD SUPPLEMENTS

HIGHER NATURE LTD
Almost Human® SuperDog MSM;
Almost Human® SuperDog Ultimate
Nutrition; Almost Human® SuperPet
Organic 3:6:9 Oil; Animal Aloe;
OmegaPet Kibble for Dogs

MH FOODS ™🚫🐾
Bon Appetit: **Beef flavour food
enhancer spray, Chicken flavour
food enhancer spray, Fish flavour
food enhancer spray**

**RICHARD HENRY
CONSULTING LTD** ™☺🐾
Pulpa Acai

SEAGREENS LTD ™☺🚫
Seagreens: **Equine Granules, Pet
Granules**

SIMPLE SYSTEM LTD ™☺🚫
**Blue Bag Grass Pellets; Eclipse
Recovery; Endurocomplete; Green
Gold; Instant Linseed; Just Grass;
Justamint; LucieBrix; Luciecobs;
Lucienuts; Luciestalks; Lunar Eclipse;
Metaslim; Organic Cider vinegar;
Purabeet; PuraMint Pellets; Pure
Garlic Flakes; Pure Garlic Powder;
Pure Ocean Seaweed; Pure organic
Salt Bucket; Red Bag Grass Pellets;
RuffStuff; Sundried Lucerne Bales;
Timothy Cobs; Top Nosh; Total
Eclipse; Traditional Brewers Yeast**

SOURCE-OMEGA LLC
Pure One: Algae Oil - Capsule, Algae
Oil - Liquid

VEGEPET
Vegecat; Vegecat Kibble Mix; Vegecat
pH; Vegedog; Vegekit pH

**YARRAH ORGANIC
PETFOOD BV** ™🚫✩
**Multi Dog Biscuits; Organic
Vegetarian Dog Food; Vegetarian
Chunks With Vegetables;
Vegetarian Dog Biscuits; Vegetarian
Duo Snacks**

HEALTH & CARE PRODUCTS

AUBREY ORGANICS
Organimals: Grooming Spray for Dogs,
Shampoo for Dogs

**BABY'S BUM PREMIUM NATURAL
SOAPS** ☺🚫🐾👁☘1980
Dog Shampoos - Liquid: Minty Muttley

BERWITZ HOMEOPATHY ☺
Tea Tree Coat Conditioner for Dogs &
Cats; *Assisi Homeopathic Remedies :*
Euphrasia Eye Drops, Five Flower Remedy,
Sore Paws Ointment, Verbascum Ear
Drops; *Natural Drops:* Ear, Eye; *Natural
Grooming Lotions:* Cats, Dogs, Small
Animals; *Shampoos:* Aromatic for Dogs,
Tea Tree for Dogs & Cats

**EARTH FRIENDLY
PRODUCTS UK** ™☺✦👁
Earth Friendly Products: **Natumate**

FOREVER LIVING PRODUCTS
Veterinary Aloe Spray

JR LIGGETT ☺
Shampoo: My Dog Fergie's Shampoo

JUNGLESALE LIMITED ™
**Animal insect spray with neem;
Neem Horse Shampoo; Neem Pet
Shampoo; Pet Insect Spray; Stable
Cleaner**

JUST SOAPS ™
Dog Shampoo Bar

MASON'S PRODUCTS
☺☺✦✂1976
Dog Oil for Massaging (For Dogs Horses
& Humans)

ORGANIX SOUTH INC
Thera Neem: Pet Shampoo

VERDESATIVA S.R.L. ™☺❶⊘✦☼👁
Balsamo for Canines: **Balsamo Per
Cani Prof A;** *Shampoo for Canines:*
**Shampoo Cani Pelo Lungo,
Shampoo Cani Pelo Medio,
Shampoo Per Cani Pelo Corto**

NOTES

■ The inclusion of an 'Animal Care' section should not be construed as indicating support for the pet industry or ownership of pet (companion) animals. Pets exist solely for human gain — in the case of the pet trade: financial; in the case of pet owners: pleasure — and their freedom is necessarily restricted. In the quest for the 'perfect' pet, breeds of animals including dogs, cats, birds and fish have, through genetic manipulation, been created with 'aesthetically-pleasing' deformities. Many animal-free shoppers find the breeding of animals for 'pets' incompatible with their animal rights philosophy and those who find themselves caring for animals often do so because tens of thousands of domestic animals are unwanted and would otherwise be destroyed.

■ For our information on feeding cats or dogs a vegan diet, see www.vegansociety.com/lifestyle/comp anion-animals or contact the Vegan Society office for a paper copy of the information.

GARDEN & LEISURE

ARTS & CRAFTS

DALER-ROWNEY LTD ⊘ ✔
Artist Oil Colours: All except Ivory Black & Blue Black; *Artists' Brushes:* Cryla, Dalon, Series 260 270 & 280; *Cryla :* All except Ivory Black; *Designer's Gouache:* All except Neutral Grey 2, Paynes Grey, Lamp Black, Cool Grey 1,2,3 & Warm Grey 1,2,3; *F.W. Artist Inks:* All; *Georgian Oil Colours:* All except Ivory Black, Prussian Green & Coeruleum Hue; *Painting Surfaces & Equipment:* All except Saunders Waterford, Langton & Bockingford Papers, Canvas Panels & Rabbit Skin Size; *Pearlescent Liquid Acrylic Inks:* All; *Rowney Block Printing Colours (Water Based & Oil Based):* All; *System 3 Colours:* All except Raw Sienna

ETHICAL WARES ☺❶✔
Accessories: Guitar Strap Black, Guitar Strap Rainbow

FREERANGERS ™☺✔
Guitar Strap

INNOCENT OILS ™☺⊘✔
Gluten & Wheat Free Play Dough: **O'Dough**

WINSOR & NEWTON ⊘✔
Artisan Water Mixable Oil Colour: All except Ivory Black; *Artists' Acrylic Colour:* All except Ivory Black, Payne's Grey; *Artists' Oil Colour :* All except Blue Black, Carmine, Ivory Black; *Artists' Soft Pastels:* All; *Artists' Oilbar:* All except Ivory Black, Payne's Gray; *Artists' Pigment (Dry Ground):* All except Ivory Black, Carmine; *Brushes:* Artisan Water Mixable Oil Colour Brushes, Cotman, Galeria, Monarch, Special Value Brushes: Synthetic, University; *Calligraphy Inks:* All; *Cotman Water Colour:* All except Viridian Hue, Raw Umber, Ivory Black; *Designers Gouache:* All except Ivory Black, Raw Sienna, Winsor Green, Spectrum Yellow, Intense Blue, Sky Blue, Purple Lake, Prussian Blue, Linden Green, Grenadine, Flame Red, Burnt Umber, Bengal Rose, Primary Blue, Lamp Black, Spectrum Violet; *Galeria Flow Formula Acrylic Colour:* All except Ivory Black, Payne's Grey; *Griffin Alkyd Fast Drying Oil Colour:* All except Ivory Black; *Poster Paint:* All; *Water Colour Mediums:* All except Ox Gall, Lifting Preparation; *Water Colour Papers:* Bockingford; *Winton Oil Colour:* All except Ivory Black, Raw Umber

CLEANERS - OUTDOOR

ASTONISH
Car Care Range: All Weather Screen Wash, Anti Fog Glass Clear, Anti-Fog Glass Cleaner, Black Shine Restorer, Carpet & Upholstery Cleaner, Crystal Clear Wash & Wax, De-Icer, Engine Degreaser, Spray & Shine, Tar & Insect Remover, Vinyl Trim & Dashboard Cleaner, Wheel Cleaner

GARDENING & COMPOST PRODUCTS

FERTILE FIBRE ™
Vegrow Organic: **Multipurpose Compost, Potting Compost, Seed Compost, Special Mix range**

SEAGREENS LTD ™☺◎
Seagreens: **Agricultural Granules, Ascophyllum Granules, Garden Granules, Hebridean Horticultural Granules**

TAMAR ORGANICS ◎
Seaweed Extract Liquid Feed; *Fertiliser:* Cumulus 5-5-5, Cumulus K, Cumulus NK, Rock Phosphate, Seaweed Meal

THE ORGANIC GARDENING CATALOGUE
Fertilisers: Alfalfa Plus, Chase Organics Animal Free, Comfrey Pellets, Rock Phosphate

WILLIAM SINCLAIR HORTICULTURE
Autumn Lawn Food & Mosskiller; Complete John Innes Range; Growmore; J Arthur Bower's Ericaceous; Lawn Dressing; Lawn Feed Weed & Mosskiller; Lawn Food; New Horizon Coir Compost; Traditional Potting Compost

GLUES, STICKY TAPE, ETC

VEGAN STORE ™☺❶◎ ⌀
Weldbond: **Multi Purpose Glue**

SMOKING PRODUCTS

RIZLA ☺
Filter Tips; *Papers:* King Size Blue, King Size Red, King Size Slim Blue, King Size Slim Silver, Regular Blue, Regular Green, Regular Red, Regular Silver

NOTES

- **instruments:** All modern guitar strings are made from metal or nylon. Guitar picks are now made of plastic. The heads of most modern percussion instruments are non-animal 'skin'. World or traditional percussion instruments may be made with animal skins.

- **Photographic film and papers** used in traditional photography contain gelatine. However for digital cameras there are several types of paper available for printing digital photographs that are animal-free.

- **Tattoo Inks** may contain animal derived ingredients. The Vegan Society has some information on tattoo inks that are free of animal products. Contact the Vegan Society office for more details

- **Tennis balls** may contain wool.

- **Vegan-organic or stockfree gardening** is becoming more and more popular; see USEFUL ADDRESSES page 46 for details of the Vegan-Organic Network.

**VEG 1
(£4.99 for
three
months'
adult
supply)**

Specifically
designed to
benefit vegans
of all ages in a safe
and effective way.

Taken daily, VEG 1 ensures adequate supplies of
selenium, iodine, vitamin D, folic acid, vitamins B2, B6
and, of course, B12.

Based on extensive research by Vegan Society health
and nutrition spokesperson Stephen Walsh, author of
Plant Based Nutrition and Health, the supplement is
ideal for vegans of all ages. Available only from The
Vegan Society

SUPERMARKETS

FOOD

BISCUITS

Reduced Fat Rich Tea Biscuits; Rich Tea Biscuits; Rich Tea Finger Biscuits

BREADS, ROLLS, PIZZA BASES ETC

3 Ready To Bake Half Baguettes; 4 Apple & Cinnamon Hot Cross Buns; 4 Ciabatta Rolls; 4 Classic Hot Cross Buns; 4 Crusty White Morning Rolls; 4 Crusty White Submarine Rolls; 4 Fruit Buns; 4 Green Olive Rolls; 4 Large White Baps; 4 Malted Grain Rolls; 4 Super Seeded Rolls; 4 White Rolls; 5 Caramelised Onion & Poppy Seed Bagels; 5 Cinnamon & Raisin Bagels; 5 Plain Bagels; 5 Sesame Seed Bagels; 6 Soft White Finger Rolls; 6 Soft White Rolls; 6 Soft Wholemeal Finger Rolls; 6 Soft Wholemeal Rolls; 6 Teacakes; 8 Mini 3% Fat Hot Cross Buns; Bake At Home 6 White Petit Pains; Bake At Home White Half Baguettes; Baker's White Farmhouse; Brown Soda Bread; Ciabatta; Citrus Fruit Slices; Count On Us Malted Grain Thick Sliced; Count On Us Wholemeal Thick Sliced; Crusted Malted Grain; Crusty White; Golden Wholemeal Farmhouse; Highbran; Irish Wheaten Bread; Medium Sliced Wholemeal; Mini Rosemary Flatbread; Mini Tomato And Basil Focaccia; Mixed Seed & Grain Roll Selection; Multi-seed Bloomer Slices; Organic Multiseed Loaf; Organic Wholemeal Loaf; Peperonata Ciabatta; Plain White Loaf (Scottish Batch); Poppyseed Swirl Rolls; Sandwich White Medium Slice Loaf; Seeded Batch Loaf Unsliced; Soft Farmhouse White; Soft Malted Grain Loaf; Soft Multigrain Loaf; Soft Oatmeal Farmhouse; Soft White Bloomer Slices; Soft White Farmhouse; Speciality Italian Hand-crafted Flatbreads; Stonebaked Sourdough; Super Seeded Loaf; Super Soft Brown; Super Soft Brown With Grains; Super Soft White; Super Soft White Medium; Super Soft White Thick; Thick Sliced Wholemeal; Two In One Loaf; Whiskey Fruit Loaf; White Batch Bread; White Bread Mix; Wholegrain Bread Mix; Wholemeal Bloomer; *Eat Well:* 12 Mini Wholemeal Pittas, 5 Multi-seed Bagels, 6 Wholemeal Pittas, 8 Two In One Pitta Bread Pockets, Brown Loaf, Golden Wholemeal Rolls, Organic Stoneground Cob; *In-store bakery:* Baked 5 Seed Golden Wholemeal Crusty Cob, Baked Green & Black Olive Pave Roll, Baked Green Olive Ciabatta Roll, Baked Green Olive Pave, Baked Hot Cross Bun, Baked Muesli Loaf, Baked Organic Baguette, Baked Organic Half Baguette, Baked Organic Malted Wheat Loaf, Baked Organic Wholemeal Spelt Loaf, Baked Pretzel, Baked Rosemary Focaccia, Baked Rustique Flute, Baked Rustique Loaf, Baked Sesame Seed Pretzel, Baked Tartine Slices, Baked White Crusty Loaf, Baked White Levain Boule, Baked White Pave Loaf, Baked Whole French Sourdough, Bakers Choice Roll, Brown Farmhouse, Granary Farmhouse, Iced Doughnuts, Plain Bagel, White Farmhouse Loaf, Wholemeal Farmhouse

BREAKFAST FOODS

Count On Us Fruit And Nut Muesli; Organic Crunchy Sultana Granola; Organic Exotic Fruit And Nut

Wholegrain Muesli; Organic Luxury Fruit And Nut Wholegrain Muesli

'BURGERS', 'SAUSAGES', 'MEAT' SLICES ETC
Eat Well: Roasted Vegetable Burgers

CONFECTIONERY & SWEET SNACKS
125 Year Jar Of Rhubarb And Custard; 20 Halloween Lollipops; 5 Pack Blueberry And Cranberry Oat bar; Eat Well Organic Date, Raisin, Oat & Cinnamon Bars; Eat Well Organic Hazelnut, Brazil, Peanut & Almond Cereal Bars; Fruit Sherbets; Jelly Fruits; Mint Imperials; Pear Drops Mini Bag; Peppermint Gum; Retro Carton Of Liquorice Twists; Rhubarb & Custard; Rhubarb & Custards Mini Bag; Sherbet Lemons Mini Bag; Soft Liquorice; Spearmint Gum; Sugar Free Coolmint Chewing Gum; Sugar Free Menthol Airplus Chewing Gum; Sugar Free Mints Box; Sugar Free Orange & Lemon Fruit Drops Box; Sugar Free Raspberry & Strawberry Drops; Sugar Free Very Berry Chewing Gum; Tin Of Travel Sweets; Turkish Delight

COOKING AIDS - SAVOURY
Ciabatta Croutons; Croutons - Tomato And Basil; Dumpling Mix; French Bread Croutons

COOKING AIDS - SWEET
Apple Crisps; Ready To Roll Marzipan; Ready To Roll Soft Icing; Speciality English Blackcurrant & Cassis Dessert Sauce

CRACKERS, CRISPBREADS ETC
Eat Well Organic Mini Rice Cakes; Oatcakes

DESSERTS
Apricots In Amaretto Liqueur; Blueberry & Elderflower Jelly; Christmas Compote; English Rhubarb Compote; Peach Melba Jelly; Peaches & Cranberries In Orange Liqueur; Peaches In Brandy Connoisseur; Pears In Red Wine Connoisseur; Pickled Pears In Champagne Vinegar; Pomegranate & Elderflower Jelly; Speciality Whole Mandarins In Mulled Wine; Speciality Whole Mini Pears In Raspberry Liqueur; Summer Berry Compote; Summerfruit Pudding; Whole Mandarins In Orange Liqueur Connoisseur; *Eat Well:* 2 Summer Fruit Puddings, Berry & Cherry Jelly Terrine, Cherry Jelly With Sweet Cherries, Fresh Fruit Jelly, Mango & Passion Fruit Jelly Terrine, Raspberry Jelly

DIPS & DRESSINGS
3 Pack Mini Houmous Pots; Balsamic & Blueberry Dressing; Butternut And Chilli Harissa Dip; Dip To Share Houmous And Chilli And Herb; Dressing Bottles Chilli And Coriander; Dressing Shots - Italian Style; Eat Well Tomato Salsa; Fire Roasted Pepper Salsa Dip; Houmous; Lemon And Parsley Dressing; Organic Balsamic Vinaigrette; Organic Lemon And Tarragon Vinaigrette; Reduced Fat French Dressing; Speciality Mediterranean Tomato, Pepper And Olive Dip; Speciality Rose Harissa Dip; Speciality Smoked Jalapeno Barbecue Dip; Spicy Red Pepper Houmous; Sunblush Tomato & Roasted Onion Dressing; Sweet Soy And Chilli Dressing; Vinaigrette With Sherry Vinegar; White Balsamic And Raspberry Dressing

'ICE CREAMS', SORBETS ETC
Freshly Squeezed Valencian Orange Juice Lolly; Mango Madness Sorbet

MARGARINES, FATS, OILS ETC
Sunflower Spread; Sunflower Spread Light; Sweet Popcorn

PASTRY
Puff Pastry; Shortcrust Pastry

PICKLES, SAUCES, VINEGARS ETC
12 Spice Indian Cooking Sauce; Arrabiata Pasta Sauce; Arrabiata Sauce; Artichoke & Tomato Italian Paste; Balti Cooking Sauce; Balti Paste; BBQ Sauce; Black Bean Cooking Sauce; Black Bean Sauce; Bramley Apple Sauce With Vintage Cider; British Raspberry Coulis; Brown Sauce; Chowmein Stirfry Sauce - Pouch; Christmas Mustard And Dill Sauce; Christmas Wild Cranberry Sauce With White Port; Chunky Fajita Marinade; Chunky Sweetcorn Relish; Count On Us Balsamic Vinegar, Olive And Herb Dressing; Cranberry And Port Sauce; Cucumber Relish; Curry Cooking Sauce; Dopiaza Sauce; English Mint Sauce With Fresh Mint; English Vineyard Mustard; Green Thai Curry Cooking Sauce; Hoi Sin; Jalfrezi Cooking Sauce; Korma Paste; Laksa Sauce; Madras Cooking Sauce; Mango & Sweet Chilli Sauce; Mint Jelly; Organic Balsamic, Garlic & Rosemary Marinade; Organic Red Wine Vinegar; Organic Red Wine, Rosemary And Thyme Marinade; Organic Tomato, Kalamata Olive And Chilli Marinade; Peri Peri Relish; Plum & Hoisin Stirfry Sauce; Provender Balsamic Vinegar; Raspberry Vinegar; Red Thai Cooking Sauce; Redcurrant Sauce With Cabernet Sauvignon; Rendang Sauce; Roasted Italian Vegetable Stir Through; Rogan Josh Cooking Sauce; Smoky BBQ Relish; Soy Sauce; Speciality Black Olive Tapenade; Speciality Mediterranean Tomato And Red Pepper Marinade; Speciality Stanley Plum And Soy Marinade; Spicy Mango Chutney; Spicy Sweet & Sour Cooking Sauce; Sticky Barbecue Marinade; Sweet & Sour Sauce; Sweet & Sour Stirfry Sauce; Sweet And Sour Marinade; Sweet And Sour Stir Fry Sauce; Sweet Chilli & Ginger Stirfry Sauce; Sweet Chilli And Ginger Stir Fry Sauce; Sweet Chilli Sauce; Sweet Mango Chutney; Sweet Red Pepper Marinade; Tagine Paste; Tequila, Peri Peri & Lime Marinade; Tewksbury Mustard Pot; Tex Mex Paste; Thai Green Paste; Thai Red Paste; Tikka Paste; Tomato & Basil Bruschetta Topping; Tomato & Roasted Vegetable Sauce; *Pasta Sauce:* Puttanesca, Tomato & Basil, Tomato & Chilli, Tomato & Garlic, Tomato & Grilled Vegetable, Tomato & Herb, Tomato & Hidden Vegetable, Tomato & Mushroom, Tomato & Porcini Mushroom, Tomato & Red Pepper, Tomato And Chilli Pepper

SAVOURIES - CANNED/BOTTLED
Giant Beans In Tomato Sauce; Greek Olives Stuffed With Pimiento; Greek Olives With Orange & Peppers; Green Olives Stuffed With Sundried Tomato; Mixed Marinated Olives; Mixed Pitted Olives Connoisseur; Olives Stuffed With Almonds; Vine Leaves

SAVOURIES - CHILLED/FRESH

6 Vegetable Siu Mai; 6 Vegetable Steamed Dim Sum; Antipasti Mix; Asian Rice; Bombay Aloo; Butternut Squash Samosa; Chargrilled Olives And Peppers; Chunky Chips; Chunky Vegetable & 3 Bean Chilli; Chunky Winter Vegetable; Coconut Rice; Crinkle Cut Chips; Crispy Onion Rings; Crispy Vegetable Ball; Dine In Frites; Fresh Chunky Chips; Frites; Fruity Spanish Couchillo Olives; Green Bean Selection With Provencale Sauce; Grilled Mixed Peppers; Indian Selection With Tomato & Chilli Dip; Large Olive Selection; Manzanilla Olives; Marinated Greek Olive Selection; Marinated Roasted Artichokes; Mild Spanish Mixed Olives; Mini Onion Bhajis And Vegetable Pakoras; Mixed Stuffed Olives; Moroccan Marinated Olives; Oriental Mushroom Puffs; Pesto Queen Green Olives; Pitted Manzanilla Olives; Potato, Courgette And Tomato Bake; Refried Bean Mini Tacos; Rice Pancake Vegetable Spring Roll; Savoury Vegetable Rice; Speciality Italian Slow Roast Vine Tomatoes; Squash & Potato Bake With Sage Dressing; Stuffed Greek Olives; Super Mammoth Greek Olives; Sweet Potato Bhaji; Tapas Garlic Mushrooms; Tapas Patatas Bravas; Tarka Dahl; Tomato & Basil Sauce; Vegetable Chop Suey; Vegetable Spring Roll; Vegetable Stir Fry With Pancakes & Hoisin Sauce; *Count On Us:* Sweet Chilli Veg Sushi Wrap; *Eat Well:* Mini Vegetable Kebabs; *Ready meals:* Braised Vegetable Casserole With Mini Parsley Dumplings, Count On Us Vegetable Chilli & Rice, Mediterranean Vegetable Pasta With Red Pepper Sauce, Vegetable Curry; *Salads:* 3 Bean Salad, BBQ Sweetcorn And Red Pepper Pasta, Cous Cous And Chickpea Salad, Couscous And Roasted Vegetables, Deli - 'superfood' Salad, Deli Side Salad - Broccoli And Red Pepper With Sweet Chilli And Ginger Dressing, Deli Side Salad - Sprouting Seed, Eat Well Marinated Lentil Salad With A Balsamic Dressing, Eat Well Minted New Potato Salad, Eat Well. Roasted Red Pepper, Tomato & Chilli Dressing, Giant Couscous & Wheatberries With Roasted Butternut Squash, Large Deli Side - 3 Bean, Large Deli Side - Roasted Veg Cous Cous, Large Deli Side Salad - Rice Lentil Aubergine, Mediterranean Orzo Salad, Mediterranean Side Salad Selection, Mediterranean Vegetables & Pasta Salad, Multigrain Salad With Houmous, Oriental Style Edamame Soya Bean Salad With Chilli & Coriander Dressing, Orzo Pasta Salad With Slow Roasted Tomatoes, Rice, Lentil & Roast Aubergine With A Garlic Dressing, Santini Tomato Salad With Classic French Dressing, Super Wholefood Salad With Basil And Mint Vinaigrette, Super Wholefood With Blueberries & Mango, Tomato Pasta Salad

SAVOURIES - DRIED

Pouch Rice Stirfry Noodles; *Microwaveable Rice:* Basmati, Long Grain, Pilau, Wholegrain

SNACKS - SAVOURY

6 Pack Lightly Salted Handcooked Crisps; British Duke Of York Lightly Salted Handcooked Crisps; Chilli And Lime Salsa Flavour Handcooked Crisps;

Full On Flavour Sea Salt and Malt Vinegar crisps; Herb Flavoured Roasted Mixed Nuts; Hickory Smoked BBQ Lattice Snack; Kalamata Olive Twists; Lightly Salted Pretzel Sticks; Lightly Salted Reduced Fat Crinkles; Lightly Sea Salted Handcooked Crisps; Mixed Vegetable Crisps Lightly Sea Salted; No Salt Handcooked Crisps; Prawn Cocktails; Reduced Fat Crinkles Salt & Vinegar; Roast Beef And Onion; Salt & Pepper Pretzels; Salt & Vinegar Chiplets; Salt & Vinegar Twists; Salted Mini Pretzels; Sea Salt & Balsamic Vinegar Handcooked Crisps; Sea Salt And Balsamic Vinegar Handcooked Crisps; Sea Salt And Cracked Black Pepper Baked Potato Crisps; Sea Salted And Cracked Black Pepper Purple Star Handcooked Crisps; Smoky BBQ Full On Flavour; Spicy Red Pepper Houmous & Crudite Dipper; Summer Mexican Lime With A Hint Of Chilli Handcooked Potato Crisps; Sweet Chilli Baked Potato Crisps; Sweet Potato Lightly Sea Salted Handcooked Crisps; Sweet Thai Chilli; Tomato Salsa Potato Bakes; *Count On Us:* Bacon Hoop Crisps, Sea Salt Crisps, Sweet Chilli Crisps

SOUPS
Gazpacho; Minestrone Soup; Spicy Red Lentil And Tomato Soup; Super Green Soup; Tomato And Basil Soup; *Eat Well:* Italian Tomato And Vegetable Soup, Minestrone Soup, Three Bean Broth, Tomato And Basil Soup, Winter Vegetable Soup

SOYA AND OTHER 'MILKS'
Soya Milk

SPICES
Bombay Potatoes Spice Kit; Chicken Jalfrezi Spice Kit; Chicken Tikka Masala Spice Kit; Christmas Hot Toddy Bundles; Lamb Rogan Josh Spice Kit

SPREADS - SAVOURY
Speciality Sundried Tomato & Almond Tapenade

SPREADS - SWEET
Hedgerow Conserve; Medium Cut Blood Orange Marmalade; Medium Cut Mandarin Marmalade; Medium Cut Ruby Red Grapefruit Marmalade; No Peel Orange Marmalade; Raspberry Conserve; Rhubarb & Ginger Conserve; Speciality Fairtrade Damson And Sloe Jam; Victoria Plum Conserve

DRINK

SOFT
Apple Softbrew; Blackberry & Echinacea Drink; Blackcurrant High Juice; Blackcurrant Softbrew; Blackcurrant Still Fruity Water; Blueberry & Pomegranate Sparkling Water; Blueberry Juice Drink; Cherry Juice Drink; Citrus Softbrew; Cloudy Lemonade; Cola; Cranberry & Raspberry High Juice; Cranberry & Raspberry Juice Drink; Cranberry & Raspberry Sparkling Spring Water Drink; Cranberry & Raspberry Sparkling Water; Cranberry Juice Drink; Diet American Ginger Ale; Diet Bitter Lemon; Diet Cola; Diet Lemon & Lime; Diet Lemon And Lime Carbonate; Diet Lemonade;

Diet Sparkling Alphonso Mango And Passion fruit Carbonate; Diet Sparkling Florida Orange; Fiery Ginger Beer; Florida Orange High Juice; Florida Pink Grapefruit High Juice; Lemon & Lime High Juice; Lemon & Lime Sparkling Spring Water Drink; Lemon & Lime Still Spring Water Drink; Lemonade; No Added Sugar Blackcurrant High Juice; No Added Sugar Orange High Juice; Pomegranate And Raspberry Juice Drink; Speciality Elderflower Cordial; Speciality Ginger & Lemongrass Presse; Speciality Organic Pear And Ginger Cordial; Speciality Organic Pear And Ginger Presse; Speciality Organic Raspberry Cordial; Speciality Organic Raspberry Presse; Speciality Raspberry & Pear Presse; Still Lemonade Juice Drink; Strawberry & Aloe Vera Drink; Strawberry & Banana Smoothie; Strawberry & Raspberry Smoothie With Oat Beta Glucan; Summer Fruits High Juice; Superberry Smoothie; Traditional Cream Soda; Traditional Dandelion & Burdock; Traditional Extremely Fiery Ginger Beer; Vitamin Water Blueberry And Pomegranate; Vitamin Water Cranberry And Raspberry; Vitamin Water Orange; *Eat Well:* Super Berry Smoothie

SPORTS DRINKS
Sparkling Glucose Energy Drink

WINES
In larger stores there are always a few wines labelled as vegan

FOOD

BISCUITS
Ginger snaps; Morning coffee biscuits; Oaty Biscuits; Rich tea finger biscuits; *Basics:* Ginger snaps; *Be Good To Yourself:* Reduced fat Ginger snaps

BREADS, ROLLS, PIZZA BASES ETC
10 Mini white pitta; 12 Crumpets; 12 Kids mini pitta; 2 Ready to bake baguettes; 6 Organic wholemeal pitta; 6 Ready to bake petits pains; 6 Teacakes; 6 White pitta; 6 Wholemeal pitta; 6 Wraps; 8 Crumpets; Heat & serve ciabatta; Italian 2 pizza bases; Kids Ready to eat 6 Whole & white mini wraps; Thin & Crispy 2 Pizza Bases; What's Cooking Tortilla wraps; *Basics:* 2 Ready to bake baguettes, 4 Teacakes, 6 Pitta, 6 White muffins, Medium sliced white bread, Medium sliced wholemeal bread; *Be Good To Yourself:* 6 Tortilla wraps; *Mixes:* Mixed grain bread mix, Pizza base mix, Sunflower bread mix; *Rolls:* 4 Heat & Serve ciabatta rolls, 6 White floury batch rolls, 6 Wholemeal floury batch rolls, Basics 12 White rolls, Taste the Difference 4 Heat & serve mixed olive ciabatta rolls; *Sliced bread:* Medium white bread, Medium white Fresh for longer bread, Medium white Scottish batch bread (Scotland only), Medium whole & white bread, Medium wholemeal bread, Medium wholemeal Fresh for longer bread, Plain White Medium Bread (N.Ireland only), Soft White Batch, Thick white bread, Thick wholemeal bread, White thick sliced bread; *SO Organic:* 4 wholegrain muffins, 4 wholemeal rolls, 4 wholemeal seeded rolls, 6 Wraps, Multiseed wholemeal thick sliced batch loaf, Stoneground wholemeal thick sliced bread, Sunflower & pumpkin seed thick sliced batch loaf, Wholemeal bread; *Taste the Difference:* 2 Heat & Serve ciabatta with slow roasted Aegean tomatoes, 2 Heat & Serve half ciabatta, 2 Heat & Serve seeded half ciabatta, Heat & Serve half ciabatta, Soft white batch thickly sliced bread, Soft white multiseeded batch thickly sliced bread, Soft wholemeal multiseeded batch thickly sliced bread, Soft wholemeal oat topped batch thickly sliced bread

BREAKFAST FOODS
24 SO organic Wholewheat biscuits; Fruit & nut muesli; Fruit muesli; Golden syrup flavoured easy porridge oats; Malties; Pecan & maple crisp cereal; Wholegrain apricot wheats; Wholegrain blueberry wheats; Wholegrain cranberry wheats; Wholegrain mini wheats; Wholegrain raisin wheats; Wholewheat biscuits; Wholewheat muesli; *Basics:* Instant hot oat cereal, Rice pops, Wholewheat 36 Breakfast wheat biscuits; *Be Good To Yourself:* Less than 3% fat High fruit muesli; *freefrom:* Fruit & Nut Muesli, Golden porridge

'BURGERS', 'SAUSAGES', 'MEAT' SLICES ETC
Meatfree: 18 Vegetable dunkers, 4 Spicy bean quarter pounders, Basics 4 Vegetable burgers, Sainsbury's Nut Cutlets

CHOCOLATE
freefrom: Choc 'n' crispie bar, Rice crackle soya choc bar, Soya choc bar, Tangerine flavour soya choc bar

CONFECTIONERY & SWEET SNACKS
Cough candy; Flying saucers; JS Fizzy Strawberry Lances; Kids Fizzy rainbow belts; Kids Strawberry Pencils; Mint imperials; Rhubarb & custard boiled sweets; Sherbet cocktails; Strawberry laces; *Basics:* Cinema style sweet popcorn

COOKING AIDS - SAVOURY
Golden breadcrumbs; Harissa paste; Natural breadcrumbs; *Stuffing:* Apple and herb, Basics Sage and onion, Parsley, thyme and lemon, Roasted garlic and herb, Sage and onion; *Stuffing mix:* Cranberry and orange, SO organic sage and onion; *Stuffing mix - Taste the Difference:* Apricot and flaked almond, Cranberry, orange and roasted chestnut, Sage, roasted onion and lemon

COOKING AIDS - SWEET
Luxury mincemeat; Mincemeat; Plain scone mix; SO organic mincemeat; Summer fruit sauce; Topping for crumble; *Taste the Difference:* Matured mincemeat

CRACKERS, CRISPBREADS ETC
Cream crackers; High bake water biscuits; Melba toast; Mini Breadsticks; Rice Cakes no added salt; Rough oatcakes; Savoury Snack Crackers; Slowbaked Italian Olive Oil Grissini; *Basics:* Snack crackers; *Be Good To Yourself:* Reduced fat Cream crackers; *Taste the Difference:* Italian olive oil crostini

DESSERTS
Forest Fruit Compote; Heritage raspberry jelly; Mandarin jelly; Raspberry jelly; Treacle tart; *Basics:* 6 apple pies, Apple Pie

DIPS & DRESSINGS
Be Good To Yourself Vinaigrette 3% Fat; Chunky salsa dip; French Dressing; Mango and Chilli Dressing; Organic Balsamic Dressing; Organic French Dressing; Sunbaked Tomato & Red Pepper Dressing; *Basics:* French Dressing; *Be Good To Yourself:* French Dressing, Red Pepper dressing, Reduced fat Guacamole, Tomato and Chilli Dressing; *Houmous:* Be Good To Yourself, Caramelised Onion, Jalapeño, Mixed Olive & Tomato, Moroccan Style, SO organic; *Salsa dips:* Basics, Cool, Hot; *SO organic:* Balsamic Dressing, Garlic & Herb Dressing; *Taste the Difference:* Balsamic Raspberry Rioja Dressing, Chilli vinaigrette, French Dressing with Chardonnay, Lemongrass, Lime Leaf & Galangal Dressing, Sundried tomato dipping oil, Sweetflame Pepper & Piri Piri dressing

GRAVIES & STOCKS
Signature vegetable stock; *freefrom:* Vegetable gravy

'ICE CREAMS', SORBETS ETC
10 Fruit ice lollies; 10 Orange Lollies; 10 Real Fruit Lollies; 10 Rocket Lollies; 3 Kiwi Indulgence Lollies; 8 Fruit Flavour Lollies; High Juice Push ups; Lemon Sorbet; Mango Sorbet

PASTRY
Puff Pastry; Shortcrust Pastry; Shortcrust pastry mix; *Ready Rolled:* Filo Pastry, Puff Pastry, Shortcrust Pastry

PICKLES, SAUCES, VINEGARS ETC

Bramley apple sauce; Brown sauce; Cranberry sauce; Dill sauce; Fresh Mint Sauce; Fruity brown sauce; Fruity sauce; Mint jelly; Mint sauce; Pepper & Chilli Sauce; Pour over Black Bean Sauce; Pour over Sweet Chilli Sauce; Redcurrant jelly; Smooth Bramley apple sauce; SO organic mint sauce; Spicy Faijta Sauce; Thai chilli dipping sauce; *Basics:* Brown sauce, Mint sauce; *Chutney:* Basics onion, Basics tomato, Spiced mango, Sweet mango, Taste the Difference red onion, Taste the Difference red pepper, Tomato; *Cooking sauces:* Balti curry sauce, Madras curry sauce, SO organic Rogan josh cooking sauce, Taste the Difference Balti; *freefrom:* Korma cooking sauce, Thai green curry cooking sauce, Tikka masala cooking sauce; *Marinade:* Mango and Chilli, Sticky BBQ; *Marinade - Taste the Difference:* Lemon & Piri Piri, Smokey BBQ & Brown Ale, Sweetflame Pepper; *Mexican cooking sauces:* Hot chilli con carne, Light chilli con carne, Medium chilli con carne, Spiced tomato tagine; *Oriental cooking sauces:* Basics Sweet & sour, Light sweet & sour, Lime & coconut curry, Peking lemon, SO organic Sweet & sour, Spicy sweet & sour, Sweet & sour, Sweet & sour with extra pineapple; *Pasta sauces:* Basics Tomato, Chunky vegetable, Emiliana, Light tomato & herb, Ligure, Mushroom, Onion & garlic, Pizza topping sauce, Siciliana, SO organic Tomato & basil, SO organic Tomato, red pepper & chilli, Spicy pepper, Tomato & chilli, Tomato & herb; *Relish:* Onion, Sweetcorn, Tomato, Tomato and chilli, Tomato and jalapeno; *Taste the Difference:* Chargrilled vegetable caponata, Cranberry sauce; *Tomato Ketchup:* Basics, Reduced sugar and salt, SO organic tomato ketchup; *Vinegar:* Aceto Balsamico di Modena, Aceto Balsamico di Modena 2L, Basics Malt, Cider, Malt, Organic Balsamic (3 leaf), Organic cider vinegar flavoured with tarragon, Red wine, SO organic white wine, Taste The Difference vintage balsamic of Modena, White wine

SAVOURIES - CANNED/BOTTLED

Capucines capers in brine; Chargrilled artichokes; Italian mixed mushroom antipasto; Italian mixed pepper antipasto; Italian sun-dried tomato antipasto; Mixed beans in mild chilli sauce; Mixed Vegetable Antipasti; Mushy peas chip shop style; Processed peas in water; SO organic spaghetti in tomato sauce; Sun dried tomatoes; Vegetable chilli; Vegetarian spaghetti bolognese; *Baked Beans:* 2 microwavable snack pots, Baked beans in tomato sauce, Basics, Reduced sugar reduced salt, SO organic; *Basics:* Mushy processed peas, Processed marrowfat peas in water, Spaghetti in tomato sauce; *Olives:* Bella di Cerignola Olives, Black pitted olives, Couchillo Olives with Pine Nuts, Gordal and Kalkidis Olives, Green pitted olives, Mixed Olives, Mixed Olives with sun dried tomatoes, Pimento Stuffed Green Olives, Queen Green Olives, SO organic Italian nocellara olives; *Taste the Difference:* Chargrilled artichoke hearts in Puglian olive oil, SunBlush® Tomatoes 300g

SAVOURIES - CHILLED/FRESH
12 Falafels; 2 Onion Bhajis; 3 Bean salad; 6 Spinach Pakora; 6 Stuffed Vine Leaves; Basmati rice; Channa masala; Indian: Bombay potato; Mushroom pilau rice; Pilau rice; Spicy potato wedges; Thai sticky rice; Three colour pilau rice; Vegetable dhansak; Vegetable rice; *Basics:* Tomato & herb pasta; *Be Good To Yourself:* Less than 3% fat Beetroot salad, Mediterranean vegetable pasta, Orzo and Sunbaked™ Tomato Salad, Penne arrabbiata, Vegetable chilli & rice; *Taste the Difference:* Bombay potato British Maris Piper Potatoes, Coriander pilau rice with fresh coriander & mustard seeds, Roasted baby potatoes & garlic

SAVOURIES - DRIED
Dried soya mince; *2 Minute meals:* Basmati rice, Long grain rice, Pilau rice, Vegetable Arrabiata, Vegetable biryani rice, Wholegrain rice; *Basics:* Instant mashed potato mix; *freefrom:* Bombay potatoes, Chickpea curry, Saag aloo

SAVOURIES - FROZEN
American Curly Fries; Carrot & Parsnip Mini Waffles; Chips; Crinkle Cut Chips; French Fries; Hash Browns; Pilau rice; Roast Potatoes; Steak Cut Chips; *Be Good To Yourself:* Oven Chips; *Party food:* 15 Party vegetable spring rolls, 16 Party Indian snack selection, 60 Piece Party Indian snack selection; *Taste the Difference:* British Extra Chunky chips, British Jumbo Wedges

SNACKS - SAVOURY
Jumbo chilli peanuts; Jumbo multiseed pretzels; Lightly salted tortilla chips;

Mini Carrots and Houmous Dip; Mini poppadoms; Potato squares; Ready salted potato triangles; Salt & vinegar crunchy sticks; Salted pretzels; *Basics:* Beef & tomato flavour snack noodles, Chicken & mushroom flavour snack noodles, Pasta shells in a tomato & onion sauce mix, Tortilla chips; *Instant noodles:* Basics chicken curry flavour, Basis chicken flavour, Chicken curry flavour, Chicken flavour, Vegetable flavour; *Multipack crisps:* 30% less fat British potato crisps ready salted, Bacon crispies, Basics British potato ready salted crisps, Basics Potato rings, British potato crisps ready salted, Prawn cocktail flavour, Ready salted, Ready salted crisp bakes, Salt your own crisps; *Taste the Difference:* British Charlotte potato crisps lightly salted, British potato crisps with sea salt, British potato crisps with sea salt & cider vinegar, Root vegetable crisps with sea salt

SOUPS
Microwave soup tomato, basil & chilli; *freefrom:* Juicy tomato & basil soup; *Fresh soups:* Chunky Carrot & Sweetcorn, Minestrone, SO organic Carrot, Chickpea and Coriander, SO organic Mediterranean style vegetable, SO organic Red Lentil, SO organic Vegetable and Barley, Taste the Difference Vine Ripened Tomato and Puy Lentil; *Instant soup:* Minestrone Soup in a Cup; *Tinned:* Basics vegetable soup, Be Good To Yourself Moroccan inspired chickpea & spinach soup, Be Good To Yourself spicy tomato & lentil soup, Chunky soup vegetable, French onion soup simmer and serve, Spring vegetable soup, Vegetable soup

SPREADS - SAVOURY
Peanut butter: 33% Less fat Smooth, Basics Crunchy, Crunchy, Smooth, Wholenut; *SO organic peanut butter:* Crunchy, Smooth

SPREADS - SWEET
Bramble jelly; Ginger preserve; *Basics:* Medium cut orange marmalade, Mixed fruit jam, Strawberry jam; *Jam:* Apricot jam, Blackcurrant jam, Damson jam, Raspberry jam, Seedless Raspberry jam, Strawberry jam; *Marmalade:* Extra thick cut mature orange, Fine cut orange, Medium cut orange, Orange shred, Shredless orange, SO organic Seville orange fine cut, SO organic Seville orange thick cut, Thick cut orange, Thick cut orange & ginger; *Reduced sugar jam:* Apricot, Blackcurrant, Morello cherry, Raspberry, Strawberry; *Reduced sugar orange marmalade:* Fine cut, Thick cut; *SO organic Continental soft set conserve:* Apricot, Raspberry, Strawberry; *Taste the Difference:* Apricot & orange conserve (limited edition), Apricot conserve, Bitter Seville orange marmalade, Blackcurrant conserve, Cherry conserve, Hedgerow conserve, Plum conserve, Raspberry conserve, Ruby Red grapefruit marmalade, Sicilian Blood orange marmalade, Strawberry conserve, Sweet Valencia orange marmalade, Three fruit marmalade

DRINK

WINES
In larger stores there are always a few wines labelled as vegan

FOOD

BISCUITS
Fruit Shortcake; Ginger Nuts; Reduced Fat Rich Tea Biscuits; Rich Tea Finger; Value Rich Tea Biscuits

BREADS, ROLLS, PIZZA BASES ETC
10 Mini Wholemeal Pitta Bread; 12 Bake at home mini petits pains; 12 Crumpets; 13 Bakers Dozen White Pitta Breads; 2 Bake at home Baguettes; 2 Half Ciabatta; 2 Part baked Baguettes; 4 Bake at home baguettes; 4 Ciabatta rolls; 4 Oven Bottom Muffins; 4 Panini rolls; 4 Potato Farls N.I; 4 Value Teacakes; 5 Caramelised Onion & Poppy Seed Bagels; 5 Cinnamon & Raisin Bagels; 5 Plain Bagels; 6 Garlic & Herb Pitta Bread; 6 Large Pitta; 6 Large Wholemeal Pitta Bread; 6 sesame seeded burger buns; 6 Soft White Rolls; 6 Teacakes; 6 White English Muffins; 6 White Pitta Bread; 6 Wholemeal Pitta Bread; 6 Wholemeal Rolls; 8 Potato Farls; BS White Bread Medium Sliced; BS White Bread Thick Sliced; Crumpets 6; Discount Soft Farmhouse Wholemeal; Discount Seeded Batch; Discount Soft Farmhouse White; Finest 6 Multigrain Pain Rustiques; Finest Bake at Home Ciabatta Rolls; Finest Ciabatta; Finest Multiseed Batch Bread; Finest Oatmeal Batch Bread; Finest Part Baked Ciabatta Loaf; Finest White Farmhouse Batch Bread; Fruit Slice; Healthy Living 4 Seeded Panini; Healthy Living Pitta x 6; Healthy Living Wholemeal Oat Bran Rolls; Light Choices Naan Bread; Light Choices Tortilla wraps 8; Lighter Choice Mini Naan Bread; Mini Pitta Bread x 10; Organic 6 Wholemeal Pitta Bread; Organic White Thick Sliced Bread; Organic Wholemeal Thick Sliced Bread; Plain Bread N.I; Plain Ciabatta; Plain Pappadums; Scottish Plain Batch Bread; Spicy Pappadums; Stay Fresh White Bread Medium Sliced; Stayfresh Medium Sliced Wholemeal Bread; Thick sliced soft white bread; Value 12 White Rolls; Value 5 bagels; Value Medium Sliced White Bread; Value Thick Sliced White Bread; Value White Bread; Value White Pitta Bread x 6; Wheatfield 2 Ciabatta rolls; Wheatfield Bakery Bake at home 8 pack dinner rolls; Wheatfield Bakery bake at home baguette rolls 4; Wheatfield Bakery Bake at home ciabatta; White Medium Sliced Loaf; White Thick Sliced Danish Loaf; Wholemeal Bread Medium Sliced; Wholemeal Bread Thick Sliced; Wholemeal Oatbran Bread; *In store bakery:* 6 Mickey Doughnuts, Ciabatta Roll, Express Seeded Roll, Finest Baguette, Kalamata Olive Bouchon, Mediterranean Rustique, Seeded Bloomer, Spelt & Sunflower Bloomer; *In store bakery:* Finest 2 Pack Finest Pain Rustique, Finest Grand Rustique, Stonebaked Sourdough Bloomer; *Mixes:* Crusty White Bread Mix, Crusty Wholemeal Bread Mix, Pizza Base Mix, Pizza Twists Mix, Shortcrust Pastry Mix

BREAKFAST FOODS
Apricot wheats; Blackcurrant Bites; Blueberry wheats; Country Barn Wheat Biscuits; Country Barn Corn Flakes; Finest Porridge with Fruit and Nuts; Finest Sultana & Apple Porridge; Malt

Wheats; Micro oats Golden Syrup; Micro oats Original; Raspberry Bites; Strawberry Bites; Value Coco Snaps; Value Corn Flakes; Value Frosted Flakes; Value Rice Snaps; Value Wheat Biscuits; Wheat Biscuits

'BURGERS', 'SAUSAGES', 'MEAT' SLICES ETC

Meatfree: 15 Vegetable Fingers, 4 Mexican Style Bean Burgers, 4 Nut Cutlets, 4 Vegetable Quarter Pounders, Mince

CAKES & CAKE MIXES

Free From: Pancake Mix, Victoria Sponge Mix

CHOCOLATE

Andean Extra Bitter Plain Chocolate 70%; Finest plain cooking chocolate

CONFECTIONERY & SWEET SNACKS

Barley Sugar; Chewing Gum Peppermint; Chewing Gum Spearmint; Coconut Ice; Cola Cubes; Fizzy Multi Coloured and Flavoured Belts; Flying saucers; Rhubarb And Custards; Sherbet Fruits; Strawberry Flavour Lances; Sweet Shop Lemon Sherberts; Value Mint Imperials; *Free From:* Blueberry Bars

COOKING AIDS - SAVOURY

Beef Casserole Mix; Black pepper and olive oil croutons; Chilli Con Carne Mix; Cottage Pie Mix; Crumble Mix; Dumpling Mix; Garlic and herb croutons; Olive oil croutons; Sausage Casserole Mix; Yeast Extract; *Stuffing mix:* Apple & Herb Stuffing Mix, Oak Lane sage & onion stuffing mix, Sage

and Onion stuffing, Value Sage & Onion Stuffing Mix

COOKING AIDS - SWEET

Custard Powder; Finest Raspberry Dessert Sauce; Fondant Icing; Glacé Cherries; Glacé Cherries with Natural Colour; Golden Marzipan; Natural Marzipan; Strawberry Dessert Sauce; Value Golden Syrup; Value squeezy chocolate flavour ice cream sauce; Value strawberry flavour ice cream sauce

CRACKERS, CRISPBREADS ETC

Cream Cracker; High Baked Water Biscuit; Light Choices Dutch Melba Toast; Light Choices Savoury Jumbo Rice Cakes; Oatland Rye Crisp Bread; Organic Thick Slice Rice Cakes No Added Salt; Reduced Fat Cream Crackers; Rough Oatcakes; Snackers; Wheat Thins

DESSERTS

Apple Strudel; Blackcurrant flavour Jelly; Oak Lane Mango Jelly with Peach; Oak Lane Pineapple Jelly with Pineapple; Oak Lane Strawberry Jelly with Pieces of Peach; Orange flavour Jelly; Orange Jelly with Mandarin; Pineapple Jelly with Pineapple Pieces; Strawberry flavour Jelly; Strawberry flavour jelly with Peach Pieces; Value Apple Pie; Value Orange Flavour Jelly; Woodland Fruit Strudel

DIPS & DRESSINGS

Balsamic Dressing; Cool Salsa Dip; Finest Balsamic Dressing; Finest Chilli & Sherry vinegar dressing; Finest French Dressing; French Dressing; Hot Salsa

Dip; Light Choices Balsamic dressing; Organic French Dressing; *Houmous:* Caramelised Onion, Chunky, Houmous, Jalapeno and Red Pepper, Olive & Sundried Tomato, Organic, Reduced Fat, Reduced Fat Caramelised Onion, Reduced Fat Red Pepper, Roasted Vegetable Topped, Sea Salt & Cracked Black Pepper, Sweet Chilli; *Salsa:* Cool, Hot, Vine ripened tomato

GRAVIES & STOCKS
Vegetable Stock Cubes

'ICE CREAMS', SORBETS ETC
4 Freshly Squeezed Orange Juice Ice Lollies; Lemon Sorbet; Mango & Blackcurrant Sorbet; Raspberry Sorbet

MARGARINES, FATS, OILS ETC
Finest Olive Spread

PICKLES, SAUCES, VINEGARS ETC
Black Bean Cooking Sauce; Bramley apple sauce; Chilli sauce; Cranberry sauce; Dark soy sauce; Discount Sweet & Sour Cooking Sauce; Finest Apple Chutney with Flame Roasted Tomato & Garlic; Finest Apple Sauce with Cider; Finest Caramelised Red Onion Relish; Finest Cranberry Sauce; Finest Mango, Apricot & Coriander Chutney; Finest Mint Sauce; Finest Redcurrant Sauce with Port; Garden Mint Sauce; Hamburger Relish; Light Choices Sweet & Sour Cooking Sauce; Light soy sauce; Mango Chutney; Mango Chutney - Top Down; Mint Jelly; Mint Sauce; Moroccan Tagine Sauce; Mustard Piccalilli; Oak Lane Apple Sauce; Oak Lane Cranberry Sauce; Oak Lane Mint

Sauce; Onion Chutney; Onion Relish; Organic soy sauce; Organic Tomato & Basil Sauce; Redcurrant jelly; Rice Vinegar; Sandwich Piccalilli; Sandwich Pickle; Spicy Lime Pickle; Spicy Mango Chutney; Sticky BBQ Marinade; Sundried Tomato & Cinnamon Sauce; Sweet & Sour Cooking Sauce; Sweet Piccalilli; Sweet Pickle; Sweetcorn Relish; Teriyaki sauce; Tomato Chutney; Tomato Relish; Value Apple sauce; Value Mint Sauce; Value Sweet & Sour Sauce; Value Sweet Pickle; *Brown sauce:* Brown Sauce, Discounter, Fruity, Value; *Fresh pasta sauces:* Arrabbiata, Chargrilled vegetable, Finest cherry tomato, Napoletana, Tomato; *Indian cooking sauces:* Curry Leaf Rogan Josh, Finest Rogan Josh, Jalfrezi, Madras, Rogan Josh, Value Curry Sauce; *Ketchup:* Organic, Reduced Sugar and Salt, Tomato Ketchup, Value; *Mexican:* Casa Mexico Chilli Cooking Sauce, Chilli Hot Sauce, Chilli Mild Sauce, Hot Salsa Dip; *Mustard:* Dijon, English, Finest Dijon, Finest Wholegrain, French, Genuine American, Oak Lane English, Oak Lane Wholegrain, Organic Wholegrain, Value, Wholegrain; *Pasta sauce:* Chunky Veg, Discount Brand Arrabbiata, Disney, Finest Tomato and Mushroom, Light Choices pasta sauce, Mushroom, Onion and Garlic, Organic Arrabiata, Original, Spicy Pepper, Sundried Tomato, Garlic and Basil, Tomato & Chargrilled Vegetable, Tomato & Olive Pasta, Trattoria Verdi Mushroom, Trattoria Verdi Tomato & Herb, Value Pasta Sauce, Whole Cherry Tomato & Chilli Pasta Sauce; *Stir fry sauce:* Chinese, Finest Soy, Wasabi and Lemongrass, Hoi

Sin and Plum, Limited Edition Szechuan, Sweet Chilli; *Stir fry sauce pouch:* Black bean, Chow mein, Hoisin, Sweet and sour; *Thai curry paste:* Green, Red, Yellow; *Vinegar:* Balsamic Vinegar of Modena, Balsamic Vinegar of Modena 3 leaves, Cider Vinegar, Discounter Balsamic Vinegar, Distilled Vinegar, Finest Aged Balsamic Vinegar of Modena, Ingredients: Balsamic glaze, Malt Vinegar, Oak Lane Malt Vinegar, Organic Balsamic vinegar of Modena, Red Wine Vinegar, Value Vinegar, White Balsamic Condiment, White Wine Vinegar

SAVOURIES - CANNED/BOTTLED
Almond & Piri Piri Stuffed Olives; Bombay Potato; Mushy Processed Peas; Pimiento Stuffed Green Olives; Sun Grown Pimento Stuffed Olives; Value Mushy Peas; *Baked beans in tomato sauce:* Baked Beans, Light Choices, Oaktree, Value; *Free From:* Three Bean Chilli, Vegetable Curry; *Spaghetti in tomato sauce:* Rings, Short Cut, Value; *Spicy beans:* Chilli beans, Hot and spicy mixed beans, Taco Mixed Beans

SAVOURIES - CHILLED/FRESH
Bubble and Squeak; Chunky Chips; Fries; Garlic Stuffed Olives; Pimento Stuffed Olives; *Finest:* Fresh Chunky Chips, Rosemary Roasted Potatoes; *Healthy Living:* Bean stew, Moroccan veggie pot; *Indian Meals:* Basmati rice, Pilau rice; *Oriental Meals:* Vegetable Spring Rolls; *Prepared potatoes:* Potato Wedges with an Oil and Parsley Dressing, Roast potatoes, Spicy potato wedges, Summer roasting potatoes with a pepper sauce & rosemary;

Salads: Fruity Couscous, Spicy Couscous, Sweet Chilli Pasta, Tomato and basil pasta

SAVOURIES - DRIED
Trattoria Verdi Gnocchi; Value Golden Vegetable Savoury Rice; Value Pasta in a Tomato & Onion Sauce; Wholefoods Soya Mince; *Microwaveable rice:* Basmati rice, Long grain rice, Pilau rice, Wholegrain rice

SAVOURIES - FROZEN
16 Tomato & Basil Rolls; Breaded Onion Rings; Crispy Potato and Mediterranean Vegetable Mix; Finest Beer Battered Onion Rings; Roasting Parsnips; Steamrice White & Wild Rice with mixed vegetables; Steamrice White Rice; Value White Rice; *Chips:* Country Store Golden fries, Crinkle cut oven chips, Curly oven potato chips in a seasoned coating, Finest Oven Chips, Hash Browns, Steak Cut Chips, Straight Cut Fry chips, Straight cut oven chips, Sweet Potato Chips, Thin and crispy oven chips; *Potatoes:* Crispy Lattice Potatoes, Finest British Jumbo Wedges, Masala Wedges, Potato Croquettes, Roasting Potatoes, Rosemary and garlic roasting potatoes, Spicy Wedges

SNACKS - SAVOURY
Bombay Mix; Centennial Chilli Flavoured Coated Peanuts; Chilli peanuts; Cinema Style Popcorn; Eastmans Chilli tortilla chips; Japanese peanut crackers mix; Japanese Rice Crackers; Sweet chilli coated nuts; Value Spicy Curry Flavour Noodle Quick Snack; *Crisps:* Bacon Rashers, Crunchy Sticks Ready Salted, Crunchy Sticks Salt & Vinegar Flavour,

Finest Lightly Salted Handcooked Crisps, Finest Sea Salt & West Country Cider Vinegar flavour, Finest Sundried Tomato, Garlic & Basil flavour, Vegetable; *Instant mashed potato:* Oak Lane, Value

SOUPS
Finest SunBlush Tomato & Basil Soup pouch; Microwave Spicy lentil pot soup; Oak Tree Estate Vegetable Soup; Premium Spiced Chickpea & Spinach Soup; Premium Tomato Cannellini Bean & Basil Soup; Tomato & Puy Lentil Soup; Value Vegetable Soup; Vegetable Soup; *Free From:* Minestrone Soup; *Fresh soups:* 10 vegetable, Chilli bean, Finest puy lentil and vine ripened tomato, Tomato and basil

SPREADS - SAVOURY
Pizza Toast Tomato and Herb; Quince Jelly; Sundried Tomato Tapenade; *Peanut butter:* Crunchy, Smooth, Value Crunchy, Wholenut

SPREADS - SWEET
Blackcurrant; Bramble jelly; Ginger preserve; Oak Lane Blackcurrant Conserve; Oak lane strawberry conserve; *Jam:* Apricot, Finest red cherry conserve, Plum, Raspberry, Seedless Raspberry, Strawberry, Value mixed fruit, Value strawberry; *Marmalade:* Fine cut orange shred, Finest Three Fruit, Fresh Fruit Bitter Orange, Fresh Fruit Rich Dark Orange, Oak Lane lemon and lime, Oak Lane lime, Oak Lane Thick Cut Orange, Oak Lane Thin Cut Grapefruit, Oak Lane Thin Cut Orange, Shredless lemon, Shredless orange, Thick cut orange shred, Value orange

DRINK

BEERS
Best Bitter; Bière Blonde; Bière d'Or; Bière Spéciale; Boheme Czech Lager; Draught Bitter; Finest Abbey Beer; Lager 5%; Strong Bitter; Strong Lager; Value Bitter

CHAMPAGNE
Blanc de Noirs Champagne; Demi Sec Champagne; Finest Premier Cru Champagne; Rose Champagne

CIDERS & PERRIES
Lambrusco Bianco Light; Lambrusco Rose Light; Low Alcohol Cider; Oakleys Original Cider

'HOT'
Cocoa; Value Cocoa Powder

SOFT
American Ginger Ale; Apple and Elderflower Cordial; Bitter Lemon; Cream Soda; Dandelion & Burdock; Diet Dandelion & Burdock; Diet Lemonade Shandy; Diet Summer Fruits; Dry Ginger Ale; Finest American Ginger Ale; Finest Grape & Elderflower; Finest Orange, Mango and Mandarin; Finest Pear and Raspberry Cordial; Finest Pomegranate; Ginger Beer; Iron Brew; Lemon, Mandarin & Lime Crush; Lemonade Shandy; Low Calorie American Ginger Ale; Low Calorie Bitter Lemon; Low Calorie Indian Tonic Water with a Twist of Lemon; Low Calorie Indian Tonic Water with a Twist of Lime; Peach & Passion Fruit Crush; Pink

Lemonade; Premium English Elderflower Presse; Premium Italian White Grape Crush; Premium Jamaican Ginger Ale; Premium Mango Pineapple Crush; Premium Mexican Key Lime Crush; Premium Morello Cherry Crush; Premium Red Syrah Grape Crush; Premium Scottish Raspberry Crush; Premium Sicilian Bitter Lemon; Sparkling Diet Lemon & Lime; Sparkling Diet Orange; Sparkling Diet Tropical; Sparkling Orange; Strawberry Lemonade; Strawberry Milkshake Mix; Sugar Free Cherryade; Sugar Free Limeade; Sugar Free Orangeade; Tropical Juice from Concentrate with added Calcium; *Cans:* Cloudy Lemonade, Diet Lemonade, Ginger Beer; *Cola:* Caffeine Free Diet Cola, Cola, Cola Zero, Diet Cola, Diet Cola with Almond, Fiery Cola, Premium Cola, Premium Diet Cola, Value Sugar Free Cola; *Flavoured water:* Apple Still, H2 Lemon & Lime Still, H2 Raspberry Still, H2 Sparkling lemon & lime, H2 spring water with peach, Lemon & Lime Still, Peach flavour spring water, Spring water hint of Apple & Raspberry, Spring water hint of Elderflower & Lemon, Spring water hint of Grapefruit, Spring water hint of Lemon & Lime, Spring water hint of Orange, Spring water hint of Peach, Spring water hint White grape & Blackberry, Strawberry Still, White grape & Blackberry spring water; *Fruit and Barley Squash:* Orange, Peach & Apricot, Summer Fruits; *High Juice:* Apple, Apple and blackcurrant, Apple, pear and plum, Apple, pomegranate and raspberry, Blackcurrant, No Added Sugar Orange, Orange, Pineapple, Pink grapefruit, Pomegranate, apple and raspberry, Tropical; *Juice drink:* Apple, Apple and raspberry, Apple with calcium, Blackcurrant, Cranberry, Orange, Pomegranate, Sun Grown apple & banana, Sun Grown Peach, Sun grown Pear, Sun Grown Pineapple & Lemon, Sun grown tropical and multivitamins, Tropical; *Juice drink no added sugar:* Apple, Cranberry, Cranberry & orange, Cranberry and raspberry, Light Choices Apple, Light Choices Orange, Light Choices Orange with calcium, Orange, Tropical; *Juice drinks:* Apple and raspberry, Blueberry, Cranberry, Cranberry and raspberry, Exotic, Pomegranate, Summer fruits, Tropical, Yumberry; *Lemonade:* Cloudy Lemonade, Diet Cloudy Lemonade, Lemonade Juice drink "squeezed from fresh lemons", Premium Diet Lemonade, Premium Lemonade, Sparkling Diet Lemonade, Sparkling Lemonade, Value Sugar Free Lemonade; *No added sugar Squash:* Apple, Apple and blackcurrant, Apple and strawberry, Cherries and berries, Discounter Orange, High Juice No Added Sugar Summer fruits, Lime Cordial, Mexican Lime, Orange, Orange, lemon and pineapple, Summer fruits, Sun Sip Apple and blackcurrant, Tropical, Value apple and blackcurrant, Value lemon, Value orange, Whole lemon; *Smoothies:* Mango and Passionfruit, Pineapple, Banana and Coconut, Plum, Red Grape and Pear, Strawberry Raspberry and Blackberry, Summer Fruits; *Squash:* Apple and blackcurrant, Orange, lemon and pineapple, Whole orange

SPIRITS & APÉRITIFS
Brandy: Spanish Brandy, Value French Brandy; *Gin:* Dry London Gin, Finest Classic No 1 London Dry Gin, Special London Dry Gin, Value Gin; *Portuguese:* Finest 10 Year Old Tawny Port, Late Bottled Vintage Port, Special Reserve Port; *Rum:* Dark Rum, Finest Trinidadian Golden Rum, Value Dark Rum, Value White Rum, White Rum; *Sherry:* Finest 7 Year Old Fino, Finest Manzanilla Pasada; *Vodka:* Imperial Vodka, Value Vodka; *Whisky:* Finest 10 Year Old Islay Malt Scotch Whisky, Special Reserve Irish Whiskey, Value Whisky

SPORTS DRINKS
Active Glucose Energy Drink; Active Orange; Active Orange Isotonic; Active Orange Sport Fuel; Active Raspberry Isotonic; Active Raspberry Sport Fuel; Active Tropical Isotonic; Kx Stimulation Drink; Sugar Free Kx Stimulation Drink

WINES - FRUIT
Argentinian: Argentinian Malbec, Finest Argentinian Malbec; *Australian:* Finest McLaren Vale Shiraz/Grenache 2008; *Bordeaux:* Claret, Claret Reserve, Finest Medoc, Finest Saint Emilion, Finest Vintage Claret; *Chilean:* Chilean Cabernet Sauvignon, Finest Los Fresnos Pinot Noir; *East European:* Bulgarian Reka Valley Cabernet Sauvignon, Bulgarian Reka Valley Merlot; *French:* Beaujolais Villages, Cotes du Rhone, Cotes du Rhone Villages Reserve, Finest Châteauneuf du Pape 2008, Finest Cornas, Finest Crozes Hermitage, Finest Gerard Bertrand Tautavel, Finest Hermitage, Finest Oak Aged Red Burgundy 2008, Finest Saint Joseph 2006, Fleurie 2008, French Vin de table, Red Burgundy 2008; *Italian:* Chianti Classico DOCG, Chianti DOCG, Finest Barolo DOCG, Italian Merlot, Valpolicella; *North American:* California Merlot, California Red Wine, Californian Cabernet Sauvignon, Californian Petite Sirah, Californian Red Wine, Californian Zinfandel, Californian Zinfandel Reserve 2008; *Portuguese:* Finest Touriga Nacional; *South African:* Finest Beyers Truter Pinotage 2006, Finest Farquharson Shiraz, South African Cabernet Sauvignon Shiraz, South African Medium Sweet Red Wine, South African Pinotage 2009, South African Red Wine; *Spanish:* Finest Tempranillo, Finest Vina Mara Rioja Reserva, Vina Mara Rioja Crianza 2006

WINES - ROSÉ
California Blush Zinfandel; California Rose; Finest Cotes de Provence Rose 2008

WINES - SPARKLING
Asti Spumante DOCG; Cava Brut; Cava Demi-sec; Cava Reserva DO; Finest Vintage Cava D.O.; Rose Cava DO

WINES - WHITE
Argentinian: Argentinian Reserve Fairtrade Chardonnay; *Bordeaux:* Finest Sauternes, Premieres Cotes de Bordeaux; *Chilean:* Chilean Sauvignon Blanc, Finest Los Nogales Sauvignon Blanc; *French:* Anjou Blanc, Chablis AOC, Finest Alsace Pinot Gris, Finest Chablis 1er Cru 2008, Finest Oak Aged White Burgundy, Finest Pouilly Fume, Finest Sancerre, Finest Vouvray Demi-

sec, Muscadet, Sancerre 2008, T Citrus Squeezer French Colombard, White Burgundy; *Italian:* Asti Spumante DOCG, Bardolino DOC, Italian White Merlot, Soave, Soave Classico, Soave DOC, Verdicchio Classico; *North American:* California Pinot Grigio, Californian Chardonnay, Californian White Wine; *South African:* Finest Darling Sauvignon Blanc, Ken Forrester Reserve Chenin Blanc 2008, South African Sauvignon Blanc

HEALTH CARE

SUPPLEMENTS
B-Active 30 Tablets; Chewable Vitamin C; Cranberry Extract; Echinacea; Effervescent B-Active Orange flavoured; Effervescent Echinacea Lemon and Lime Flavoured; Effervescent Vitamin C and Zinc Orange flavoured; Effervescent Vitamin C Orange flavoured; Energy Extra Tablets; Folic Acid; Ginkgo biloba 60 Tablets; Gold Sun Chewable Vitamin C & Zinc; Gold Sun Chewable Vitamin C 90 Tablets; Korean Ginseng extract 60 tablets; Milk Thistle; Omega 3 For Vegetarians and Vegans; Rosehip Extract; Skin Tablets; Sleep Aid; Slimming Aid; Slow Release Vitamin C; St John's Wort; Stress Relief; Vitamin B Complex; Vitamin B6; Vitamin C + Zinc; Vitamins A, C, E + Selenium; Water Relief; Women's Health; Zinc

FOOD

BISCUITS
Digestive; Morning Coffee; Rich Tea Finger; Simply Value Ginger Nut

BREADS, ROLLS, PIZZA BASES ETC
12 Soft White Rolls; 4 Fruited Teacakes; 4 Onion Batons; 4 Panini; 4 plain muffins; 4 White Crusty Rolls; 6 Burger Buns with Sesame Seeds; 6 Ciabatta Rolls; 6 Plain Pitta Breads; 6 Soft White Rolls; 6 Soft Wholemeal Rolls; 6 White Finger Rolls; 6 White Rolls; 6 Wholemeal Pitta Breads; 8 Ready To Eat Poppadums; Brown Crusty Rolls; Brown Loaf; Brown Rustic Roll; Ciabatta roll; Danish White Bread-Medium Sliced; Football Rolls; Fruit Loaf; Irish White Batch Loaf; ISB - Malted Grain Loaf; Longer Life White Bread - Medium Sliced; Malted Grain Loaf; Medium Petit Pain; Medium Sliced White Bread; Mini Gingerbread Men; Naturally Healthy - Wholemeal Bread - Medium Sliced; Naturally Healthy - Wholemeal Bread - Thick Sliced; Naturally Healthy 6 Wholemeal Rolls; Organic brown bloomer; Organic white bloomer; Parisien White Baguette; Plain Bagel; Plain Bloomer; Plain Bread; Poppy bloomer; Ready to Bake White Baguettes; Ready to Bake White Petits Pains; Simply Value 6 Plain Pitta Breads; Simply Value Medium Sliced White Bread; Simply Value Medium Sliced Wholemeal Bread; Thick Sliced White Bread; Truly Irresistible 4 Seeded Batch Rolls; Truly Irresistible Oat Topped Batch Rolls; White bloomer; White Crusty Roll; White Demi Baguette; White Farmhouse Loaf; White Tin Loaf; Wholemeal Knot Roll; *Truly Irresistible:* Ciabatta (Twin pack), French White Baguette, Mixed Olive Rolls, Multigrain Rustique, Oatmeal Batch Loaf, White Farmhouse Batch Loaf, White Seeded Batch Loaf, Wholemeal Seeded Batch Loaf

BREAKFAST FOODS
Cereals: 16 Shredded Wheat, Healthy Living Porridge Oats with Wheatbran, Wholewheat Biscuits

CONFECTIONERY & SWEET SNACKS
10 Sour Lollipops; Assorted Fruit Flavour Lollies; Cookie Assortment; Fizzy Strawberry Lances; Flying Saucers; Mint Imperials

COOKING AIDS - SAVOURY
Golden breadcrumbs

COOKING AIDS - SWEET
Apple & Blackberry Fruit Filling; Apple Fruit Filling; Blackcurrant Fruit Filling; Custard Powder; Golden Marzipan; Mincemeat; Red Cherry Fruit Filling; White Marzipan; White Ready to Roll Icing

CRACKERS, CRISPBREADS ETC
Cream Crackers; High Bake Water Biscuits; Italian Plain Breadsticks; Melba Toast; Mini Breadsticks

DESSERTS
5 Jam Doughnuts; *Christmas Pudding:* Free From, Rich Fruit, Truly Irresistible;

Jelly: Blackberry Flavour with blackberries, Orange Flavour with Pineapple, Summer Fruit Flavour with Raspberries

DIPS & DRESSINGS
Houmous; Lemon and Coriander Houmous; Reduced Fat Houmous; Roasted Red Pepper Houmous; Salsa Dip; Truly Irresistible Balsamic Salad Dressing

GRAVIES & STOCKS
Gravy Browning; Gravy Granules for Meat

'ICE CREAMS', SORBETS ETC
10 Rocket Lollies; 6 Assorted Push Up Ice Lollies; Orange Juice Lollies

MARGARINES, FATS, OILS ETC
Soft Spread

PICKLES, SAUCES, VINEGARS ETC
British Bramley Apple Sauce; Brown Sauce; Dijon Mustard; Distilled Malt Vinegar; English Mustard; French Mustard; Half Fat Salad Cream; Malt Vinegar; Mango Chutney; Mint Jelly; Mint Sauce; Redcurrant Jelly; Reduced Fat French Dressing; Sandwich Pickle; Simply Value Tomato Ketchup; Sweet Piccalilli; Sweet Pickle; Truly irresistible sweet red pepper and balsamic; *Chutney - Truly Irresistible:* Caramelised Red Onion, Fruit, Tomato and Chilli; *Cook In Sauce:* Blackbean, Chilli - Hot, Chilli - Medium, Sweet and Sour, Truly Irresistible Tikka Masala; *Healthy Living Cooking Sauce:* Jalfrezi, Madras, Rogan Josh; *Pasta Sauce:* Chunky Vegetable Pasta Sauce, Healthier Choice Tomato

and Herb, Hot and Spicy, Mushroom, Tomato and Garlic, Tomato and Herb; *Pasta Sauce - Truly Irresistible:* Sun-Dried Tomato and Basil, Tomato and Chilli; *Relish:* Barbecue, Hamburger, Onion, Sweetcorn; *Stir Fry Sauce:* Sweet Chilli and Garlic, Sweet Hoisin, Teriyaki; *Truly Irresistible:* Truly Irresistible Apple Sauce, Truly Irresistible Balsamic Vinegar of Modena, Truly Irresistible Cranberry Sauce, Truly Irresistible Dijon Mustard, Truly Irresistible Mint Sauce., Truly Irresistible Raspberry Coulis, Truly Irresistible Wholegrain Mustard

SAVOURIES - CANNED/BOTTLED
Spaghetti in Tomato Sauce; Spaghetti Rings in Tomato Sauce; *Baked beans in tomato sauce:* Baked Beans, Organic, Simply Value; *Olives:* Pimento Stuffed Manzanilla Olives in brine, Pimento Stuffed Olives, Pitted Black Hojiblanca Olives in Brine, Pitted Green Manzanilla Olives in Brine, Truly Irresistible Green Olives stuffed with Sun-Dried Tomatoes, Truly Irresistible Whole Greek Green Queen Olives in Brine, Whole Kalamata Olives in Brine

SAVOURIES - CHILLED/FRESH
4 Vegetable Spring Rolls; 6 Onion Bhajis; Gourmet Pasta Salad; Moroccan Cous Cous; Takeaway Bombay Potatoes; Takeaway Pilau Rice; Takeaway Sticky Thai Rice

SAVOURIES - DRIED
Apple and Herb Stuffing Mix; Parsley & Thyme Stuffing Mix; Sage and Onion Stuffing Mix; *Microwaveable Rice:* Basmati, Long Grain, Mediterranean, Pilau

SAVOURIES - FROZEN
12 Mini Vegetable Spring Rolls; Battered Onion Rings; Potato Croquettes; Roast British Parsnips; Roast British Parsnips with Rosemary; *Chips:* Crinkle Cut, Crinkle Cut for frying, Healthy Living, Simply Value straight cut, Straight Cut

SNACKS - SAVOURY
Oatcakes; *Crisps:* Assorted Potato Crisps 6x 25g, Chilli Tortilla Chips, Lightly Salted Tortilla Chips, Ready Salted Potato Crisps, Salt & Vinegar Crunchy Sticks, Salt and Vinegar Twirls, Truly Irresistible Lightly Sea Salted Crisps, Truly Irresistible Mixed Root Vegetable Crisps

SOUPS
Chilled: Garden Vegetable Soup with Barley, Limited Edition Minestrone Soup, Limited Edition Pea and Mint Soup, Truly Irresistible Three Bean and Italian Tomato Soup, Truly Irresistible Tomato and Chilli Soup; *Tinned:* Simply Value Vegetable Soup

SOYA AND OTHER 'MILKS'
Simply Value UHT unsweetened soya drink; UHT Organic Sweetened Soya Drink; UHT Organic Unsweetened Soya Drink

SPREADS - SWEET
Bramble Jelly; Premium Red Cherry Soft Set Conserve; Premium Strawberry Soft Set Conserve; *Jam:* Soft set extra jam bursting with fruit, Apricot, Blackcurrant, Damson, Orange and Ginger, Plum, Raspberry, Raspberry Seedless, Simply Value Mixed Fruit, Strawberry; *Marmalade:* Fine Cut Lemon Marmalade, Fine Cut Orange Marmalade, Shredless Orange Marmalade, Simply Value Medium Cut Orange Marmalade, Thick Cut Orange Marmalade; *Truly Irresistible:* Blackcurrant Conserve, Coarse Cut Fresh Fruit Orange Marmalade, Fine Cut Fresh Fruit Seville Orange Marmalade, Strawberry Conserve, Thick Cut Fresh Fruit Three Fruits Marmalade

DRINK

BEERS
Belgian Premium Lager; Best Bitter; Czech Premium Lager; Dutch Lager; Fairtrade Organic Ale; French Premium Lager; Lager; Pilsner Lager; Premium Export Lager; Spanish Premium Lager; Strong Export Ale; Strong Premium Ale; Summer Breeze Ale; Super Strength Lager; Wheat Beer

CIDERS & PERRIES
Strong Dry Cider

'HOT'
Truly Irresistible Fairtrade Drinking Chocolate

SOFT
Apple and Blackcurrant Squash; Apple and Raspberry Juice Drink; Apple, Strawberry & Redcurrant Squash; Bitter Lemon; Blackcurrant Cordial; Cloudy Lemonade; Cola; Cranberry Juice Drink; Diet Cloudy Lemonade; Diet Cola; Diet

Lemonade; Exotic Fruit Juice Drink; Fruit & Barley Drink; Ginger Ale; Grape Apple and Raspberry Juicy Water; Indian Tonic Water; Lemonade; Lime Cordial; Low Calorie American Ginger Ale; Low Calorie Bitter Lemon; Low Calorie Ginger Ale; Low Calorie Indian Tonic Water; Mango and Orange Juicy Water; Mixed Fruit Flavour Squash; No Added Sugar Ginger Beer; Orange and Passion Fruit Juice Water; Orange, Lemon and Pineapple Squash; Simply Value Low Calorie Orange Squash; Soda Water; Sparkling Cranberry Juice Drink with Spring Water; Sparkling Lemonade Shandy; Summer Fruits Smoothie; Tonic Water with a Twist of Lemon; Tropical Fruit Smoothie; Tropical Juice Drink; Tropical Juicy Water; Whole Lemon Squash; Whole Orange Squash; *High Juice:* Apple Squash, Blackcurrant, Orange Squash, Pineapple and Grapefruit, Summer Fruits Squash, Tropical Fruit Squash; *No Added Sugar:* Apple and Blackcurrant Squash, Apple Flavour Squash, Blackcurrant Juice Drink, Caffeine Free Cola, Cherryade, Cola, Cranberry Juice Drink, Cream Soda, Dandelion & Burdock, Fruit and Barley Orange Squash, Fruit and Barley Pink Grapefruit Squash, Fruit and Barley Summer Fruit Squash, Lemon and Lime Crush, Lemon and Lime Squash, Lemonade, Limeade, Orange Drink, Orange Juice drink with sweeteners, Orange, Lemon and Pineapple Squash, Orangeade, Peach and Apricot Flavour, Raspberryade, Strawberry Squash, Strawberryade, Summer Fruit Squash, Tropical Fruit Drink with sweeteners, Whole Lemon Squash, Whole Orange Squash; *Simply Value:* Cola, Lemonade;

Sparkling Spring Water Drink: Apple & Blueberry Flavour, Cherry and Blackcurrant Juice Water, Lemon & Lime Flavour, Orange & Cranberry Flavour, Peach Flavour; *Still Spring Water Drink:* Apple, Blueberry and Raspberry Flavour, Mandarin & Cranberry Flavour, Summer Fruits Flavour; *Truly Irresistible:* Sparkling Blackcurrant Flavour Juice Drink, Sparkling Elderflower Flavour Drink, Sparkling Raspberry Juice Drink, Still Lemonade, Tillington 1000 pressed apple juice

SPIRITS & APÉRITIFS
Scotch Whisky

WINES
Argentine Malbec; Balance Cabernet Shiraz; Beaujolais; Bin 99 Argentine Cabernet franc; Bulgarian Cabernet Sauvignon; Bulgarian Chardonnay; California Colomard Chardonnay "The big chill"; California the pink chill white zinfandel; Cape cellar springs Sauvignon blanc; Cape French Oak Chardonnay; Casa del sol Sauvignon verdejo; Cava rosada brut; Chablis; Champagne les pionniers; Chilean Cabernet Sauvignon; Chilean Cabernet Sauvignon reserve; Chilean Chardonnay; Chilean gewurztraminer; Chilean merlot; Chilean Sauvignon blanc; Cotes du Rhone; Elephant trail colombard Chardonnay; Explorers unoaked Chardonnay; Explorers Vineyard Sauvignon Blanc; Fair trade Argentine Shiraz; Fair trade Cape Cabernet Sauvignon; Fair trade Cape Chardonnay; Fair trade Cape chenin colombard; Fair trade Cape cinsault Shiraz; Fair trade Cape Sauvignon blanc reserve; Fair

trade Cape sparkling brut; Fair trade Chilean Cabernet merlot Shiraz; Fair trade Chilean carmenere; Fair trade Chilean merlot rose; Fair trade Chilean Sauvignon blanc; Fair trade organic Argentine malbec reserve; Fitou; Frascati superiore; Fynbos Cape Shiraz; Island Vines Cyprus red; Long slim white; Orvieto classico; Piper Heidsieck Brut; Premium domaine st gabriel viognier; Premium leyda valley Sauvignon blanc; Premium Vina vedra albarino; Romanian Prairie Merlot; Spanish medium sweet white; Sparkling Chardonnay; Vin de pays Cotes de Gascogne; Vin de pays d'oc Cabernet Sauvignon; Vin de pays d'oc Chardonnay; Vin de pays d'oc Shiraz; Vin de pays d'oc Shiraz rose

TOILETRIES & COSMETICS

SHAVING PRODUCTS
Disposable Razors

HEALTH CARE

SUPPLEMENTS
Chewable Vitamin C; Effervescent Vitamin C Tablets; Folic Acid 400 µg; Ginkgo Biloba Extract 40mg; Korean Ginseng Extract 75mg; Vitamin B Complex; Zinc 15mg

FOOD

BISCUITS
Organic GingerNut Biscuits; *Essential Waitrose:* Bourbon Creams, Ginger Nuts, Morning Coffee Biscuits, Reduced Fat Rich Tea, Rich Tea Finger Biscuits

BREADS, ROLLS, PIZZA BASES ETC
2 Half Ciabattas; 6 Seeded Batch Loaf; Crusty Rolls; Farmhouse Batch Crusty White; Farmhouse Batch Multigrain; Farmhouse Batch Multiseed; Farmhouse Batch Soft White; Farmhouse Batch Wholemeal; Fig, Raisin & Walnut; Flute; Grand Mange Blanc; Grand Mange Paysan; Hovis Granary Baguette; Hovis Granary Rustique; Hovis White Granary Knot; Korbe Medium Rye Bread; Large Baguette; Mixed sliced bloomer; Multigrain Bagel; Olive Ciabatta; Pain Au Levain; Petit Mange Blanc; Petit Parisienne; Plain Bagel; Plain Ciabatta; Rustic Wholemeal Roll; Seeded Bloomer; Sesame Bagel; Small Baguette; Soft White; Soft White Medium Sliced Bread; Soft White Thick Sliced Bread; Stone Baked Pain Rustica Roll; Stone Baked Paysan Rustica Roll; Stonebaked Baguette; Stonebaked Boule; Stonebaked Ficelle; Stonebaked Grand Rustica; Stonebaked Pain de Campagne; Stonebaked Spelt Bread; Stoneground Wholemeal Bread Medium Sliced; Stoneground Wholemeal Bread Thick Sliced; Tiger Bloomer; Waitrose German Style Rye Bread; Walnut bread; Wheat 'N' Rye Quarter; White and Wholegrain Medium Sliced Bread; White and Wholegrain Thick Sliced Bread; White Bloomer; White Farmhouse; White Long Split Tin; White Sandwich; White sliced bloomer; White Tin; Wholegrain Farmhouse; Wholegrain Long Tin; Wholemeal and Seeds Bread Medium Sliced; Wholemeal and Seeds Thick Sliced Bread; Wholemeal Farmhouse; Wholemeal Roll; WR Stonebaked Harvester Petit Pain; *Essential Waitrose:* 10 Mini Plain Bagels, 2 Iced Belgian buns, 5 Cinnamon, Raisin & Apple Bagels, 5 Plain Bagels, 5 Sesame Seed Bagel, 6 Fruited Teacakes, 6 Hot Cross Buns, 6 Iced finger buns, Brown Thin Sliced Bread, Essential Baguette, Longer Life White Medium Sliced Bread, Longer Life Wholemeal Medium Sliced Bread, White Medium Sliced Bread, White Picnic Pitta, White Pitta Bread, White Thick Siced Bread, Wholemeal Medium Sliced Bread, Wholemeal Pitta; *Frozen:* Italian stone baked 2 pizza bases with passata; *Organic:* 4 Wholegrain Muffins, 5 Organic Multi-grain Bagels, Brown Loaf, Brown pitta bread, Farmhouse Batch Malted and Seeded, Farmhouse Batch Soft White, Farmhouse Batch Wholemeal, Farmhouse Batch Wholemeal and Seeded, Malted tin, Multi Seeded Pave, Multigrain Pave, Organic Ciabatta, Sliced Seeded Bloomer, White Baguette, White Farmhouse, White Loaf, White Tin, Wholegrain Farmhouse, Wholegrain Tin, Wholemeal Heyford Loaf; *Prepacked Rolls:* 4 Granary Rolls, 4 Italian Style Ciabatta Rolls, 4 pack panini, 4 White Rolls, 4 Wholemeal Rolls; *Prepacked Rolls - Essential Waitrose :* 4 White Crusty Rolls, 4 White Giant Baps, 6 White Finger Rolls, 6 White Floured Baps; *Prepacked Rolls -*

Essential Waitrose: 6 White Sesame Seed Burger Buns; *Prepacked Rolls - Essential Waitrose:* 6 Wholemeal Baps; *Waitrose Frozen:* 4 White rustic baguettes, 4 Wholemeal rustic baguettes, 6 Pain rustiques

BREAKFAST FOODS
Fruit and Seed Muesli; High fibre Muesli; Maple triple nut Muesli; Orchard fruits & berries Muesli; Seriously fruity mixed berry crisp; *Essential Waitrose:* Fruit & nut Muesli, Malted Wheats, Wholegrain apricot wheats, Wholegrain cranberry wheats, Wholewheat Biscuits; *Organic:* Muesli; *Perfectly Balanced:* Fruit Muesli

'BURGERS', 'SAUSAGES', 'MEAT' SLICES ETC
4 Chunky vegetable quarter pounders

CONFECTIONERY & SWEET SNACKS
Chocolate Ginger; Chocolate Mint Thins; Fizzy Strawberry Lances

COOKING AIDS - SAVOURY
Cooks' Ingredients: A Handful of Breadcrumbs, A Handful of Soft White Bread Crumbs

COOKING AIDS - SWEET
Cranberry and Port Mincemeat; Mincemeat; *Cooks' Ingredients:* A Good Layer of Brandy Marzipan, A Good Layer of Golden Marzipan, A Good Layer of White Marzipan

CRACKERS, CRISPBREADS ETC
Grissini Plain breadsticks; Grissini Sesame Breadsticks; Mini Breadsticks with extra virgin olive oil; Oatcakes with cracked black pepper; Scottish oatcakes with extra virgin olive oil; Scottish rough oatcakes; *Black and White Low Fat:* Breadsticks; *Essential Waitrose:* Cream Crackers, High Bake Water Biscuits

DESSERTS
2 Summer Puddings; 2 Winter Puddings; Fruity blackcurrant coulis; Fruity mango & lime coulis; Fruity raspberry coulis; Summer Pudding; *Essential Waitrose:* Cherry Jelly, Raspberry Jelly; *Patisserie:* Cinnamon & Raisin Bagel, Coconut and Cherry Slice, Iced Finger Bun, Individual apple & blackberry pie, Individual apple pie, Large apple & blackberry pie, Large Apple Pie; *Waitrose Entertaining:* Champagne Sorbet Shots, Elderflower Sorbet Shots

DIPS & DRESSINGS
Cannellini Bean and Lime Houmous; Caramelised Onion Houmous; Chunky Dip Vine Ripened Tomato Salsa; French Dressing; Guacamole Supreme; Hot Spicy Salsa; Mango & Chilli Dressing; Moroccan Style Spiced Houmous; Roasted Red Pepper Houmous; Salsa Supreme; Slow Roasted Tomato Houmous; Supreme Houmous; *Black and White Half Fat:* French Dressing; *Essential Waitrose:* French Dressing, Houmous, Tomato Salsa; *Essential Waitrose Black and White Reduced Fat:* Houmous; *Organic:* Houmous

GRAVIES & STOCKS
Cooks' Ingredients: Cooks Ingredients - A Measure of Vegetable Stock, Pop in a shot of vegetable stock; *Organic Cooks' Ingredients:* A Ladle of Vegetable Stock gently simmered

'ICE CREAMS', SORBETS ETC

Seriously: Fruity Alphonso mango sorbet, Fruity passion fruit sorbet, Fruity Sicilian lemon sorbet, Fruity Williamette raspberry sorbet

PICKLES, SAUCES, VINEGARS ETC

Apple and walnut chutney; Apple sauce with cider; Bruschetta Topping in Olive Oil; Cano's Membrillo Quince Paste; Caramelised red onion chutney; Cranberry & Mulled Wine Sauce; Cranberry and Port Sauce; Cranberry Sauce; Cranberry sauce with Burgundy; Goan Cooking Sauce; Green Olive, Coriander & Lemon Tapenade; Hot & Spicy Mango Chutney; Kalamata Olive & Sundried Tomato Tapenade; Mango Chutney; Mint Jelly; Mint sauce; Mint sauce with wine vinegar; Patia Cooking Sauce; Redcurrant & Red Onion Chutney; Redcurrant jelly; Redcurrant sauce with Port; Roasted vegetable chutney; Salsa Relish; Spicy Onion & Garlic relish; Spicy Peach Chutney; Sticky Barbecue Marinade; Tewkesbury Mustard; Thai Marinade; Tomato and Onion Relish; Tomato Chutney; *Black and White Half Fat:* Half Fat Jalfrezi Cooking Sauce; *Cooks' Ingredients:* A dash of Chinese rice vinegar, A dash of dark soya sauce, A dash of Japanese soya sauce, A splash of Chinese black rice vinegar, A splash of Japanese rice vinegar, A splash of mirin rice wine, A splash of shaoxing rice wine, A spoonful Of Miso Paste, A spoonful Of Umeboshi Plum Puree, Balsamic Vinegar of Modena Spry, Be bold with the Thai sweet chilli sauce, Be generous with the hoisin sauce, Be generous with the plum sauce, Caper paste, Chilli Sauce, Dijon Smooth Mustard, Dijon Wholegrain Mustard, Glaze with the Teriyaki sauce, Go easy on the Thai hot chilli sauce, Roasted Garlic Sauce, Sherry Vinegar; *Essential Waitrose:* Brown Sauce, Dijon Mustard, English Mustard, French Mustard, Tomato Ketchup, Wholegrain Mustard; *Pasta Sauce:* Arrabbiata, Chianti & Olive, Essential Waitrose Tomato & Basil, Essential Waitrose Tomato and Basil Pasta Sauce, Essential Waitrose Tomato and Chilli Pasta Sauce, Mediterranean Vegetable, Napoletana, Organic Tomato and roasted garlic, Sugo alla Bolognese, Tomato & Chilli, Tomato, Basil & Rocket Pasta Sauce; *Vinegar:* 3 Leaves Organic Balsamic Vinegar of Modena, 4 leaves Balsamic Vinegar of Modena, Balsamic Vinegar; *Vinegar - Essential Waitrose:* Balsamic Vinegar of Modena, Cider Vinegar, Red Wine Vinegar, White Wine Vinegar

SAVOURIES - CANNED/BOTTLED

Halkidiki Citrus Stuffed Olives; Natural Pimiento Stuffed Queen Olives in brine; Olympian Mixed Marinated Greek Olives; Pimiento Stuffed Green Olives in Brine 340g; Pitted Green Olives Stuffed with Hot Pimiento Puree in brine; Pitted Green Olives Stuffed with Lemon puree; Spanish Mixed Stuffed Green Olives in brine; Spanish pitted green olives stuffed with almonds; Stuffed Green Olives with Garlic in Brine; Whole Greek Kalamata Olives in brine and wine vinegar; *Essential Waitrose:* Short cut Spaghetti in Tomato Sauce, Spaghetti hoops in tomato sauce; *Organic:* Organic Baked Beans in Tomato Sauce

SAVOURIES - CHILLED/FRESH
Chargrilled vegetable antipasti pizza with basil oil; Chef's Special Nine Jewel Rice; Chinese Pancakes; Chunky Chips; Coconut rice; Falafel Bites; Lemon pilau rice; Roast potatoes; Sambhar; Spinach & carrot pilau rice; Thai fragrant rice; Vegetable Samosas; Vegetable spring rolls; *Cafe:* Boiled rice, Bombay Potatoes, Grilled Vegetable & Houmous Wrap with Baby Spinach, Crunchy Carrot & Pine Nuts, Hot & Spicy 6-Cut Wedge, Pilau rice, Spinach & carrot pilau, Spinach Dal, Tomato & Fresh Basil Soup; *Delicatezze:* Artichokes with grilled asparagus & courgettes, Red pepper topped houmous, Roasted red pepper mezze, Stuffed Vine Leaves; *Food for Now:* Grilled Vegetable & Houmous Wrap with Baby Spinach, Crunchy Carrot & Pine Nuts, Large Vegetable Samosa, Rosemary Breadsticks with Houmous; *Hot Takeaway:* Boiled rice, Bombay potatoes, Masala dal, Pilau rice, Spinach & carrot pilau, Spinach dal; *Indian Tastes:* Cauliflower and Broccoli Masala, Channa Masala, Coriander Rice, Spiced Potatoes, Spinach Dal; *Salad and olive bar:* Beetroot and Carrot Salad, Black, Green and Pepper Stuffed Olives, Carrot & Coriander Salad, Cherry Tomato Salad, Chick Pea and Bean Salad, Chilli stuffed Kalkidis olives, Fruity Moroccan style Couscous, Italian Antipasti, Minted Potatoes, Mixed Salad, Oriental Nanjing Rice, Red Cabbage Slaw, Tabbouleh Salad, Tomato & Basil Fusilloni Pasta, Tomato & Chilli Potatoes; *Waitrose Entertaining:* Bombay potatoes, Couscous and Roasted Vegetable Salad, Pilau rice, Rice and Potato Wedges, Roast Potatoes, Rosemary and Garlic Roast Potatoes, Tomato & Basil Pasta Salad

SAVOURIES - DRIED
Tomato and Onion Couscous; *Cooks' Ingredients:* A Nest of Medium Noodles; *Microwaveable Rice:* Arborio, Basmati, Long Grain, Pilau Basmati, Whole Grain

SAVOURIES - FROZEN
4 Moroccan-spiced couscous grills; Basmati Rice; Potato Rosti; Vegetable Ratatouille; Waitrose Roasting Parsnips; *Chips:* American Coated Oven Fries, Chunky Skin on oven Chips, Crinkle Oven Chips, Organic Straight Cut Oven Chips, Spicy Jacket Wedges, Steak Cut Oven Chips, Straight Cut Frying Chips, Straight Cut Oven Chips; *Essential Waitrose:* Basmati Rice, White Rice; *Waitrose Frozen:* Tomato Ragu

SNACKS - SAVOURY
Giant Pretzels; Roasted mixed nuts with a rosemary infused oil and Mexican chilli seasoning; Sea Salt & Cracked Black Pepper Pretzels; *Crisps:* Hand Cooked Crisps Sea Salt, Hand Cooked Crisps Texan BBQ, Spicy plantain crisps with sweet chilli & lime, Vegetable Crisps, Winter-spiced parsnip crisps with chilli; *Crisps - Black and White Reduced Fat:* Crinkle Cut Lightly Salted Crisps; *Crisps - Essential Waitrose:* Bacon Rashers, Potato squares, Ready Salted Crisps, Salt & Malt Vinegar Crisps, Salt and malt vinegar sticks, Salt and malt vinegar twirls, Salt Your Own Crisps; *Crisps - Essential Waitrose Black and White Reduced Fat:* Crinkle Cut Lightly Salted Crisps, Crinkle Cut Unsalted Crisps

SOUPS

Fresh soups: Gazpacho, Italian Bean, Organic Lentil & Tomato, Organic Tomato & Red Pepper, Tomato & Fresh Basil, Vegetable and Lentil; *Tinned soup:* Chunky Minestrone, Chunky Tuscan Bean, Moroccan Vegetable Tagine, Organic Red Pepper and Mediterranean Vegetable, Parsnip & Ginger, Tomato and Basil

SOYA AND OTHER 'MILKS'

Sweetened U.H.T. Soya non dairy alternative to milk; Unsweetened U.H.T. Soya non dairy alternative to milk; *Organic:* Sweetened U.H.T Soya non dairy alternative to milk, Unsweetened U.H.T Soya non dairy alternative to milk

SPREADS - SAVOURY

Essential Waitrose: Crunchy Peanut Butter, Smooth Peanut Butter, Wholenut Peanut Butter; *Organic:* Organic Crunchy peanut butter, Organic Smooth peanut butter

SPREADS - SWEET

Foundation Fruit Fresh Fruit Orange Marmalade; Fresh Fruit 3 Fruits Marmalade; Fresh Fruit Grapefruit Marmalade; Fresh Fruit Lemon Marmalade; Fresh Fruit Seville Orange Marmalade; Fresh Fruit Star Ruby Grapefruit Marmalade; Ginger Conserve; Orange and Ginger Marmalade; Organic Seville Orange Marmalade; *Black and White Reduced Sugar:* High Fruit Blackcurrant Jam, High Fruit Cherries and Berries Jam, High Fruit Orange Marmalade, High Fruit Raspberry Jam, High Fruit Strawberry Jam; *Essential Waitrose:* Apricot Jam, Blackcurrant Jam, Raspberry Jam, Seedless Raspberry Jam, Seville no peel Orange Marmalade, Seville Thick Cut Orange Marmalade, Seville Thin Cut Orange Marmalade, Strawberry Jam

DRINK

SOFT

Blueberry Juice Drink; Cranberry Juice Drink; Pineapple, banana & coconut smoothie; Pomegranate Juice Drink; Strawberry, raspberry & banana smoothie; Tropical Crush; Tropical Juice; *Cordial:* Elderflower, Lime Juice, Raspberry and Pear; *Essential Waitrose:* Apple & Raspberry Juice Drink, Bitter Lemon, Ginger Ale, Lemonade with Lemon Juice, Scottish Natural Mineral Water Sparkling with Lemon, Tropical Juice Drink; *Essential Waitrose Black and White Sugar Free:* Bitter Lemon, Ginger Ale; *Seriously:* Blackcurrant and Blueberry Smoothie, Kiwi, Apple and Pear Smoothie, Mango and Lychee Smoothie, Peach and Pineapple Smoothie, Strawberry and Cherry Smoothie; *Sparkling Water:* Cranberry, Elderflower, Grapefruit, Mango; *Squash:* Apple & Blackcurrant No Added Sugar, Grapefruit No Added Sugar; *Squash - Essential Waitrose Black and White No Added Sugar:* Apple & blackcurrant, High Juice Blackcurrant, High Juice Mediterranean Orange, High juice summer fruits, Lemon, Orange, Orange, lemon & pineapple, Summer fruits, Tropical;

Squash - High Juice: Apple, Apple & Elderflower, Blackcurrant, Cranberry & Blueberry, Mediterranean Orange, Orange and Mango, Pink Grapefruit, Summer Fruits, Tropical, White Grape & Peach

NOTES

- Asda were unable to provide a list at the time of going to print but anticipate having an up to date list available by early 2011. When the list becomes available you will be able to view it on our Animal Free Shopper website: www.vegansociety.com/afssearch.aspx

- Sainsbury's and Marks and Spencer both label their vegan wines.

COMPANY CONTACT DETAILS

- **7UP** www.7up.co.uk 0800 032 1767
- **A. Vogel** www.bioforce.co.uk 01294 277 344
- **A'Beckett's Vineyard** www.abecketts.co.uk 01380 816669
- **Absolut** www.absolut.com
- **Absolute Aromas** www.absolute-aromas.com 01420 540400
- **Absolutely Pure** www.absolutelypure.com 0870 760 6915
- **Acorn Products Co, LLC** www.acorn.com 0011207 786-3526
- **Adeena** www.adeena.co.uk 08707 605 49321
- **Adorn Mineral Cosmetics** www.adornmineralcosmetics.com.au 0061 (0) 3 9802 4003
- **Advanced Formulations (Europe Ltd)** www.advancedformulations.com 0208 640 4444
- **Age Vert Lynx Industries** www.agevert.com 0033 344 09 02 74
- **Ainsworths** www.ainsworths.com 0207 935 5330
- **Ajitas Vege Chips** www.ajitas.com 61 7 55 250670
- **Akamuti** www.akamuti.co.uk 0845 458 9242
- **Akoma International (UK) Ltd** www.akomaskincare.co.uk 01332 200 473
- **Alara Wholefoods Ltd** www.alara.co.uk 020 7387 9303
- **Alexami Cosmetics** www.alexami.com
- **All Seasons Health** http://www.allseasonshealth.co.uk/ 01329 230991
- **Allergenics** www.lifewitheczema.com
- **Allied Bakeries** www.alliedbakeries.co.uk 01628 764300
- **Allinson** www.allinsonbread.com
- **Aloe Dent** www.optimah.com
- **Aloe Pura** www.optimah.com
- **Alpro UK Ltd** www.alprosoya.co.uk 01536 720 605
- **Alternative Stores** www.alternativestores.com 0191 236 8519
- **Alvin Connor Limited** www.alvinconnor.com 0151 448 0368
- **Amanda Trading Ltd T/A African Delights** www.africandelights.co.uk 020 8400 4842
- **AmaZene** http://www.amazene.co.uk 01279 739 222
- **Ame** www.britvic.co.uk 0800 0321767
- **Amisa** www.windmillorganics.com
- **Anheuser-Busch** www.budweiser.co.uk
- **Anheuser-Busch InBev** www.inbev.com 0158 239 1166
- **Anila's Authentic Sauces Ltd** www.anilassauces.com 020 8577 6162
- **Animal Aid** www.animalaid.org.uk 01732 364546
- **Ann Elise Skincare** www.anneliseskincare.co.uk 01304 368298
- **Annemarie Borlind** www.borlind.com

- **Aqua Natural** www.aquanatural.co.uk 01933 441818
- **Aquados Ltd** www.simplywashing.com 01924 894513
- **AquaSource** www.aquasource.co.uk 01392 822155
- **Arabesque** Unit F7, Acton Business Centre, School Road, Park Royal, London, NW10 6TD 02089619222
- **Arbonne** www.arbonneinternational.co.uk 07879 401 021
- **Archers** www.archers.com
- **Arcim Hypogeen b.v.** www.hypogeen.nl 00 31 356 945 297
- **Arise and Shine Cosmetics Ltd** www.ariseandshinecosmetics.co.uk 07961 726 337
- **Aroma Comforts** 31 Hackney Grove, London , E8 3NR 0208 985 5956
- **Aroma Crystal Therapy** www.aromacrystal.com
- **Aromafoods** www.aromafoods.org.uk 0800 0744 876
- **Aromatherapy Products Ltd** www.tisserand.com 01273 325666
- **Artisan Biscuits** www.artisanbiscuits.co.uk 01335 342 373
- **Artisan Brasseur** www.artisanbrasseur.com
- **Asics** www.asics.co.uk 01925 241041
- **Aspall** www.aspall.co.uk 01728 860 510
- **Astonish** www.astonishcleaners.com 0113 236 0036
- **Astroglide** www.astroglide.co.uk 0208 203 9493
- **Aubrey Organics** www.aubrey-organics.com 0800 0851 697
- **Auro** www.auroorganic.co.uk 01452 772020
- **Australian Nougat Company** www.ausnougat.com.au 07548 853132
- **Australian Tea Tree** www.optimah.com
- **Aveda** www.aveda.co.uk
- **B&Q** www.diy.com 0845 609 6688
- **Babyboo Organics Ltd** www.babyboo-organics.co.uk 08448793302 ex5
- **Babycakes Direct** www.vegancakedirect.co.uk 07951 215121
- **Babynat** www.babynat.co.uk
- **Baby's bum premium natural soaps** http://www.redstarnaturalliquidsoaps.co.uk 01384 873748
- **Bacheldre Watermill Organic Flowers** www.bacheldremill.co.uk 01588 620 489
- **Barefoot Botanicals** www.barefoot-botanicals.com 0870 220 2273
- **Baron Wine Cellars Ltd T/A Tishbi Estate Winery** www.tishbi.com 972-4-6380434/5
- **Barry M Cosmetics** www.barrym.com 020 8349 2992
- **Baxters** www.baxters.co.uk 01343 820393
- **Beaming Baby** www.beamingbaby.com 0800 0345 672
- **Bean Thinking** www.beanthinking.co.uk 01353 723 600
- **Beanie's Health Foods** www.beanieshealthfoods.co.uk 01489 574 593
- **Beauty Naturals** www.beautynaturals.com 0845 094 0402
- **Beauty Without Cruelty** www.bwcshop.co.uk 01473 271500

- **Bellecare AG** www.sanmar.ch 0041 76 376 63 16
- **Belvoir Fruit Farms** www.belvoircordials.co.uk 01476 870 286
- **Ben & Jerry's** www.benjerry.co.uk 0800 1696 123
- **Bendicks of Mayfair** www.bendicks.co.uk 01962 844800
- **Benecol** www.benecol.co.uk
- **Bertolli** www.bertolli.com
- **Berwitz Homeopathy** www.homeopathy-heals.com 0161 439 8041
- **BetterThanks Inc** www.betterthanks.com
- **Beyond Skin** www.beyondskin.co.uk 01494 871655
- **Bickiepegs** www.bickiepegs.co.uk 01224 790626
- **Bill's Natuurbakkerij** www.billysfarm.nl +31(0)512 532000
- **Bio-D** www.biodegradable.biz 01482 229950
- **Biofair** www.windmillorganics.com
- **Biofun bvba** www.biofun.be 0032 50 2898 07
- **Bio-Health Ltd** www.bio-health.co.uk 01634 290115
- **Biona** www.windmillorganics.com 020 8547 2775
- **Bio-Oil** www.bio-oil.info
- **Biosym A/S** www.biosym.dk 004597252015
- **Bird's** www.premierfoods.co.uk 0727 815 850
- **Bisto** www.aahnight.co.uk 0800 234 6328
- **BL Cosmetics** www.bodyline.co.uk 01803 527000
- **Black Opal International Australia** http://www.blackopalinc.com/index.html
- **Black Sheep Brewery Plc** www.blacksheepbrewery.com 01765 689227
- **Blackfriars Bakery** www.blackfriarsbakery.co.uk 0116 262 2836
- **Blue Dragon** www.bluedragon.com
- **B'Nice** www.bnice.be 00 32 1461 1306
- **Bodylove** www.cherrybliss.com
- **Bonano Gmbh** www.alviana.de 0049 6259322683
- **Boots Company Plc** www.boots-plc.com 0115 950 6111 / 0115 968 7035
- **Bourgeois Boheme** www.bboheme.com 020 88 788 388
- **Brackencraft** www.brackencraft.com
- **Braham & Murray Ltd** www.goodwebsite.co.uk
  01271 858 377/ 0207 727 7785
- **Brakspear's** www.brakspear-beers.co.uk/ 01993 890 800
- **British Sugar plc** www.britishsugar.co.uk 020 7589 6363
- **Britvic** www.britvic.co.uk 0800 032 1767
- **Bronnley & Co Ltd** www.bronnley.co.uk 01280 702291
- **Brooks- Hill Ltd** www.naturaleve.co.uk 01923 249241
- **Broughton Pastures** www.BroughtonPastures.co.uk 01442 823 993
- **Brunel Healthcare** www.bruhealth.co.uk
- **Buckingham's Oativa** www.oativa.com 01246201041
- **Budweiser** www.budweiser.com 020 8332 2302
- **Buitoni** www.buitoni.co.uk

- **Burton's Foods Ltd** f 0151 488 4536
- **Burt's Bees** www.forever-natural.com 01628 898410
- **Bute Island Foods Ltd** www.buteisland.com 01700 505357
- **Cadaleah Home Bakers** caren@cadaleah.co.uk 01932 882019
- **Cadbury Trebor Bassett** www.cadbury.co.uk 0121 451 4444
- **Calder Valley Soap Co. Ltd** www.caldervalleysoaps.com 01706 818666
- **Caledonian Brewing Co** www.caledonian-brewery.co.uk 0131 337 1286
- **Caledonian Curry Co.** www.caledoniancurry.co.uk 01863 766025
- Mobile: 0787 67 62 395
- **Carlsberg UK Ltd** www.carlsberguk.co.uk 01604 668866
- **Cauldron** www.cauldronfoods.co.uk 0845 7413 666
- **Caurnie Soaperie** www.caurnie.com 0141 776 1218
- **Cawarra Cosmetics Ltd** www.sanctumaustralia.com 00 61 2 6680 3266
- **Cebra Ethical Chic** www.cebraonline.com 01328 826928
- **Cedar Health Ltd** www.cedarhealth.co.uk 0161 483 1235
- **Cellande Midlands** www.cellande.co.uk 0121 472 2903
- **Celtic Chocolates** info@celticchocolates.eu 00353-405 57077
- **Chegworth Valley Juices** www.chegworthvalley.com 01622 859 272
- **Chikpe** www.chikpe.co.uk 01743 244466
- **Chimans** www.chimans.co.uk 01271 850378
- **Chocaid** www.chocaid.com 01604 493020
- **Clearspring** www.clearspring.co.uk 020 8749 1781
- **Clive's Pies** www.clivespies.co.uk 01364 642279
- **Coca-Cola** 1 Queen Caroline Street, Hammersmith, Greater London, W6 9HQ
- **Cocada Fresco (UK) Ltd** www.cocadafresco.com 02084552898
- **Cockburn's** www.cockburns-usa.com
- **Colman's** www.colmans.co.uk
- **Constellation Wines** www.cbrands.eu.com 01483 690 000
- **Cookeen** www.princes.co.uk 0151 236 9282
- **Cosmetic Innovations Australia PTY Ltd** www.claytime.com.au 0061299754637
- **Country Life** www.country-life.com
- **Courvoisier** www.courvoisier.com
- **Cow & Gate** www.cowandgate.co.uk 08457 623 623
- **Cracker Drinks Co.** www.crackerdrinks.com (0)1189 845 378
- **Crips** www.cripsnacks.com 01332 865220
- **Cropton Brewery** www.croptonbrewery.co.uk 01751 417310
- **Cubana Produce LTD** www.spirel.co.uk 0207 427 5145
- **Cuisine de France** www.cuisinedefrance.ie 00353 1405 7200
- **Curry Slim** www.tinydeol.com 0116 238 67 56
- **Cyberdyne Technologies Ltd, T/A Mama Shamba** www.mamashamba.com +44 2033 724 838
- **D & D Chocolates** www.d-dchocolates.com 02476 370909

- **Dalepak** www.dalepak.co.uk 01677424111
- **Daler-Rowney Ltd** www.daler-rowney.com 01344 461 000
- **Daloon Foods** www.daloon.com
- **Daniel Field** www.danielfield.com 0800 077 8270
- **Daniel Thwaites** www.thwaites.co.uk 01254 686868
- **Dark Secrets Chocolate** darksecretschoc@yahoo.co.uk 01273 476966
- **Dartmoor Chilli Farm** www.dartmoorchillifarm.co.uk
- **Dees Caribbean Imports** deesimports@hotmail.com 0208 5398484
- **Delaforce** www.delaforce.com
- **Dendron Ltd** 42 Caxton Way, Watford Business Park, Watford, Hertfordshire , WD1 8QZ
- **Desert Essence** www.desertessence.com 020 8614 1411
- **Desibox Indian Cuisine** www.desibox.co.uk/
- **Deva Nutrition LLC** www.devanutrition.com (+001) 888 517 7620
- **Diet Freedom** www.sweetfreedom.co.uk 020 7328 8490
- **Dietary Needs Direct** www.dietaryneedsdirect.co.uk 01453 840 420
- **Diomed Developments Ltd** www.4headaches.co.uk
- **Dipak Foods Ltd** 13 Willowbrook Workshops, Syston Street West, Leicester, Leicestershire, LE1 2JU 0116 2511300
- **Dirk Rossmann GmbH** www.rossmann.de 0049 5139 898 - 4279
- **Discovery Foods** www.discoveryfoods.co.uk 01494 464460
- **Divine Chocolate** www.divinechocolate.com 020 7378 6550
- **Dixie Diners Club** www.dixiediner.com
- **Dolma** www.dolma-perfumes.co.uk 0115 963 4237
- **Dolmio** www.dolmio.co.uk 0800 952 1234
- **Dome** www.domecosmetics.com 020 8746 1900
- **Doves Farm Foods Ltd** www.dovesfarm.co.uk 01488 684880
- **Dr Hauschka** www.drhauschka.co.uk 01386 791 022
- **Dr Oetker** www.oetker.co.uk 01977 687 300
- **Dr Organic** www.drorganic.co.uk
- **Dragonfly Foods** www.beany.co.uk 01364 642700
- **Dri-Pak Ltd** www.dripak.co.uk 0115 932 5165
- **Droyt Products** www.droyts.com 01257 417251
- **Dunkerton's Cider Company** www.dunkertons.co.uk 01544 388653
- **Durex** www.durex.com
- **Earth Footwear** www.earthfootwear.com 001-781-893-7474
- **Earth Friendly products UK** www.greenbrands.co.uk 01892 616871
- **EarthBorn Natural Paints** www.earthbornpaints.co.uk 01928 734171
- **Earthpure** www.earthpure.co.uk 01994 241 484
- **Earth's Beauty** www.earthsbeauty.com
- **Ecco Bella** www.eccobella.com
- **Eco Cosmetics GmbH & Co. KG** www.eco-naturkosmetik.de +49-(0)5102-933 99 54

- **Eco Lips, Inc** www.ecolips.com 00 1 319 364 2477
- **Ecos Paints** www.ecosorganicpaints.com 01524 852371
- **Ecosoapia** www.ecosoapia.com 0207 289 2121
- **EJs Conscious Chocolate** www.consciouschocolate.co.uk 07949 171245
- **Elizabeth Shaw** www.elizabethshaw.co.uk 0117 301 3300
- **Ella Drinks** www.bouvrage.com 01786 834342
- **Emergen-C** www.emergenc.com 1-800-854-0249
- **Emiliana Organico** www.emiliana.cl
- **Empathy Skincare Ltd (Natural Empathy)** www.naturalempathy.com 01665 710016
- **Energizer Personal Care** www.wetones.co.uk 01494 5333 00
- **Epson** www.epson.co.uk 08702 416900
- **ESB Developments LTD** Unit 2, Glade Business Centre, Galaway, Nottingham, Nottinghamshire, NG5 9RW
- **Essential Care** www.essential-care.co.uk 01638 716593
- **Essential Trading Co-Operative Ltd** www.essential-trading.coop 0117 9583550
- **Essentially Natural** www.e-nat.co.uk 08000 664916
- **Essentially Yours Ltd** www.essentially-yours.co.uk 020 8398 6300
- **Eternity Designs International PTY Ltd** www.mineralmakeup.com.au 0061299754637
- **Ethical Wares** www.ethicalwares.com 01570 471155
- **Everards Brewery** www.everards.co.uk 0116 201 4100
- **Faith Products Limited** www.faithinnature.co.uk 0161 724 4016
- **Fauser Vitaquellwerk KG** www.vitaquell.de 0049 40 572020
- **Feel Good Handbags** www.feelgoodhandbags.co.uk 01695 580713
- **Fentimans Ltd** www.fentimans.com 01434 609847
- **Fertile Fibre** www.fertilefibre.co.uk 01432 853111
- **First Grade International LTD** http://www.fg-int.co.uk/liquid.htm 01564731980
- **Flex Enterprises Ltd** www.flexenterprises.co.uk 02032878286
- **Floris** www.florislondon.com 01884 242626
- **Fonseca** www.fonseca.pt
- **Food Safe** www.food-safe.com 01788 510415
- **Forever Living Products** www.aloevera.co.uk 01327 830855
- **Forever Young International Limited** forever-young@lineone.net 0208 648 6777
- **Frank Cooper** www.premierfoods.co.uk 01727 815850
- **Freedom Brewery Ltd** www.freedomlager.com 01283 840721
- **Freerangers** www.freerangers.co.uk 01207 565957
- **Fry Group Foods** www.frys-special.com +27 31 700 3022/3
- **FTF Sweets Ltd** www.goodygoodstuff.com 0845 643 9333
- **Fullers** www.fullers.co.uk 020 8996 2000

- **Funk Bubble** www.funkbubble.co.uk 07775 898 889
- **G & G Vitamins** www.gandgvitamins.com 01342 312 811
- **G. Costa & Co** www.gcosta.co.uk 01622 717777
- **Gama Healthcare Limited** www.gamahealthcare.com 08452 011 644
- **Gatorade** www.gatorade.co.uk 0800 0321767
- **Geeta's Foods Limited** www.geetasfoods.com 0208 450 2255
- **General Dietary** www.generaldietary.com 020 8336 2323
- **Gentle Beauty Co Ltd** www.gentle-beauty.com 0203 072 1000
- **Geo Organics** www.venturefoods.co.uk 01743 289 133
- **Georgas Family** www.geowines.gr 00302106633345
- **George Bateman & Son** www.bateman.co.uk 01754 880317
- **Gerber Juice Company** www.gerberfoods.com 01278 441600
- **Gilchesters Organics Ltd** www.gilchesters.com 01661 886119
- **Glasgow Health Solutions** www.healthyandessential.com 08700 536000
- **Glenfiddich** http://uk.glenfiddich.com/
- **Gluten Free Foods Ltd** www.glutenfree-foods.co.uk 020 8953 4444
- **Glyde Health PTY LTD** www.glydehealth.com 0061 2 9415 8933
- **Gobblin Wholefoods** Unit 5, Station Rd Ind Est , Elmswell, Bury St. Edmund, Suffolk, IP30 9HR 01359 241841
- **Golden Wonder** www.goldenwonder.com 01724 281222
- **Goodlife Foods** www.goodlife.co.uk 01925 837810
- **Gordon's** www.gordons-gin.co.uk
- **Gourmet Classic Ltd** www.gourmetclassic.com (0) 1202 863040
- **Govinda Natur GmbH** www.govindanatur.de/ 00496782109670
- **GR Wright & Sons Ltd** www.wrightsflour.co.uk 0208 344 6900
- **Grand Marnier** www.grand-marnier.com
- **Granose** www.symingtons.com
- **Granovita UK Ltd** www.granovita.co.uk 01933 273717
- **Green People Co.** www.greenpeople.co.uk 01403 740350
- **Green Planet Solutions Ltd** www.greenplanetsolutions.co.uk 01270 898 041
- **Green Shoes** www.greenshoes.co.uk 01364 644 036
- **Green Valley Trading Co** www.gvtc.co.uk 01283 769898
- **Green Wych ltd** www.greenwych.co.uk (01803) 315012
- **Greencity Wholefoods** www.greencity.co.uk 0141 554 7633
- **Green's** www.kerrygroup.com
- **GreenVee** www.greenvee.com www.greenvee.com
- **Grolsch** www.grolsch.co.uk 01283 513358
- **Guarana Company Ltd** www.guaranaco.com 01273 621406
- **Gwynt Y Ddraig Cider** www.gwyntcider.com 01443 209 852
- **Hall & Woodhouse Ltd** www.hall-woodhouse.co.uk
- **Halls** www.cadburyschweppes.com
- **Halo Skincare Ltd** www.haloskincare.co.uk 07950 794 552
- **Handmade Flapjack Company Ltd** www.handmade-flapjack.co.uk 024 7658 8350

- **Happy And Healthy Foods** info@happyandhealthyfoods.com +61242360529
- **Happy Kitchen** www.happykitchen.org.uk 0207 275 0872
- **Harbourne Vineyard** www.harbournevineyard.co.uk
- **Harveys** www.harveys-usa.com
- **Health + Plus Ltd** www.healthplus.co.uk 01323 872277
- **Health Perception** www.health-perception.co.uk 01252 861 454
- **Healthpol** www.healthpol.co.uk 020 8360 0386
- **Healthquest Limited** www.healthquest.co.uk 0845 310 4411
- **Healthspan Ltd** www.healthspan.co.uk 0800 7312377
- **Healthy Herbs** c.chamberlain-davis@ntlworld.com 01565 755022
- **Hedgecraft** www.hedgecraft.co.uk
- **Heineken** www.heineken.com +31 (0)20 523 92 39
- **Heinz** www.heinz.co.uk 0208 573 7757
- **Hellmann's** www.hellmanns.co.uk 0800 435562
- **Hemp Garden** www.hempgarden.co.uk 01424 434370
- **Hemp Global Solutions Ltd** www.hempglobalsolutions.com 0208 671 7731
- **Hendersons** www.hendersons-relish.co.uk 0114 272 5909
- **Herbs Hands Healing Ltd** www.herbshandshealing.co.uk 0845 3453727
- **Herbsgo Limited T/A Clive Foot** www.clivefoot.com 0114 2668100
- **High Barn Oils** www.highbarnoils.co.uk 01403 730326
- **Higher Nature Ltd** www.highernature.co.uk 01435 883484
- **Hipp Organic Baby Foods** www.hipp.co.uk 0845 050 1351
- **Hippy Heaven Natural Beauty** www.hippyheavennaturalbeauty.net 0403 587 609
- **Holistix Herbal Products** www.holistixherbs.co.uk 0151 734 1940
- **Holland and Barrett Retail Ltd** www.hollandandbarrett.com 02476244400
- **Holsten** www.holsten.de
- **Honesty Cosmetics Ltd** www.honestycosmetics.co.uk 01629 814888
- **Hotel Chocolat** www.hotelchocolat.co.uk 0870 442 8282
- **Hovis** www.hovisbakery.co.uk
- **Howad Ltd T/A Incognito** www.lessmosquito.com 0207 221 0667
- **HP** www.hp.com
- **Hula Hoops** www.hulahoops.com 020 8234 5000
- **Humdinger Ltd** www.humdinger-foods.co.uk 01482 625790
- **I Am Natural** www.iamnatural.co.uk 07737 764 660
- **Ice Guard** www.optimah.com
- **Idris** www.britvic.com 0800 0321767
- **Il Mangiarsano S.p.A** www.ilmangiarsano.com 0039 0423 420099
- **In a Soapnut Shell** www.inasoapnutshell.com 01342 811220
- **Inika** www.inika.com.au +51 2 4268 5342
- **Innginni Limited (Ohsobo)** www.ohsobo.com 01923 842884
- **Innocent Oils** www.innocentoils.com 01473 622816
- **Inwinex Pharmaceuticals** info@inwinex.in 00914023047717

- **Its Elixir (UK) Limited** www.itselixir.com 01228 808 304
- **J&D Black Ltd** www.jdblack.co.uk 01252 344010
- **J.L. Bragg** www.charcoal.uk.com 01473 748345
- **Jacob's** www.unitedbiscuits.com 020 8234 5000
- **Jason Natural Products** www.jason-natural.com 0800 626 697
- **Jeremy's Soups** jeremys.soups@tiscali.co.uk 017683 53311
- **Jethros** www.jethros.co.uk 01273 417 405
- **Jif** www.unilever.co.uk 020 7822 5252
- **Jim Beam** www.jimbeam.com
- **Johnnie Walker** www.johnniewalker.com
- **Jonathan Crisp** www.jonathancrisp.co.uk 01865 882514
- **Jordans** www.jordans-cereals.co.uk 01767 318222
- **JR Liggett** www.jrliggett.com
- **Juice Beauty** www.juicebeauty.com
- **Junglesale Limited** www.junglesale.com 0871 2501271
- **Jus-Rol** www.jus-rol.co.uk 0800 125577
- **Jus-Rol** www.jusrol.co.uk 0800 125 577
- **Just Soaps** www.just-soaps.co.uk 01509 813535
- **Just Wholefoods** www.justw.demon.co.uk 01285 651 910
- **Kallo Foods** www.kallofoods.com 01428 685100
- **Katharine Botanicals Ltd** www.katharinebotanicals.com/ 01326 375294
- **Kelloggs** www.kelloggs.co.uk 0161 869 2000
- **Keltek Brewery** http://www.kelteknaturalmagik.co.uk/
- **Kerry Foods Ltd** www.puredairyfree.co.uk 01924 272534
- **Kettle Chips** www.kettlefoods.co.uk
- **Key Sun Laboratories PTY Ltd** www.keysun.com.au 0061 2 9905 7300
- **Kingfisher Natural Toothpaste** www.kingfishertoothpaste.com
  01603 630484
- **Kingsmill** www.lovekingsmill.com 0800 197 0110
- **Kinnerton Ltd** www.kinnerton.com 020 7284 9500
- **Kiss My Face** www.kissmyface.com 01347 878 751
- **Kitchen Buddy (Culinary Courses) Raw Chocolate** www.kitchenbuddy.eu
  020 8697 2755
- **Kitchen Garden** www.kitchen-garden.co.uk (01926)851415
- **Kitchen Garden Preserves** www.kitchengardenpreserves.co.uk 01453 759612
- **Kitten Vixen Cosmetics** www.kittenvixen.com 07814823263
- **Knobbly Carrot Food Company** www.theknobblycarrot.co.uk 01570 422 064
- **Knorr** www.knorr.com
- **Kobashi** www.kobashi.com 01392 217628
- **Konrad Haberberger Handels- und Consulting GmbH** www.pro-oleic.de
  0049 (0)8782 85 96
- **Kordel's** www.kordels.com
- **KP** www.kpnuts.com 08080 576887

- **Kuching Herbal Tea** www.kuchingherbal.com 08456434825
- **Kudos Vitamins and Herbals** www.kudosvitamins.com 0800 389 5476
- **Lambs Navy** www.thomaslowndes.com
- **Lancaster Brewery Ltd** www.lancasterbrewery.co.uk
- **Lanes Health** www.laneshealth.com 01452 524012
- **Lanson Ventures** www.lansongroup.com 0091 44 2479 9920
- **Laphroaig** www.laphroaig.com
- **Larabar** www.larabar.com
- **Laverana GmbH & Co. KG** www.lavera.co.uk
  00 49 51 0393 91-0/ 01557 870 203
- **Leopard's Leap** www.leopardsleap.typepad.com
- **Lifefood Czech Republic s.r.o.** www.lifefood.eu +420 222 210 851
- **Lifeplan Products Ltd** www.lifeplan.co.uk/index.php 01455 556281
- **Limney** www.davenportvineyards.co.uk 01892 852 380
- **Linda McCartney** www.lindamccartneyfoods.co.uk 0800 626 697
- **Lindt & Sprungli** www.lindt.com 020 8602 4100
- **Lip Ink** www.lipink.co.uk 01854 333833
- **Lipton** www.liptonicetea.co.uk
- **Little Valley Brewery Ltd** www.littlevalleybrewery.co.uk 01422 883888
- **Live Native** www.livenative.com 01599 530 367
- **Liz Earle** www.lizearle.com 01983 813913
- **Luscombe Organic Drinks** www.luscombe.co.uk 01364 64 30 36
- **Lush** www.lush.co.uk 01202 667830
- **Lyme Bay Winery** www.lymebaywinery.co.uk 01297 551355
- **Lyme Regis Fine Foods Ltd** www.lymeregisfoods.com 01428 722 900
- **Lyons** www.premierfoods.co.uk 0727 815 850
- **M.A.C. Cosmetics** www.maccosmetics.com
- **Ma Baker** www.firstqualityfoods.co.uk 08707 771910
- **MacSween of Edinburgh** www.macsween.co.uk 0131 440 2555
- **Majestic Wine Warehouse Ltd** www.majestic.co.uk 01923 298 200
- **Majik Blankit Skin Care** www.majikblankit.co.uk 01424 421 907
- **Malibu** www.malibusun.com 020 8758 0055
- **Malibu** www.malibu-rum.com
- **Manakedi Skincare** www.manakedi.co.uk 01438 239 370
- **Manic Panic** www.manicpanic.com
- **Manna Gifts** www.mannagifts.com 0845 094 1552
- **Marigold** www.marigoldhealthfoods.com 0207 388 4515
- **Marks & Spencer** www.marksandspencer.com 0845 302 1234
- **Marmite** www.marmite.co.uk
- **Mars** www.mars.com
- **Mason's Products** www.dogoil.co.uk 01706 379817
- **Masterfoods** www.masterfoods.co.uk
- **Matt & Nat** www.mattandnat.co.uk

- **Maxim Marketing Company** www.maximmarketing.co.uk 020 8689 0773
- **McCain** www.mccain.co.uk 01723 584141
- **McCoy's** www.mccoys.co.uk
- **McKeith** www.gillianmckeith.info
- **McVities** www.unitedbiscuits.com
- **Mediterranean Foods (London) Ltd** www.mediterraneanfoods.uk.com 020 89 688444
- **Meinklang** www.vintageroots.co.uk 0800 980 4992
- **Melbrosin UK Limited** www.kudosvitamins.com 01256 773299
- **Meridian Foods** www.meridianfoods.co.uk 01490 413 151
- **Merrydown** www.merrydown.co.uk 01737 735007
- **MH Foods** www.mhfoods.net 01322 337711
- **Michelin** www.michelin.co.uk
- **Michelob** www.michelob.com
- **Miss Bellasis** www.missbellasis.com 07776 081 846
- **Misshu Ltd T/A Lani-Jo** www.veganproducts4u.co.uk 07866 454 747
- **MJ Health(NZ) Ltd** www.doctorwendy.net 0064 63531948
- **Moet & Chardon** www.moet.com
- **Montagne Jeunesse** www.montagnejeunesse.com 01639 861550
- **Montezumas Chocolates** www.montezumas.co.uk 0845 450 6304
- **Moo Free Chocolates** www.moofreechocolates.com 01189507766
- **Mood Food Company** www.moodfoodcompany.co.uk
- **Moom UK** www.moom-uk.com 08452345668
- **Mooncup Ltd.** www.mooncup.co.uk 01273 355020
- **Morrocco Method** www.morroccomethod.com 805 534 1600
- **Mothers Pride** www.premierfoods.co.uk 01727 815850
- **Mrs Crimble's** www.stilettofoods.com 08451 300869
- **MuLondon** www.mulondon.com
- **Mulu Chocolate Ltd** www.muluchocolate.co.uk 01268 906443
- **Munchy Seeds** www.munchyseeds.co.uk 01728 833004
- **My Handmade Soaps** www.myhandmadesoaps.com 01626 364938
- **My Skincare Ltd** 128A Above Bar Street, Southampton, Hampshire, SO14 7DU 02380222519
- **NAE, LDA** www.nae-vegan.com 00 351 910 535 595
- **Naked Lunch .DA** nakedlunch.da@hotmail.com 004791604920
- **Natracare** www.natracare.com 0117 9823492
- **Natrol** www.natrol.com
- **Natura Organics** www.naturaorganics.com 01273 808380
- **Natural by Nature Oils** www.naturalbynature.co.uk 01582 840848
- **Natural Insulation** www.naturalinsulations.co.uk 01920 821069
- **Natural Sense** www.naturalsenseproducts.com 01424 716461
- **Natural Shoe Store** www.birkenstock.co.uk 020 7602 2866
- **Naturally Gifted** www.naturally-gifted.co.uk 0208 715 1245

- **Naturally ME Inc** www.naturalfeast.com 207 737 2237
- **Nature Complete Ltd** www.naturecomplete.com 020 8539 5585
- **Natures Aid - DUPLICATE -** www.naturesaid.co.uk 01772 686231
- **Natures Aid Limited** www.naturesaid.co.uk 01772 686231
- **Nature's Gate** www.natures-gate.com
- **Nature's Path Foods INC** www.naturespath.com 1-888-808-9505
- **Natures Remedies** naturesremedies.uk.com 01494 727 888
- **Naturgreen** www.naturgreenfood.com
- **NaturKraftWerke** www.naturkraftwerke.com 0041 44 9722777
- **Neal's Yard Remedies** www.nealsyardremedies.com 01747 834 634
- **Nestlé** www.nestle.co.uk 01904 604 604
- **Neuaura** www.newaurashoes.com 001 732 207 7682
- **New Balance** www.newbalance.co.uk 01925 423000
- **New Seasons** www.newseasons.co.uk 01235 821110
- **New York Bagel Co.** www.newyorkbagel.co.uk 01709 580840
- **Neways International UK Ltd** www.neways.co.uk 01480 861764
- **Niepoort** www.niepoort-vinhos.com
- **Nimble** www.nimblebread.co.uk 08707 288888
- **No Cows** www.nocows.com 07747 605271
- **NOHARM** www.noharm.co.uk 01733 564077
- **Nothing Nasty** www.nothingnasty.com 01600 861 816
- **Nutrilabs** www.nutrilabs.biz 01600 780256
- **Nutshell Natural Paints** www.nutshellpaints.com 01392 421 535
- **NVS Ltd** www.fusioncondoms.com
- **Oatly** www.oatly.com
- **Obbekjaers** www.healthremedies.co.uk 01257 404659
- **Odysea** www.odysea.com 0207 796 1166
- **Oleador UG (haftungsbeschränkt)** www.oleador.com 0049 160 366 8954
- **Oliverhill Winery** www.oliverhillwinery.com.au 0061 883238922
- **Onitsuka Tiger** www.onitsukatiger.com
- **Optimah** www.optimah.com
- **Orchid Healthcare Limited** www.orchidhealth.co.uk 020 8961 0085
- **Organatural** www.forestsecretsskincare.com 01749 677884
- **Organic Botanics** www.organicbotanics.com 01273 573825
- **Organic Meltdown** www.organicmeltdown.com
- **Organic Seed & Bean Co Ltd** www.organicseedandbean.co.uk
- **Organic Soap Company** www.organicsoap.net 020 8488 2469
- **Organico** www.organico.co.uk 0118 9 238 766
- **Organix Brands Plc** www.babyorganix.co.uk 0800 393511
- **Organix South Inc** www.organixsouth.com
- **Orgran** www.orgran.com
- **Oshadhi** www.oshadhi.co.uk 01223 242242
- **OSMO UK** www.osmouk.com 01296 481 220

- **Oxford Landing** www.oxfordlanding.com
- **Panacea ApS** www.panacea.dk +45 48 27 7110
- **Pasante Health Care** www.pasante.com 01903 753844
- **Pasta King (UK) Ltd** www.pastaking.co.uk 0800 458 78 98
- **Pataks Foods** www.pataks.co.uk 01942 267000
- **Patchwork Traditional Food Company** www.patchwork-pate.co.uk 01824 705832
- **Paul's Tofu** www.soyfoods.co.uk 01664 560572
- **Paxo** www.premierfoods.co.uk 01727 815850
- **Pennard Organic Wines & Cider** www.pennardorganicwines.co.uk 01749 860393
- **Pennine Spring** www.britvic.com 0800 0321767
- **Pepsi** www.britvic.co.uk 0800 0321767
- **Pertwood Organic Cereal Company** www.pertwood.co.uk 01985 217770
- **Peter Lehmann** www.peterlehmannwines.com
- **Peter Rabbit Organics** www.peterrabbitorganics.com 020 7637 5505
- **PharmaBrand USA LLC** www.cidbotanicals.com 3056308456
- **Phileas Fogg** www.phileasfogg.com 01207 580999
- **Pick Me** jacqueline@jb-pr.com
- **Pitfield Brewery** www.pitfieldbeershop.co.uk 0845 833 1492
- **Pitrok Ltd** www.pitrok.co.uk 020 8563 1120
- **Plamil** www.plamilfoods.co.uk 01303 850588
- **Polar Sun Products Ltd** www.polarsunproducts.com +372 60 13 701
- **Porter Foods Co Ltd** www.porter-foods.co.uk 01279 501711
- **Pot Noodle** www.potnoodle.co.uk 0800 032 3251
- **Potions and Possibilities** www.potions.co.uk 01394 386 161
- **Potter's Herbal Medicine** www.pottersherbal.co.uk 01942 219 960
- **Power Health Products** www.power-health.co.uk 01759 302595
- **Principle Healthcare** www.principlehealthcare.co.uk 01756 792600
- **Pukka Herbs** www.pukkaherbs.com 0845 375 1744
- **Puraty Ltd** www.puraty.com 0560 235 2055
- **Purdey's** www.britvic.com 0800 0321767
- **Pure Gaisha** www.puregaisha.com.au
- **Pure Health Limited** www.eastwestherbshop.com 01582 380000
- **Purely Wicked Shakes Limited** www.purelywicked.co.uk 0786 335 1169
- **Purity Trading Ltd** www.currytree.co.uk 08451277400
- **PZ Cussons UK Ltd** www.originalsource.co.uk 01614351000
- **QianNa Agricultural Products Ind & Trading Co. Ltd** www.qiannafoods.com 00 86 22 26889240
- **Quaker Oats** www.quakeroats.com 020 8574 2388
- **Quality Sea Veg** http://www.seaveg.co.uk/ 01438 213194
- **Quest Vitamins** www.questvitamins.co.uk 0121 359 0056
- **Quinessence Aromatherapy** www.quinessence.com 01530 835918

- **Quintessential Soaps** www.quintessentialsoap.co.uk 01453 766 931
- **Quinua Real Brasil Ltda** www.quinuareal.com.br 0055 11 3063 4007
- **R & R Tofu** www.clearspottofu.co.uk 01653 690235
- **R Whites** www.britvic.com 0800 0321767
- **Ragazzi Vegan** www.ragazzivegan.com 909-979-2012
- **Rakusen's** www.rakusens.co.uk 01132 784821
- **Rare Natural Care, Inc.** www.rarenatural.com 001 310 839 2696
- **Raw Alchemy Ltd** www.rawalchemy.org.uk 07846 824364
- **Raw Gaia** www.rawgaia.com 01273 311 476
- **Raw Living** www.rawliving.eu 0844 561 7448
- **Rawcreation Ltd** www.detoxyourworld.com 08700 113 119
- **Real Organic Foods** www.realorganic.co.uk 01491 615 280
- **Rebecca's Cakes** http://www.thevegancakegirl.co.uk/ 0781 328 2587
- **Red Bull** www.redbull.co.uk 020 7434 0100
- **Redbush Tea Co** www.redbushtea.com 0845 601 2658
- **Redwood Wholefood Company** www.redwoodfoods.co.uk 01536 400557
- **Relentless** www.relentlessenergy.com 020 8237 3000
- **Reliv UK** http://www.reliv.com/UK/EN/home.html 01527 559811
- **Ren** www.renskincare.com 020 7724 2900
- **Renbow** www.renbow.co.uk 0870 366 5410
- **Renk's Industrial LTDA** http://www.ebarbrasil.com.br/
- **Ribena** www.ribena.co.uk
- **Rice Dream** www.tastethedream.eu
- **Richard Henry Consulting Ltd** www.pulpastore.co.uk 0161 798 0671
- **Rimon Winery** www.rimonwinery.co.uk 0207 935 8343
- **Ripe Gifts** www.ripegifts.co.uk 08452269182
- **Ritter Sport** www.ritter-sport.de +49 7157-97-210
- **River Veda** www.riverveda.com/
- **Rizla** http://www.rizla.co.uk/
- **RJ Foods Limited** www.rjfoods-flapjack.com 01202 481471
- **RJ Mineral Cosmetics International PTY Ltd** www.rjmineralcosmetics.com.au 0061882400635
- **RJ's** www.rjslicorice.co.nz
- **Robert Cain & Company Limited** www.cainsbeers.com 0151 709 8734
- **Robertsons** www.premierfoods.co.uk 01727 815 850
- **Robinsons** www.britvic.co.uk
- **Rocks Organic Cordials** www.rocksorganic.com 0118 934 2344
- **Rococo Chocolates** www.rococochocolates.com 020 7352 5857
- **Rosie's Gourmet Products (UK) Ltd**
  - www.rosiesproducts.co.uk 02087 317707
- **Rubicon Drinks Ltd.** www.rubiconexotic.com +44 (0)20 8900 9944
- **Ryvita** info@ryvita.co.uk
- **Saaf International Limited** www.saafpureskincare.com 0113 2265849

- **Sacla** www.sacla.co.uk 01494 687900
- **Sahfee Halal Care** www.sahfee-halalcare.com 0031 320411193
- **Sainsbury's Supermarkets Ltd** www.sainsburys.co.uk 020 7695 8602 or 0800 636 262
- **Salus** www.salusuk.com 01925 825679
- **Salus Haus** www.salusuk.com 01925 825679
- **Samuel Smith** christian@samuelsmiths.biz 01937 832225
- **Sanchi** www.sanchi.co.uk 020 8450 9419
- **Sanitarium Health Food Co** www.sanitarium.com.au
- **Sant'Or go to 020627** www.santorwines.gr 00302693091104
- **Sauces of Choice** www.saucesofchoice.co.uk 01935 431 924
- **Sauflon Pharmaceuticals** www.sauflon.co.uk 0208 322 4200
- **Savant Distribution Ltd** www.savant-health.com 0113 3885235
- **Science In Sport** www.scienceinsport.com 01254 246 060
- **Scottish Herbal Supplies**
-   www.veganherbal.com 01770 820338
- **Seabrook Potato Crisps Ltd** www.seabrookcrisps.com 01274 546405
- **Seagreens Ltd** www.seagreens.com 0845 0640 0403
- **Seasoned Pioneers** www.seasonedpioneers.co.uk 0800 0682348
- **Sedlescombe Organic Vineyard** www.englishorganicwine.co.uk 01580 830715
- **Seeds of Change** www.seedsofchange.co.uk 0800 952 0000
- **Sensory Revolution, LLC** www.sensoryrevolution.com 001 415 648 5472
- **Seven Seas** http://www.sseas.com 01482 375234
- **Shandy Bass** www.britvic.com 0800 0321767
- **Shanti Products** www.shantiproducts.co.uk 01233 733 061
- **Shea By Nature** www.africanblacksoaponline.co.uk 07716 853180
- **SheaCare** www.sheacare.co.uk 08708 034 527
- **Shearer Candles** www.shearer-candles.com 0141 445 1066
- **Sheppy's Cider** www.sheppyscider.com 01823 461 233
- **Shifa Lifeherbs International (UK)** www.shifalife.com 01223 243368
- **Silver Wing Ltd** www.silverwingltd.co.uk 01603 300260
- **Simon Howie** www.thescottishbutcher.com
- **Simple** www.simpleskincare.co.nz 0121 712 6523
- **Simple System LTD** www.simplesystem.co.uk 01371 870753
- **Simply Soaps** www.simplysoaps.com 01603 720869
- **Sir Richard's Condom Company** www.sirrichards.com
- **Sjaak's Organic Chocolates** http://sjaaks.com 707-775-2434
- **Skin Blossom Limited** www.skinblossom.co.uk 05600 533 049
- **Skincare Cafe Ltd** www.skincarecafe.com 0870 44 327 44
- **Skinvac** www.skinvac.com
- **Skol** 0845 7820 820
- **Smart Beauty** www.smartcolour.info 0870 608 9990

- **Smilde** www.smildefood.uk.com 01892 669616
- **Smirnoff** www.smirnoff.com 020 7927 5200
- **Smithfield Wine** www.smithfieldwine.com 0161 273 6070
- **Sodasan** www.sodasan.com 00 49 4956 40720
- **Solano Trading** 11 Summerhill, Frome, Somerset , BA11 1LT 01373 473809
- **Solaray Nutritional Supplements** www.solaray.co.uk 01273 693 022
- **Solgar Vitamins** www.solgar.com 01442 890355
- **Soma Organic** www.somajuice.com 0870 950 7662
- **Somerset Cider Brandy Company & Burrow Hill Cider**
  www.ciderbrandy.co.uk 01460 240782
- **Sonett OHG** www.sonett.eu 00 49 7555 92950
- **Sophyto** http://www.sophytoorganics.co.uk/ 0800-680-0671
- **Source Foods** www.miso.co.uk
- **Source-Omega LLC** www.source-omega.com 001 919 360 5275
- **SpaRitual** www.sparitual.co.uk 0161 788 2868
- **Special Effects Hair Dyes** www.specialeffectshairdye.co.uk
- **Spectrum Brewery** www.spectrumbrewery.co.uk 07949 254383
- **Spiral Foods** www.spiralfoods.com.au
- **Stella McCartney** www.stellamccartney.com
- **Stroud Brewery LTD** www.stroudbrewery.co.uk
- **Suki Pure Skin Care** www.sukipure.com 1.413.584.7854
- **Suma Wholefoods** www.suma.coop 0845 458 2290
- **Sun Zapper** www.sunzapper.com
- **Sunblest** www.alliedbakeries.co.uk
- **Sun-Pat** www.premierfoods.co.uk 0727 815 850
- **Superdrug** www.superdrug.com 020 8684 7000
- **Supernutrients ltd** www.supernutrients.co.uk 01225 830517
- **Swedish Glace** www.swedishglace.com 1270 589311
- **Sweetbird** www.beyondthebean.com
- **Swiss Herbal Confectionery** www.optimah.com
- **Swizzels Matlow Ltd** www.swizzels-matlow.com
- **Synthesis 345** www.synthesis345.com
- **Taifun** www.taifun-tofu.com
- **Talooza Inc** www.bebe-o.com
- **Tamar Organics** www.tamarorganics.co.uk 01579 371087
- **Tango** www.tango.co.uk 0800 0321767
- **Tanjero** www.tanjero.co.uk 01142 562977
- **Taoasis GmbH Aroma-Kosmetik & Verlag** www.taoasis.de 49 5261 9383 0
- **Tara Smith Limited** www.tarasmith.com 024 76 222088
- **Taylor Jackson Health Products** www.taylor-jackson.com 0871 874 0464
- **Teachers** www.teacherswhisky.com
- **Tesco** www.tesco.com
- **Thai Kitchen** www.thaikitchen.com

- **The Best of Taste Company** www.bestoftaste.co.uk 01691 680410
- **The Booja-Booja Company Ltd** www.boojabooja.com 01508 558888
- **The Chocolate Alchemist** www.thechocolatealchemist.co.uk 01798 860 995
- **The Co-operative** www.co-op.co.uk 0161 8275688
- **The Deodorant Stone (UK) Ltd** www.deodorant-stone.co.uk 01559 384856
- **The Durham Brewery Ltd** www.durham-brewery.co.uk 0191 377 1991
- **The English Provender Co.** www.englishprovender.com
- **The Famous Chocolate House 1657** www.chocolatehouse1657.co.uk 01539 740702
- **The Food Doctor LTD** www.thefooddoctor.com 0800 093 5877 ex4
- **The Gorgeous Chocolate Heart Co** www.gchc.org.uk
- **The Green Superfood Company LLP** www.naturalgreens.co.uk
- **The Hemp Company Ltd** www.tattooaftercare.co.uk 01244 315486
- **The Hibiscus Drinks Company Limited** www.hibiscusdrinks.com 01604 581717
- **The Highland Soap Company** www.highlandsoaps.com 01397 713 919
- **The Himalaya Drug Company** www.himalayahealthcare.com 0091 802371 4444
- **The Hop Back Brewery** www.hopback.co.uk 01725 510 986
- **The Innis & Gunn Brewing Company** www.innisandgunn.com 0131 337 4420
- **The Organic Gardening Catalogue** www.organiccatalogue.com 0845 130 1304
- **The Organic Herb Trading Company** www.organicherbtrading.com 01823 401205
- **The Organic Pharmacy** www.theorganicpharmacy.com
- **The Organic Spirits Company** www.junipergreen.org www.uk5.org 01483 894 650
- **The Perfumers Guild** www.perfumersguild.com 01923 260502
- **The Raw Chocolate Company Limited** www.therawchocolatecompany.com 01273 493 331
- **The Really Wild Drinks Co** www.britvic.co.uk 0800 0321767
- **The Sunrise Granola Company LLC** www.sunrisegranola.com 0015038307624
- **The Vegan Society** www.vegansociety.com 0121 523 1730
- **Thomas Lowndes & Co** www.thomaslowndes.com 01403 270007
- **Thorntons** www.thorntons.co.uk 0800 454537
- **Tints of Nature** www.tintsofnature.co.uk 01590 613490
- **Tofurky** www.tofurky.com
- **Tofutti** www.trianobrands.co.uk 020 8861 4443
- **Toms of Maine** www.tomsofmaine.com 001 207 985 2944
- **TOPAS** www.wheaty.de 00497473 94865-0
- **Torq Uk** www.torqfitness.co.uk 0845 128 4312

- **Traditional Scottish Ales** www.traditionalscottishales.com 01786 817000
- **Traidcraft Plc** www.traidcraft.co.uk 0191 491 0591
- **Treacle Moon** www.treaclemoon.net
- **Treasured Earth Skincare** www.treasuredearth.com.au 00615 9391 4860
- **Tree-Harvest** www.tree-harvest.com 01531 635 284
- **Trialia Foods Australia** www.trialiafoods.com.au 0061 3 9701 1666
- **Trident** www.cadbury.co.uk 0121 451 4444
- **Trinity Lifecare(Holdings) Limited** www.dentaplex.co.uk 01323 833 558
- **Tropical Wholefoods** www.tropicalwholefoods.com 0191 548 0050
- **Truthful Co. Ltd (Purely Skincare)** www.purelyskincare.co.uk 01204 531 281
- **Tunch Foods Ltd** www.tunchfoods.com 08452248352
- **Tyrrells Potato Chips** www.tyrrellspotatochips.co.uk 01568 720244
- **Ultra Glow Cosmetics** www.ultraglowshop.co.uk 01473 612641
- **Uncle Ben's** www.unclebens.co.uk 0800 952 1234
- **United Biscuits Ltd** www.unitedbiscuits.co.uk 01494 463388
- **Upcakes** www.upcakes.co.uk
- **Urban Decay** www.urbandecay.com
- **Urban Jungle SARL** www.boastyle.net + 212 522 27 20 57
- **Urtekram** www.urtekram.dk +45 9854 2288
- **Valrhona** www.valrhona.com 04 75 07 90 42
- **Vanilla Tree Natural Skin Care** www.vanillatree.com.au
- **Vega Nutritionals** www.vegavitamins.co.uk 08452 267 300
- **Vegan Chic** www.veganchic.com 00 1 818 307 5994
- **Vegan Perfection** www.veganperfection.com.au (00) +61 39398 6302
- **Vegan Store** www.veganstore.co.uk 01273 302979
- **Veganline** www.veganline.com 020 8286 9947
- **Vegantisch** www.vegantisch.de 00499942/949341
- **VegeFarm Corp** www.vegefarm.com.tw 00-886-3-3271818
- **Vegepet** www.vegepet.com
- **Vegetarian Shoes** www.vegetarian-shoes.co.uk 01273 685685
- **Vegetarians Choice** Unit 4, , Crow Arch Lane Industrial Estate, off Crow Arch Lane, Ringwood, Hampshire, BH24 1PD 01425 838 801
- **Veggies Catering Campaign** www.veggies.org.uk 0845 458 9595
- **Venture Foods Uk Ltd** www.seriouslyvegan.co.uk 01743 289133
- **VERDESATIVA s.r.l.** www.verdesativa.com +39 06 912 510 87
- **Vicco** www.worldsend.co.uk 0845 094 1635
- **Victoria Manor Spa Retreat T/A Livinia Natural Skincare** www.liviniaskincare.com.au 0061 3 796 8941
- **Vimto** www.vimto.co.uk 01925 222222
- **Vinceremos Organic Wines** www.vinceremos.co.uk 01132 440002 or 0800 107 3086
- **Vintage Roots** www.vintageroots.co.uk 0118 932 6566

- **Violii** www.violii.com 0046 70 977 93 99
- **Visionary Soap Company** www.visionarysoap.co.uk 01424 460 022
- **Viva!** www.viva.org.uk 0117 944 1000
- **Waitrose** www.waitrose.com 01344 424680
- **Walkers Snack Foods** walkers.corpex.com/cr15p5/index.htm 0800 274 777
- **Warburtons** www.warburtons.co.uk 01204 556600
- **Wassen International** www.wassen.com 01372 379828
- **Weetabix Ltd** www.weetabix.co.uk 01536 722181
- **Weleda** www.weleda.co.uk
- **Well Cultivated Ltd** www.wellcultivated.co.uk 0115 921 2979
- **Wellfoods Ltd** www.bake-it.com 01226 381712
- **Wells & Young's** www.charleswells.co.uk 0500 00 33 08
- **Westerham Brewaery Co Ltd** www.westerhambrewery.co.uk 01732 864427
- **Westler Foods Ltd** www.westlerfoods.com 0800 027 6336
- **Weston & Sons Ltd** www.westons-cider.co.uk 01531 660233
- **White Lotus Cosmetic Acupuncture** www.cosmeticacupuncture.net.au/
  07 3868 3856
- **White Mark Marketing UG** www.white-mark.de 0049511 3703193
- **Whitworths Ltd** www.whitworths.co.uk 01933 653000
- **Wholebake Ltd** www.wholebake.co.uk 01490 412297
- **Wholistic Research Company** www.wholisticresearch.com 0845 430 3100
- **Wibbler's** www.wibblers.com 01621 789003
- **Wicken Fen**
- **William Santus & Co. Ltd** www.uncle-joes.com 01942 243 464
- **William Sinclair Horticulture** www.william-sinclair.co.uk
- **Winning Ways Fine Foods Limited** www.fabulousfudgefactory.co.uk
  01799 599999
- **Winsor & Newton** www.winsornewton.com 020 8424 3200
- **Worthenshaws** www.worthenshaws.co.uk 01772 469899
- **Wrigley** www.wrigley.com 01752 701107
- **Wychwood Brewery** www.wychwood.co.uk 01993 890 800
- **X35 Energy Ltd** www.x35energy.com 0116 268 12 82
- **Yaoh** www.yaoh.co.uk 01179 239053
- **Yarrah Organic Petfood BV** www.yarrah.com 0031 341 439850

INDEX

C

D

ADVERTISERS INDEX

The Vegan Passport is available from The Vegan Society for just £4.99. It is a pocket-sized book, with a simple message explaining what vegans do and don't eat, and why in seventy-three different languages.